# PRINTING PATENTS

# Printing Patents

ABRIDGEMENTS OF PATENT
SPECIFICATIONS RELATING TO
PRINTING

1617-1857

First published in 1859
and now reprinted with
a Prefatory Note by

## JAMES HARRISON

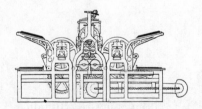

LONDON:
PRINTING HISTORICAL
SOCIETY

Reprinted by photolitho from the
original editions of 1859 and 1878
Prefatory Note © James Harrison 1969

Published by
The Printing Historical Society
St Bride Institute
Bride Lane, London E C 4

1969

Publication No. 6
SBN 900003 00 6

Printed in Great Britain
at the Gresham Press by
Unwin Brothers Limited
Woking & London
(HC03463)

12/15/76

# PREFATORY NOTE

The system of encouraging the introduction of new skills by grants of monopolies for limited periods did not originate in England but in no other country has the system flourished continuously for so long. This type of monopoly grant was first adopted as a deliberate policy in the economic development of the country during the reign of Elizabeth I, but long before the award of the first monopoly grant for a new manufacture it had been the practice of English sovereigns to verify their dispensations of privileges or honours by lettters patent ('open letters') that could be produced by the recipient as proof of the royal favour. It followed naturally that when monopoly privileges came to be granted they too were confirmed by letters patent.

Sometimes petitioners for the earlier patents for inventions were called upon to explain or demonstrate their inventions personally before the sovereign or a senior officer of state. Occasionally, written descriptions were submitted, but it was not until the 1730's that such descriptions became a regular feature of the patent system. Even then it was not laid down at which of the several offices that had to do with patent grants, the description, or 'specification', was to be deposited. Prior to the Patent Law Amendment Act of 1852 none of these specifications was officially printed, nor were there clear official records of the places where specifications could be perused, nor had a systematic record of patent grants been kept. One of the reforms introduced by the 1852 Act was the establishment of a new administrative body—the Commissioners of Patents—with authority to print and publish specifications, indexes and other relevant matter. The Commissioners lost no time in making their authority effective by creating a post of 'Superintendent of Specifications' and appointing to this post Bennet Woodcroft, an engineer and patent agent who had shown unusual knowledge of both the formal and technical aspects of patents and great interest in and zeal for reforms in patent procedure during the enquiries preceding the Act.

From the experience of personal searches Woodcroft was aware that the most nearly complete list of invention patents in official hands was that maintained by the Office of the Clerk of the Letters Patent in the Court of Chancery. From this he had prepared for his own use alphabetical, chronological and subject-matter ·indexes. These and other relevant material were purchased in 1853 by the Commissioners under a special Act of Parliament and the indexes constituted the Commissioners' first publications.

Although his immediate primary concern was the publication of the specifications of patents currently granted and at that time running at about 3,000 a year, Woodcroft made an early start on the printing of the specifications enrolled under the 'Old Law'. For this purpose he used again the list available from the Chancery Clerk's Office, an office that had been opened in 1618 and which had started its list with patents granted in the previous year. As well as omitting about a hundred patents awarded before 1617, the list failed to include a score or ·so granted during the Commonwealth and Protectorate period. A small number of other grants seem to have been accidentally missed. Even this incomplete list included more than 13,500 patents and it was no small task to search out the specifications (or titles where no specifications existed) and to organise their publication.

With the printing of current and past specifications under way publication of abridgments of the specifications classified by subject-matter was started. The classified abridgments are in general rather less complete than the printed specifications but the omissions from any specific group of subject-matter, such as this, are comparatively few and detract but little from the value of the collection. Printing was one of the subjects for which a second volume was issued covering the years 1858–1866. This contained a Supplement (included in this reprint) making good some of the omissions of the first volume.

Of the hundred or so volumes of abridgments covering every aspect of inventive subject-matter conceived by the 1850's, a few are known to have been compiled by Woodcroft and others

of his small staff, but most, including the present volume, were
the work of experts not on the Patent Office establishment.
When it is appreciated that the Commissioners had no statu-
tory power to engage in this work—their powers did not extend
to patents granted before their jurisdiction—the zeal and
driving force of Woodcroft is better understood.

It is difficult to see how a man more suited than Woodcroft
could have been found to give a vigorous lead in the publishing
work of the new Patent Office and, after his assumption of the
duties of Clerk to the Commissioners in 1864, to stimulate its
general administration. The foundations of his commercial and
administrative attributes had been laid when he was in partnership with his father as a textile manufacturer in Manchester
and were strengthened in commercial undertakings of his own.
In addition his technical knowledge was deep and wide. At
an early age he had been sent to learn weaving. This was followed by instruction in chemistry under John Dalton with
whom he was a favourite pupil. But his strongest technical
bent was for engineering and in this he received encouragement from close association with some of the great Manchester
engineers, men of such standing as William Fairbairn at
whose home he was a frequent visitor, James Nasmyth,
Richard Roberts and Joseph Whitworth. Woodcroft left
Manchester for London in 1846 and a year later became Professor of Machinery at University College. Before and after his
move to London he practised as a consulting engineer and
also as a patent agent. It was from this professional experience
and also from knowledge personally acquired as an inventor
and patentee that he became convinced of the necessity for
changes in patent practice and he played a significant part
in the patent reform activity of the years immediately preceding 1852. His own patents were for inventions in the fields of
textile printing, weaving and marine propulsion and included
some of great technical merit. He was elected a Fellow of the
Royal Society in 1859.

Much material published by the Commissioners would have
remained difficult of access to the public but for Woodcroft's
concern and zeal. He published little in his own name. That
which does bear his name mainly relates to the history of
inventions and technology, a subject on which he was pecu-

liarly well-informed. Before his official appointment he had amassed a considerable quantity of literature devoted to this subject along with many models of machines and apparatus and a collection of portraits of inventors. These were purchased by the Commissioners and the literature provided the nucleus for the Patent Office Library (now itself providing a nucleus for the National Reference Library of Science and Invention). The models formed the initial material of a Patent Museum which in 1884 passed from Patent Office control to provide, with other collections, a basis for the modern Science Museum. There is some slight indication that the collection of portraits of inventors put on public exhibition at the Patent Office in 1853 suggested to others the idea of a National Portrait Gallery.

For more than twenty years Woodcroft pursued his official duties vigorously. He retired in 1876 and died three years later. His achievements did not gain for him the fame that went to many of his associates but his contribution to technical progress was considerable. Only a minute fraction of his work is represented by this volume but nevertheless it is a reminder of his services to engineering and technology and to their history.

JAMES HARRISON

# PUBLISHER'S NOTE

At the back of the book will be found sixty pages of additional abridgements omitted from the original volume, and later published as a supplement to the volume covering the years 1858–66. The original pagination has been retained which means that any page references to this section will have to be prefaced by the word Supplement. There is a separately compiled index.

The total extent of the book as it now stands is 722 pages, made up as follows:

| | |
|---|---|
| New preliminaries | i–x |
| Original preliminaries | xi–xxii |
| | *(Page numbers adjusted for this edition)* |
| Main text | 1–612 |
| Appendix | 611*–612* |
| Main Index | 613–632 |
| Half title | |
| Supplement | 311–370 |
| | *(Original pagination)* |
| Index to Supplement | xxv–xxvii |

Errors and omissions in the main index that have been discovered in the course of use have been corrected and added. Three errors found in the main text, again in the course of use, are as follows:

p. 10 *For* Ponchée *read* Pouchée
p. 23 1.22 *For* Atteignaud *read* Attaignant
p. 24 3 lines from foot *For* Feischman *read* Fleischmann

## PATENTS FOR INVENTIONS.

# ABRIDGMENTS

OF

# Specifications

RELATING TO

# PRINTING,

INCLUDING THEREIN

**THE PRODUCTION OF COPIES ON ALL KINDS OF MATERIALS,
(EXCEPTING FELTED AND TEXTILE FABRICS,)**

BY MEANS OF

TYPES, STEREOTYPE, BLOCKS, PLATES, STONE, DIES,
STENCIL PLATES, PAPER WRITINGS, ELECTRO-CHEMICALS,
AND LIGHT.

---

PRINTED BY ORDER OF THE COMMISSIONERS OF PATENTS.

---

## LONDON:

PRINTED BY GEORGE E. EYRE AND WILLIAM SPOTTISWOODE,
PRINTERS TO THE QUEEN'S MOST EXCELLENT MAJESTY.

PUBLISHED AT THE GREAT SEAL PATENT OFFICE,
25, SOUTHAMPTON BUILDINGS, HOLBORN.

1859.

# PREFACE.

THE Indexes to Patents are now so numerous and costly as to be placed beyond the reach of a large number of inventors and others to whom they have become indispensable.

To avoid this difficulty, short abstracts or abridgments of the Specifications of Patents under each head of Invention have been prepared for publication separately, and so arranged as to form at once a Chronological, Subject-matter, Reference, and Alphabetical Index to the class to which they relate. As these publications do not supersede the necessity for consulting the Specifications, the prices at which the latter are sold have been added.

B. WOODCROFT.

# INDEX OF NAMES.

[Those printed in *italics* and within brackets are the names of the parties by whom the inventions have been communicated to the Patentees. For names of persons otherwise connected with Inventions noticed in this work, see " Index of Subject Matter," post, p. 612. (*n*) refers to a note.]

# PRINTING.

PRINTING (a) is the art of mechanically multiplying permanent facsimiles (inverted or direct) of an original. The facsimiles are usually termed "impressions." The originals (according to the character of which the art is divided (b) into various branches) are principally metal types, stereotype, wood carvings in relief,

---

(a) Dutch, *prenten, drukken;* Ger., *drucken;* Swed., *trycka;* French, *imprimer;* Span., *imprimir;* Portug., *imprimir, estampar;* It., *stampare, imprimere.* The term imports pressure, such in the infancy of the art having been its distinguishing feature. The following passages will illustrate its early use :—

"Shew ye to me the *prente* of the money."
"Matt. xxii."—*Wickliffe,* before 1381.

"Except I se in his honds the *prent* of the neyles."
"John xx."—*Tyndale,* 1526.

"How soon a loke will *print* a thought that never may remove."
"Frailtie and Hurtfulness of Beautie."—*Surrey,* died 1547.

"Ye shall not *print* any marks upon you."
"Lev. xix."—(Authorized version, 1611.)

See Shakspere (died 1616), Tempest, act i. sc. 2; Much Ado, act i. sc. 1; Love's Labour's Lost, act ii. sc. 1; Winter's Tale, act ii. sc. 3, and act v. sc. 1; King John, act iv. sc. 3; Cymbeline, act ii. sc. 3; Tit. Andron., act iv. sc. 1.

"Upon his breastplate he beholds a dint,
Which in that field young Edward's sword did *print*."
"Bosworth Field."—*Beaumont,* died 1628.

"My life is but a wind
Which passeth by and leaves no *print* behind."
*Sandys,* died 1643.

"Whilst from off the waters fleet
Thus I set my *printless* feet."
"Comus."—*Milton,* died 1674.

"Perhaps some footsteps *printed* in the clay
Will to my love direct your wandering way."
*Roscommon,* died 1684–5.

"And in their minds so deep did *print* the sense."
*Dryden,* died 1700.

In many extensive branches of modern printing, such as photography, pyrography, and the like, pressure can hardly be said to enter as an element at all.

(b) "L'art d'imprimer ou de representer les idées par la parole écrite se pratique aujourd'hui par trois procédés differents, la *typographie,* la *calcographie,* et la *lithographie.* Le premier sent plus particulièrement à l'impression des textes, les deux autres rivalisent entre eux pour la réprésentation des estampes, cartes, plans, &c., ce qui ne les empêche par d'empieter souvent sur le domaine de la typographie qui a son tour s'en venge quelquefois avec succès."—*La Boulaye,* "Dictionnaire des Arts et Manufactures," 4to., Paris, 1847, Art. "Imprimerie."

metal and other plates perforated or engraved, paper writings, dies, and stone (a).

The materials on which the impressions are taken are various. For literary purposes (to which branch this series is principally devoted) that usually employed is paper (b).

---

(a) In the case of photography, *i.e.* the art of producing copies by the action of light, any visible object will serve for an original. "Calico printing," under which term the production of impressions on textile fabrics generally is comprised, forms the subject of another series of abridgments.

(b) The importance of this article, as contributing to the success of modern printing, appears to have been very generally overlooked (Landseer's Lectures on Engraving, 1807; see Pliny's Observations. lib. 13, § 21). It will, however, be apparent, on a comparison of it with the various substances which have from time to time supplied its place.

In the infancy of society the materials employed to receive writings and other representative signs were stone, wood, the bark and leaves of trees, the shoulder bones of animals, and other similar substances in their natural form. The Decalogue (Exod. xxxi. 18) was on stone, as were also the earliest records of the Greeks, Romans, and most nations in the East (Astle, The Origin and Progress of Writing, 2nd ed., 1803, Lond., p. 198). The oldest literal inscription known (that of the Sygeian marble in the British Museum) is on stone. Herodotus (lib. 7, cap. 22) mentions a letter engraven on plates of stone being sent by Themistocles, B. C. 500, to the Ionians.

Wood in the form of tablets was in use for the purpose before the days of Homer (Iliad vi. ver. 168). It is mentioned in that capacity in Holy Writ (Isa. xxx. 8, Habak. ii. 2). The laws of Solon were promulgated on wood (Diog. Laert. lib. 2, cap. 12). Wooden tablets, at first plain and afterwards coated with wax of various colours or chalk (Nouveau Traité de Diplomatique, tom. i. p. 535), were in ordinary use among the Romans (Plaut. Bac. act iii. sc. 3; Propert. iii. 258; Ov. Trist. lib. 1, eleg. 2). "Wooden tablets," says Sir J. G. Wilkinson (Manners and Customs of the Ancient Egyptians, vol. iii. p. 153), "covered with wax, were long in use among the Romans, as well as the papyrus (whence the word paper, as in byblos or biblus, originated the name bible or book), and the inner bark of trees (called liber, whence the Latin name *liber*, a book), and pieces of linen (Liv. iv. 7., xiii. 20) had been previously adopted by them. Wooden tablets covered with a glazed composition, capable of receiving ink, were used by the Egyptians long after they had papyrus, and are still in common use in schools at Cairo in lieu of slates." Specimens of Kufic writing on wood are in the Sloanian Library (No. 4,852). According to some, the Hebrew copy of St. Matthew found in the tomb of the Apostle Barnabas was on wood. The Chinese, before the invention of paper, wrote with an iron tool upon thin boards or bamboo (Astle, 199). Tables of wood were used for the laws of the Empire in the 4th century. The Greeks and Romans continued the use of waxed table books long after the use of papyrus, leaves, and skins became common, transcribing their performances, when corrected, into parchment books (Astle, 200), nor were they entirely discontinued until the 14th century (Dictionnaire Diplomatique, vol. i. p. 424).

The bark of trees was also very early in use, and is still adopted in the East. The Cottonian Library contains a specimen of Latin writing on bark. In the Sloanian Library (No. 4,726) is a specimen written in perpendicular columns in the Batta character, used in the island of Sumatra, on a long piece of bark folded up so as to represent a book. Another specimen of writing on bark in India occurs in the same library (No. 3,478), being a nabob's letter on a piece of bark about two yards long, richly ornamented with gold. The people also on the Malabar coast frequently write on bark, with a style, several specimens of which are in the British Museum and other public and private collections. In the Bodleian Library (No. 3,207) is a book of Mexican hieroglyphics painted on bark.

Leaves have also been used for writing upon in most nations. Pliny, speaking particularly of the Egyptians, says, that men at first wrote upon the leaves of palm trees. The Sibyl's prophecies were on leaves (Virg. Æn. lib. iii. p. 443),

a substance which afterwards became proverbial among the Romans (Astle, 202).
Thus Juvenal, " Credite me vobis folium recitare Sibyllæ." Diodorus Siculus relates that the judges of Syracuse were anciently accustomed to write the names
of those whom they sent into banishment upon the leaves of olive trees, and the
sentence was termed *petalism,* from πεταλον, a leaf. The practice of writing
upon palm leaves in still very prevalent in the East. In the Sloanian Library
are upwards of 20 MSS. written in different parts of Asia in the Sanskrit,
Burman, Peguan, Ceylonese, and other characters used in those parts (Astle, 203).
*Waraka* in Arabic signifies both a leaf and paper (Wilkinson, Manners and
Customs, vol. iii. p. 153).

Various metals were also employed. "Next" (to writing on leaves), says Fuller,
"they wrote on labels or sheets of lead, wherein the letters were deeply engraven,
being a kind of printing before printing, and to this I refer the words of Job (an
author allowed contemporary with if not superior to Moses himself), 'Oh! that
my words were now written; oh! that they were printed in a book!' (Job xix.
23 and 24). Pausanias states that the 'Works and Days' of Hesiod was written
on leaden tables, and Pliny informs us that lead when thus used was rolled up
like a cylinder. Two documents of lead are still preserved, which passed
between Pope Leo III. and Luitbrand, King of the Longobards; and according
to Kircher's Museum many more of such writings are to be found. Montfaucon
notices a very ancient book composed of eight leaves of lead, the first and last
being used as covers, and the whole held together by a leaden rod passed
through rings at the back of the plates. It contained numerous mysterious
words of the Basilidians, and words partly in Greek and partly Etruscan characters." "The precepts and laws of the ancients," says Landseer, J. (Lectures on
Engraving, p. 6) "were engraved on stone or on metal. The poems of Orpheus
and Hesiod are said to have been cut in lead, and the shields of Hercules and
the heroes who distinguished themselves in the early Theban wars, as well as
the more celebrated shield of Achilles, are described as having been ornamented
with heraldic and historical engravings." See also the Essay prefixed to Strutt's
Biographical Dictionary of Engravers. Two tables of brass were discovered in
1732 at Heraclea, one of which in the Greek language contained a decree concerning the boundaries of lands belonging to a temple of Bacchus written about
300 B.C., and the other a law about 41 B.C. Eight tables of bronze discovered in
1444, seven of them bearing inscriptions in Latin and the eighth in Etruscan,
will be found described in Merula, Gruter, and others. Not long since a copper
plate was discovered at Mongheer in Bengal, containing in Sanskrit a gift of land
dated 100 B.C. The pacts between the Romans, Spartans, and Jews were written
on brass. In many cabinets may be seen discharges of soldiers written on copper
plates. The speech of Claudius engraved on a plate of bronze is still preserved
at Lyons. It is said that upwards of 3,000 tables of brass kept in the Capitol at
Rome, and containing laws, treaties of alliance, &c., perished by fire in the reign
of Vespasian (Astle, 199 ; Nouveau Traité, vol. i. p. 422). The laws of the Twelve
Tables when ratified were engraved on brass, previously to which they were
written on ivory and hung up for inspection. Tablets of ivory were in use in
Chaucer's time (see the Sompner's Tale, "a pair of tables all of iverie").

The use of skins is very ancient, Isa. viii. 1 ; Jer. xxxvi. 2; Ezek. iii. 9. Herodotus
says they were in use from the earliest times among the Ionians ; and Diodorus
Siculus that they were used by the ancient Persians. Josephus tells us that the
Jews sent their laws written on skins in letters of gold to Ptolemy (Philos.
Trans., No. 420). Specimens of ancient Mexican paintings on skin are in the
Bodleian. (See as to the invention of parchment, Astle, 203.)

In China, letters appear to have been painted on linen and silk before the
discovery of paper. Specimens of hieroglyphical writing on linen have been
found in Egytian mummy cases.

"The early Arabs committed their poetry and compositions to the shoulder
bones of sheep. They afterwards obtained the papyrus paper from Egypt, on
which the poems called Moallaqât were written in gold letters, and after their
conquests in Asia and Africa these people so speedily profited by and improved
the inventions of the nations they had subdued that parchment was manufactured in Syria, Arabia, and Egypt, which in colour and delicacy might vie with
our modern paper. It speedily superseded the use of the papyrus, and continued to be employed until the discovery of the method of making paper from
cotton and silk, called carta bombycina, which is proved by Montfaucon to have
been known at least as early as A.D. 1100, and is supposed to have been invented
about the beginning of the ninth century. Being introduced into Spain from
Syria, it was denominated carta Damascena, and some MSS. are said to exist in

the Escurial written in the eleventh century."—(Wilkinson's Manners and Customs, &c., vol. iii. p. 153.)

The Egyptian papyrus (*Cyperus papyrus*, Linn.) or paper rush was manufactured by the ancients for writing upon. It mostly grew in Lower Egypt (a similar plant, native of Sicily, is described in Lobel's Adversaria) in marshy lands, shallow brooks (Isaiah xix. 7), or ponds formed by the inundations of the Nile (Pliny, lib. xiii. c. 11, and Theophr. Hist. Plant. lib. iv. c. 9). A learned dissertation on it by Montfaucon may be found in the 6th vol. of the Mem. de l'Acad. des Inscriptions, and a drawing of it in Bruce's Travels, vol. vii. p. 117. "The paper made from it differed in quality, being dependent upon the growth of the plant and the part of the stalk whence it was taken, and we find many of the papyri which have been preserved vary greatly in their texture and appearance. They are generally fragile and difficult to unrol until rendered pliant by gradual exposure to steam or the damp of our climates, and some are so brittle that they appear to have been dried by artificial means." — (Wilkinson's Manners and Customs, vol. iii. p. 142.)      .      .      .      "The monopoly of the papyrus in Egypt so increased the price of the commodity that persons in humble life could not afford to purchase it for ordinary purposes; few documents, therefore, are found written on papyrus, except funeral rituals, the sales of estates, and official papers, which were absolutely required, and so valuable was it that they frequently obliterated the old writing and inscribed another document on the same sheet."—(Ib. p. 150.)      .      .      .      "For common purposes pieces of broken pottery, stone, board, and leather were used; a soldier's leave of absence, accounts, and various memoranda were often written on the fragments of an earthenware vase, an artist sketched a picture which he was about to introduce in a temple or a sepulchre on a large flat slab of limestone, or on a wooden panel prepared with a thin coating of stucco, and even parts of funeral ritual were inscribed on square pieces of stone or stuccoed cloth, or on leather. Sometimes leather rolls were substituted for papyri, and buried in the same manner with the deceased; they are of an early period, and probably adopted in consequence of the high price of the papyrus, but few have hitherto been found at Thebes."—(Ib. p. 151.)

Varro says that the practice of writing on this plant was first introduced into Egypt in the time of Alexander the Great (330 B.C.), and that Ptolemy Philadelphus (283 B.C.) caused his books to be transcribed on papyrus. Sir J. G. Wilkinson (Manners and Customs, &c. vol. iii. p. 150) considers Pliny to be in error as to the date, and states that the style of hieroglyphic found on some corresponds with the age of Cheops (B.C. 2000). See N. T. de D., vol. ii. p. 166. The place most famous for the manufacture was Alexandria. Several charters written on papyrus are extant in Italy and France; a magnificent specimen of the kind may be seen in the British Museum. The famous Gospel of St. Mark at Venice is on papyrus (in the British Museum). Pliny (A.D. 77), (xiii. 11), after describing the plant, says, "When they manufacture paper from it they divide the stem by means of a kind of needle into thin plates or laminæ, each of which is as large as the plant will admit.      .      .      .      All the paper is woven upon a table, and is continually moistened with Nile water, which being thick and slimy, furnishes an effectual species of glue. In the first place, they form upon a table perfectly horizontal a layer, the whole length of the papyrus, which is crossed by another placed transversely, and afterwards enclosed within a press. The different sheets are then hung in a situation exposed to the sun in order to dry, and the process is finally completed by joining them together, beginning with the best. There are seldom more than twenty slips or stripes produced from one stem of the plant. Different kinds of broad paper vary in breadth. The best is 13 digits broad, the hieratic only 11; the Fannian (from the factory of Fannius at Rome), 9; the Saitic is still narrower, being only the breadth of the mallet, and the paper used for business is only 6 digits broad; besides the breadth, the fineness, thickness, whiteness, and smoothness are particularly regarded. .      .      .      When it is coarse, it is polished with a (boar's) tooth or a shell, but then the writing is more easily effaced, and it does not take the ink so well."—(Ib. xiii. 12). This account is confirmed by Cassiodorus, who says that in his time (A.D. 550) the paper used was white as snow.

It is uncertain until what year paper made of the papyrus continued in general use, but there is evidence of its having been occasionally employed to the end of the seventh century, when it was superseded by parchment. All public documents under Charlemagne and his dynasty were written on parchment, and the papyrus was then entirely given up, except (Astle, 206) for epistolary correspondence. The use of it was continued by the Popes (see specimens in N.T. de D.)

until the 12th century. Parchment, indeed, had been invented long before, and was used for writing as early as the year 250 B.C. by Eumenes, King of Pergamus. . . . . It was made of the skins of sheep and calves, but to the former the name of parchment is more correctly applied, as to the latter that of vellum. ▷ Cotton paper (*carta bombycina*) was an eastern invention, and Montfaucon says (Palæograph. Græc. lib. i. c. 2), was used in the ninth century. It was more common in the beginning of the eleventh century, and was in general use about the beginning of the thirteenth. This cotton paper was little made use of in Italy, except in that part of the country which had intercourse with the Greeks, as Naples, Sicily, and Venice; but even they did not write their charters or records upon it till the eleventh century, so that a Latin charter on cotton paper of the tenth century would be suspected, though a Greek charter of that age may be genuine. The paper made of cotton in the East is so fine that many have mistaken it for silk; but Du Halde (Description of China, p. 360) says, that silk cannot be beat into such a pulp or paste as to make paper, though he afterwards mentions a strong and coarse paper which is made of the balls of silkworms. Other authors also mention silk paper (Astle, 206).

It may, however, be questioned whether it was made from linen at that early period, and we have no positive proof of linen paper being known even by the Saracens prior to the eleventh century. The Moors, as might be expected, soon introduced it into Spain, and the Escurial library is said to contain MSS. written on this kind of paper as old as the twelfth century. An Arabic version of the Aphorisms of Hippocrates in the Escurial dates from the beginning of the thirteenth century (Montfaucon, Palæograph. Græc., lib. 1. c. 2., and Horne's Introd., p. 63.) The earliest of this sort with a date is 1050. Petrus Mauritius, a contemporary of St. Bernard, who died in 1153, says, in his treatise against the Jews: " The books we read every day are made of sheep, goat, or of calf skin, or of Oriental plants, that is, of the papyrus of Egypt, or of rags," (*ex rasuris veterum pannorum*). See "An Account of the Styles of the Ancients and their different Sorts of Paper," by Sir J. Clerk, Philos. Trans., No. 420, A.D. 1731. Some of the earliest books, as may be seen by the specimens in the King's and Spencer Libraries in the British Museum, were printed on vellum.

But paper of mixed cotton and linen, which was made at the same time, appears to have been in more general use, and linen paper continued to be rare in most European countries till the fifteenth century. That it was known in Germany as early as the year 1312 has been satisfactorily ascertained by existing documents, and a letter written on linen paper from Germany to Hugh Despencer about the year 1315 is preserved in the Chapter House at Westminster, which, even to the watermark, resembles that made in the present day.

As regards linen rag paper, the merit of invention is assigned by Chambers to the Chinese, who for several centuries have made paper in the same manner that we do. " It is a matter of doubt," says Wilkinson (Manners and Customs, &c., vol. iii. p. 153), " to which nation and period the invention of paper manufactured from linen ought to be ascribed. The Chinese were acquainted with the secret of making it from various vegetable substances long before it was known in Europe; the perfection to which they have carried this branch of art continues to excite our admiration, and the librarian at Cassiri relates, according to Gibbon (vol. ix. c. 51, p. 379), that paper was first imported from China to Samarcund A.H.30 (A.D. 652), and invented, or rather introduced, at Mecca, A.H.88 (A.D. 710)." —Du Halde (who in his History of China describes the manufacture), Kircher, Marsini, and Lecompte place the invention about 50 B.C., but others contend that it is of much earlier antiquity (Astle, 199). There are many opinions concerning the use of this kind of paper in Europe. The editors of the "Nouveau Traité de Diplomatique" mention a charter made by Adolphus, Count of Schomberg, written on paper made of the like materials, dated in the year 1239, and they are of opinion that it was first introduced into Europe in the thirteenth century. Father Mabillon (De re Diplomatica) thinks it was invented in the twelfth century. The learned antiquary, Montfaucon, however, in a diligent search in Italy and France, was unable to find a book or leaf of such paper with a date anterior to 1270. See Meerman and others in a work, "De Chartæ vulgaris seu lineæ origine" (8vo. 1767, The Hague), written at the instance of the Royal Academy of Göttingen, who proposed a premium of twenty-five ducats for the solution of the question. Dr. Prideaux (Prid. Connexion, p. 1, l. vii. p. 710, &c.) delivers it as his opinion that it was brought from the East, because most of the old MSS. in the Oriental languages are written on this kind of paper. He thinks it most probable that the Saracens of Spain first brought it out of the East into that country, from whence it was dispersed over the rest of Europe. The same learned author assures us he had seen a register of some acts of John Cranden, Prior of Ely, made on paper which bears date in the fourteenth year of King Edward II. (A.D. 1320). In the Cottonian Library are said to be several writings on this kind of paper as early as the year 1335. Mention is made of an inventory in the Library of the Dean and Chapter of Canterbury of the goods of Henry, Prior of Christ Church, who died in 1340, written on paper made with linen rags (Phil. Trans., No. 288). In the Bishop's Registry at Norwich there is a registry book of wills all made of paper wherein registrations are made bearing date as far back as 1370. Some of Caxton's books are printed on paper, "very fine and good," as Lewis (Life of Caxton, 125) observes, " almost like the thin vellum on which they used to write their books at that time," with the same watermark as that used by Faust, and probably of German manufacture. See Dibdin, Typ. Ant., Preface by Herbert, ). 56, and plate, p. cxxv.; and " Observations on Paper Marks," read by the Rev. Samuel Denne, at the Society of Antiquaries, May 21 and June 4, 1795; also the third vol. of the recent work by Mr. S. L. Sotheby, Principia Typographica, p. 84, which treats exclusively of paper marks, and where there is a notice of those in Caxton's works.

The first paper mill in England was erected in the reign of Henry VII. by John Tate the younger at Hertford. The fact is noticed in the subjoined lines from the prologue to the English edition of *Bartholomœus de Glanville, De Proprietatibus rerum* (in the Grenville Library, British Museum, Case viii. No. 10), printed by Wynkyn de Worde in 1495 :—

> " And to John Tate the younger joi mote he broke
> Which since hath in England doo make this paper thinne,
> That now in our English tongue this boke is printed inne."

In one of the notes to Vallan's " Tale of Two Swannes," 1590, it is stated that in 1507 there was a paper mill at Hertford, which belonged to John Tate, whose father was mayor of London.—(Herbert's Preface, p. 56, Dibd. Typ. Ant.)

In 1558 Thomas Churchyard published a poem entitled " A Description and playne Discourse of Paper, and the whole Benefits that Paper brings, setting forth in verse a paper myll built near Dartfoord by an High Germaine, called Master Spilman, jeweller to the Queen's Majestie." This poem (which is given entire in Nichols' Progresses, vol. ii. p. 592) contains some interesting notices of the art at an earlier period. A previous attempt to introduce the manufacture had it appears been made :—

> " One *Thirlby* went embassador farre from hence
> To Charles the Fift, an emperor of great fame.
> And at return did bring with him from thence
> A learned man, *Remegius* by name;
> Who *Thirlby* loved, and made by his devise
> A paper-mill, but not so much in price
> As this that now neare Darthford standeth well,
> Where *Spill-man* may himself and houshold dwell."

Sir Thomas Gresham appears, previously to his being engaged (June 7, 1566) in rebuilding the Exchange, to have entered on a similar project :—

> " Glasse was at first as strange to make or vewe
> As paper nowe that is devised of newe.
> Of newe I mean in England, save one man,
> That had great wealth, and might much treasure spare ;
> Who with some charge a paper-mill began,
> And after built a stately work most rare,
> The Royall Exchaunge; but got by that more gayne
> Than he indeede did lose by former payne.
> But neither he nor none before his dayes
> Made paper-mill that merits so much prayse."

In 1589 a special licence was granted to this John Spilman (Harleian MSS., 2296), " for the gatherings of all manner of linen ragges, scrolles, or scrappes of parchment, peace of lyme leather, shreds and clippings of cordes and oulde fishing nettes, fitte and necessary for the makinge of all or anie sortes of white wrightinge paper for the space of tenne years next ensuing."

Fuller, writing in 1662, characterizes the paper of his day thus : " Paper participates in some degree of the character of the country which makes it, the Venetian being light, subtle, and courtlike ; the French, light, slight, and slender ; and the Dutch, thick, corpulent, and gross, sucking up the ink with the sponginess thereof," and complains of the "vast sums of money expended in our land for paper out of Italy, France, and Germany, which might be lessened were it made in our nation."

In a curious German work on the subject of paper, by Dr. Schaeffer of Regensburg, 1765-71, various processes are described of making paper without rags, and specimens given of vegetable papers. Among these are samples from the cotton flowers of the poplar tree, wasps' nests, wood shavings, moss, beech, willow, aspen tree, mulberry tree, clematis, and pine tree, from hemp and hopstalks, the barks of the vine, the leaves of aloes, and the lily of the valley, from orack, mugwort, the sypha or reedmace, barley straw, cabbage stalks, the stems of thistles, burdoch, confervas, maize, broom, and Bavarian turf.

A paper insensible to the action of fire has by modern ingenuity been manufactured from the flexible fibre of the mineral called asbestos, which the ancients were in the habit of converting into cloth. Dr. Burman, Professor, at Brunswick, published a treatise on this fossil, of which four copies were taken off on asbestos paper (Peignot, "Essai sur l'Histoire du Parchemin," p. 2). The process of fabricating this paper is described in the Philos. Trans. vol. xiv. p. 823.

In 1763 some low grounds near Cortona, which had been flooded, were on the subsidence of the water found covered with a substance very much like a finer sort of common brown paper. It was found to owe its formation to a casual aggregate of the fibres of the common species of conferva, without the intervention of any other plant whatever. (Philos. Trans., A.D. 1769.) The mode adopted in Hindostan of manufacturing paper from old ropes, clothes, and nets made from the fibre of the sun plant is described by Lieut.-Col. Ironside, in the Philos. Trans. of 1774. (See 1 Rep. Arts, A.D. 1794, p. 41.)

The instruments used for marking with by the ancients varied, of course, with the materials inscribed on. For wooden wax-covered tablets (*pugillares*) at Rome, a stylus (hence the metaphorical word *style*) was used of iron, silver, brass, or bone, one end of which was pointed, and served to make the inscription; and the other flat, so as to smooth over the written places; they were of considerable size. Specimens may be seen in the British Museum and other collections. Drawings of several kinds of these styles may be seen in the Nouveau Traité, tom. i. p. 534. Suetonius tells us that Cæsar in full senate seized and pierced the arm of Cassius with his stylus. See also Seneca de Clementia, lib. i. c. 4, where a Roman knight narrowly escapes being killed by the mob, who attack him with the styles attached to their *pugillares*; and Prudentius (Martyrs' Hymn), who describes the death, by similar means, of Cassianus at the hands of his scholars.

When writing on softer materials than wood, other instruments and a pigment were used, of which reeds and cane appear to be the first. Specimens taken from Egyptian tombs may be seen in the British Museum. Pliny, Hist., lib. xvi. c. 36; Martial, xiv. epigr. 34; and see Astle, 207. They are still in use among Tartars, Persians, Indians, and Turks. The Chinese use hair pencils dipped in ink.

Quills of geese, peacocks, crows, and other birds were also in early use in the West, but when it is not easy to ascertain (Astle, 208). St. Isidore of Seville (Hisp. Orig., lib. vi. c. 14), in the middle of the seventh century, describes a pen made of a quill as used in his time. Dr. Holland, who translated Pliny's Natural History in the sixteenth century, says:—

> "With one sole pen I wrote this book,
> Made of a gray goose-quill;
> A pen it was when it I took,
> A pen I leave it still."

Mr. Knight, in his Pictorial Gallery of Arts (1846), says:—"The use of the steel pen has not sprung immediately from that of the quill pen. There were several intermediate stages adopted before the fitness of steel for this purpose was sufficiently known. From about the commencement of the present century down to ten or a dozen years ago, the number of proposed substitutes for the quill pen was very considerable. Horn pens, tortoiseshell pens, nibs of diamond or ruby embedded in tortoiseshell, nibs of ruby set in fine gold, nibs of rhodium and iridium embedded in gold; all have been adopted at different times; but most of them have been found too costly for general adoption." Mr. Bohn, in his edition (1846) of Beckmann's History of Inventions (where, Art. "Writing-pens," this subject is exhaustively treated), states, p. 413 n., that he "has in his possession an extremely well-made metallic pen (brass) at least fifty years old, and with it a style for writing by means of smoked paper, both

The condition of this art at the period of its introduction to
literature (*a*) appears to be but slightly in advance of that in
which it had existed from almost unknown antiquity. Seals (*b*) and

in a Morocco pocket-book, which formerly belonged to Horace Walpole, and
was sold at the Strawberry Hill sale." In 1803 Mr. Wire constructed barrel
pens of steel mounted in a bone case for carrying in the pocket; they were
costly and not very successful.—(Tomlinson's Cycl. of Useful Arts, 1854, Art.
" Pens.")  In 1830, Perry introduced the use of apertures between the shoulder
and the point as a means of affording elasticity.  " The total quantity of steel
annually employed in the manufacture of pens has been estimated at 120 tons,
from which upwards of 200,000,000 pens are produced.  . . . .  When first
introduced steel pens were 8*s*. a gross, they afterwards fell to 4*s*. a gross, and
now they are procured at Birmingham for 4*d*. a gross."—Waterston's Cyclo-
pædia of Commerce, 1846.

The manufacture of INKS appears to have been carried to considerable
perfection among the ancients.  In some of the oldest specimens of the
papyri the colours of the ink and other pigments are beautifully preserved.
See also Ov. de Arte Amandi, lib. iii. v. 629.  Pliny, lib. xxxv. c. 6, enumerates
all the materials used in his time for black ink.  Gold and silver inks, and
inks of vermilion, cinnabar, and purple were also used.  (Beckmann, vol. ii.
p. 265, Art. " Indigo.")  Astle (p. 211) mentions a collection of certificates
dating about 1200, in some of which the characters were fresh and black as if
written yesterday; others had changed into brown and yellow hues.  See Weever's
Funeral Monuments, 4to, London, 1767, p. 379, where there is a specimen.  It is
interesting to note, that in these certificates four-fifths are in Norman letters,
some in modern Gothic, and a very few in Lombardic small letters.

Curious particulars connected with this subject will be found in Caneparius
de Atramentis, 4to, Venice, 1619, and Weckerus de Secretis, 8vo, Basle, 1612;
the latter work being compiled from Porta, Cardan, and several older writers.
(Beckmann, Art. " Sympathetic Ink.")

See also, as to the various matters above mentioned, " Historical Account of
the substances which have been used to describe events and convey ideas from
the earliest date to the invention of paper, printed on the first useful paper
manufactured solely from straw," by Matthias Koops, 8vo, London, 1800.
Koops's Patents for the manufacture of paper from straw, hay, thistles, nettles,
refuse hemp, and flax, many kinds of wood-bark and other fibrous materials,
are dated 2 Aug. 1800 (No. 2433) and 17 Feb. 1801 (No. 2481), and Dis. Cur. Lit.
Art. " Origin of the Materials of Writing."

(*a*) There is an amusing article in Disraeli's Curiosities of Literature, respecting
the prices of MSS.; and Roscoe, in his Biography of Lorenzo de Medici, has
adduced a variety of instances of the avidity with which ancient MSS. and early
printed books were sought after and esteemed by the Italian scholars of the
fourteenth and fifteenth centuries.  See Ames's Pref. in Dibd. Typ. Ant. p. 5 (n.),
where some curious particulars on this subject are given.  " Before the finding
out of this illustrious art," says Burges (Some Observations on the Use and
Original of the Noble Art and Mystery of Printing, Harleian Miscellany, vol. iii.,
p. 154) " the Epistle of St. James was thought a mighty pennyworth when
purchased for a load of hay, whereas now (1701) both the Old and New Testament may be bought for five shillings.  It is stated that in numerous
instances the transfer of MSS. was attended with the same formalities as
that of lands.  See also Introductory Memoir on the Public Libraries of the
Ancients, Horne's Introd. to Bibliography, 8vo, Lond., 1814, p. i—xxv.  An
account of the lending libraries before the introduction of printing will be found
in Merryweather's Bibliomania in the Middle Ages; and some remarks on the
regulation and encouragement of books in the twelfth and thirteenth centuries
in the Preface to Horne's Introduction, and in Dibdin, Typ. Ant., p. 7 (n.).

(*b*) Exod. xxviii. 9 and 36; Deut. xxxii. 34; 1 Kings ii. 8; 2 Chron. iii. 7 and 14;
Neh. ix. 38; Esther iii. 12; Jer. xxxii. 10 and 34; Dan. vi. 17; Timperley's Dictionary of Printers and Printing, 8vo., London, 1839, Introd. p. 15; Dibdin
Typ. Ant. p. 3; Hansard's Typographia, 8vo., London, 1825. Herodotus, (cliv.,
cxcv.,) in detailing the customs of Chaldæa or Assyria as they existed in his day,
says that every Assyrian possessed a signet or seal.  " The manner," says Mr. J.
Landseer (Sabæan Researches, p. 3), " in which the engraver's art is spoken of

stamps, as a means of multiplying impressions, were in use in the earliest stages of civilization. Clay bricks, imprinted with a stamp bearing hieroglyphics in relief, have been found on the supposed site of ancient Babylon, of Gour, the ancient capital of Bengal, and other cities of the East (*a*). The names stamped by the Romans on their earthen vessels and coins (*b*) were, in fact,

---

in the Pentateuch, shows that in the time of Moses it was an art of no recent invention, and that among the surrounding nations signets were then common and in well-known use. The onyxes for the sacred ephod, the plate of gold for the mitre of the High Priest, and the precious stones for his breastplate, were all expressly ordered to be engraven like the engravings of a signet, that is, in intaglio; and these words, 'like the engravings of a signet,' are in the book of Exodus frequently repeated."

(*a*) Specimens may be seen in the British Museum, Trinity College, Cambridge, the East India Company's Library, and other collections. See, for a description of one of these, Niebuhr Reise-beschreibung nach Arabien, &c., 4to., Copen., 1774, vol. i. p. 98, where there is a drawing (Tab. XI. fig. A.); Fourmont's Heliopolis, 12 Par. 1755.

(*b*) Dictionnaire de Numismatique Chrétienne; Encyc. Migne; Heineccius de Sigillis. "The invention of COINING was not only a very curious and useful adaptation of this art of engraving to the purposes of society, but is an important event in the history of the world. Stamping impressions on medals and money was a mode of printing the most eminently calculated to resist the attacks of time, and also a mode of circulating and transmitting information the most certain, because itself constituted the woof that gave texture to commerce and strength and extension to the bands of civil society. If truth, therefore, be the basis of history, as surely it is, history must appear to have been peculiarly ungrateful to an art of which it may be no hyperbole to say that it has contributed more than all other arts to the detection of remote error and the verification of fact, for notwithstanding these, its extensive energies, and this, its inestimable importance, it is not known when or in what country money first became the substitute for cattle and unstamped bullion as the general representative of property and the measure of value."—(Landseer's Lectures on Engraving, 1807, 2nd Lecture.) Among the Greeks there existed a tradition that Phidon the Argive was the inventor of weights and measures, and the first who stamped coins; but it is well known that certain ancient writers are not of this opinion. Herodotus (lib. i. c. 94) says that the Lydians first coined money of gold and silver, and some of our modern numismatists are inclined to believe that the money with the type of the tortoise is not the earliest. "The coins," says Akerman, ("Numismatic Manual," 8vo., London, 1840, Art. "Origin of Coinage,") "which by universal consent are allowed to be most ancient have on one side a cavity or indentation, and those assigned to the island of Ægina are thus distinguished and placed among the earliest examples. The type of these coins is a turtle or tortoise, the reverse being merely an indented square divided into segments. Others of a later period have letters and symbols within the square." "Manuel de Numismatique," tom. i. p. 16. But see "Memoirs of the French Academy," vol. xxvi. p. 543.

As regards the antiquity of Grecian coinage we have most certain evidence that it had attained some degree of excellence in the reign of Alexander I., King of Macedon, 497 to 454 B. C., of whom we have authentic coins exhibiting the indented square (Mionnet, Descrip. tom. i. p. 505), a mark which does not disappear until the reign of Augustus II., who reigned from 397 to 371 B. C. Of this monarch we have coins both with and without the indented square (Ib. p. 508). Plutarch (in Lycurg.) informs us that Lycurgus substituted copper money for that of gold and silver current in Lacedæmonia, from which we learn that gold and silver coins were current nine centuries before the Christian era. "This statement," observes M. Hennin ("Manuel de Numismatique," tom. i. p. 18), "requires authentication, for in a passage in the Eryxias, a dialogue attributed to Plato, the Lacedæmonians are said to have used iron weights as money." In the laws of Solon six centuries B.C. the punishment of death is awarded to persons found guilty of counterfeiting the public coin, a fact which justifies the remark

printed; and the letters on the matrices for marking them necessarily inverted (a).

In vol. i. of a " Collection of several Pieces of John Toland," 8vo.,
London, 1726, is a small tract entitled " Conjectura vero similis

---

of Neumann ("Romanorum Numi Anecdoti," p. 197), that "the act of forging
was almost coeval with the coining of money." The Roman coinage differs from
the Greek in the greater size of the copper coins in early times and their superior
workmanship at a later period, as well as in the prevailing simplicity of the
devices adopted. In the first period of the republic they were cast. The con-
sular copper coins have separate symbols for the pieces according to their
respective value, as the head of Janus for the *as*, Jupiter for the *semis*, &c. A
silver coinage was first introduced into Rome 266 B.C., and that of gold sixty
years afterwards. The imperial Roman coins form by far the most complete
and varied series which we possess of ancient or modern times. The symbols
on the reverse have been arranged under four head, as relating to religion, war,
Janus, and the embellishment of the city. The obverses contain the portraits
of emperors and empresses. The characters on the reverses of the coins are
generally speaking explanatory of the type.

In England Roman coins were current until the arrival of the Saxons. We
have the coins of five out of the seven kingdoms of the Heptarchy, among which
are some small copper coins, the only specimens of that metal coined before the
reign of Elizabeth. Coins struck prior to the reign of Charles II. had their
devices impressed by the blows of a hammer. The system of lettering on the
edges which succeeded by graining was invented in order to obviate the
fraudulent practice of clipping and filing the current coin. Brand's account of
the different historical works on the subject of English, Irish, and Scottish coins
will be found in the preface (p. vii. et seq.) to Ruding's "Annals of the Coinage
of Great Britain and its Dependencies, from the earliest Period of authentic
History to the Reign of Victoria," 3 vols. London, 4to. 1840. The third volume
of this work contains beautiful illustrations of the various coins. And see "The
Silver Coins of England arranged and described, with Remarks on British
Money previous to the Saxon Dynasties," by Edward Hawkins, Keeper of Antiquities in British Museum, 8vo. London, 1841, the frontispiece of which contains
drawings of recent coins executed by the Anaglyptograph : also Martin Folkes'
Tables of English Silver and Gold Coins, reprinted by the Society of Anti-
quarians, 1763, 4to. Lond.; The Medallic History of Marcus Aurelius Valerius
Cauransius, Emperor in Brittain, by W. Stukely, 4to. Lond., 1757 ; The Connexion
of the Roman, Saxon, and English Coins, deduced from Observations on the
Saxon Weights and Money, by Wm. Clarke, 4to. Lond., 1769.

The principal improvement effected in this art consisted in the introduction
of the mill and screw, circa A.D. 1561, thus superseding the old and imperfect
mode of hammering. The punching die was fixed to the screw, which was
worked by a flywheel, and the other die fixed in the framework. Before the use
of this mill the edges of the coins were in a very imperfect state. The earliest
specimen of "milled money" (under Elizabeth) has a graining to form a regular
circle on the outside of the legend quite to the edge of the coin.

(a) Several of these (some few in intaglio) in one solid piece of metal may be
seen in the British Museum (Bronze Room). Many hundred pieces of pottery
impressed with these stamps have been found in the sands near Reculver in
Kent and on the east side of the Isle of Sheppey (Astle, ed. 1803, p. 213). " The
*stampillæ* or metal stamps, consisting of monograms, names, marks of goods,
&c., in use among the Romans, afford examples of such a near approach to the
art of printing as first practised that it is truly extraordinary that there has
been no remaining evidence of its having been practised by them, unless we
suppose that they were acquainted with it, and did not choose to adopt for some
reason of state policy."—Samuel Weller Singer, "Researches into the History of
Playing Cards, with Illustrations of the Origin of Printing and of Engraving
on Wood," 4to., Lond., 1816, pp. 89 and 90, where there are impressions from the
original stamps. See also Nouveau Traité, p. iii. sec. 5, chap. 2, act 1, where
there are drawings. Macpherson (Annals of Commerce, vol. i. p. 119) supposes
the types alluded to in the above quotation to have been used without colouring
matter.

de primæ Typographiæ Inventione," which is founded upon the passage in Cicero (De Natura Deorum, cap. xx. lib. 2), where Balbus, a stoic, uses the following words in an argument against Velleius, an epicurean : " Hic ego non miror esse aliquem qui sibi " persuadeat corpora quædam solida atque individua vi et gravitate " ferri mundumque effici ornatissimum et pulcherrimum ex eorum " concursione fortuita ? Hoc qui existimet fieri potuisse non intel- " ligo cur non idem putet si innumerabiles unius et viginti formæ " literarum (vel aureæ vel quales libet) aliquo conjiciantur : posse " ex his in terram excussis annales Ennii, ut deinceps legi possint " effici, quod nescio anne in uno quidem versu possit tantum valere " fortuna." *Formæ literarum*, it should be observed, is the very term used for types by the early printers. Again, in the book " De Divinatione," cap. x. lib. 3, Cicero uses the phrase " impri- mere literas."

Brands for marking cattle were in use in Virgil's time (Georg., lib. iii. v. 158) :—

> " Continuoque notas et nomina gentis inurunt."

Procopius, in his " Historia Arcana," says that the Emperor Jus- tinian, not being able to write his name, had a thin smooth piece of board, through which were cut holes in the form of the four letters J U S T, which, being laid on the paper, served to direct the point of his pen, which was dipped in red ink.

By some the origin of printing is ascribed to the East, where it is said to have been practised from a very early period (*a*). Marco Polo, who returned from China about the end of the thirteenth century, describes (*b*) the fabrication of paper money by means of a stamp and vermilion pigment. A Persian work, published in 1317 (*c*), speaks of printing as an art in common use.

The first application of this art in the West was to the manufacture of PLAYING CARDS (*d*) and devotional pictures (*e*), which were printed

---

(*a*) P. Jovius Hist., lib. xiv. p. 226, ed. Florent., 1550, from which Osorius and several other writers have embraced the same opinion.

(*b*) De Regionibus Orientis.

(*c*) The Historia Sinensis of Abdalla. See Meerman, vol. i. pp. 16 and 218, vol. ii. p. 186 (n).

(*d*) "At what time the application of xylography to the purpose of multiplying cards took place, it is not now possible to ascertain with certainty, but there can be no doubt that they were among the first objects it produced, and we have reason to conclude that they were printed from engraved blocks of wood at least as early as the fourteenth century, if they were not derived with this art from the Eastern world at an earlier period, a supposition which is not entirely devoid of probability."—Singer, p. 230, and see authorities cited in vol. i. Bibliotheca Spenceriana, " Works executed in the Infancy of Printing," p. ii. (note).

(*e*) As to the order in which these uses were made of the art, see Breitkopf Ursprung der Spielkarten, 4to., Leipzic, 1784.

from originals carved in relief on wood. There is an account of the execution of woodcuts in Italy as early as 1285 (a). Cards were certainly known in Germany in 1376 (b), in Castile and France in 1387 (c), and in England in 1464 (d). A Venetian decree, dated 11 October 1441, recites that the art and mystery of making "playing cards and colored figures printed" (carte e figure stampide) had fallen into decay in that city (e).

The earliest print of ascertained date is one in the Spencer Gallery, representing St. Christopher carrying the infant Jesus across the sea (f). This piece is of the folio size and coloured in the manner of our playing cards. It is accompanied by an inscription (g), and bears the date 1423.

"The gradual progress from these images with inscriptions to
" copies of the historical drawings annexed to the Biblical histories
" was natural and easy. A series of these would of course follow,
" with explanations annexed, engraved on the same block" (h). The

(a) See as to the engravings of the two Cunios, dedicated to Honorius II., Papillon, *Traité Historique, &c., de la Gravure en Bois*, 8vo., Paris, 1766, vol. i. p. 84, where also are many curious particulars relative to Oriental block printing; Singer, p. 95; Ottley, Inquiry into the Early History of Engraving, 2 vols., 4to., Lond., 1816, vol. i. pref. p. xi. and p. 84.

(b) Heineken Idée Generale d'une Collection complette d'Estampes avec une Dissertation sur l'origine de la Gravure et sur les premiers Livres d'Images, 8vo., Leipz., 1771, p. 241; Hüber's Notices des Graveurs, p. 47; Manuel des Amateurs de l'Art, vol. i. p. 86; Dibdin, Typ. Ant. iv. See Buller, Recherches Historiques sur les Cartes à jouer, 8vo., 1759.

(c) "It appears certain that the outlines of three packs of cards furnished for the use of Charles VI. of France in 1392 at the low price of fifty sous for the whole must have been printed and afterwards gilt and colored by hand."—Ottley, pref. p. xi. (See Singer, 45, 69.) For specimens of illuminated prints (the originals of which are in the Bodleian), see Strutt's Dictionary of Engravers; *Cartes à jouer*, published for the Société des Bibliophiles de Paris.

(d) When their importation was prohibited by Statute 3 Edw. IV. c. 4.

(e) Ottley, vol. i. pp. 46, 93.

(f) Facsimiles of this print may be seen in the Bibliotheca Spenceriana, by Dibdin, vol. i. p. 3, Heineken, Jansen (*Essai sur la Gravure*, vol. ii. p. 107), and various other writers. A coloured facsimile, full size, will be found in Mr. Ottley's beautiful work, vol. i. p. 91. See also Huber, Notices des Graveurs, p. 47; Id. Manuel des Amateurs de l'Art, vol. i. p. 86; Dibd. Typ. Ant., vol. i. p. iv. This print was discovered by Heincken at Buxheim, near Augsburg, one of the most ancient monasteries in Germany. It was pasted within one of the covers of a Latin MS. of the year 1417. Ottley (vol. i. p. 97) supposes it to be of Italian origin.

(g) Cristofori faciem die quacumq : tueris:· ⎱ Millesimo cccc
Ella nempe die morte mala non morieris:· ⎰ rr° tertio.

(h) Singer, 109. Heineken Idée Générale, p. 252. For specimens of the most important of these block books issued in Holland, Flanders, and Germany, see Mr. Sotheby's beautiful work, Principia Typographica, 3 vols. 4to. Lond., 1858. An impression from an original block of an edition of the Apocalypse, supposed to have been executed between 1420 and 1430, may be seen in the Bibliotheca Spenceriana, vol. i. p. 214. See for an account of this block, Astle, 215.

text gradually assumed more important proportions, and thus
ushered in the era of "block books." The mode of preparing the
wooden blocks from which they were printed and the mode of
printing them (by passing a cloth rubber over the paper, the latter
being laid upon the block) (*a*) has a very considerable similarity to
that adopted in China at the present day (*b*). The paper was printed
on one side only, the blank sides being pasted together so as to
form one leaf (*c*).

"The books of this period are divided into two classes, viz.,
"books of images without text, and books of images with text.
"Of the former class (*d*), the most celebrated specimen is the *Biblia*

---

(*a*) Ottley, vol. 1, p. 81. A similar plan is adopted for taking proofs of woodcuts
at the present day.

(*b*) The mode now in use in China is in all probability that which has been
employed for many centuries. The matter to be printed is written on thin
paper, and made to adhere face downwards to a wooden block; the wood is then
cut away from around the characters with wonderful rapidity, leaving the
letter standing in low relief. The whole block (relief and hollow) is then
brushed over with a thin ink, a sheet of paper laid upon the block, and rubbed
dexterously with a soft brush, so as to take the impression of the relief alone.
It is stated by Du Halde that one man can in this manner print off 10,000
copies in a day. The sheet is printed on one side only, and folded, when printed,
so as to present a double edge to the reader, the loose edges being all gathered
at the back of the book. "The invention of these tablets has been ascribed by
many writers even to an earlier period than the commencement of the Christian era; but it is with more probability assigned by the very accurate Phil
Couplet to the year 930."—Bowyer and Nichols' Essay on Printing, 8vo. Lond.,
1776, p. 22 (n.) In Hone's Every-Day Book, p. 185, the celebrated printer,
letter founder, and bookseller, Breitkopf, is stated to have printed Chinese
characters with moveable types. The "Canton Gazette" of the present day, a
kind of Court Journal of appointments, arrivals, and departures, is stated
("Sketches in China") to be printed with moveable types. See also a notice
in Gutzlaff's "China Opened," 1848. Horne's Introd. 202.

(*c*) Astle, 215.

(*d*) The following list is given in Horne's Introduction to the Study of Bibliography, App. 1:—

Sec. I., Books of Images without text.

1. Biblia Pauperum.
2. Historia Sancti Johannis Evangelistæ.
3. Historia Virginis Mariæ ex Cantico Canticorum.
4. Historia Virginis Mariæ ex Evangelistis.
5. Exercitium Super Pater Noster.

Sec. II., Books of Images with text.

1. Der Entkrist.
2. Quindecim Signa extremi Judicii.
3. Ars Memorandi notabilis per Figuras.
4. Ars Moriendi.
5. Sujets tirés de l'Ecriture Sainte.
6. Speculum Humanæ Salvationis.
7. Die Kunst Cyromantia.

The adventures of the Chevalier Teurdanncks, executed at Nuremberg,
A.D. 1507.

" *Pauperum* (*a*), and of the latter (*b*), the *Speculum Humanæ Salva-*
" *tionis*. Both are without date, and their production has been attri-
" ~~buted to different periods, varying from 1420 to 1450 (*c*). In the~~
" latter work the text accompanying the figures is printed for the
" most part with moveable characters in one edition, and in the
" other entirely so."

" The change and improvement from the manner in which these
" books of images were executed to moveable wooden characters
" seems obvious and not very difficult, but there is no evidence
" that they were ever used except in the capital letters of some
" early printed books " (*d*).

" The religious treatises were followed by donatuses, or brief
" manuals of grammar for the instruction of youth, ' which are re-
" corded not only to have led the way to the invention of typo-
" graphy, but to have been among the first books attempted to be
" executed with moveable types' " (*e*).

The further progress of the art, by the employment of moveable

---

(*a*) The latest writer, Mr. Sotheby (Principia Typographica, 4to., Lond., 1858, Introd., p. vi.) says, " In arranging the several editions of the principal block-books in what appeared to me to be the order of their issue I found that the edition of the Apocalypse, placed by Heineken as the *first* of the work, I had considered to be the *last;* so likewise in respect to the *Biblia Pauperum* and the *Ars Moriendi*."—See (as to the place of their production) Ottley, chap. iii., and Heineken, Idée Générale, p. 325.

(*b*) " This book consists of forty leaves, printed on one side of the paper only, by friction from as many blocks. The colour is brown, the pages are placed opposite to each other, and the blank backs being pasted together form one strong leaf. The cuts are about 10 in. in height and 7½ in width. Each print contains three sacred subjects in compartments, and four half-length figures of prophets in smaller divisions, two above and two beneath the principal subjects. Latin inscriptions are on either side of the upper figures; rhythmical verses on either side of the lower; and additional inscriptions are on labels at the bottom of the whole. The central subjects are from the New Testament, and the others from the Old, and in some manner allusive to the former. There are many copies of the work, evidently from different blocks, and of different dates. Indeed, it appears to have been a most popular book, and was printed re-peatedly long after the introduction of legitimate printing. There are several editions in which the inscriptions are actually printed with moveable types. . . . Dr. Horne possessed a copy contained in one volume with the *Ars Moriendi* and *Apocalypse*, all works of the same style, the binding of which bore the date of 142(?)." — Encyc. Brit., art. " Printing." Ottley in a note (vol. i. p. 34) says, that the paper was used in a dry state for printing these books. A specimen, of the date 1475, is in the Grenville Library, case I., of the British Museum. Facsimiles are in Mr. Sotheby's recent work, vol. i. p. 44.

(*c*) See " An Inquiry into the Origin and Early History of Engraving upon Copper and in Wood, with an Account of Engravers and their Works, from the Invention of Chalcography to the time of Marc' Antonio Raimondi, by W. Y. Ottley," 4to., Lond., 1816.

(*d*) Timperley, p. 94.

(*e*) Singer, p. 109. Astle, p. 214, supposes that the repair of particular types, by gluing in fresh ones, suggested the hint of moveable types of metal.

types, was rendered feasible by the existence in the West of an alphabetic system of writing (*a*).

Where, when, and by whom printing with moveable types was first practised, it seems impossible to determine with any certainty. The claims to this honour are now limited to those of Laurenz

---

(*a*) The introduction and invention of letters has from a very early period formed a subject of inquiry. Herodotus, Pliny, Plutarch, and others ascribe its introduction to the West to Cadmus—a Phœnician who founded Thebes, B.C. 1500. There seem grounds for supposing it to have been imported from the East. The oldest Greek letters (Astle, p. 66, Nouveau Traité de Diplomatique, vol. i. p. 616) are written from right to left, the mode to this day prevalent to the East, and curious specimens, termed Boustrophedon (Nouveau Traité de Diplomatique, vol. i., Ency. Brit., art. " Boustrophedon") writings, in which the writings read from left to right, and right to left alternately, mark the transition to the system now obtaining. (See for a specimen of a very ancient inscription, (the Sigeian,) 500 B.C., of this kind, Astle, 66, and Hansard, 43, where there are drawings.) The inscriptions on the pedestal of the Colossus of Delos and the Tripods of Thebes, supposed to be almost contemporary with it, read from right to left only. (See as to Eastern character, the works of the Abbés Fourmont and Barthélemy, Wilkinson's Materia Hieroglyphica, 4to., Malta, 1828.)

For speculations on the origin of this art, and specimens of its several stages, from the merely imitative representations of natural objects to the adoption of arbitrary characters, the reader should consult the Nouveau Traité de Diplomatique (où l'on examine les fondemens de cet art ou etablit des règles sur le discernement des titres et l'on expose historiquement les caractères des bulles pontificales et des diplomes donnés en chaque siècle avec des éclaircissemens sur un nombre considerable de points d'histoire, de chronologie, de critique, et de discipline et la réfutation de diverses accusations intentées contre beaucoup d'Archives célébres, et surtout contre celles des Anciennes Eglises); par deux Benedictins de la Congrégation de St. Maur, 6 vols. 4to., Paris, 1750; Reflexions sur l'Alphabet et sur la Langue dont on se servait autrefois à Palmyre, par M. l'Abbé Barthélémy, 4to., Paris, 1774; De Wailly, Elémens de Palæographie, 2 vols., 4to. Paris; the Origin and Progress of Writing, as well hieroglyphic as elementary, illustrated by engravings taken from marbles, MSS., and charters, ancient and modern; also some Account of the Origin and Progress of Printing, 2nd ed. with additions, by Thomas Astle, Keeper of the Records of the Tower of London, folio, Lond., 1803. Timperley, Dictionary of Printers and Printing, 8vo., Lond., 1839, Introduction. Du Halde professes to have discovered that the Chinese characters are entirely of hieroglyphic character.

Various efforts have been made to establish characters that should be universal, or expressive of things, instead of merely representatives of different sounds. The earliest attempts were made by Dalgarno and Bishop Wilkins, (" Essay towards a Real Character and a Philosophical Language," folio, London, 1668.) Leibnitz has also propounded a scheme. Lodwick (Philos. Trans., 1686) gives a plan of an universal alphabet to " contain an enumeration of all such single sounds or letters as are used in any language." The Journal Littéraire of 1730 contains a project for a universal character by means of the Arabic numerals. See also 11 Rep. Arts. See post, sub A.D. 1655; Marquis of Worcester's Century of Inventions.

Literal characters are divided partly according to the people by whom they are in use and partly according to various styles adopted by the same people. Thus the type foundries of the present day, in addition to the varieties of English type, contain Arabic, Armenian, Coptic, Domesday, Engrossing, Ethiopic, Etruscan, German, Greek, Alexandrian Greek, Gothic, Hebrew, Irish, Malabaric, Malayan, Nazari or Bramin, Persian, Philosophical, Runic, Russian, Samaritan, Sanskrit, Saxon, Sclavonian (or ancient Russian), Script (imitation of writing), Swedish, Syriac, Tamoul, Telegu, and Turkish, besides " black letter," music, and a great variety of fancy types. The Imperial press at Paris is said to possess the type of fifty-six eastern languages, being all that are known of the characters of Asia, ancient and modern, also the type of sixteen European tongues which do not use the ordinary Roman characters.

Coster, of Haarlem, Faust, of Mentz, and Guttenberg and Mentilius, of Strasburg (*a*).

---

(*a*) Pretensions were also advanced in favour of Nicholas Jansen of Venice, until it became clear that books were printed before the date attributed to the earliest of his works The claim on behalf of Coster was first brought forward by Hadrianus Junius many years after Coster's death, in his work entitled Batavia, published at Leyden, January, 1575. The account (p. 253) is given by the historian on the authority of his tutor, Nicholas Gelius, who had heard it from a bookbinder who had worked for Coster. The passage is given in Johnson's Typographia, vol. i. p. 7. On the singular controversy to which this point has given rise, the very learned bibliographer, Dr. Dibdin, who himself inclines to Gutenberg and Faust, has the following remarks (Typ. Ant., " Preliminary Disquisition on early Engraving and ornamental Printing," p. xxxi. (n.) :—" The great error, as I humbly submit, in almost all preceding treatises upon the origin and progress of printing, has been the determination of each writer to support through the most formidable objections the claims of that country and of that typographical artist in whose cause he sat out as the avowed champion. The strong attachment of Junius to *Holland* and *Coster*, in aid of which he exercised a poetical fancy, has been even exceeded by the enthusiasm [or, as some call it, obstinacy] of Meerman towards the same objects. When the latter commenced his inquiries, it is certain that he had no very extensive information upon the subject. Dr. Ducarel threw out some hints relating to the claims of Holland, which, as Meerman was a native of that country, he seized with avidity, and resolved to expand and consolidate them into a systematic history. Accordingly, after publishing a small octavo volume as a specimen of his large work, he appeared before the public with his portrait in his *Origines Typographicæ* in two quarto volumes, along with a fictitious head of his beloved Coster, beautifully engraved by Houbraken. Meerman's is a learned and valuable work, and is in the hands of every bibliographer. The author had himself a fine library, and was exceedingly kind and liberal in giving the curious permission to see it. But though it be absolutely necessary to possess his performance, yet it is not free from gross errors, which have been attacked perhaps with too much severity by the acute and experienced Heineken. This latter was a *German*, and a like patriotic ardour induced *him* to give the palm of having discovered the art of printing to Mentz and Strasburg. Heineken, as now seems to be allowed, has paid too little attention to the claims of Haarlem, and Meerman infinitely too much : thus, although both set out with professing to adhere to truth, both have described her not as she really was, but as they had *conceived or wished her to be*. The Parisian bibliographers, as their own metropolis had never been considered the cradle of the typographic art, and as they had in consequence no national prejudices on this score to espouse, have been more just and satisfactory. The recent treatises of Lambinet, Oberlin, Fischer, Daunou, and Santander are highly creditable to their respective authors."

A mere list of the works published on this subject would far exceed the limits of a note. Mallinkrot, who collected with great industry the testimony on both sides of the question, classifies the authors who had written on the subject at the date of his treatise "De ortu et progressu Artis Typographicæ," 4to. Col., 1640, as follows :—

| | |
|---|---:|
| For Mentz, before the dispute was started by Dr. Junius | 62 |
| Those who have written on the same side since Junius | 47 |
| | **109** |
| Those who have written in favour of Haarlem | 13 |
| Those who are neutral | 11 |
| | **24** |

Since that period numerous and valuable treatises have appeared on the same subject. A list of authors consulted and referred to by Dibdin in the compilation of his Typographical Antiquities, is given at the end of the first volume of that work. A list of works on the history and art of printing, including a brief

The earliest complete printed book known (*a*), commonly called the Mazarine Bible, or the "Mentz Bible without date," is supposed to have issued from the press of Guttenberg and Faust, at Mentz, about 1455. The initial letters in this are illuminated by hand (*b*). In 1455, Guttenberg seceded from the business, which was continued by Faust and Schöffer, his son-in-law, at Mentz. The next book was the celebrated Psalter, printed by them in August 1457. The small letters of this edition were of metal, the

---

analysis of the author's hypothesis relative to the origin and invention of typography, will be found in Horne's Introduction to Bibliography, pp. 469-507.

An article prefixed to Dibdin's Typographical Antiquities, entitled " Some Account of Caxton," the following passage occurs (lxxxvii. n.):—" The reader will be pleased to accept of the following sketch relating to this important, but most intricate and involved subject, so true being the remark of Oxonides, that "the Art of Printing, which has given light to most other things, hides its own head in darkness ;" or, according to Daunou, " We live too near the epoch of the discovery of printing to judge accurately of its influence, and too far from it to know exactly the circumstances which gave birth to it."

The following remarks are by the latest writer on the subject, Mr. Sotheby (Principia Typographica, 1858, Introd. ii.):—"It will, however, be seen that while endeavouring to keep free from any direct controversy, I have been led to believe that the statement of Junius, ascribing to Lawrence Coster the discovery of the art in question, may be substantially correct, supported as it is by the disinterested evidence of Ulric Zell, who has recorded that the art of printing in Germany was derived from the donatuses which had been printed in Holland."

To account for the obscurity of this question, it should be observed that the earliest productions of the press are without name or date. The first book issued with a date was *Literæ Indulgentiarum Nicholai V.*, printed on a single piece of parchment, by Faust and Schöffer, in 1455; after which date the practice of prefixing or subjoining the printer's name became common.

The invention is even said to have been purposely concealed, and an oath of secrecy to have been imposed upon all who were employed in it. The form of the types (that used in the MS. writings of the date) is supposed to have been adopted with that view. Timperley, 102 ; Essai sur la Calligraphie des Manuscrits du Moyen Age, et sur les Ornements des premiers Livres d'heures imprimes, par E. H. Langlois, 8vo. Rouen, 1841. It is stated that Faust, having printed off a considerable number of copies of the Bible, carried them to Paris, where he endeavoured to dispose of them as MSS. " Enabled to sell his copies at 60 crowns, while the other scribes demanded 500, this raised universal astonishment, and still more when he produced copies as fast as they were wanted, and even lowered his price. The uniformity of the copies increased the wonder. Informations were given in to the magistrates against him as a magician, and in searching his lodgings a great number of copies were found. The red ink (and Faust's red ink is peculiarly brilliant) which embellished his copies was said to be his blood, and it was solemnly adjudged that he was in league with the devil. Faust at length was obliged, to save himself from a bonfire, to reveal his art to the Parliament of Paris, who discharged him from all prosecution in consideration of his useful invention."—Disraeli's Curiosities of Literature, art. " Early Printing;" Meerman, vol. i. p. 6. See Quart. Rev. (A.D. 1840), vol. 65, p. 19. Timperley's Dictionary, p. 108. Hence the story of the Devil and Dr. Faustus.

(*a*) A copy is in the King's Library at the British Museum.

(*b*) Astle, 218. The following dates are given in Hansard's Typography :— Printing from blocks, about 1422; from letters cut separately in wood, 1438 ; from letters cut separately in metal, 1450; and from letters cast in moulds, 1456. For a list of works published by Gutenberg, see *Peignot*, Dict. de Bibliol., 3 vols., pp. 129, 130. Fischer, Essai sur les Monumens Typographiques de Jean Gutenberg, 4to. Mayence, 1802.

capitals of wood (a); but Meerman asserts that the former were
cut not cast, and that the earliest instance of printing with cast
types is Durand's "Rationale Divinorum," printed with an
entirely new fount of type by Faust and Schöffer, in October 1459.
In 1459 they reprinted the Psalter; in 1460, the Constitutiones
Clementiæ (b), and in 1462, the celebrated Latin Bible, with well
proportioned evenly standing type.

Faust was carried off at Paris, about 1466, by the plague. Schöffer
survived him many years, and in conjunction with Conrad Henliff,
produced a great number of works. His name is found in the
Colophon (c) of the fourth edition of the Bible in 1502, about which
time he is supposed to have died.

By the adoption of the three improvements above indicated,
namely, the employment of moveable types, the casting of those
types in metal, and the formation of matrices for this purpose by
punches of hardened steel, the art of printing was brought
essentially to the state in which we now possess it. The subsequent improvements, so far as letter-press printing is concerned,
until a very recent period, are rather in the mechanism for obtaining the copies from the printing surface than any variation in the
printing surface itself.

On the dispersion of the printers at Mentz, by the sacking of
that town in 1462, the art was carried into various countries, and
so rapid was its progress that before the close of the century it had
become established in every city and town of note in Europe (d).
In Italy and France the Gothic character was succeeded by the
Roman and Italic. The first book printed with Greek type was the
production of an Italian press in 1476 (e).

---

(a) See Astle, 207.

(b) A copy on vellum is in the British Museum.

(c) " The conclusion of a book formerly containing the place or year, or both,
of its publication."—Webster. The derivation of this word is variously given
in almost every dictionary. Some (see Liddell and Scott, Scheller, Brande,
and Ency. Met., vol. xvii. p. 28,) are highly fanciful. Scapula and Suidas render
the Greek word Κολοφών, *fastigium, apex, seu summa manus, finis,* which is
probably the correct source, &c.

(d) A list of the places where, the times when, and the persons by whom the
art was practised prior to the year of 1500 will be found in Johnson's Typographia, vol. i. p. 58.

(e) In addition to the Roman and Italic characters of the modern type founders.
An exclusive privilege in respect of the use of these types was granted 1495
by the Venetian State to Aldus, who employed them in the composition of the
"Aldine" classics.

The first to practise printing in England was William Caxton (*a*), who, in the year 1474, printed in a chapel (*b*) near the Abbey at Westminster "The Game and Playe of the Chesse" (*c*). He had learnt the art abroad, and tells us himself that he began to print his translation of the " Recueil des Histoires de Troye," at Bruges, in 1468, that he continued the work at Ghent, and finished it at Cologne in 1471 (*d*). In 1475 he printed "The Book of Jason ;" and in 1477, " The Dictes and Sayings of the Philosophers" (*e*).

---

(*a*) This point has also been the subject of a very animated controversy. Mr. Dibdin's remark on it is as follows :—" Although Caxton is called by me the first English printer, yet I fully believe in the authenticity of the Oxford edition of the Expositio Sancti Jeronimi in symbolum Apostolorum, &c., of the date 1468, which was printed by a foreigner," Corsellis, " at Oxford, who was afterwards interrupted in the prosecution of his labours." This volume was discovered soon after the Restoration in the Public Library at Cambridge. The more common opinion is that the date is a typographical error (by the omission of an X.) for 1478, from which period the productions of the Oxford press were continuous. Similar instances of omission or transposition of letters or figures denoting the date occur frequently in early books ; one is that of a Bible printed at Augsburgh with date 1449 for 1494. Chevillier (Origine de l'Imprimerie de Paris, c. v. p. 76) mentions three ; one at Paris, dated 1443 ; another at Lyons, 1446 ; a third at Basil, dated 1450 ; although printing was not used in any of those places till long after. Orlandi describes three books with the like mistake from Mentz ; and Koelhoff who first printed about 1470, has dated one of his books MCCCC. omitting a C., and another 1458, which Palmer (History of Printing, p. 179) imputes to design rather than mistake. A copy of this work is in the Grenville Library. "Caxton's claim remained undisputed for nearly two centuries, until the year 1642, when a dispute arose between some persons who printed by virtue of a patent from the Crown and the Company of Stationers respecting the patents. A committee was appointed, who heard counsel for and against the petitioners, and in the course of the pleadings Caxton was acknowledged incontestably as the first printer in England." Horne, 177.
(*b*) Hence, it is supposed, is derived the term "chapel," applied to a printing office in the present day. The men meeting to consider and frame regulations for the good order of the office are said to "hold a chapel." Harleian Miscellany, vol. iii. p. 155.
(*c*) The title was " *The Game and Playe of Chesse, translated out of the Frenche, and emprynted by me, William Caxton. Fynisshed the last day of March, the yer of our Lord God a thousand foure hundred and lxxiiij.*" " To the west of the sanctuary in Westminster Abbey stood the eleemosynary or almonry, where the first printing press in England was erected, in 1471, by William Caxton, encouraged by the learned Thomas Milling, then Abbot. He produced " *The Game and Play of Chesse,*" the first book ever printed in these kingdoms. There is a slight difference about the place in which it was printed, but all agree that it was within the precincts of this religious house." Leigh.
"This Art of Printing," says Burges (Harleian Miscellany, vol. iii. p. 155), "was first brought into England by Simon Islip in the year 1471, at the charge of King Henry VI., whence printing was for many years accounted the King's prerogative as much as coining, but in process of time it became a free trade. The first printing press in England was set up by the fore-named Simon Islip, in Westminster Abbey, London, and printing was used there by William Caxton."
(*d*) A copy of this book is in the Library of the British Museum, Case viii. In this work Caxton takes care to explain to his readers that the work is printed, "not wreton with pen and inke, as other bokes ben, to thende that euery man may haue them attones (at once), ffor all the bokes of this story, named the Recule of the History of Troyes, thus emprynted as ye see here were begon in oon day and also fynished in oon day."
(*e*) For an account of Caxton's other works, see Dibdin's Typ. Ant. vol. i. p. cxxxv., and Johnson's Typographia, vol. i. p. 209, where a list is given, with

their supposed degree of rarity. The following observations on the peculiarities of Caxton's productions are from Lewis's Life of Caxton, p. 124:—
"As to Mr. Caxton's printing, it has been observed that his first performances are very rude and barbarous. He used a letter resembling the handwriting then in use. His d at the end of a word is very singular (an illustration is given in the work quoted from). . . . . He used the characteristics which we find in the English MSS. before the Conquest. . . . . Instead of commas and periods, he used a transverse or oblique stroke, thus /, as the Dutch printers do to this day in their gothic impressions. Mr. Palmer observed that he used a letter peculiar to himself, and which is easily known from any other, being a mixture of secretary and gothic as to shape, and sometimes of great primer as to size, especially in printing proper names. He had a way of joining almost any two characters together, which, perhaps, might induce Mr. Bayford to suppose that the types which he used were not distinct or fusible types made of metal and cast in moulds as they are now. In his titles he used the German text, or what our printers call the gothic, of the size of great primer, and sometimes he mixed it with his secretary or common print, as our printers now do the italic. Like the other printers of his time, he never used any direction or catch words, but placed the signatures where that now stands, and rarely numbered his leaves, but never his pages. . . . . Mr. Palmer has observed that the Liber Festialis or Festivalis is the only one of his books whose lines are not spaced out to the end, which, he says, is an after improvement and elegancy introduced by Mr. Caxton in imitation of foreign printers. In most of his books which I have seen he only printed, as the custom then was, a small letter at the beginning of his chapters, to intimate what the initial or capital letter should be, and left that to be made by the illuminator, who wrote it with a pen and red, blue, or green ink. Thus are the initial letters in his edition of the Polychronicon made with red ink, but in some of his books he used flourished initials, or what the printers call blooming capitals." See Johnson's Typographia, vol. i. pp. 110, 111, where specimens are given.

The following are specimens of the various sized types in use at the present day :—

*Great Primer.*

PRINTING is the Art of mechanically

*English.*

PRINTING is the Art of mechanically multip

*Pica.*

PRINTING is the Art of mechanically multiplying

*Small Pica.*

PRINTING is the Art of mechanically multiplying perm

*Long Primer.*

PRINTING is the Art of mechanically multiplying permanent

*Bourgeois.*

PRINTING is the Art of mechanically multiplying permanent facsi

*Brevier.*

PRINTING is the Art of mechanically multiplying permanent facsimiles,

*Minion.*

PRINTING is the Art of mechanically multiplying permanent facsimiles (in

*Nonpareil.*

PRINTING is the Art of mechanically multiplying permanent facsimiles (invert

*Ruby.*

PRINTING is the Art of mechanically multiplying permanent facsimiles (inverted or direct)

*Pearl.*

PRINTING is the Art of mechanically multiplying permanent facsimiles (inverted or direct) of an

*Diamond.*

PRINTING is the Art of mechanically multiplying permanent facsimiles (inverted or direct) of an original. The

Caxton died in 1491. His immediate successors were Wynkyn de Worde (a), Richard Pynson, and Julian Notary, the latter of whom printed as late as 1520 (b).

In 1478 presses were set up at both Universities, and two years afterwards at St. Albans.

There is no certainty of the establishment of the press in Scotland until 1507, when Walter Chapman, a merchant of Edinburgh, obtained the King's patent for himself and Andrew Miller to carry on the business of printing (c). The first book of which there appears to be any account is "A Breviary" of the Church of Aberdeen, printed by Walter Chapman at Edinburgh, 1509 (d).

The first book known to have been printed in Ireland is the Book of Common Prayer, printed with sole privilege, "in officina Humphredi Poweli," A.D. 1551.

THE PRESS used by the early printers was very rude (e). It was composed entirely of wood, and consisted of a table, along which the coffin containing the form, and furnished with a tympan and frisket, was pushed by hand. The platen worked vertically between standards, and was brought down for the impression and raised after it by a common screw, worked by a bar handle. The platen was only half the size of the form, which had therefore to be shifted to complete the impression. The inking was performed by hand with skin pelts.

Little or no improvement was made in respect of the press until the year 1601 (f), when Blaew, of Amsterdam, contrived a press, the platen of which recovered itself by a spring. This became universally adopted, and remained in use with little variation (g) until

(a) This printer was the first in England to use the round Roman letter, which had been cut abroad by Sweyheim and Pannartz, under the patronage of the sub-librarian of Paul II.

(b) A list of the works of each English printer, from this period down to 1599, may be seen in Johnson's Typographia, vol. i. p. 481, et seq.

(c) Chalmer's Life of Ruddiman, p. 80.

(d) Ames, Typ. Ant., by Herbert (ed. 1790), vol. iii. p. 1468.

(e) A good idea of the presses on the old principle will be derived from a device of Badius Ascensius of Lyons, 1495–1535, inserted on the title pages of his books in various sizes, and an engraving (bearing date 1560) frequently used as a device by printers on the Continent at that period. A copy is in Dibdin's Typ. Ant., Preliminary Disquisition, p. lvii., and Johnson, vol. ii. p. 498. The same colophons show the method of applying the ink to the types. It was laid in some thickness on the corners of a stone slab, and thence taken in small portions and ground with a muller, and so taken up by the balls and applied to the type. The types were disposed in cases similar to the present, but the composing stick was somewhat different.

(f) Haydn's Dictionary of Dates, art. "Printing." A drawing of this press, as worked in 1771, may be seen in Luckombe, p. 293. There seems to be some confusion as to the author of this improvement, it being by some attributed to the father, Nicholas Blaew, and by others to the son, Willem Jansen Blaew.

(g) See Johnson's Typographia, vol. ii. p. 502, where the "improved wooden press" is described and a drawing given.

the end of the last century. At this period a great change took
place by the introduction of presses, known as the "Apollo,"
Roworth's, and the "Stanhope." In all these the platen was made
of a size sufficient to cover the entire form.

The "Apollo," the first in order, was imported from France.
The platen was of iron. Its lower surface, which was of brass,
was ground perfectly flat, and was of such thickness as not to bend
or yield at the parts most distant from the centre of pressure. The
spindle was joined by connecting rods to a long lever placed by
the side of the press, which was wrought by the pressman with
both hands in a vertical plane, like the handle of a pump. The
press, however, was worked only with great labour, and fell into
disuse (a).

Roworth's press is considered by some to have been the first
real improvement on the common press. Here the spindle is
entirely plain, and works at its upper end in a socket at the head
of the press, and at its lower in a cup on the upper side of the
platen. On a shoulder at the upper end of the spindle is a circular collar of steel (b), about 8 inches in diameter, the upper
surface of which forms, at opposite sides of the spindle, two
similar inclined planes, rising rapidly at first and gradually decreasing in inclination. In the head of the press are fixed two
solid rollers or studs of steel, which as the spindle is turned (about
one-third of a revolution by a lever at the off side of the press)
act upon the inclines so as to bring the platen down with constantly decreasing velocity and increasing force until it reaches
the type. The platen recovers itself by a weighted lever. It is
strengthened by fastening to its upper side an iron piece almost
the size of the entire platen in the "two-pull" presses which had
been formerly in use.

In 1798, Earl Stanhope perfected the press that bears his name (c).
It consists of a heavy cast-iron frame in one piece, screwed to a
wooden cross. It was furnished with rails, along which the type-
carriage was run under the platen by means of a rounce and bands (c).
The descent of the platen was caused by a screw worked by a

---

(a) Encyc. Met., viii. 775.
(b) Chilled cast iron was subsequently found to be better adapted for the
formation of the collar and studs.
(c) In the construction of this press, Hansard (Typographia, p. 637,) remarks
his Lordship "must have found many useful hints in M. Anisson's Premier Mé-
moire sur l'Impression en Lettres, suivi de la Description d'une Nouvelle Presse,
exécutée pour le Service du Roi."
(d) A general view of the press is given in Johnson's Typographia, vol. ii. p. 537;
Encyc. Met., p. lxxx., figs. 2 and 9.

peculiar combination of levers (*a*), so arranged as to act with progressively increasing force until the platen reaches the types. A moveable stop regulated the range of the handle, and consequently the pressure exerted on the types.

With this machine about 250 impressions could be taken, or 125 sheets printed, on both sides in an hour; and although by excessive labour a greater number was produced in newspaper printing offices, yet it was necessary to have duplicate presses, and set up forms of type to carry on such work, and still the production of copies was quite inadequate to satisfy the increased demand. Hence arose the necessity for machine printing (the earliest attempt at which will be found embodied in N° 1748 *post*), which has produced an entire revolution in the mechanism of the art (*b*).

MUSIC PRINTING.—As early as 1490 music was printed by letter-press. The edition of the Psalms printed at Mentz in 1490 had the music (plain chant) in two colours, the notes being in black and the ledger-lines in red. The shape of the notes in this edition is different from the square notes subsequently adopted for sacred music. The notes of the music executed by Peter Hautin, an engraver, typefounder, and printer (*c*), were lozenge-shaped, and each note was cast separately with the ledger lines.

Peter Atteignaud, of Paris, printed in 1530 twenty-nine songs, with this description of music.

Burney, in his General History of Music, 4to., London, 1782, vol. ii., p. 446, says, "The most curious specimens of early counter-" points among the printed music in the (British) Museum are a " collection of masses in four parts, the first that issued from the " press after the invention of printing. They consist of the first " and third sets of the masses which Jusquin composed for the " Pope's chapel during the Pontificate of Sextus IV., who reigned " from 1471 to 1484; the masses of Pierre de la Rue, sometimes " called Petrus Platensis; a set of masses by Anthony de Feven " or Feum, Robert de Feven, and Pierzon; the masses of John

(*a*) Drawings of this arrangement of levers may be seen in Hansard's Typographia, p. 637; Encyc. Brit., art. "Printing."

(*b*) By some of the fast newspaper machines in use at the present day the production amounts to no less than 15,000 copies per hour.

(*c*) Caxton, Wynkyn de Worde, and Pynson were type founders as well as printers, Ames, Typ. Ant., vol. iii. p. 1764. Most of the early printers styled themselves "printers and binders." In a reprint of Caxton's edition of 1482 of the Polychronicon, de Worde has printed the scheme of the musical concords, the discovery of which is there attributed to Pythagoras from the ringing of differently weighted hammers. In Caxton's copy a blank is left to be filled up by the illuminator, in the same manner as the initials. Dibd. Typ. Ant. vol. ii. p. 51.

" Monton; ditto of several composers, viz., Obrecht, Phil. Bas-
" siron, Brumel, Gaspar, and De la Rue. All these were printed
" by Ottavio Petruccio da Fossembrone; he first published the
" masses of De la Rue at Venice, 1503, and in 1508 those by
" different authors. In 1513, removing to Fossembrone in the
" Ecclesiastical State, he obtained a Patent from Leo X. in behalf
" of his invention of types for the sole printing of figurative song
" (*cantus figuratus*) and pieces for the organ (*organorum intabla-*
" *turæ*) during the term of 20 years."

In 1552 Adrian Leroy, musician to Henry II. of France, and
Robert Ballard, his brother-in-law and partner, obtained the title
of King's printers for music. The types were engraved by William
Le Bé, an eminent artist of that period, and were on the same plan
as those of Peter Hautin.

In 1579 Angelo Gardano printed in Venice from music types
"Madrigali à sei voce di Sabino." The process was the same as
Peter Hautin's, but the execution was very inferior. The opera
of "Thesée" was printed by Ballard in 1688. The typographical
execution was imperfect. The same work in folio was printed in
1720 by Beauseune from copper-plates, and was so superior to the
music printed from types that the old method was abandoned for
that of printing from engraved plates. The exclusive privilege
granted to Ballard was maintained in his family without opposition until 1639, when Sanlecque, another engraver in Paris, obtained Letters Patent from Louis XIII. of France for a ten years'
sole right of printing the *plain chant* music by a new process of
his invention. In consequence of this Patent, copperplate music
printing superseded typographic music printing as early as 1675.
In 1746 M. Dornel, of Paris, entered into partnership with M.
Klebin, an engraver and typefounder, for the purpose of casting
music types in sand. By this kind of stereotyping the printing
appeared to possess some advantages, but the plan was abandoned.
In 1764 M. Breitkopf, a typefounder and printer at Leipzig,
succeeded in casting music types. In this type music the notes
were each composed of separate pieces, and in Germany, until
then, there had been only one piece for each note and ledger-line.
The system possessed some advantages, but the composition was
tedious and the types costly. At the same time MM. Enschédé,
of Haarlem, caused M. Feischman, an artist employed in their
foundry, to engrave music types, the perfection of which has
scarcely been surpassed, but the system which they adopted was

too complicated for general use.   In 1762 M. Rosart, of Brussels, being desirous of diminishing the number of pieces, cast a new fount of music with only 300 separate sorts.   M. Fournier junior further improved the casting by reducing the number of types to 100; his improvements were favourably noticed by the Royal Academy of France in 1762.   M. Reinhard, of Strasburg, obtained a patent for a new process, consisting in printing the ledger-lines from engraved plates and the notes from moveable types.   The work was good, although the notes were of a different tint from the lines, in consequence of the two printings.   About 1810 M. Olivier, a French engraver, produced beautiful moveable music types, but the mechanical difficulties of setting up rendered the plan useless. In 1832 M. Duveryes, of Paris, invented an ingenious mode of casting the notes separately from the lines.   His plan was to compose a page of music without the lines, after which he took a plaster cast, in which, with a straight-edge, he ruled lines to a lever with the notes.   From this plaster he obtained a stereotype plate serviceable for surface printing.   MM. Tanterstein and Cordel, pupils of M. Duveryes, invented another mode; they set up the music with moveable types combined with the lines; they then took plaster casts, and repaired in the casts the imperfections of the line-joints, and obtained stereotype plates from the corrected plaster.   Good specimens of this system were exhibited in the Great Exhibition of 1851.   Another system, exhibited on the same occasion, was by M. Derriey of Paris.   The notes were cast in one or more pieces, so as to admit of the line crossing the notes when they were required to be on the line.   Each line was of one piece, and of the width of the page, either in brass, zinc, or hard type-metal.   "Music printed from such types," was said in the Reports of the Juries, "a nearer approach to impressions from " engraved plates than any hitherto produced, yet it is doubtful " whether by continued wear the interstices may not become visible, " and render this system imperfect."

THE ART OF COPPER-PLATE PRINTING (under which title is comprised the mode of obtaining copies from engraved metallic plates) may be said to be the reverse of letter-press printing, the copy obtained being that of the sunken parts of the printing surface.   Its date may be considered as about the same as that of letter-press printing.   Vasari, in his introduction to his Life of Marc Antonio, expressly says that the art of engraving and printing copper-plates (dell' intagliare le stampe) had its beginning with Maso Finiguerra, a

goldsmith and engraver of Florence, about the year 1460, for that
artist made sulphur casts of all the things that he engraved in
silver, which were intended to be filled with *niello* (a pulverized
substance composed of silver, copper, lead, sulphur, and borax);
that he also took impressions from his engravings with a tint
made of soot and oil upon damped paper by means of a wooden
roller, which he passed over it ; and lastly, that the impressions so
produced looked like drawings done with a pen (*a*). This mode of
printing is said to have been introduced into England by John
Speed in the reign of James I. (*b*).

The following may be said to be the principal modes of engraving
at present in use (Bryan's Dictionary of Painters and Engravers,
by Stanley, 8vo. London, 1849; Introd. p. xviii.):—

*Stroke Engraving.*—This manner is effected by tracing the design
upon the plate with a sharp tool called the dry point, and the
strokes or lines are cut on the copper with an instrument called
the graver or burin.

*Etching.*—In etching the traces are cut with a point or needle
through a varnish prepared for the purpose and laid on the plate,
and these strokes are corroded or bitten in the copper by aquafortis.

*With the Point and Graver.*—In this, the most general mode of
engraving, the subject is first etched and afterwards finished with
the graver. By this process the advantages of both the above are
combined.

---

(*a*) Ottley, vol. i. p. 286; Encyc. Met., vol. viii. p. 779. One of the following
circumstances is supposed to have given rise to the discovery:— Finiguerra
chanced to cast or let fall a piece of copper engraved or filled with ink into
melted sulphur, and observing that the exact impression of his work was left
on the sulphur, he repeated the experiment on moistened paper, rolling it
gently with a roller. This origin has been admitted by Lord Walpole and Mr.
Landseer, but another has also been mentioned by Hüber:—" It is reported,"
says he, " that a washerwoman left some linen upon a plate or dish on which
Finiguerra had just been engraving, and that an impression of the subject
engraved, however imperfect, came off upon the linen occasioned by its weight
and moistness." Dibdin's Typ. Ant., Prelim. Disquisition on Early Engraving
and Ornamental Printing, p. iv. (n.)

(*b*) " The art of engraving and working from plates of copper which we call
prints was not yet appearing or born with us till about the year 1490." Evelyn.
" The first book," says Strutt (Dictionary, vol. i. p. 18), " which appeared with
copper cuts in England was the ' *Birth of Mankind*,' otherwise called the
' Woman's Book,' dedicated to Queen Catherine, and published by J. Raynalde,
A. D. 1540. Yet it is by no means certain that these plates were engraved in
England, or the work of English artists. Chambers must have given himself
very little trouble to examine the state of the arts in England, when he igno-
rantly asserted in his Dictionary that engraving was first introduced here by
John Speed, being brought by him from Antwerp in the reign of James the First.
Dibdin, however, supposes the earliest copper-plate impressions in this country

*Mezzotinto* (*a*).—This style of engraving is executed by raising on the plate with a toothed tool a uniformly dark barb or ground. The designs being traced upon the plate, the light parts are scraped off by instruments in proportion as the effect may require.

The copper-plate press has undergone but little alteration (*b*). The common press consists of two upright cheeks, with ribs at right angles to them. A short distance above these ribs is a solid iron cylinder, made to revolve by a star handle connected with the axis, the radii of this star being as long as the height from the ground will permit. A carriage containing the plate is made to run along the ribs. Beneath the ribs is another cylinder, which is made to rise by means of a lever, and press the carriage against the upper cylinder as it passes along the press with any required force. The copper-plate is heated over a charcoal brazier, and the ink worked into its lines with a linen rag. The face is then cleaned with

---

executed by means of a roller to be the frontispiece to *Galenus de Tempera-menti*, printed at Cambridge in 1521." Dibd. Typ. Art. vol. i. p. xxv., where also is a facsimile (printed from a wood cut) of a copper-plate engraving of the Birth of Mankind.

The copper-plates in Vesalius's Anatomy, printed in Latin in 1545, by Thomas Gennius, is the first work by an English engraver of whom we have any distinct account. A translation of this work by Redal, dedicated to Edward VI., contained in the preface the following passage " Accepte, jentill reader, this Traetise of Anatomie, thankfully interpreting the work of Thomas Gennin, the workman. He that with his great charge, watch, and travayle hath set out these figures in pourtrayture will most willingly be amended or better perfected of his own workmanship if admonished." The first maps of English counties were engraved by Christopher Saxton, A.D. 1579.

(*a*) The invention of engraving in mezzotinto was for some time ascribed to Prince Rupert, Palatine of the Rhine. The circumstance which led to its dis-covery is thus related, from a tradition received by Vertue. from Mr. Killegrew, of Somerset House. to whom it had been communicated by Evelyn, the author of *Sculptura* :—" The Prince going out early one morning discovered a soldier employed in cleaning his musket from the rust which the night dew had occa-sioned, and on examining it, perceived something like a figure corroded upon the barrel, with innumerable small holes close together, like freezed work on gold or silver, part of which the soldier had scraped away. He conceived an idea that some contrivance might be found to cover a copper plate with such a grained ground of fine pressed holes which would give an impression all black, and that by scraping away those parts which required to be white, the effect of the draw-ing might be produced. He communicated this idea to Wallerant Vaillant. a painter in his service. They made several experiments, and at last invented a steel roller, cut with tools, to make teeth like a rasp or file, which produced the black ground, which in some measure answered the purpose intended. The au-thenticity of this account is questionable. Heineken (Idée générale) affirms that De Siegen, an officer in the Hessian service, was the inventor, and that Prince Rupert learnt the secret from him, and brought it into England when he came over the second time with Charles II." Bryan's Dictionary of Painters and Engravers, nom. " Rupert."

(*b*) A printed book in the Bodleian, " Missale Secundum usum Herbipolensis," (Wurtzburg), contains an instrument dated 8th November 1541, to which is appended, instead of a seal, an engraving which bears indisputable proof of having been printed from by a rolling press. — (Chambers's Dictionary, art. " Printing.")

another linen rubber, and the workman, with the balls of his hands covered with whitening, cleans off the plate so as to leave the ink in the recessed parts only.

PAPER-HANGINGS, as a substitute for the "hangings" of tapestry or cloth, came into use in the middle of the 17th century. The invention of velvet or flock paper is generally attributed to Jerome Lanyer, who in 1634 obtained a patent for the art (a).

The manufacture has undergone a gradual succession of improvements, and has now reached a high state of beauty and perfection. At first the outline of the figure was printed from wooden blocks, and the design completed by hand painting. The patterns were subsequently produced by stencil plate and cylinder printing (b).

LITHOGRAPHIC PRINTING consists in obtaining copies from stone or other substances, upon which the subject has been drawn with a peculiar ink, or etched. The discovery of this art is due to Aloysius Senefelder, A.D. 1800, (see post, No. 2518,) and rests upon the following properties of the substance forming the printing surface (c):—1. That a drawing made upon it with fat ink adheres to it so strongly as to require mechanical force to remove it. 2. That the parts of it free from the drawing receive, retain, and absorb water. 3. That a roller or other instrument being covered with fat ink, being applied to the printing surface when inked and wetted, the ink will attach itself only to the drawn parts, and will be repelled from the wetted parts. Plates of zinc have lately been treated by this process in the same way as stone, and the process is then called ZINCOGRAPHY.

By this process it will be seen that a drawing being made or an impression taken upon paper with prepared ink, and transferred by pressure to the stone, &c., the latter will form a printing surface, from which facsimiles of the drawing or impression may be obtained by this process. The press used by Senefelder at the date of his Patent (1801) will be found in the drawing annexed to his

---

(a) Rymer's Fœdera, vol. xix. Lond., 1732, fol. p. 554. The merit is, however, claimed for a Frenchman, named François, who is stated to have made printed paper-hangings at Rouen as early as the year 1620 (Journal Œconomique, 1756, Février, p. 92).

(b) See Beckmann's History of Inventions and Discoveries, art. "Paper-hangings."

(c) Partington's Engravers' Complete Guide; Newton's Journal, vol. 2 (new series), p. 340.

Specification. It has been entirely superseded by subsequent inventions. The art made little progress until the year 1815, since which time it has risen into a very considerable degree of importance.

ANASTATIC PRINTING is the ἀνάστασις (fresh raising up) of copies from a printed sheet. The philosophy of this art rests on a few known properties of the articles employed. Thus, water attracts water, and oil, oil; though each mutually repels the other. Metals are much more easily wetted with oil than water, but they will be readily moistened with a weak solution of gum; and, finally, this property of their becoming wet by water is greatly increased by phosphatic acid. To these properties of oil, water, and the metals may be added the readiness with which part of the ink of any newly printed book or engraving can be transferred by pressure to any smooth surface beneath. If, for example, a corner of a newspaper be fixed on a white sheet of paper, and then pressed or rubbed with a paper knife, the letters will be distinctly seen in reverse on the paper. This effect is ordinarily known as "setting "off." The process is simple. The printed paper is moistened with dilute nitric acid, and then pressed with considerable force by a roller on a perfectly clean surface of zinc. The acid with which the unprinted part of the paper is saturated etches the metal, and the printed portion "sets off" on it, so that the zinc surface presents a complete reverse copy of the work. The zinc plate thus prepared is washed with a solution of gum in weak phosphatic acid. This liquid is attracted by the etched surface, which it freely wets, while it is repelled by the oil of the ink in which the writing or drawing on the plate is traced. A leathern roller covered with ink is then passed over the plate, when a converse effect ensues. The repulsion between the oily ink and the watery surface over which the roller presses prevents any soiling of the unfigured parts of the zinc plate, while the attraction between oil and oil causes the ink to be distributed over the printed portions. In this condition the anastatic plate is complete, and impressions are pulled from it in the common lithographic press. When it is required to apply the anastatic printing to very old originals, which do not set off their ink, the following expedient is resorted to. The page or print is soaked in a solution, first of potash, and then of tartaric acid. This produces a perfect diffusion of minute crystals of bitartrate of potash through the texture of the unprinted part of the paper. As this salt resists oil, the ink roller may now be passed over the surface without transferring any of its contents except to the printed parts. The tartrate is then washed out of the paper and the operation proceeded with as before, commencing with the moistening by nitric acid (*a*).

The invention was a foreign one, and was first practised as a profound secret. Early in October 1841 the editor of the "Athenæum" received from a correspondent at Berlin a reprint of four pages of the copy of that paper (which contained three woodcut illustrations) published in London only on the 25th September. "The " copy," the editor observes (No. 736,) "was so perfect a facsimile " that, had it reached us under any other circumstances, we should " never have suspected that it had not been issued from our own " office; and, even with our attention thus specially directed to " the subject, the only difference that we could discover was that " the impression was lighter, and that there was less body in " the ink, from which we infer that the process is essentially " lithographic, the impression of the original page being, in the " first instance, transferred by some means on to the surface of " the stone or zinc plate. This, however, is but a conjecture, and " our correspondent is unable to throw light on the subject."

The inventor was Mr. Baldermus of Berlin, who communicated the process to Mr. Joseph Woods (see N° 10,219, *post*).

PANEICONOGRAPHY is a similar invention by M. Gillot of Paris, for reproducing, by means of the typographic press, any lithographic, autographic, or typographic proof, any drawing with crayon or stump, or any engraving from wood or copper. Upon a plate of zinc, polished with pumicestone, the artist executes the design with lithographic crayon or ink, or transfers impressions from lithography, wood engraving, or copper-plates. The surface is then inked over with a roller, so as to increase the thickness of the ink, which is afterwards consolidated by dusting finely powdered rosin over the plate by means of a pad of wadding. The rosin adheres only to the ink, and is readily removed from the other parts of the plate. Afterwards, for the purpose of obtaining a relief block, the plate is placed on the bottom of a shallow trough containing very dilute sulphuric or hydrochloric acid. By means of a rocking motion given to the box the acid is caused to pass

---

(*a*) During the description of this process given by Professor Faraday in a lecture at the Royal Institution on the 25th April 1845, a complete anastatic copy of a page of a printed work was made by Mr. Woods, who had brought his press and workmen.—"Athenæum," No. 914.

slowly and continuously to and fro over the surface of the plate. After the lapse of half an hour, if it be a crayon drawing, the etching is completed, and a relief block is obtained, in which it is only necessary to remove the large "whites" by saw piercing. In case, however, of the plate containing written matter, or many fine lines, it is necessary to withdraw it from time to time, and again to ink the surface with lithographic ink, and dust the powdered rosin, so that the edges may be protected as much as possible from the undermining action of the acid. These operations must be repeated until the necessary depth is obtained. Transfers may be made from very old impressions of wood engravings by sponging them several times at the back with acidulated water, and then operating as is usual with lithographic transfers (*a*).

GALVANOGRAPHY.— An artist covers a plate of silvered copper with different coats of a paint composed of any oxide, such as that of iron, burnt terra-sienna, or black lead, ground with linseed oil. The substance of these coats is of necessity thick or thin, according to the intensity given to the lights and shades. The plate is then submitted to the action of the galvanic battery, from which another plate is obtained, reproducing an intalio copy with all the unevenness of the original painting. This is an actual copper-plate resembling an aquatint, and obtained without the assistance of the engraver.

By the *galvanoplastic* process antediluvian fishes were exhibited by the Imperial printing office of Austria at the Great Exhibition, 1851, which were reproduced upon paper with the exactness of nature itself. " By means of successive layers of gutta-percha " applied to the stone enclosing the petrified fish a mould is " obtained, which being afterwards submitted to the action of " a galvanic battery, is quickly covered with coatings of copper, " forming a plate upon which all the marks of the feet are re- " produced in relief, and which, when printed at the typographic " press, gives a result upon the paper identical with the object " itself."—(Reports of the Juries, Class XVII.)

GALVANOGLYPHY.—Upon a plate of zinc coated with varnish a drawing is etched. Then, with a small composition roller, a coat of ink is spread upon this varnish and left to dry. The ink is deposited only on those parts where the varnish has not been broken through by the graver and leaves the sunken portions of the en-

---

(*a*) Reports of the Juries of the Great Exhibition, 1851, class xvii. p. 407.

graving free. When the first layer is dry a second is applied, then a third, and so on, until it is considered that the original hollows are deep enough. The plate thus prepared is placed in the galvanic battery, and another plate is the result, in which all the hollows of the engraving are reproduced in relief. This relief is more or less raised, according to the number and thickness of the coats of ink successively applied. This process was invented in England, and patented by Edward Palmer. (See *post*, A.D. 1841, N° 8987, and A.D. 1842, N° 9227.)

CHEMITYPY.—A polished zinc plate is covered with an etching ground. The design is etched with a point and bitten in with diluted aquafortis. The etching ground is then removed, and every particle of the acid well cleaned off. For this purpose the hollows of the engraving are first washed with olive oil, then with water, and afterwards wiped, so that there may not remain the least trace of the acid. The plate, on which must be placed filings of the fusible metal, is then heated by means of a spirit-lamp, or any convenient means, until the fusible metal has filled up all the engraving. When cold it is scraped down to the level of the zinc plate in such a manner that none of it remains, except that which has entered into the hollow of the engraving. The plate of zinc to which the fusible metal has become united is then submitted to the action of a weak solution of muriatic acid, and as of these two metals, the one is negative, the other positive, the zinc alone is eaten away by the acid, and the fusible metal which has entered into the hollows of the engraving is left as a relief printing surface which can be worked in the typographic press.

PHOTOGRAPHY is the art of producing copies of objects by the action of light (Gr. φῶς). It is of very recent origin. The only observations of the ancients on the chemical properties of light as affecting colour that have reached us are the doubtful ones that some precious stones, especially amethyst and opal, lost their brilliancy by prolonged exposure to the sun.

The alchemists in their searches after the *philosopher's stone* and the *elixir vitæ* made and recorded the discovery that a peculiar combination of silver with chlorine, called "horn silver," became blackened by exposure to the light, but no attempt was made to utilize the discovery for the purpose of obtaining images.—(Hunt's Manual of Photography, p. 4.)

In 1772 Petit noticed that solutions of nitrate of potash and muriate of ammonia crystallized more rapidly in the light than in the dark.

In Kearsley's Pocket Ledger for the year 1775 is the following extract from Dr. Hooper's *Rational Recreations*:—"*Writing on* "*Glass by the Rays of the Sun.*—Dissolve chalk in aquafortis to " the consistence of milk, and add to that a strong dissolution of " silver. Keep this liquor in a glass decanter well stopped. Then " cut out from a paper the letters you would have appear, and " paste the paper on the decanter, which you are to place in the " sun in such a manner that its rays may pass through the spaces " cut out of the paper and fall on the surface of the liquor. The " part of the glass through which the rays pass will turn black, " and that under the paper will remain white. You must observe " not to move the bottle during the operation."

In 1777 Scheele in his *Traité de l'Air et du Feu* writes,—"It is " well known that the solution of silver in acid of nitre poured on " a piece of chalk and exposed to the beams of the sun grows " black. The light of the sun reflected from a white wall has the " same effect, but more slowly. Heat without light has no " effect on this mixture," and "fix a glass prism at the window, " and let the refracted sunbeams fall on the floor. In this " coloured light put a paper strewed with *luna cornua*, and " you will observe that this horn silver grows sooner black in " the violet ray than in any of the other rays (*a*)." Senebier repeated these experiments, and found chloride of silver darkened in the violet ray in fifteen seconds to a shade which required the action of the red ray for twenty minutes. He also experimented on the influence of light in bleaching wax.

In the Philosophical Transactions for 1798 will be found a memoir by Count Romford, entitled " An Inquiry concerning the " Chemical Properties that have been attributed to Light," showing that the effects produced upon metallic solutions by light can also be attained by heat, a position controverted by Robert Hartup in a communication to Nicholson's Journal in 1802.

In 1801 Ritter proved the existence of rays a considerable distance beyond the visible spectrum which had the property of speedily blackening chloride of silver. MM. Berard, Secbeck, Berthollet and others directed their attention to the peculiar condition of the different rays in relation to their luminous and chemical properties. Dr. Wollaston pursued and published an interesting

(*a*) Hunt, p. 4,

series of experiments on the decomposition effected by light on gum guiacum. He found that paper washed with a solution of this gum in spirits of wine had its yellow colours rapidly changed to green by the violet rays, while the red rays had the property of restoring the yellow hue. Sir H. Davy observed that the pure coloured oxide of lead became, when moistened, red by exposure to the red ray, and black by exposure to the violet rays, and that the green oxide of mercury, although not changed by the most refrangible rays, speedily became red in the least refrangible (*a*).

Other experiments were being made about the same time on phenomena connected with solar radiations. In 1801 Desmortiers published in Gilbert's Annals a paper entitled "Recherches "sur la Décoloration spontanée du Bleu de Prusse," a translation of which was subsequently published in Nicholson's Journal. Böckman, about the same time, observed that the two ends of the spectrum acted differently on phosphorus. Naye in 1802 published an observation he had made that crystals of red arsenic effloresced in the light. The result of investigations on the subject of chlorine by Guy Lussac and Thehard, of Berzelius on the salts of gold and Fischer on horn silver is stated in Hunt's Manual of Photography (5th ed. p. 9.)

The merit of being the first to create an artificial retina so sensitive as to retain the picture of an illuminated object is due to Wedgwood, the celebrated potter, who, with the assistance of Sir Humphry Davy, succeeded in 1802 in obtaining pictures by means of a lens on paper and white leather (*b*), moistened with a solution of nitrate of silver. The process he adopted is described in a paper published by him in 1802 in the Journal of the Royal Institution, with the following title, "An Account of a Method of Copying "Paintings upon Glass, and of making Profiles by the Agency "of Light upon Nitrate of Silver; with Observations by "H. Davy." The results thus obtained were not, however, satisfactory, as no means were discovered of rendering the pictures permanent.

In 1806 Vogel proved that the sun's rays changed the colour of fat, and soon rendered it rancid, and that independent of the action of the air. He also made some curious experiments on the

---

(*a*) Hunt, p. 5.
(*b*) The latter substance is stated to have shown the greater amount of sensibility, owing, as it is supposed, to the action of matter used in the process of tanning upon the nitrate of silver (see Philosophical Mag. for May 1854). See also an account of an experiment conducted by Dr. Young in 1803, on his delivering the Bakerian Lecture of 1803 (Philos. Trans. for 1804).

influence of sunshine on ammonia and phosphorus and on corrosive sublimate in solution.

From the time when the difficulty of fixing the photographs obtained stopped the progress of Wedgwood and Davy, no discoveries were made until 1814, when M. Niepce, of Chalons-sur-Saone, entered on a course of experiments. His early attempts were not successful; but becoming, after a period of ten years, acquainted with Daguerre, he succeeded with that gentleman in fixing pictures produced by a lens on metal and glass plates coated with resin. The pictures were afterwards engraved by a chemical process. Specimens, with a paper on the subject, were forwarded to the Royal Society of London in 1827, and some of them are now in the possession of Mr. Robert Brown of the British Museum (a). The discovery was called Heliography or sun-drawing, and the pictures, which required several hours of good sunlight for their production, were termed " heliographs." M. Niepce died in 1833, before the discovery by M. Daguerre of the process termed Daguerrotype.

The daguerreotype process was formally communicated to the public by M. Arago, who, in January 1839, read an account of it before the Academy of Sciences, but the process was not made known until the July following, when a bill was passed securing to M. Daguerre a pension for life of 6,000 francs, and one to the son of M. Niepce of 4,000 francs for life, with one-half in reversion to their widows (see *post*, Berry's Patent, A.D. 1839, N° 8194) (b).

On the 31st of January 1839, Mr. Fox Talbot communicated to the Royal Society his photographic discovery, and in February published an account of the process he had devised for preparing a sensitive paper for *photogenic* drawing. From the paper read before the Royal Society, it appeared that he had been pursuing

(a) Hunt, p. 11. For a full account of M. Niepce's process, see Hunt, pp. 12 to 17.

(b) The following remarks are made in the Specification of this Patent :—"This invention or discovery relates to photographic drawing, or the spontaneous reproduction of images, pictures, or representations of nature by the action of light, that is, by the process or method now well known under the name of ' daguerreotype.' I believe it to be the invention or discovery of Messrs. Louis Jaques Maude Daguerre and Joseph Isidore Niepce, junior, both of the kingdom of France, from whom the French Government have purchased the invention for the benefit of that country. This invention or discovery was fully communicated to me by a certain foreigner residing in France on or about the 15th day of July in the year 1839, with instructions immediately to petition Her Majesty to grant Her Royal Letters Patent for the exclusive use of the same within these kingdoms." After mentioning the proceedings adopted by him to obtain the Patent, the Patentee states that such Patent was sealed on the 14th August 1839, "which," he says, " is some days prior to the date of the exposition of the said invention or discovery to the French Government at Paris by Messrs. Daguerre and Niepce, according to the terms of their agreement."

his researches on the subject since the spring of 1834 (*a*). A detailed account of his experiments was published by Mr. Fox Talbot in the Philosophical Magazine.

Various improvements have from time to time been introduced, the most important being the employment of compounds of iodine and bromine, iodine and chlorine, instead of the former substance only. The sensibility of the plates is by this means infinitely increased, so that, under favourable circumstances, portraits can be produced in a few seconds of time. The application of chloride of gold to the surface of the silver plate after the picture is finished, as was recommended by Fizeau, has given a much greater degree of permanence than those productions previously exhibited.

The art of photography on glass is more recent than either the Daguerreotype or Talbotype; but its principles are similar to those of the latter art. In consequence of the inequality of the texture of the photographic paper, it became desirable to obtain some more homogeneous medium for the reception of the negative Talbotype picture. Glass and porcelain have been employed with great success for this purpose, prints from such plates being of an exquisitely beautiful character. In order to render the surface sufficiently retentive of the sensitive coating of silver, the plates of glass are covered in the first instance with a thin layer of the albumen of egg containing a few drops of a solution of the iodide of potassium. The sensitive washes are then applied, and the plate is exposed to the lenticular image in the camera. The picture is developed in the usual manner.

Dr. Woods introduced the use of the iodide of iron in his process of the " catalissotype," and Mr. Robert Hunt that of sulphate of iron in his "ferrotype," both processes of extreme sensibility. The "chromotype," the " fluorotype," and the other processes of Mr. Hunt are fully described in his Researches on Light. Sir J. Herschel has fully described his processes in his memoirs in the Philosophical Transactions.

---

(*a*) The following is from the number of "Photographic Notes," published November 1, 1858:—"In 1838, Mr. Mongo Ponton, described in the 'Edinburgh New Philosophical Journal,' a mode of producing photographic prints by applying to paper a mixture of bichromate of potass and sulphate of indigo. In this process the bichromate, the colouring matter, and the organic matter of the paper are the three materials, on the reactions among which under the influence of light the principle of printing in carbon or pigments depends. The prints produced by Mr. Mongo Ponton appear to have been the first permanently fixed photographs, and we may consider that gentleman as the discoverer of photography, for the Talbotype and the Daguerreotype processes were not published until the following year, 1839."

The production of photographs naturally coloured has been achieved by M. Niepce. By voltaic agency he produces upon the surface of a silver plate a dark purple coating of oxide of copper and chloride of silver. This is *eaten out* in colours when exposed to the influences of solar radiations. It has not yet been found practicable to give permanence to these reproductions of colours.

THE STEREOSCOPE, the invention of Professor Wheatstone is an optical instrument in which two photographic pictures taken under a small difference of angular view are so placed that one only shall be seen by each eye. Two images are thus conveyed to the brain as in ordinary vision, and uniting there exhibit the objects in relief.

---

The successive improvements in the various branches of the art above referred to will be found in the following notices, chronologically arranged. The dates affixed to the headings of such inventions as are protected by Letters Patent indicate the date of the grant, and the number is that by which they are recorded. in the Indexes of Patents. In cases in which the Letters Patent previous to the operation of the Patent Law Amendment Act, 1852, provided for the filing of the Specification within more or less than the usual period of six months, the number of months is affixed in a bracket to the heading.

Printing was early taken under the patronage and control of the State. A Statute (1 Ric. III. c. 9.), passed A.D. 1483, imposing certain restrictions on merchant strangers, was expressly stated not to " extend to be in prejudice, disturbance, danger, or " impediment to any artificer or merchant stranger, of what nation " or country he be or shall be of, for bringing into this realm, or " selling by retail or otherwise, any books, written or printed, or " for the inhabiting within this said realm for the same intent, " or any scrivener, alluminator, reader, or printer of such books, " which he hath or shall have to sell by way of merchandise, or " for their dwelling within this realm for the exercise of the said " occupations."

It has been supposed (a) that Caxton enjoyed the dignity of

---

(a) Herb. Typ. Ant. p. 2. The passage from which the inference is drawn occurs in the Epilogue to " The Image or Mirror of the World," which is stated to have been finished in " the xxj. yere of the most crysten kyng, Kynge Edward the Fourth, vnder the shadowe of who's noble proteccion I have emprysed and fynysshed this sayd lytyl werke and boke."

"King's printer." The first to assume the appellation was William Faques, who, in 1504, in a proclamation issued by Henry VII. against clipped money, (a) and in a Psalter of the same date, (b) is styled "Regius Impressor." The office appears to have been first held by patent (c) in the reign of Edward VI., when Richard Grafton (d) was appointed to it, with special licence to print generally, with some exceptions as to grammars, which were then the property of Berthelet, printer to Henry VIII., at whose expense the books had been composed (e). From that period to the present there has been a regular succession of persons holding that office.

The first instance of an exclusive privilege (f) to print a book occurs in 1518, when Richard Pynson (g), who succeeded Faques as King's printer, printed a book, "Oratio Richardi Pacei, &c.," as the colophon there states, "cum privilegio a rege indulto, ne quis "hanc orationem intra biennium in regno Angliæ imprimat, aut "alibi impressam et importatam in eodem regno Angliæ ven- "dat."(h)    After this privileges became frequent, several Patents

(a) Dibd. Typ. Ant., vol. iii. p. 7.
(b) Johnson's Typographia, vol. ii. p. 478.
(c) *Tonson* v. *Collins*, 1 H. Blackstone's Reports, p. 303.
(d) Grafton was continued in this office under Mary. He styles himself in a proclamation, dated 1553, "Queen's printer." (State Papers, ed. 1856.) Cawood and Jugg appear also to have printed proclamations and State books in the reign of Edward VI. and Elizabeth and Mary (State Papers, ed. 1856, pp. 235 and 238). In the reign of the latter, Richard Tothil had the chief printing of law books (Stow's Survey of London, vol. ii. p. 309). "It seems," says Ames (Dibd. Typ. Ant. vol. ii. p. 8), "that Lettou and Machlinia were the first printers of law in this kingdom; yet after all my searches I cannot find they had any patent for so doing." The first work described by Ames and Herbert as executed by these printers was Littleton's Tenures.
(e) Cottonian. MSS. Cleopatra, E. v. 63. See as to the condition of the office in 1660, Harleian Miscellany, vol. iii. p. 292. "The London printer, his lamentation, or the press oppressed or over pressed, September, 1660," a quarto pamphlet of eight pages, containing a short account of printing in general and a declaration of its esteem by the several Kings and Queens.
(f) The first case of literary piracy is thus noticed in Lowndes on Copyright, p. 5 (n.):—" Wynkyn de Worde had printed a Treatise on Grammar, by Robert Witinton, in 1523, which one Peter Trevers or Treveris had taken the liberty of reprinting, and Robert Witinton, in a subsequent edition printed by De Worde in 1533, attacks Trevers with great severity for the act, to prevent a recurrence of which the author and publisher obtained a privilege from the King for the second edition."
(g) The demand requisite to support publication of works without patronage is stated to have arisen as early as 1506. (*Tonson* v. *Collins*, 1, Henry Blackstone's Reports, p. 303.) Caxton's, Wynkyn de Worde's, and Pynson's books were all printed at the expense of private persons.
(h) Dibd. Typ. Ant. vol. ii. p. 477. An earlier instance, given in Beckman, Art. "Privilege for printing Books," is that of the "History of King Boccus," which is stated to be have been printed in London, cum privilegio regali, A.D. 1510. The oldest known privilege is that granted by Henry Bishop of Bamberg, in 1490, in respect of the Liber Missalis Secundum Ordinem Ecclesiæ Bambergensis. See Panze's History of the Nuremberg editions of the Bible, and Am Ende in Meusel's Collection for enlarging Historical Knowledge. The latter says:—"One may readily believe that the bishop was not the inventor of such privileges and that they are consequently of much greater antiquity than has hitherto

being granted, during the reign of Henry VIII. to particular
printers (mostly for the term of seven years from the date of the
publication), in respect as well of books to be printed as books already printed; as, for instance, to Gowghe, or Gough, in 1540,(*a*) to
Thomas Berthelet (*b*) (for six years), and to Richard Banks in 1540.
In 1547 a Patent, (*c*) conferring on Reginald Wolfe the office of
King's printer in Latin, Greek, and Hebrew, secured to him the
sole printing not only of all books in those languages, but also in
such others as "propriâ suâ industriâ, diligentiâ, atque labore con-
" quisivit."

The religious and political questions which soon after agitated
the public mind led to still further restrictions. (*d*)

## A.D. 1533.

A STATUTE (25 Hen. VIII. c.15.), "concerning printers and binders
" of books," passed in this year, states that as the effect of the
proviso in the Statute 1 Ric. III. c. 9., "there hath come into this
" realm, sithen the making of the same, a marvelous number of
" printed books, and daily doth," although "at this day there
" be within this realm a great number of cunning and expert in
" the said science or craft of printing," and notwithstanding the
capabilities of the native bookbinders, great numbers of books are
imported bound, whereby the binders are "like to be undone
" unless some reformation be herein had." It is accordingly
enacted that the said proviso "from the feast of the Nativity of
" our Lord God next coming, shall be void and of non effect,"
and any person "resiant or inhabitant within this realm," selling

been supposed." Beckmann conjectures that this and other subsequent grants
refer only to a permission to print in consequence of the institution of book
censors by Archbishop Berthold in the year 1486. See Dis. Cur. Lit., Art.
"Licensers of the Press." The oldest Venetian privilege known is of the
year 1491 (Beckmann). The oldest Papal privilege known is of the year 1505
to Hervei Briton in IV. Petri Lombardinus Sententiarum volumina scripta
subtilissima.

Other instances of early privileges are quoted by Pitter ("Der-Büchernach-
druck nach ächten Grundsätzen des Rechts geprüft") and Hoffmann ("Von
den ältesten Kayserlichen und landesherrlichen Bücherdruck-oder-Verlag-
privilegien, 8vo., 1777,) are given in Beckmann.

    (*a*) Dibd. Typ. Ant. vol. iii. p. 410.
    (*b*) Fuller's Church History, Cent. xvi. p. 392.
    (*c*) Rymer's Fœdera, vol. xv. p. 150.
    (*d*) Until the year 1640 the Crown exercised an unlimited authority over the
press, which was enforced by summary powers of search, confiscation, and imprisonment given to the Stationers' Company all over the realm and the
dominions thereunto belonging, and by the then supreme jurisdiction of the
Star Chamber, without the least obstruction from Westminster Hall or the
Parliament in any instance. (Per Willes, J., in *Millar* v. *Taylor*, 4 Burrow's
Reports, 2312.)

books imported in a bound state, is to forfeit for each book sold
6s. 8d. No person is to buy by retail imported books of strangers
" other than of denizens," under penalty (to be paid by the
buyer) of 6s. 8d. for each book, half the fine going to the Crown
and half to "the party that will seize or sue for the same in any
" of the King's courts, to be by bill, plaint, information, wherein
" the defendant shall not be admitted to wage his law, nor no
" protection ne essoin shall be unto him allowed." A proviso
is added that if the printers or booksellers enhance unreasonably
the prices of the books in sale or binding, complaint being made
thereof unto the King, "the Lord Chancellor, Lord Treasurer, or
" any of the Chief Justices of the one Bench or the other," then the
Chancellor, Treasurer, and Justices, or two of them, are to "en-
" quire thereof, as well by the oaths of twelve honest and discreet
" persons, or otherwise," and on the "enhancing and encreasing"
being "so found," to regulate the price of the books at their discretion, and fine the offenders 3s. 4d. for each book, half of such
fine going to the Crown and the other half to "the parties grieved
" that will complain upon the same in manner and form before
" rehearsed."

## A.D. 1539.

PROCLAMATION (a) addressed "to all and singular prynters and
" sellers of books within this our realme, and to all other officers,
" ministers, and subjects, theise oure letters herying or seying
" greetyng." After stating the desire of the King that his people
should attain to God's word, the danger to be apprehended from
diversity of translations of the same, and the appointment of Lord
Cromwell to take charge thereof, the proclamation forbids any
person within the realm printing "any Bible (b) in the English

---

(a) Acta Regia, p. 308; Rymer, vol. xiv. p. 649.
(b) "The first attempt at giving forth any portion of the Scripture in English
is to be found in the Exposition of the Seven Penitential Psalms, by John Fisher,
Bishop of Rochester, which was published in the year 1505." (Historical account of the English versions of the Scriptures prefixed to Bagster's English
Hexapla.)

A letter from Richard Grafton to T. Cromwell, desiring that others may be
inhibited for three years "from printing the Bible in English, until he shall have
sold his edition of 1,500 copies, or that all curates and popish monasteries may be
obliged to buy them;" and another, dated Dec. 1st, 1538, complaining to Lord
Cromwell that James Nicholson had published the New Testament in English,
with Coverdale's name to it, without his leave, are mentioned in the Cottonian
MSS. (Cleopatra, E. v. 329). Grafton and Whitchurch also held a patent under
Francis I. for printing the English Bible at Paris, ib. 326 (b).

In enumerating the patents granted for printing by Elizabeth, Stow, in his
Survey (vol. ii. p. 309) observes "John Jugge besides being Her Majesty's

" tonge, of any manner of volume, duryn the space of fyve yeres
" next ensuing after the date hereof, but only all such as shall be
" deputid, assignid, and admytted by the said Lord Crumwell."

In this year Grafton and Whitchurch, after many difficulties,
printed in London a Bible in English, their types and other materials having been obtained from Paris. The edition consisted
of 2,500 copies. (a) Cromwell next procured for them a privilege
(but not exclusive) for printing the Scriptures for five years.
Very shortly after the death of Lord Cromwell, Grafton was imprisoned for printing Mathew's Bible and the Great Bible, his
former friend Bonner much exaggerating the case against him.
The prosecution was not, however, followed up, and in a short
time he was appointed with Whitchurch printer to Prince Edward,
with special patents for printing all church service books and
primers.

---

printer, had the privilege of printing Bibles and Testaments, the which had been
common to all the printers."

" Exclusive privileges for printing the English Bible and Prayer have been
granted by the Crown at different periods up to the present time, with the exception of the period of the Commonwealth, during which they were abolished.
In the 27th year of Charles II. a Royal Patent was granted to Thomas New-
comb and Henry Hills; in the 12th of Anne to Benjamin Tooke and John
Barber; in the 22nd of George I. to John Basket. Then came John Reeves, who
received his patent from George III. in the 39th year of his reign, and in association with George Eyre and Andrew Strahan, printed the many editions of the
Bible and Prayer described as Reeves' editions. The present patent was conferred by George IV. upon Andrew Strahan, George Eyre, and Andrew Spottiswoode for a term of thirty years, which commenced January 21, 1830, and consequently ceases in 1860. By this last patent every one but the patentees is
prohibited from printing in England any Bible or New Testament in the
English tongue, of any translation with or without notes; or any Prayers, Rites,
or Ceremonies of the United Church of England and Ireland, or any books commanded to be used by the Crown; nor can either of the above be imported from
abroad if printed in English, or in English mixed with any other tongue. The
Universities of Oxford and Cambridge also enjoy the right of printing Bibles, &c.
in common with the patentees, but in their case it is a simple affair of permission, they having no power to prohibit or prosecute.  *   *   *
" In Scotland prior to 1700, various persons held concurrent licences; consequently it is very difficult to say who were King's printers and who were not.
On July 6th, 1716, George I. granted a patent to John Basket, the English
patentee, and Agnes Campbell jointly for forty-one years. To them succeeded
Alexander Kincaird, whose patent dates from June 21st, 1749; and then James
Hunter Blair and John Bruce, whose patent commenced in 1798 and expired in
the hands of their heirs, Sir D. H. Blair and Miss Bruce. In 1833 the Patent
ceased and has never been renewed. Unlike either England or Ireland, the four
Scotch Universities have never participated in the monopoly.
" In Ireland, George III. in 1766, granted a Bible patent to Boulton Grierson
for forty years. He was succeeded by his son George Grierson, who in 1811
obtained a renewal, and is still, with Mr. Keene, the Irish patentee; Trinity
College, Dublin, has also a concurrent right, but both Oxford and Cambridge are
by the Irish printers' own patent permitted to import their Bibles into Ireland."
—(Dr. Campbell's Letter on the Bible Monopoly.) See also Anderson's Annals
of the English Bible, 8vo., Lond., 1845.

(a) Dibd. Typ. Ant. vol. iii. p. 439 (n.) See also Fox's Martyrs, vol. ii. p. 515,
&c., ed. 1641, and Lewis's Hist. of Eng. Translations of the Bible.

In the same year certain other injunctions were set forth by authority of the King, (a) against persons without special licence of the King importing and selling English books under pain of loss of goods and imprisonment during the King's pleasure; or printing or bringing over any English books with annotations or prologues, unless the same be licensed by the King's Privy Council or others appointed by his Highness; "and yet not to put thereto those " words 'Cum priuilegio Regali,' without adding, 'ad imprimendum " 'solum.'" The translator's name to appear, or the printer to be liable and treated as the translator. No "English books of Scripture" to be printed, uttered, or sold, until the same have been viewed and admitted by the King or Council, under pain of the King's most high displeasure, loss of goods, and imprisonment during the King's pleasure.

## A.D. 1541.

PROCLAMATION (b) for the Bible in English to be had in every church.

## A.D. 1542, March 12.

GRANT (c) by Letters Patent to ANTONY MARLAR, "citezyn and " haberdasher of our citie of London, only to printe the Bible in " our English tonge auctorysed or hereafter to be auctorysed by " us, hymselfe, or his assignes," for the term of four years.

## A.D. 1543, January 28.

PATENT (d) for RICHARD GRAFTON and EDWARD WHITCHURCH to print the book of divine service.

## A.D. 1545.

" THE Primer set forth by the Kynge's Majestie and his clergie to " be taught, learned, and read, and none other to be used through- " out all his dominions." (e)

## A.D. 1547, April 19.

APPOINTMENT (f) of REGINALD WOLFF to the office of printer and seller of books in Latin, Greek, and Hebrew.

---

(a) Fox's Acts and Monuments, p. 1108, ed. 1576.
(b) Cottonian MSS., Cleopatra, E. v. 65.
(c) Acta Regia, p. 308; Rymer, vol. xiv. p. 745.
(d) Acta Regia, p. 309.
(e) Ames, Typ. Ant., vol. iii. p. 1559.
(f) Rymer, vol. xv. p. 150. This patent is stated, (*Tonson* v. *Collins*, Sir W. Blackstone's Reports, p. 304,) to have been granted in consideration of the great expense of purchasing MSS.

### A.D. 1547, April 22.

SPECIAL PATENT (a) to RICHARD GRAFTON to have the sole printing of the Statute Books.

### A.D. 1548, December 18.

PATENT (b) granted to RICHARD GRAFTON and EDWARD WHITCHURCH, by which they are authorized to take up and provide for one year printers, compositors, &c., together with paper, ink, presses, &c., at reasonable rates and prices.

### A.D. 1549, January 2.

A STATUTE "for abolishing and putting away of divers books and " images,"(c) of this date, enacts that all books called "antiphoners, " missales, grailes, processionalles, manueles, legedes, pies, portu- " asses, primers, in Latine or Englishe, couchers, journalles, ordi- " nalles," or other books for church service, in English or Latin, than those set forth by the King's majesty, shall be "clearly and " utterly abolished, extinguished, and forbidden for ever to be " used or kept in this realm, or elsewhere within any the King's " dominions." All "images of stone, timber, alabaster, or earth, " graved, carved, or painted," excepting sepulchral monuments, in any church or chapel, shall, under a penalty of four pounds, be defaced or destroyed "before the last day of June next ensuing." The above-mentioned books to be delivered up to the mayor, " bayliff, constable, or churchwardens of the town," to be by them given over within three months to the archbishop, bishop, chancellor, or commissary of the said diocese, to be burnt, under a penalty of 40l., within forty days after their receipt. Primers, as set forth by Henry VIII., in English or Latin, may, however, be retained, " so that the sentences of invocation or prayer to saints in " the same primers be blotted or clearly put out of the same." (d)

### A.D. 1551, April 18.

GRANT (e) to LAURENTIUS TORRENTINUS, a German, of the sole printing of the Digests and Pandects of the Roman Civil Law, for the term of seven years.

---

(a) Dugdale's Origines Juridiciales, p. 59.
(b) Dibd. Typ. Ant. vol. iii. p. 431.  Dugdale's Origines Juridiciales, p. 59.
(c) Ames, Typ. Ant. p. 1566.
(d) Hence the blotting of the word Pope in old books. Ames, Typ. Ant. vol. iii. p. 1568.  This Statute was repealed by 1 Mary, c. 2, which is in its turn repealed by 1 Jac. I. c. 23.
(e) Rymer's Fœdera, vol. xv. p. 255.

### A.D. 1553, March 4.

LICENCE (*a*) to WILLIAM SERES for the sole printing all manner
of Primers, containing the Psalter, devotions, &c., agreeable to the
Book of Common Prayer, on allowance by the Lords of the Privy
Council, the Lord Chancellor, or the King's four ordinary chaplains,
or two of them. The price to be " set, as well in the leaves, as
" being bound in paste or board, in like manner as was expressed
" in the Book of Common Prayer."

### A.D. 1553, March 25.

LICENCE to the same WILLIAM SERES for the printing of a
catechism in English with the brief of an A B C thereunto annexed ; also for printing and reprinting such of the works of the
Bishop of Winchester or Thomas Beacon as were not contrary to
the " Holy Scriptures, or proceedings in religion, or the laws of
" the realm."

### A.D. 1553, April 12.

A SPECIAL LICENCE (*b*) to RICHARD TATHILLE, citizen, stationer,
and printer of London, for him and his assigns, to imprint for the
space of seven years next ensuing the date hereof, all manner of
books of the temporal law called the common law, so as the copies
be allowed and adjudged meet to be printed by one of the justices
of the law, or two serjeants, or three apprentices to the law, whereof
the one to be a reader in court. And that none others shall imprint any book which the said Richard Tothill shall first take
and imprint during the same term, upon pain of forfeiture of all
such books.

### A.D. 1553, December 29.

A SPECIAL LICENCE (*c*) to JOHN CAWOOD for the imprinting of
all Acts of Parliament, proclamations, injunctions, and other
books and things of what sort soever, " which are already publisht
" in English, or shall be publisht by the Queen or her successors."

---

(*a*) This was taken away from him in Queen Mary's days, but obtained again
for him, (A.D. 1558,) under Elizabeth by Cecil's means. A subsequent grant on
the surrender of this latter Patent was made to him and his son William Seres
during the life of the longer liver of them, with an addition to print all books
of private prayers, for which they had a patent. (Stow's London, vol. ii. p. 309.)
(See as to subsequent Patents to Seres in respect of the above "Egerton Papers,"
Camden Society's Publications.)

(*b*) Dugdale's Origines Juridiciales, p. 59, ed. 1680.

(*c*) Dugdale's Origines Juridiciales, p. 60.

### A.D. 1554.

ABOUT this time several persons were imprisoned for having and selling certain books sent into England by the preachers that fled into Germany. (a) By an Act passed in this year, any one who should write, cypher, or print anything against the King or Queen, or that move sedition or rebellion, was for the first offence to have his right hand cut off, and for the next offence, loss of goods and perpetual imprisonment. (b)

### A.D. 1555, June 6.

PROCLAMATION (c) by the King and Queen, whereby whosoever should be found to have any of " wicked and seditious books," or finding them, should not "forthwith burne the same, without " shewing or reading the same to any other person," should be " reputed and taken for a rebell, and shall without delaye be exe-" cuted for that offence according to thorder of martiall law."

### A.D. 1555, June 13.

A PROCLAMATION (d) issued under cover of Statute 2 Henry IV., for the repressing of heresy, the importation of " the bookes, " writinges, or workes," made or set forth " by or in the name of " the following persons, is forbidden : Martyn Luther, Œcolampadyus, Siuinglius, John Caluyn, Pomerane, John Alasco, Bullynger, Bucer, Melancthon, Barnardinus Ochinus, Erasmus Sarcerius, Peter Martyr, Hughe Latimer, Roberte Barnes otherwise Freere Barnes, John Bale otherwise Freere Bale, Justus Jonas, John Hoper, Miles Couerdale, William Tyndale, Thomas Cranmer "late archebyshop of Canterburye," Wylliam Turner, Theodore Basyll " otherwise called Thomas Beacon," John Frythe Roye, " and the booke commonly called 'Halle's Cronycles,' or any of " them, in the Lattyn tonge, Dutch tonge, English tonge, Italyan " tonge, or French tonge, or any other lyke booke, paper, wrytinge, " or wourke, made, prynted, or sett forth by any other persone or " persons, conteyning false doctryne contrarye to the and agaynste " the Catholyque faythe and the doctryne of the Catholyque " churche." Books relating to the church service as conducted

---

(a) Fox, vol. iii. p. 105, ed. 1641.  (b) Ames, Typ. Ant. p. 1578.
(c) Ames, Typ. Ant. vol. iii. p. 1584.  (d) Ib. p. 1585.

under Edward VI. to be brought within fifteen days to the ordinary of the diocese under pain of their Majesties high indignation
and displeasure, and having further to "awnswer at thire uttermost
" periles." Bishops, ordinaries, and justices are directed, after the
expiration of the fifteen days, to search the "howses, closettes, and
" secrete places of every person, of whatsoever degree, being negli-
" gente in this behalf and suspected to kepe anye such booke," &c.,
and the "justices, mayors, sheriffs, and other hede officers," are to
commit " everye suche offendour to warde, theire to remayne without
" bayle or maynepryse till the same offendour or offendours heue
" receauid suche punishment as the said Statute dothe lymitte and
" appoynte in this behalfe." (a)


## A.D. 1556, May 1.

Licence (b) to Richard Tottle, stationer of London, to imprint or cause to be imprinted for the space of seven years next
ensuing, all manner of books which touch or concern the common
law, whether already imprinted or not.


## A.D. 1556, May 4.

Charter (c) of the Stationers' Company.   The governing body
is authorized to make "ordinances, provisions, and laws" for

---

(a) As early as the year 1556, decrees and ordinances in the Star Chamber
regulated the manner of printing and the number of presses throughout the
kingdom, and prohibited all printing against the force and meaning of any of
the Statutes or laws of the realm, or of any injunction, letters patent, or ordinances
set forth or to be set forth by the grant.   These decrees were subsequently confirmed by ordinances of the Star Chamber, signed by Sir N. Bacon, Lord Bur-
leigh, and all the most eminent Privy Councillors of that age.
(b) Dugdale's Origines Juridiciales, p. 60, ed. 1680.
(c) The stationers or textwriters, who wrote and sold all sorts of books, dwelt
about Pater Noster Row, and were called Pater Noster makers.   (Stow's Survey
of London, edit. 1598, p. 273.) They were of great antiquity, "even before the art
of printing was invented, yet hitherto we have not been able to find their privilege or charter, though several of the old printers are said to be of the Stationers'
Company, nor had they any authority with relation to printed books as a company," until the grant of their charter in 1556, "wherein may be observed the
names of several of our ancient printers." (Ames, Typ. Ant. vol. iii. p. 1590.) "Of
this corporation are printers, booksellers, and such as sell paper and parchment,
and blank books bound up for the use of tradesmen and merchants, and these last
are now peculiarly called stationers." (Stow's Survey of London, vol. ii. p. 307.)
    " In 1558, and down from that time, there are entries in the books of the Com-
pany of copies for particular persons.   In 1559, and downward from that time,
there are persons fined for printing other men's copies. In 1573, there are entries
which take notice of the sale of the copy and the price.   In 1582, there are
entries, with an express proviso that if it be found that any other has right to
any of the copies, then the licence touching such of the copies so belonging
to another shall be void.   A.D. 1640, the Star Chamber was abolished.   The
troubles began soon after.   The King's authority was set at nought ; all regulations of the press and restraints of unlicensed printing by proclamations,

" the good and well ordering and governing of the freemen of the
" foresaid art and of the foresaid society." By sec. 12, no person
is to " practise or exercise the art or mystery of printing or stamp-
" ing any book or anything to be sold or to be bargained for within
" this our kingdom of England, unless the same person is or shall
" be one of the society of the foresaid mystery or art of a stationer
" of the city aforesaid at the time of his foresaid printing or
" stamping," or "had the royal licence." By sec. 13, the master,
" keepers, or wardens for the time being are empowered to search
" as often as they please " the house, &c. of " any stamper, printer,
" binder, or seller of any manner of books within " the " kingdom
" of England or dominions thereof," and " seize, take away, have,
" burn, or convert to the proper use of the said society all books
" and things printed or stamped contrary to any act or proclama-
" tion." By sec. 14, persons illegally stamping or printing, or
withstanding the master, &c. in their search, may be committed by
the master, &c. to prison, there to remain "without bail or main-
" prise for the space of three months," and pay for each such
offence 100 shillings, one moiety thereof to go to the crown and
the other moiety to the company.

### A.D. 1559, November 10.

CONFIRMATION of the above charter by Elizabeth (a). In the
injunctions given by the Queen, A.D. 1559, No 51, against heretical
and seditious books, the Wardens and Company of Stationers are
especially to be obedient. In consequence of great disorder arising
from the "publication of unfruitefull, vaine, and infamous bookes
" and papers," none are to be printed of any kind or in any language without being licensed by Her Majesty " by expresse words
" in writing," or by six of Her Privy Council, or be " perused and
" licensed by the archbishops of Canterbury and York, the bishop

---

decrees of the Star Chamber, and charter powers given to the Stationers' Company, were deemed to be and certainly were illegal. No case of a prosecution
in the Star Chamber for printing without licence or against letters patent, or
pirating another man's copy, or any other disorderly printing, has been found.
Most of the judicial proceedings of the Star Chamber are lost or destroyed ; but
it is certain that down to the year 1640, copies were protected and secured from
piracy by a much speedier and more effectual remedy than actions at law or
bills in equity." (Per Willes, J., *Millar* v. *Taylor*, 4 Burrow's Reports, 2313.)
But see Registers of the Stationers' Company, edited by J. R. Collier, for the
Shakspere Society, containing entries under the first-mentioned head as early
as 1557.

(a) Ames' Typ. Ant. vol. iii. p. 1600. A second charter was granted, A.D. 1558,
*Millar* v. *Taylor*, 4 Burrow's Reports, 2313.

" of London, the chancellors of both Vniuersities, the bishop being
" ordinarie, and the archdeacon also of the place where any such.
" shalbe printed, or by two of them whereof the ordinarie of the place
" to be alwaies one." " And because many pamphelets, playes, and
" ballads be oftentimes printed, wherein regarde woulde be had
" that nothing therein should be either heretical, seditious, or un-
" seemly for Christian eares," no manner of person " shall enter-
" prise to print any such " without the licence of the commissioners
appointed for enforcing the statutes made in the last Parliament
" for uniformity of order in religion," under pain of being
punished " as to the quality of the fault shalbe thought meet."
Exception of profane authors and works in any language
" heretofore commonly received or allowed in any the vniuer-
" sities or schooles, but the same may be printed and vsed as by
" good order they were accustomed."

### A.D. 1561, January 8.

GRANT (a) to JOHN BODELEIGH for seven years of the sole privilege of printing of the Bible. Penalty for infringement 40s. for
each Bible, besides forfeiture of the Bibles to " whomsoever shall
" sustayne the charges and sue the said forfeicture in our behalf."

### A.D. 1563.

BY Statute (b) 5 Eliz. c. 28., the Bible and Book of Common Prayer
and Administration of the Sacraments, " as it is now used within
" the realm, in English," is to be translated " into the British or
" Welsh tonge," and imprinted half at the expense of the parish
and half of the parson or vicar, " to such number at the least that
" one of every sort may be had for every cathedral, collegiate and
" parish church and chappel of ease in such place, and countrys,"
where that tongue is commonly spoken, before March 1, 1566. The
prices of the books to be " appointed and ruled by the same bishops
" and their successors, or by three of them at the least," under
penalty of 40l. A Bible and Book of Common Prayer in English
to be kept in every church in Wales, in a convenient place, " that
" such as understand them may resort at all convenient times to read
" and peruse the same ; and also such as do not understand the
" said language may, by conferring both tongues together, the
" sooner attain to the knowledge of the English tongue."

---

(a) The Patent is given Ames' Typ. Ant. vol. iii. p. 1603 (n.).    (b) Ib. p. 1607.

## A.D. 1563.

SOLE LICENCE (a) to THOMAS COOPER, of Oxford, and his assigns, for twelve years, to print "the Englishe Dictionarie" (commonly called "Bibliotheca Eliota"), and now in this last edition entitled "Thesaurus utriusque Linguæ Latinæ et Britannicæ," in consideration that he hath " diverse and sundry times heretofore travelyed " in the correcting and augmenting of the same," and "hathe " altered and broughte the same to a more perfecte forme in fol- " lowing the notable worke called "Thesaurus Linguæ Latinæ."

## A.D. 1566, January 23.

LETTER (b) from the QUEEN to the BISHOP of LONDON, enjoining care in selection of men of discretion and diligence for the office of searching for and seizing seditious books "transported from " beyond sea."

## A.D. 1566, June 21.

By ORDINANCES of the Court of Star Chamber and High Commission Court " for the reformation of divers disorders " in printing and uttering of books," (c) it is decreed that no person shall print or cause to be printed, or bring or procure to be brought into this realm (d) printed, any book " against the " force and meaning of any ordinance, prohibition, or command- " ment contained in any of the statutes or laws of this realm, or in " any injunctions, letters patent, or ordinances past or set forth, or " to be past or set forth by the Queen's grant, commission, or " authority," under penalty of thenceforth being debarred from " using or exercising the feat of printing, and imprisonment for three months without bail or mainprise. No person to sell, bind, stitch, or sow such books, on pain of forfeiting the books, and for every book 20s. Half of such fine " to be reserved to the Queen's " use, and the other half to them or him that should first seize the " books, or make complaint thereof to the wardens of the said " company." Forfeited books to be taken to the Stationers' Hall,

---

(a) Rymer, vol. xv. p. 682.
(b) Appendix to Strype's Annals of the Reformation, p. 74.
(c) Strype's Life of Archbishop Parker, p. 221. Stow's Survey of London, 6th ed. vol. ii. p. 308.
(d) Several notices of seizures of Popish books, and examinations respecting them, will be found in the State Papers (Domestic series) of Charles I., ed. 1858, pp. 302, 310, 325, 336, 358.

" to be destroyed or made waste paper." Power to the wardens,
or two of the said company deputed by the wardens, " as well in
" any ports as other suspected places, to open and view all packs,
" dryfats, maunds, and other things wherein books or papers shall
" be brought into this realm, and make search in all workhouses,
" shops, warehouses, and other places of printers, books, book-
" sellers, and such as bring books into the realm to be sold, or
" where they have a reasonable cause of suspicion," the books to
be carried " to the hall to the uses abovesaid," and the offenders
brought before the Queen's Commissioners in Causes Ecclesiastical.
" Every stationer, printer, bookseller, merchant, using any trade of
" book printing, binding, selling, or bringing into the realm, should,
" before the Commissioners, or before any other persons thereto to
" be assigned by the Queen's Privy Council, enter into several
" recognizances of reasonable sums of money to Her Majesty, with
" sureties or without, as to the Commissioners should be thought
" expedient, that he should truly observe all the said ordinances,
" well and truly yield and pay all such forfeitures, and in no point
" be resisting, but in all things aiding to the said wardens and their
" deputies for the true execution of the premises."

These ordinances were signed by eight of the Privy Council, and
by the Commissioners for Ecclesiastical Causes. (*a*)


### A.D. 1571, June 13.

PATENT to RAFFE BOWES (*b*) and THOMAS BEDINGFIELD,
Esquires, to import playing cards into this kingdom, and dispose
of them in large or small quantities, notwithstanding any Act, &c.
formerly made, &c.


### A.D. 1574–5, January 22.

LETTERS PATENT (*c*) to THOMAS TALLIS and WILLIAM
BIRDE, and " the overlyver of them, and to the assignees
" of them, and of the surviver of them, for xxi. yeares next
" ensuing, to imprint any and so many as they will of set
" songe or songes in partes either in English, Latine, French,
" Italian, or other tongues, that may serve for musicke, either
" in church or chamber, or otherwise, to be either plaid or

---

(*a*) Ames' Typ. Ant. vol. iii. p. 1621.        (*b*) See *post*, A.D. 1588.
(*c*) Ames' Typ. Ant. vol. iii. p. 1643.

" soonge; and that they may rule and cause to be ruled by
" impression any paper to serve for printing or pricking of any
" songe or songes, and may sell and utter any printed bookes or
" papers of any songe or songes, or any bookes or quieres of such
" paper imprinted." Infringers to pay for each offence a fine of
40s. to the Crown, and forfeit the pirated articles to the patentees.
The Patent concludes thus :—" We have also by the same willed
" and commanded our printers, maisters, and wardens of the
" misterie of stacioners to assist the said Thomas Tallis and Wil-
" liam Birde, and their assignes, for the dewe executing of the
" premisses."

### A.D. 1575.

In this year certain persons endeavoured to obtain from the Queen
a privilege for the sole printing of all ballads, damask paper, and
books, in prose and metre, from the quantity of one sheet of paper
to four and twenty. The company of stationers made a petition to
the Lord Treasurer for stay of this, setting forth how it would be
the overthrow of a multitude of families, and that by the printing
of these the company was chiefly maintained, so as, if the same was
taken away from them by way of privilege they should be utterly
undone, whereof, if the Queen were advertised, they were sure she
would not pass the grant. (a)

### A.D. 1577, July 20.

Patent to Christopher Saxton, " that he and his assigns
" onely, for and duringe the space of tenne yeres nexte ensewing
" the date of this our lycence shall and may by himselfe, his
" assigne and assignes, factors and deputyes, imprynte and sett
" fourth, or cause to be imprynted and sett fourthe any and as many
" such mappes, chartts, and platts of this oure realme of Englande
" and Wales, or of anye countye or other parte thereof, by him
" allreadie or hereafter to be sett fourthe, as to him and to his said
" deputye and deputyes shall seem meet and conveniente, and shall
" and may sell or utter, or cause to be sold or uttered, any such
" imprynted mappes, chartts, or platts as aforesaid."

---

(a) Stow's London, vol. ii. p. 309.

## A.D. 1577, September 27.

LICENCE (a) to CHRISTOPHER BARKER for the imprinting of all Statutes and Acts of Parliament, Proclamations, &c., in English, for life.

## A.D. 1577, November 18.

LICENCE (b) to NICASIUS YETSWEIRT to print all manner of books concerning the common laws of this realm for 30 years.

## A.D. 1578.

ABOUT this time encouragement was given to the art of engraving and rolling-press work. Abram Ortelius mentions in his geography several ingenious Englishmen, as one Anthony Jenkinson, 1562; Robert Leeth, a man skilful in taking the plot of a country, sent over to take one of Ulster, 1567; and Humphrey Lhuyd, 1568. Strype, in his Life of Archbishop Parker, p. 541, says thus : " 'And now we are speaking of his servants and " dependants, we may well mention his sculptors or engravers, " excellent in their art, whereof one was a foreigner, named Hogen- " bergh, and another was called Lyne. He employed them much " in genealogies, wherein indeed a noble part of ancient history " consisteth.' A description of several of the productions of these " engravers is then given."

## A.D. 1583.

ABOUT this time a controversy arose among the stationers in respect of the licences, the members of that body contending that they had a right to print any lawful books. The matter was heard by the Lord Mayor, and afterwards by the Privy Council, and upon a reference by the latter to D. Hammond, a civilian, and Thomas Norton, a divine, and some others, it was declared that the complainants' " intent" was " derogatory to the Queen's pre- " rogative, not only as touching the granting of privileges for " printing, (c) but also for sundry other licences," and they were advised to desist from their suit.

---

(a) Dugdale's Origines Juridiciales, ed. 1680, p. 61.
(b) Dugdale's Origines Juridiciales, ed. 1680, p. 61.
(c) In complaining of the patents granted by Elizabeth, Stow (Survey, vol. ii. p. 309) says :—
" John Jugge, besides being Her Majesty's printer, had the privilege of printing of Bibles and Testaments, the which had been common to all the printers.

With a view to compromising the affair, certain copies were voluntarily granted to the Company by the licencees. (a)

## A.D. 1585-6, June 23. (b)

" DECREES (b) of the Lords in the Starre Chambers touching " printers, stationers, &c." In consequence of the "great enormities " and abuses as of late (most men of tyme past) have been com-" monlye used and practised by diverse contemptuous and disor-" derly persons professing the arte or misterie of printing and " selling books," videlicet, " 1. Every person having any printing " presse, rowle, or other instrument for imprinting of books, " chartes, ballades, pourtrayctures, paper called damask paper, or " any such matters or things whatsoever," is, within ten days from the publication of the decree, or from the erection of the presses, to bring " a true note or certificate of the sayde presses " to the Company of Stationers, under penalty of having " all and

---

*Richard Tothil*, the printing of all kind of law books, common before to all printers, who sold the same books at excessive prices, to the hindrance of a great number of poor students.

*John Day*, the printing of A B C and the catechism, with the sole selling of them by the colour of a commission. These books were the only relief of the poorest sort of that company.

*James Roberts* and *Richard Watkins*, the printing of all almanacs and prognostications, the which was also the chief relief of the poorest of the printers.

*Thomas Marsh* had a great licence for Latin books used in the grammar schools of England, the which was the general living of the whole Company of Stationers.

*Thomas Vantroller*, a stranger, had the sole printing of other Latin books, as the New Testament and others.

*One Byrde*, a singing man, had a licence for printing all music books, and by that means claimed the printing of ruled paper.

*William Seres* had privilege for the printing of all psalters, all manner of primers, English or Latin, and all manner of prayer-books, with the reversion of the same to his son.

*Francis Flower*, a gentleman, being none of the Company, had privilege of printing the grammar and other things, and had farmed it out to some of the Company for 100*l*. per year, which 100*l*. was raised in the enhancing of the prices above the accustomed order. " I have seen," he says, " a patent ready drawn for Queen Elizabeth's signing, for seven years privileging Richard Tothil, stationer, to print all manner of books or tables whatsoever which touched or concerned cosmography, or any part thereof, as geography, chorography, topography, writ in the English tongue, or translated out of any other language into English, of whatsoever countries they treated, and whosoever was the author. But whether this was ever actually signed I cannot tell."

In this year the number of the members of the Company in the City is stated by Stow at 175, 140 of whom had come to their freedom since the accession of the Queen.

*Raleigh* held a monopoly of cards during the same period. (Macaulay's Essays on Lord Bacon, vol. ii. p. 153.)

(a) Ames' Typ. Ant., vol. iii. 1672, where a list of the books is given.

(b) Ames' Typ. Ant., vol. iii. p. 1168.    Strype's Life of Archbp. Whitgift, pp. 222-3,

" every the saide presses and other instruments utterly defaced
" and made unserviceable for imprinting for ever, with twelve
" months' imprisonment without bayle or maynprise."

2. No presses to be erected except within the city of London
and the suburbs (except one at Cambridge and one at Oxford).
Presses in London to be placed in such open places in their houses
as the Company of Stationers, who are from time to time to view
and search the same, shall appoint; and no printer shall deny or
keep secret any press under payne of its being defaced and one
year's imprisonment.

3. " *Item.*—That no printer nor other person or persons what-
" soever that hath sett up any presse or instrument for imprinting
" within six moneths last past shall hereafter use or occupie the
" same, nor any person or persons shall hereafter erect or sett up
" any presse or other instrument for printing, till the excessive
" multitude of printers havinge presses alreadye sett up be abated,
" diminished, and by death, giving over, or otherwise, be brought
" to so small a number of masters or owners of printing howses,
" being of abilitie and good behaviour, as the archbishopp of
" Canterburie and bishopp of London for the time being shall
" thereupon think it requisite and convenient for the good service
" of the realme to have some more presses or instruments erected
" and sett up," when the Company of Stationers is to select fit
persons, being free stationers, and present them to the Commissioners in Causes Eecclesiastical. The article is not to extend to
the office of Queen's printer.

The effect of a decree of the Privy Council in the Star Chamber
of this date is stated (*a*) to be to confine the number of printers to
the number of twenty, to have the use and exercise of printing
houses for the time being (besides Her Majesty's printers and the
printers allowed for the Universities).

4. " No booke, worke, coppie, matter, or thing whatsoever is to
" be printed, unless allowed according to " th' order appoynted by
" the Queene's Majestie's injunctions, and be first seen and perused
" by the archbishopp of Canterburye and bishopp of London for
" the time being, or one of them, the Queen's Majestie's printer
" for some speciall service by Her Majestie or by some of Her
" Highness Privie Counsell thereunto appoynted, and such as are

---

(*a*) Harleian Miscellany, vol. iii. p. 290.

" or shalbe priviledged to print the bookes of the common lawe of
" this realme, for suche of the same books as shalbe allowed of by
" the two Cheef Justices or Chiefe Barons for the time being, or any
" two of them onely excepted; nor shall imprint or cause to be
" imprinted any booke, worke, or coppie, against the forme and
" meaning of any restraynte or ordinance conteyned or to be con-
" teyned in any statute or laws of this realme, or in any injunction
" made or sett forthe by Her Majestie or Her Highness Privie
" Counsell, or against the true intent and meaning of any letters
" patents, commissions, or prohibitions under the great seale of
" England, upon payne " of having the press and materials defaced, being disqualified to use the " arte or feate of imprinting,"
and six months' imprisonment "without bayle or maynprize."

5. Persons selling such illegally printed books liable to three
months' imprisonment.

6. Stationers' Company empowered to search where they shall
have reasonable cause of suspicion, and take contraband books
and bring offenders before the Commissioners in Causes Ecclesiastical.

7. The Stationers' Company are to deface the instruments so
seized at their Hall, and redeliver " the stuffe of the same so de-
" faced" to the owners again within three months of the seizure.

8. " Item.—That for avoyding of the excessive numbers of
" printers within this realm, it shall not be lawful for any upper
" warden of the Company to have more than three or any under
" warden more than two apprentizes at one time. The 'yeomanrie
" of this companie' to have but one. The Queen's printers to
" be allowed to have 'to the number of six at any one tyme.'"

9. " Item.—That none of the printers in Cambridge or Oxford
" for the tyme being shall be suffered to have any more apprentices
" than one at one tyme at the moste. But it is and shall be law-
" ful to and for the saide printers, and either of them, and their
" successors, to have and use the help of any journey man, being
" free men of the cittie of London, without contradiction."


A.D. 1586, October.

LICENCE (a) granted by Archbishop Whitgift to ASCANIUS DE
RENEALME, merchant bookseller, to introduce Popish books,

---

(a) Ames' Typ. Ant., vol. iii. p. 1174, and see Neal's Hist. of the Puritans,
vol. i. p. 482.

" upon this condition onely, that any of them bee not shewed nor
" dispersed abroad," but brought first to the archbishop, or some
of the Privy Council, that they may be delivered to such persons as
" by us or some of us shall be thought most meete men (upon
" good considerations and purposes) to have the reading and
" perusall of them."

Shortly after this John Wolf, fishmonger, and Roger Ward,
asserted their right to print any book, however forbidden by the
Queen's privilege, the latter making " it a practice to print all
" kinds of books at his pleasure,"(a) and resisting the master and
warden of the Stationers' Company in their attempt to search his
house.

### A.D. 1586.

THE Stationers that had privileges petitioned the Council to
enforce their privileges, and about the same time a privilege was
craved by the Company of Stationers for printing of those two
little books of introduction into the Latin tongue, used in schools,
the " accidence " and " grammar."

### A.D. 1588, October 18.

ALLOWANCE by the Stationers' Company to RAFFE or RALPH
BOWES. " The whole sute of mouldes belonging to the olde
" fourme of plaieinge cardes, commonly called the French cardes,
" with the Jew Cisian dozen, and all other thinges thereunto
" belonging. Item.—The newe addition of the whole sute of
" new mouldes belonging to the olde and newe forme of playeing
" cards, commonly called the French cards, with the Jew Cisian
" dozen, and all other thinges thereunto belonginge." (b)

### A.D. 1589, January 8.

ALLOWANCE by the Stationers' Company to RAFFE or RALPH
BOWES (ante, p. 50) to be printed, " the wholle sute of carved
" mouldes in woode or caste in mettall belonging to the oulde
" fourme of playing cardes, commonly called the French carde,
" with the Jew Cisian dozen, and all other thinges thereunto
" belonging."(c)

---

(a) Stow, vol. ii. p. 300.
(b) Ames, Typ. Ant., vol. iii. p. 1628 (n.)
(c) Ames, Typ. Ant., vol. iii. p. 1628 (n.)

## A.D. 1590–1, January 12.

ENTRY at Stationers' Hall for RAFFE or RALPH BOWES "to " print these markes folowing, which are to bynd up cardes in, " viz., a dozen m'ke.  Jtem, a Sizian m'ke.  Item, a Jew m'ke."

## A.D. 1591.

SOLE LICENCE, under the Privy Seal, (*a*) to RICHARD WRIGHTE for the term of his life, for printing the History of Tacitus.

## A.D. 1594.

LICENCE (*b*) to CHARLES YETSWERT to print all manner of books which concern the common laws, for 30 years.

## A.D. 1599, March 10.

SPECIAL LICENCE (*c*) to THOMAS WRIGHT and BONHAM NORTON to print all law books for 30 years.

## A.D. 1603, May 7.

PROCLAMATION (*d*) inhibiting the use and execution of any charter or grant made by the late Queen Elizabeth of any kind of monopolies.

## A.D. 1603, July 9.

GRANT (*e*) to ROBERT BARKER to print all statutes and libels for life.

## A.D. 1603, October 24.

GRANT (*e*) to the COMPANY of STATIONERS of the exclusive right of printing primers, psalters, psalms, almanacs, and prognostications.

## A.D. 1604.

LICENCE (*e*) to ROBERT BARKER, in reversion after JOHN NORTON, to print all books in Latin, Greek, and Hebrew, Tremelius' Latin Bible, and all charts and maps.

---

(*a*) Rymer, vol. xvi. p. 96.
(*b*) Dugdale's Origines Juridiciales, ed. 1680, p. 61.
(*c*) Ib.
(*d*) A Booke of Proclamations, published since the beginning of His Majesty's most happy reigne over England, &c., until this present Moneth of Febr. 3, A.D. 1609.  4to. Lond., p. 12.
(*e*) State Papers (Domestic series), vol. viii.

### A.D. 1605, July 20.

GRANT (*a*) to ALEXANDER SERLE, of the office of King's printer, in the Admiralty and Ecclesiastical Courts, for life.

### A.D. 1605, June 26.

GRANT (*a*) to JAMES RYME, bookseller, of the sole privilege of printing and selling certain Latin works of Hieronimus Zanchius, for fourteen years, the price of them to be fixed by the Archbishop of Canterbury.

### A.D. 1607.

LICENCE (*a*) to WM. STALLENGE, for twenty-one years, to print a book called " Instructions for the planting and increase of mul-" berry leaves, breeding of silkworms, and making of silk."

### A.D. 1608, April 29.

GRANT (*a*) to GEORGE HUMBLE, of privilege for twenty-one years, to print a book compiled by John Speed, called "The Theatre of " the Empire of Great Britayne, with cartes and maps."

### A.D. 1608, August 13.

LICENCE (*a*) for ten years to Sir WM. WODEHOUSE to print reports, &c. of a particular case.

### A.D. 1609.

IN this year (*b*) two books maintaining the most extravagant maxims of despotic power were printed, with the privity of the King, but the Parliament in the following year preparing to take cognizance of the matter, the King issued a proclamation for suppressing them.

### A.D. 1610.

LICENCE (*c*) for ten years to JOHN SPEED to print genealogies of the Holy Scriptures, together with the maps of Canaan.

---

(*a*) State Papers (Domestic series), vol. viii.
(*b*) Rapin's Acta Regia, vol. 4, p. 216.
(*c*) Rymer, vol. xvii. p. 484. A letter, dated May 14, 1610, from the Lord Treasurer to the Warden of the Stationers' Company, commanding him to suffer nothing to be printed concerning the late King's death without sanction from

### A.D. 1611, February 20.

LICENCE (*a*) to JOHN MINSHON of the sole printing of the " Glos-
" son Etimologicon," or Dictionary Etymological of twelve languages, for twenty-one years.

### A.D. 1613, January 6.

GRANT (*a*) to BONHAM NORTON of the office of printer and bookseller, in the Latin, Greek, and Hebrew tongues, for thirty years.

### A.D. 1613, April 2.

LICENCE (*a*) to the WARDENS and COMPANY of BOOKSELLERS
of LONDON, for 21 years to print and sell " Cato's Distichs," and
other books.

### A.D. 1615, March 3.

GRANT (*a*) to NOMINEES of EDWARD LORD MORLEY of the sole
printing of a small book, entitled " God and the Kinge."

### A.D. 1615, May 9.

ORDER (*a*) specifying the number of printing presses which are to
be allowed to certain printers mentioned.

### A.D. 1615, July 30.

GRANT, (*a*) under the sign manual, to JOHN WILLIE, in reversion after BONHAM NORTON, of the office of printing grammar
and grammar books.

### A.D. 1616, March 8.

LICENCE (*a*) to the WARDEN and COMPANY of STATIONERS of
LONDON to print primers, almanacs, &c.

---

his Lordship, is mentioned in the State Papers (Domestic series), ed. 1858 :
and another dated A.D. 1610, June 2, from M. de Tourval to Salisbury, in
which he says that he has executed six works for the King, and has now a
seventh given, but has received no recompence, although his expenses have been
great, especially in travelling in vain from city to city abroad to find a printer
for the King's book, and then staying three months hidden in Paris to su-
perintend its printing there, and keep it concealed from the Jesuits. Begs
some gratuity.

(*a*) State Papers (Domestic series), vol. viii.

### A.D. 1616, March 20,

GRANT, (a) under sign manual, to Capt. EDWARD DAVIES, of a
mitigated fine of 40*l*., imposed by the Commissioners Ecclesiastical
on Thomas Dawson, stationer, of London, for his contempt in
printing certain books contrary to the patent granted to Robert
Barker.

### A.D. 1617.

SPECIAL LICENCE (a) to JOHN SPEED, for the sole printing of
the genealogies of the Scripture, and other things, for seven years.

### A.D. 1617.

INJUNCTION (b) by the ATTORNEY GENERAL against printing or
selling a book compiled by the King's orders, "On the oath of
"allegiance," by any except EDWARD Lord MORLEY, and his
deputies, by whom the sole licence is granted therefor.

### A.D. 1617, February 4.

LICENCE (c) for a further term of seven years to JOHN SPEED (d)
for his genealogies and map.   The prices at which these are to be
sold are prescribed.

---

### A.D. 1617, March 11.—Nº 1.

RATHBORNE, or RATHBURNE, ARON, and BURGES,
ROGER.—Grant under the Privy Seal directed "to all justices of
" the peace, mayors, sheriff, bailiffes, constables, and all officers,
" ministers, and subjects of vs, our heires and successors, to whom
" it shall or maie appertaine."   It recites how " amongst forraine
" nations there are faire, curious, and artificiall descripcons, plott
" and mappes (e) made and sett forth of their principall citties and
" towns of greatest noat, which being exactlie drawn out in metall
" and printed of, are dispersed and sent abroad into all partes to

---

(a) State Papers (Domestic series), vol. viii.
(b) State Papers (Domestic series), ed. 1858, p. 454.
(c) Rymer, vol. xvii. p. 484.            (d) Ante, p. 58.
(e) The first maps engraved on wood were contained in an edition of Ptolemy.
(Jackson's History of Wood Engraving.)

" the greate honor and renowne of those princes in whose domynions
" they are," and how " of our citie of London, being the chief and
" principall in this our kingdome of England, there hath never been
" made or taken any true or pfecte descripc̄on, but false and meane
" draught̄ (a) cutt out in wood, and soe dispersed abroade to the
" greate disparagement and disgrace of soe famous and worthie a
" state," and Rathborne's " greate desire to take a pfecte survaie "
of the city of London and other places within the kingdom, and
application to the king for the sole making and setting forth of the
plots, maps, and descriptions thereof for some reasonable time,
" to the end hee maie reape the fruites of his travell, charges, and
" expences to bee susteyned in or about the p̄misses." It then gives
and grants " unto the saide Aron Rathburne and unto our well-
" beloved Roger Burges, their executors, administrators, and as-
" signes, and theire or anie of theire deputies or assignes havinge
" authoritie from them in that behalfe," that they " onelie and none
" others shall," during the term of twenty-one years, " within this
" our realme of Englande and any other our domynions," make
plans, drawings, and descriptions of London, Westminster, York,
Bristol, Norwich, Canterbury, Bath, Oxford, Cambridge, and
Windsor, with their suburbs, and to " imprinte and sett forth " the
same on " paper, parchmente, cloth, or other materialls." Then
follows an injunction to " all and singular bodies politique and cor-
" porate," and persons against counterfeiting or selling, exporting or
importing " anie other the like mappes, &c.," upon pain of forfeiting
the same, the tools used in their production, incurring the royal indignation and displeasure, and such punishment as may be inflicted
for contempt of the prerogative royal. Power is given to the
patentees during the said term, " with the assistance of a constable
" or other officer, at convenient tymes and in convenient and
" lawfull manner," to board any ship or enter any place, " where
" they or anie of them shall thinke good," to search for and seize
counterfeits and tools, " the one moiety thereof to bee to the
" patentees and the other to the Crown." There is a saving of all
rights under former Letters Patent and Royal Grants. And lastly,

---

(a) A plan of London was published in 1560. It was printed on six sheets and
two half sheets, measuring 6 feet 3 inches by 2 feet 4 inches. It was re-engraved
by Geo. Vertue in 1748, on pewter, with this inscription " Civitas Londinum,
1560," and printed on 6 sheets. These were purchased and re-published by
the Society of Antiquaries, 1776. (See an account of this and several other plans
of London in Gough's British Topography, vol. i. p. 745.)

a mandate to the justices, &c. to aid the patentees, their executors,
" &c. in the execuçon of their our Lr̃es Patentç, as they tender
" our indignaçon and displeasure and will avoid the same at their
" vttermoste perills."

[Extract (printed, 4d.) from Letters Patent in the Rolls Chapel.]

## A.D. 1617, April 20.

SOLE LICENCE (a) under the Privy Seal to FYNES MORRISON
for twenty-one years to print his " Itinerary," containing his " ten
" years' travaile " through " Germany, Boemerland, Switzerland,
" Netherland, Denmark, Poland, Italy, Turky, France, England,
" Scotland, and Ireland," every part thereof " being first seene,
" viewed, and allowed by the Archbishop of Canterbury and
" Bishop of London, or one of them."

## A.D. 1617, May 5.—N° 2.

HILLYARD, NICHOLAS, Gent, " Our principall drawer for
" the small purtrait and imborser of our medallies of gold."
—Patent " in respect of his extraordinary art and skill in draw-
" ing, graveing, and imprinting and representaçons of us
" and others, which he durst not hitherto shewe and publishe
" as he can doe for feare his workes would be counterfeited
" by others, whereby he should receave losse and discreditt,"
of the sole privilege " for and duringe the terme of 12 years "
within England or any other our realms and domynyons," of
inventing, making, imprinting, and selling " any picture or pic-
" tures of our image or other representaçon of our p̃son," with
alterations and additions, " as well in paper and parchment as in
" any other thinge or things whatsoever;" and to that end to
set up presses. Counterfeits to be forfeited, half going to the
Crown, half to the patentee. Power to enter " any howse, cellar,
" warehouse, shopp, or other place or places whatsoever, which
" they or any of them shall thinke good," to search for and seize
counterfeits. The patentee to pay for the said privilege the
yearly rent of 13s. 4d. Saving of the rights of other parties " to
" use theire science and faculties of prynting in, of, and for theire
" olde plates, and the like of them, as formerly they have done,

---

(a) Rymer, vol. xvii. p. 10.

" not being in imytaçon of any of our said servantç setting forth,
" or of any other new portraite of us."

[Extract (printed, 3d.) from Letters Patent in the Rolls Chapel.]

## A.D. 1618, April 26.

SOLE LICENCE (a) to JOHN MARRIOTT to print and sell Pharma-
copeia Londinensis, lately compiled by the College of Physicians.

## A.D. 1618, August 7.

GRANT (b) under the Privy Seal to WILLIAM ALLEY, for seven
years, of the sole printing of " The Peacemaker, or Britain's Bless-
" ing," by Thomas Middleton.

## A.D. 1623 (21 Jac. 1. c. 3.)
### STATUTE OF MONOPOLIES.

## A.D. 1623, February 17.

GRANT (c) to GEORGE WITHERS, for fifty-one years, of the sole
printing of the " Hymns and Songs of the Church." The price
of the book to be regulated by the Company of Stationers.

## A.D. 1623, April 24.

PATENT (d) to JOHN SPEED for a further term of twenty-one
years in respect of his genealogies and map. (e) This grant reciting
that he had " bene at great charge for the cutting of the modell
" and printing the said genealogies and mappes, and that thereby
" and by some other crosses which have befallen him his estate is
" much weakened," and had petitioned for an extension of his
privilege " for the better releife and comfort of himselfe, being now
" aged and sicklie, and of his wife and many children."

## A.D. 1623, September 20.

A PROCLAMATION (f) reciting the decree of 23rd June, 28 Eliz.,
" the true intent and meaning of which said decree hath been
" cautelouslie abused and eluded by printing in the parts beyond
" the sea and elsewhere, as well sundrie seditious, scismatical, and

---

(a) State Papers, ed. 1858.   (Warrant Bk. I. p. 238.)
(b) Rymer, vol. xvii. p. 111.
(c) Rymer, vol. xvii. p. 454.
(d) Rymer, vol. xvii. p. 484.
(e) Ante, p. 60.
(f) Rymer, vol. xvii. p. 522.

" scandelous books and pamphlets, as alsoe such allowed bookes,
" workes, and writings as have been imprinted within the realme
" by such to whome the sole printing thereof by Letters Patents
" or lawfull ordinance or authoritie doth appertaine according to
" the true intent of the said decree, and by importing the same
" into this our realm." " This decree in future is to be strictly
" observed and putt in execution, and to meet with the malice and
" crafts of such as by sleight or cunning shall attempt or goe
" about to undermyne or avoyde all or any parte of the said decree,"
no person to print or import any seditions, scismatical, scandalous,
or privileged books " upon paine of our indignation and heavie
" displeasure, and of the paines, punishments, and imprisonments
" conteyned in this said decree, and such further censures as by
" our Court of Star Chamber and High Commission respectively
" shall be thought meete to be inflicted on them for such their
" offences."

## A.D. 1623, September 25.

PROCLAMATION (a) against the disorderly printing, uttering, and
dispersing of books, pamphlets, &c. It recites the statute 28 Eliz.
c. 23.

## A.D. 1625, April 1.

PROCLAMATION (b) to inhibit the sale of Latyne bookes reprinted
" beyond the seas haveing been first printed in Oxford or Cam-
" bridge," reciting that " for preventinge the common errors of
" the presse which have heretofore happened in printing " Latin
books (c) for the advancement of religion and learning, "there hath
" byn for manie yeares a speciall printer allowed and authorized at
" either of our universities." The university printers are directed
within one month to give a certificate of books originally printed
at the universities; and, further forward, certificates (signed by
the respective vice-chancellors) (d) monthly of these printed there in
future to the Stationers' Company.

---

(a) Rymer, vol. xvii. p. 522.          (b) Rymer, vol. xviii. p. 8 (note).
(c) In the State Papers (Domestic series) a petition is mentioned of Robert
Young, assignee of His Majesty's printer for the Latin tongue, which states
that he has nearly printed a Bible, and prays that he may have a Royal Warrant
for adding thereto the Liturgy in Latin.
(d) Under date December 8, 1625, is a letter from the Vice Chancellor and
Senate of Cambridge, to Thomas, Earl of Arundel and Surrey, thanking him for

## A.D. 1625, April 1.

PATENT (*a*) appointing Sir EDWARD VILLIERS and Sir WILLIAM PARKHURST, RICHARD ROGERS, WILLIAM WOOD, ANDREW PALMER, and GEORGE TURNER, or any three of them, to be Commissioners of the Royal Mint in the room of Sir Randill Cranfield, the Master of the Mint.

## A.D. 1625, May 10.

GRANT (*b*) of a pension of 2,000*l.* a year to Sir FRANCIS CRANE for the encouragement of the work of tapestries "which he hath " lately brought into the kingdom and erected at Mortlake in the " county of Surrey."

## A.D. 1625, May 14.

GRANT (*c*) of the office of master embosser and maker of the medals to the King and his heirs, with a salary of 40*l.* a year, to ABRAHAM VANDERDOORT, Esq., who, " after many chargeable tryals and long practice," had attained to the art and mystery of making of medals.

## A.D. 1625, June 4.

PROCLAMATION (*d*) for continuing farthing tokens of copper, and the prohibiting the counterfeiting of them, and the use of all others.

## A.D. 1625, July 11.

PATENT (*e*) to FRANCES Duchess Dowager of LENOX and Sir FRANCIS CRANE, for the sole coining of farthing tokens of copper for seventeen years, in consideration of the payment of 100 marks per annum to the king.

## A.D. 1625, September 4.

PROCLAMATION (*f*) for making the French silver coin called Cardecue current within the realm, at the value of 19½*d.*

his assistance in the determination of a cause relating to an infringement by certain London booksellers of the privilege of printing granted to the University by Henry VIII. (State Papers, Domestic series, ed. 1858, p. 473.) There is also in the same papers (p. 341), a petition of Bonham Norton to the Council, complaining of the surreptitious printing of Grammars, Accidences, and Lilly's Rules, by Cantrell Legge, of Cambridge.

(*a*) Rymer, vol. xviii. p. 6.  (*b*) Rymer, vol. xviii. p. 60.
(*c*) Rymer, vol. xviii. p. 79.  (*d*) Rymer, vol. xviii. p. 108.
(*e*) Rymer, vol. xviii. p. 143.  (*f*) Rymer, vol. xviii. p. 186.

### A.D. 1626, April 24.

GRANT (a) to GEORGE SANDYS, Esquire, for the sole printing and selling of fifteen bookes of Ovid's Metamorphoses, by him translated into English verse.

### A.D. 1626, April 26.

GRANT (b) of a privilege for thirty-one years to JOSEPH WEBB, M.D., "for the whole teaching and instructing all that desire to " learn the tongues by the ways and means by him invented, and " for the sole printing and selling of the books by him invented " and modelled for that end."

### A.D. 1625, June 21.

RICHARD MONTAGUE brought (c) to the bar of the Commons in respect of his book " Appello Cæsarem."

### A.D. 1626, April 18.

IMPEACHMENT of (d) RICHARD. MONTAGUE by the House of Commons in respect of his "Appeal to Cæsar," and an address voted, praying "that the said Richard Montague may be punished " according to his demerits in such exemplary manner as may " deter others from attempting so presumptuously the peace of the " Church and State, and that the books aforesaid may be sup- " pressed and burnt."

### A.D. 1626, June 17.

PROCLAMATION (e) by the King forbidding the publication of " A declaration" or remonstrance of the late dissolved Parliament.

### A.D. 1626, July 26.

PROCLAMATION (f) repealing the former proclamation as to the currency of the French coins Cardecue.

---

(a) Rymer, vol. xviii. p. 676.  (b) Rymer, vol. xviii. p. 660.
(c) "This cause, says Rushworth (vol. i. p. 173), began in the one and twentieth of King James, when he had published a former book which he named 'A new Gag for an Old Goose,' in answer to a popish book entitled 'A Gag for the New Gospel.' The business was then questioned in Parliament and committed to the Archbishop of Canterbury, and ended in an admonition given to Montague;" and see ib. 176 and 209.
(d) Rymer, vol. xviii. p. 719.  (e) Rymer, vol. xviii. p. 727.
(f) Rymer, vol. xviii. p. 736.

## A.D. 1626, August 14.

PATENT (*a*) to Sir EDWARD VILLIERS and Sir WILLIAM PARKHURST, RICHARD ROGERS, and ANDREW PALMER, or any three of them, to be " Commissioners for the makeing and coining " of our moneys at our Mint."

## A.D. 1626, September 7.

PATENT (*b*) appointing Sir EDWARD VILLIERS and Sir WILLIAM PARKHURST, RICHARD ROGERS, and ANDREW PALMER Commissioners of the Royal Mint.

## A.D. 1627, February 25.

APPOINTMENT (*c*) by Writ of Privy Seal of the Earls of MARLEBURGH, MANCHESTER, EXETER, SUFFOLK, SALISBURY, DORSETT, and BRIDGEWATER; Sir JOHN COOKE, Sir RICHARD WESTON, and Sir JULIUS CESAR, Sir RICHARD WYNNE, Sir ROBERT HEATH, Sir ROBERT RICHE, Sir JOHN FINCH, Sir THOMAS HATTON, Sir HENRY CROOKE, Sir WILLIAM PARKHURST, Sir JOHN BURROUGHES; HENRY CLIFFORD, EDWARD JOHNSON, GILES RAWLINS, ANDREW PALMER, Esquires; and NATHANIEL TOMKINS, or any five of them, to be Commissioners for the execution of the Proclamation against the frauds practised upon the coinage.

## A.D. 1627, March 9.

GRANT (*d*) by Patent to CALEB MORLEY, A.M., who is said to have contrived the best method that ever was invented to help the memory and to ground scholars in the English, Latin, and other languages. If the said method should be approved by the testimony of twelve good grammarians, then the same was enjoined to be taught for twenty-one years in all schools throughout the King's dominions, and he was to have the sole privilege for that term of printing and selling any books, tracts, or tables for that purpose.

## A.D. 1627, May 25.

PROCLAMATION (*e*) " for the better execution of the office of His " Majestie's chaunger and reformation of sundry abuses and " frauds practised upon his Majestie's coines."

---

(*a*) Rymer, vol. xviii. p. 740.  
(*c*) Rymer, vol. xviii. p. 971.  
(*e*) Rymer, vol. xviii. p. 896.  
(*b*) Rymer, vol. xviii. p. 752.  
(*d*) Rymer, vol. xviii. p. 857.

### A.D. 1628, January 17.

PROCLAMATION (a) for the suppressing of the book entitled " Appello Cæsarem."

### A.D. 1628, February 12.

PETITION (b) from the printers and booksellers of London complaining of the restraints imposed in respect of books written against Popery, and that divers of their number had been sent for by pursuivants for printing them, and "that licensing is only " restrained to the Bishop of London and his chaplains, and in- " stanced certain books against Popery which were denied to be " licensed." (c)

### A.D. 1628, June 24.

PROCLAMATION (d) for calling in and suppressing of two sermons preached and printed by Roger Manwaring, D.D., entituled " Reli- " gion and Allegiance."

### A.D. 1628, July 15.

PROCLAMATION (e) by the King, commanding all copies of the " Appello Cæsarem" to be delivered up to the Bishops or Vice-Chancellors of the Universities, " and if any, by preaching, read- " ing, or making of books, pro and contra, concerning those " unnecessary questions, shall revive the difference, he was resolved " to take such order with them and those books as they shall wish " they had never thought upon those needless controversies."

### A.D. 1629.

IN a debate in the House of Commons in this year, Mr. Selden took notice " that there was no law to prevent the printing of any " books in England, but only a decree in the Star Chamber, and " he moved that a law might be made concerning printing, other- " wise, said he, a man might be fined, imprisoned, and his goods " may be taken from him by virtue of the said decree, which is a " great invasion on the liberty of the subject." (f)

---

(a) Rymer, vol. xix. p. 261 ; ante, p. 66.     (b) Rushworth, vol. i. p. 655.
(c) It was on the discussion occasioned by the presentation of this petition that Mr. Selden made the declaration noticed under A.D. 1629.
(d) Rymer, vol. xviii. p. 1024.          (e) Rushworth, vol. i. p. 634.
(f) Rymer, vol. xix.

### A.D. 1630, April 26.

SOLE LICENCE (a) by Privy Seal to PAULE WILLETT for twenty-one years to print the "Synopsis Papisimi," written by his father, Dr. Willett.

### A.D. 1632.

PLAYING CARDS monopolized by the King. There was one company in particular created for making playing-cards, of whom the King bought them at 18s. and 28s. per gross, and after sealing them, sold them again. The duty arising from the sealing was given to William Watkins, by whom it was farmed to Henry Cogan. The Company of Cardmakers, after some opposition, " submitted to a contract with the King, that rendered this profit " answerable to the project." A "like contract was made between " his Majesty and the dice-makers of London, to pay him an allow-" ance for every bale of dice, besides other mean projects for raising " money." (b)

### A.D. 1634, May 21.

PATENT (c) granted under the Privy Seal to JEROME LANYER, for his Invention called Londrindiana, being an art and mystery by affixing of wool, silk, and other materials of diverse colours upon linnen cloth, silk, cotton, leather, and other substances with oil size, and other cements, to make them useful and serviceable for hangings, &c. He was to have the sole practice and profit of the invention for fourteen years, on payment of 10l. yearly to his Majesty.

### A.D. 1634, June 24.—Nº 71.

ROTSIPEN (or ROTISPEN) ARNOLD.—Among a number of miscellaneous inventions protected by this Patent is mentioned " a " pressinge or printinge engine with wheeles & rolls after his " peculiar manner." No details are given. The Patent recites the petition of the patentee to the effect "that the same instruments " and engines are all of his own invenčon, and not formerly vsed " by anie other within this realme, and hath humbly besought vs

---

(a) Rymer, vol. xix. p. 61.
(b) Acta Regia, vol. iv. p. 804; Case of Monopolies, Co. Rep. 88a. part 11, Fraser's edition, p. 165 (n.)
(c) Rymer, vol. xix. p. 554,

" to grant unto him a priviledge for the sole makinge of the said
" instruments and engines, prohibiting all others to make use of
" anie of the said engines or instruments by him invented, and
" not hitherto practised by anie other, nor as yet by our saide
" servant exposed to the viewe of anie but only of our selfe, and
" of such as wee have especially deputed thereunto, the pticuler
" composicōns & vses whereof shall appear as they shalbe framed
" and sett up at our storehouse in the Minoritę, there to remain
" for our peculiar service."

[From Letters Patent, Rolls Chapel.]

### A.D. 1634, November 1.

GRANT (a) to JOHN DAY, citizen, fishmonger, and sworn broker
of London, for the sole printing of the weekly bills of the prices of
all foreign commodities for the term of fourteen years. The Patent
declares the system of such publication to have been his own invention, and that it had "been discontinued near three years, to the
" great hindrance of the merchants in their commerce and corre-
" spondence, to the disgrace of the city of London, and to the
" prejudice of the Customs."

### A.D. 1635, August 18.

PATENT (b) for twenty-one years under the Privy Seal to WILLIAM
BRAITHWAITE, reader and schoolmaster, for the sole printing and
sale of his books containing an easy method which he had accomplished both for expedite and exquisite composing, and for speedy
and pleasant teaching, and learning it by voice and instrument;
and his invention of a method to express the long and short syllables in the Greek and Latin tongues by the letters themselves,
without the accents, to the great advantage of poetry, oratory, and
of a graceful pronunciation of the Greek and Latin tongues.

### A.D. 1635, September 16.

APPOINTMENT under Privy Seal of CHARLES BARKER and
MATTHEW BARKER to the office "impressorum omnium statu-
" torum, librorum, libellorum, et aliorum munimentorum Domino
" Regi durantibus vitis." (c)

---

(a) Rymer, vol. xix. p. 577.          (b) Rymer, vol. xix. p. 656.
(c) Rymer, vol. xix. p. 765.

### A.D. 1637, July 11.

DECREE (a) of the Star Chamber, whereby (Art. 7) "no person is " to print or import printed abroad any book or copy which the " Company of Stationers or any other person hath or shall by any " Letters Patent, order, or entry in their register book," or otherwise have the right, privilege, authority, or allowance solely to print.

### A.D. 1640, (b) February 13.

ORDER (c) made by the House of Commons to the effect " that the " sub-committee heretofore appointed by the grand committee for " religion, concerning abuses in licencing and printing of books be " now made a Committee from the House, and inlarged to take " into consideration and examine all abuses in printing, licensing, " importing, and suppressing of books of all sorts, and in denying " licence to some books and expunging several passages out of " other books."

### A D. 1641, April 6.

ORDERED by the House of Commons, (d) "that the Master and " Wardens of the Company of Stationers be required to attend " this House presently, and that forthwith they make search and " enquiry after the printer and venter of a speech they term " Mr. Maynard's, the which speech Mr. Maynard absolutely dis- " avows, and that they use all diligence in suppressing the said " speech."

### A.D. 1641, July 23.

ORDER of the House of Commons, (e) among other things, that a certain pamphlet, a copy of a sermon preached on " Sunday last at " St. Margaret's, Westminster," and " a copy of an order informed " to be made in the House of Peers, concerning the Bishop of " Lincolnes appointing such as shall preach there," be laid before

---

(a) About the year 1637 (13 Car.), " printing and printers," according to the complaint of a writer of the period [" The London Printer, his Lamentation," A.D. 1660, Harleian Miscellany, vol. iii. p. 291], "having grown to a monstrous excess and exorbitant disorder," the Lords of the Privy Council made on the 11th day of July, a decree, which is styled by the same writer "the best and most exquisite form and constitution for the good government and regulation of the press that ever was pronounced or can reasonably be contrived to keep it in due order and regular exercise."

(b) In this year the first book (the Bay Psalm Book) was printed (by Daye) in the United States. Trübners Guide to American Literature, p. xxxix.

(c) Commons' Journals.          (d) See Journ. of the House, vol. ii. p. 116.

(e) Ibid, vol. ii. p. 221.

the Committee for Printing. The preacher of the sermon in question to be sent for.

## A.D. 1641, May 12.

RESOLUTION (a) passed by the Commons to the following effect: " This House doth desire and hold it fit that the heir of Sir " Edward Coke do publish in print his Commentary upon Magna " Charta, The Pleas of the Crown, and The Jurisdiction of Courts, " according to the intention of Sir Edward Coke; and that none " but the heir of the said Sir Edward Coke, or he that shall be " authorized by him, do presume to publish in print any of the " foresaid copies or books."

## A.D. 1641, July 10.

IT was referred by a resolution (b) of the Commons to the Committee for Printing "to take into consideration the printing of " the book entitled 'Protestation Protected,' and to examine the " printer thereof, and to inform themselves of the author of that " book, and of the scandal to this House by any passages in that " book."

## A.D. 1642, April 4.

ORDERED (c) by the House of Commons, "that a message be " sent to the Lords to desire their Lordships to appoint a com- " mittee to join with a committee of this House to take the ex- " amination of anything that shall be presented unto them by " His Majesty's learned Counsel, concerning tumults, seditions, " pamphlets or sermons."

## A.D. 1642, June 4.

LIEUTENANT-COLONEL AUDLEY MERVYN having presented to the Commons an account of certain transactions in Ireland since the beginning of the rebellion, it was ordered, (d) "that he be " desired to print it, and that no man shall reprint it but such as " he shall appoint, without the particular order of this House."

---

(a) H. of Com. Journ. vol. ii. p. 144.
(b) J. of H. of C., vol. ii. p. 206. Various other orders of a similar nature occur in the Journals. See vol. ii. pp. 220, 221, 268, 269, 404, 408, 419, 441, 472.
(c) H. of C. J., vol. ii. p. 514,　　　(d) H. of C. J., vol. ii. p. 611,

### A.D. 1643, May 5.

AN order of Parliament (*a*) was this day made "that the book " Enjoining and Tolerating of Sports upon the Lord's Day, be " forthwith burnt by the hands of the common hangman, in " Cheapside, and other usual places." Persons having copies to deliver them to the sheriffs.

### A.D. 1643, June 10.

THE liberty of the press having of late been " very grievous " to the Parliament, an ordinance of this date (*b*) was passed to restrain it, and to strengthen some former orders made for that purpose.

### A.D. 1643, June 14.

BY an Act of this date (*c*) for redressing disorders in printing, it is enacted that orders and declarations of Parliament are not to be printed but by order, nor other books unless licensed and entered in the register of the Stationers' Company; nor books the property of the Company or private persons without their consent. Powers are given to the Master and Wardens of the Company, "the " Gentlemen Usher of the House of Peers, the Sergeant of the " Commons House, together with the persons formerly appointed " by the Committee of the House of Commons for examinations," to search for and seize unlicensed presses and books, and to apprehend the " authors, printers, and other persons whatsoever em- " ployed in compiling, printing, stitching, binding, publishing, " and dispersing of the said scandalous, unlicenced, and unwar- " rantable " papers, books, &c.

### A.D. 1644, November.

THE two Houses having, in consequence of various libels, made an ordinance which prohibited printing, unless the book was first licensed and entered in the register of the Stationers' Company,

---

(*a*) Parl. Hist., vol. iii. p. 114.
(*b*) Parl. Hist., vol. iii. p. 131.
The preamble to this Ordinance sets forth the making of several orders by both Houses to suppress works defamatory of religion and government; " and that through the present distractions very many persons, as well stationers and printers as others of sundry other professions, have taken upon them to set up private printing presses in corners. It was also ordered, that it be referred to the Committee at Haberdashers' Hall, to consider of some course for improving and turning the profits and advantages of the office of King's printers to the benefit of the Commonwealth." (Commons Journals, vol. iii. p. 123.)
(*c*) Scobell's Acts and Ord,

or printing any book without consent of the owner, or importing,
if published abroad, Milton, in November 1644, published his
famous speech for the liberty of unlicensed printing against this
ordinance. Among the " glosses," which he says were used to
colour this ordinance and make it pass, he mentions " the just re-
" taining of each man his several copy, which God forbid should
" be gainsaid." (a)

### A.D. 1647, September 30.

BOTH HOUSES passed (b) an ordinance "against unlicenced and
" scandalous pamphlets, (c) and for the better regulating of print-
" ing." The maker, writer, or composer of any book, pamphlet,
treatise, ballad, libel, or sheet of news, not licensed by both or
either of the houses, or persons appointed by them, (d) 40s. or forty
days' imprisonment, the printer to suffer a fine of 20s., or twenty
days' imprisonment, and have his press and printing implements
seized and defaced. Booksellers or stationers to pay 10s. fine, or
suffer ten days' imprisonment. The Commissioners for the Militia
in London, Middlesex, and Surrey, and the officers of corporations
in other towns, to carry out the ordinance, make searches, and con-
vict offenders. The " view of any one justice of the peace, head
" officer, or commissioner aforesaid, or the oath of one credible
" witness," to be sufficient for conviction. Persons " acting any-
" thing by virtue of this ordinance to be indemnified by both
" Houses," and persons convicted under it not to be thereby exempt
from further punishment for seditious, treasonable, or blasphemous
matter.

### A.D. 1649.

ORDINANCE of the Long Parliament forbidding printing any book
legally granted, or any book entered without consent of the owner.

---

(a) 4 Burrow, 2314.
(b) Parl. Hist., vol. iii. p. 780. Scobell's Acts and Ord., where the date is
given as September 28.
(c) "Of these leaves of an hour, and volumes of a week, the labours of the
passions, the wisdom or the folly of our countrymen, during the revolution of
Charles the First, in that single period from 1640 to 1660, about thirty thousand
appear to have started up." (Disraeli's Charles I., vol. 4. p. 146. The deriva-
tions suggested for the word are, *par un filet*, held together by a thread, or
*palme feuillet*, as leaves to be held in the hand). Most of these were collected
by order of Charles I., and became the gift of George III. to the national library.
See Rushworth's Historical Collections, vol. x. p. 662.
(d) In pursuance of this Ordinance, Mr. Gilbert Mabbot was appointed licenser
of the press. (Ib.)

### A.D. 1649, September 20.

Act of Parliament (a) for punishing unlicensed and scandalous books and pamphlets, and regulating printing; the penalty for making, printing, or uttering scandalous books, papers, or pictures is, for the author, 10l.; for the printer, 5l., and for the bookseller, 2l.; the buyer to forfeit 1l. if he conceal the book bought. All books and pamphlets to be licensed. Offenders to be punished, as prescribed by the Act of September 1647. Former licenses for printing "news-books" are made null. Clerk of Parliament to license news-books. The Act not to acquit offender of further punishment for treasonable matter. Master and Wardens of the Stationers' Company, "assisted by such per- " sons as the Council of State shall for that purpose nominate or " approve," to search for unallowed presses and books. No sedi- tious books to be sent by post or carrier. No "printing press, " rolling press, or any other instruments for printing," to be used within the Commonwealth, save only in London and the liberties thereof, the Universities, and such other places as shall be authorized by special order of the Council of State, under a penalty of 20l., and presses defaced. This clause not to extend to " the printing press now used in the city of York, nor to the " printing press now used in Finsbury, for the printing of Bibles " and Psalms." Printers to enter into a bond of 300l. not to print " seditious, scandalous, or treasonable matter;" authors and licensers names to be printed. No house or room to be let to a printer, nor implements made, press imported, or letters founded, without notice being given to the Stationers' Company. Importers of seditious books to forfeit 5l. All books to be imported into London, and viewed by the Master and Wardens of the Company. No Bibles or Psalms to be imported. Penalty for printing book entered for another, 6s. 8d. Warrant for any two magistrates to search packs and packets. All unlicensed books seized to be de- livered to the Secretary of the Council. Hawkers and ballad- mongers to be sent to the house of correction; offenders to be prosecuted within six months of the offence. The Act to continue in force until September 29, 1651.

### A.D. 1652, January 7.

Act (b) for the suppression of unlicensed and scandalous books. The Act of September 20, 1649, is revived with some alterations.

---

(a) Scobell's Acts and Ord.  (b) Scobell's Acts and Ord.

Council of State to determine how many of the " printing-houses " now in being " shall be continued, and the number of apprentices and presses to be allowed to each printer, and regulate the mystery. None but those licensed by the Council or claiming the privilege " by patrimonial right " to exercise the art. Printers to exercise the trade in their dwelling-houses. Books seized to be taken to Stationers' Hall. Master and Wardens to provide a place for inspecting imported books. Penalties to be recovered in courts of record, " within the jurisdiction whereof such offence shall be com- " mitted ;" one half to the use of the Company of Stationers, or other party prosecuting, and the other to the use of the Commonwealth. The " Agent for the Army " to " licence such intelligence " as may concern the affairs of the army onely." Saving of the rights of the University printers.

## A.D. 1653, October 11.

THE COUNCIL OF STATE made (a) a report to the House " of " several seditious and scandalous pamphlets coming out, tending " to the disturbance of the Commonwealth, and that they had " employed divers persons to find out the authors, printers, and " publishers thereof." (b)

## A.D. 1655.

AMONG the " Century of Inventions," published " at the instance of a powerful friend," by the Marquis of Worcester in this year, are the following :—

" 1. Several sorts of seals, some shewing by scrues, others by " gages, fastening or unfastening all the marks at once ; others by " additional points and imaginary places proportionable to ordi- " nary escocheons and seals at arms each way, palpably and " punctually setting down (yet private from all others but the " owner, and by his assent) the day of the moneth, the day of the " week, the moneth of the year, the year of our Lord, the names " of the witnesses, and the individual place where anything was " sealed, though in ten thousand several places, together with the " very number of lines contained in a contract, whereby falsifica- " tion may be discovered, and manifestly proved, being upon good " grounds suspected. Upon any of these seales a man may keep " accompts of receepts and disbursements from one farthing to an

---

(a) Parl. Hist., vol. iii. p. 1413.
(b) One of these was entitled " A Charge of High Treason against Oliver Cromwell, Esq., for several Treasons by him committed,"

" hundred millions, punctually showing each pound, shilling,
" peny, or farthing. By these seal likewise any letter, though
" written but in English, may be read and understood in eight
" several languages, and in English itself, to seem contrary and
" different sense, unknown to any but the correspondent, and not
" to be read or understood by him, neither if opened before it
" arrive unto him, so that neither threats nor hopes of reward can
" make him reveal the secret, the letter having been intercepted
" and first opened by the enemy.

" 2. How ten thousand persons may use these seals to all and
" every of the purposes aforesaid, and yet keep their secrets from
" any but those whom they please.

" 3. A cypher and character so contrived that one line without
" returns and circumflexes stands for each and every of the 24
" letters, and as ready to be made for the one letter as the other.

" 4. This invention refined and so abbreviated, that a point
" onely sheweth distinctly and significantly any of the 24 letters,
" and these very points to be made with two pens, so that no time
" will be lost; but as one finger riseth, the other may make the
" following letter, never clogging the memory with several figures
" for words, and combinations of letters, which with ease and
" void of confusion are thus speedily and punctually letter for
" letter set down by naked and not multiplied points, and nothing
" can be less than a point, the mathematical definition being *cujus*
" *pars nulla*, and of a motion equally as swift, thus *semiquavers*
" or *relishes*, yet applicable to this manner of writing.

" 5. A way by a circular motion either along a rule or ringwise
" to vary any alphabet, even this of points, so that the selfsame
" point individually placed without the least additional mark or
" variation of place, shall stand for all the 24 letters, and not for
" the same letter twice in ten sheets' writing, yet as easily and
certainly read and known as if it stood but for one and the
" selfsame letter constantly signified.

" 6. How at a window, as far as an eye can discover black from
" white, a man may hold discourse with his correspondent, without
" noise made or notice taken, being according to occasion given
" and means afforded *ex re natâ*, and no need of provision before-
" hand, though much better if foreseen and means prepared for
" it, and a premeditated course taken. (*a*)

---

(*a*) See Sir Hugh Plat's *Jewel House of Art and Nature*, " How to speak by
signs only without the uttering of any word." A.D. 1595.

" 7. A way to do it by night as well as by day, though as dark
" as pitch.

" 32. How to compose an universal character, methodical and
" easie to be written, yet intelligible in any language, so that if an
" Englishman write it in English, a Frenchman, Italian, Irish,
" Welsh, being scholars, yea Grecian or Hebritian, shall as per-
" fectly understand it in their owne tongue, as if they were perfect
" English, distinguishing the verbs from nouns, the numbers,
" tenses, and cases, as properly expressed in their own language
" as it was written in English. (a)

" 33. To write with a needle and thred, white or any other
" colour, upon white or any other colour, so that one stitch shall
" significantly shew any letter, and as readily and as easily shew
" the one letter as the other, and fit for any language.

" 34. To write by a knotted silk string, so that every knot
" shall signifie any letter, with comma, full point, or interrogation,
" and as legible as with pen and ink upon white paper.

" 35. The like by the fringe of gloves.

" 36. By stringing of bracelets.

" 37. By pinck'd gloves.

" 38. By holes in the bottom of a sieve.

" 39. By a lattin or plate lanthorn.

" 40. By the smell.

" 41. By the taste.

" 42. By the touch.

" By these three senses as perfectly, distinctly, and uncon-
" fusedly, yea, as readily as by the sight.

" 43. How to vary these so that ten thousand may know
" them, and yet keep the understanding part from any but their
" correspondent.

" 51. A rule of gradation, which with ease and method reduceth
" all things to a private correspondence most useful for secret
" intelligence.

" 52. How to signifie words and a perfect discourse by jingling
" of bells of any parish church, or by any musical instrument
" within hearing, in a seeming way of tuning it, or of an unskilful
" beginner.

" 75. How a tape or ribbon weaver may set down a whole dis-
" course, without knowing a letter or interweaving anything sus-
" picious of other secret than a new-fashioned ribbon.

---

(a) See notes to the above in Partington's edition. 8vo. Lond.. 1825.

" 76. How to write in the dark as streight as by day or candle light.

" 84. An instrument whereby persons ignorant in arithmetick
" may perfectly observe numerations and substractions of all
" summes and fractions.

" 97. An instrument whereby an ignorant person may take any
" thing in perspective as justly and more than the skilfullest
" painter can do by his eye."

### A.D. 1656, October 20.

ORDERED (a) by the House of Commons, that it be referred to a
" Committee to consider of a way to suppress private presses and
" regulating the press, and suppressing and preventing scandalous
" books and pamphlets."

In the Reports of the Deputy Keeper of the Public Records, vol. 5,
p. 251, *et seq.* under the head of " Letters of Privy Seal granted in
" the name and style of Oliver, and Lord Protector of the Com-
" monwealth of England, Scotland, and Ireland, and the dominion,
" thereto belonging," are the four following entries.

### A.D. 1656-7, March 20.

" PETER BLONDEAN, Gent., 200$^{li}$ for carrying on the charge of
" coyning M$^l$ M$^{l\,li}$, &c."

### A.D. 1657, May 23.

" SAMUEL MORLAND, Esq$^{re}$, 700$^{li}$ for y$^e$ charge of paper, printing,
" and cutting of the mapps for two thousand coppies of the History
" of y$^e$ Protestants of y$^e$ Valleyes of Piedmont, &c."

### A.D. 1657, December 11.

" S$^r$ THOMAS VYNER, Kn$^t$, M$^{l\,li}$ to bee by him issued and paid to
" Peter Blondean, for preparing engines for coyning, &c."

### A.D. 1657-8, March 8.

" THOMAS SYMON, Cheife Graver of his Highnes mints, seales,
" and meddals, M$^l$ xxviij$^{li}$ 5$^s$ 8$^d$, resting due to him upon his
" acco$^t$, &c."

### A.D. 1660, (b) February 5.—N$^o$ 128.

TOMLYN GEORGE.—" Texting and flourishing on vellum and
" parchment." The Letters Patent recite the statement in the peti-

---

(a) Commons' Journals, vol. vii. p. 442.
(b) In 1660, we are informed by the writer of The London Printer's Lamentation [Harl. Mis., vol. iii. p. 291], " the number of printing houses and printing
masters, or such at least as exercise the faculty of printing (though some be
booksellers only by trade and education, and others are of other trades not
relative to printing), is at present multiplied and increased to above triple the
number of twenty constituted by " the decree of the Star Chamber.

tion of the patentee, a "cittizen and staconer of London," that
" by his industry and paynes with much charges and expences
" hee hath invented a new manufacture or way to text and flourish
" velomes and parchments in black and white, with our royale
" name both in Latine and English, with our portraicture, impiall
" armes, badges, and other ornament̃, better and more exact than
" the name and title of any former king hath heretofore been done
" by any other person for such reasonable rates as hee doth and
" will take for the same.  And that the manufacture is wrought
" with a rolling printing presse and ingraven plates, and is of much
" benefitt and advantage to our subject̃, in respect as good worke
" otherwise wrought cannot bee done for tenne times the price."
The grant is for fourteen years.

[Extract from Letters Patent, printed, Rolls Chapel.]

### A.D. 1662, March 28.—No 137.'

TOMLYN, George.—" A newe way to text and florish veloms
" and parchment̃ with our Name, pourtraicture, Imperiall Armes,
' Badges, and other ornament̃, by printing the same with a
" rolling printing presse and engraven plates, to the greate benefitt
" of our subjects, for that as good worke otherwise wrought
" cannott well be afforded for tenn times the price; the worke being
" likewise very neate and of good ornament to our Letters Patent̃
" and other exemplificačons."  Repeal of the Grant No 128, and
re-grant of the privileges thereby conferred, in addition to "the
" like printing of the name and title our royall and deare consort
" Queen Katherine," for "the terme of twelve yeares, remainder
" of the saide fourteene years."

[Extract from Letters Patent, printed, Rolls Chapel.]

### A.D. 1662.

Act (13 & 14 Car. II. c. 33) against seditious, treasonable, and unlicensed books, and for regulating printing and printing presses.
No pamphlets bringing scandal on Church or State to be printed or
imported.  Books to be entered with the Company of Stationers.
The Act prescribes the parties who are to license respectively
books of common law, history, affairs of state, heraldry, divinity,
physic, philosophy, &c.  Private interests in books to be saved.
Every licenser to have a written copy of the book licensed.  Books
to be imported at London only.  No books, form of blank bills, or

indentures, whereof any have Letters Patent for sole printing, to be printed or imported. Books to contain the name of the printers. No one to sell books in London or market towns except persons thereto licensed by the bishop of the diocese, or having the right by seven years' apprenticeship or "patrimonial right." No English books printed abroad to be imported. Presses and printing houses not to be set up in or about London without notice to the Stationers' Company, under a penalty of 5*l.*, half to go to the Crown, half to the prosecutor. No one to be admitted a master printer till the number be reduced to twenty, "and from thenceforth "the number of twenty master printers shall be continued and no "more, besides the King's printers and the printers allowed for "the Universities, to have the use and exercise of printing books "at one time, and but four master founders of letters for printing." Persons having the use of a printing press to give sureties against unlawful printing. None but the Master or upper Warden of the Stationers' Company (who may have three) to have above two presses. Masters of the Company, past and present, may have three apprentices, liverymen of the Company two, and the yeomanry of the Company one. Journeymen printers and letter-founders, being English, to be employed. On warrant under the Sign Manual, or by a Secretary of State, or by the Master and Wardens of the Stationers' Company, "one or more of the messengers "of His Majesty's Chamber" may search houses and shops for, and seize suspected books and papers. Printed copies to be sent to His Majesty's library and the two Universities. The Act not to apply to persons who have served apprentices to booksellers or liverymen of the Stationers' Company, or persons selling books within Westminster Hall, or twenty yards of the site of the said hall; nor to parties privileged by royal grant, nor to John Streater, nor to the press at York. The Act to continue in force for two years. This Act was continued from time to time by 16 Car. II. c. 8., 1 Jac. II. c. 17. s. 15., and several other Acts.

## A.D. 1679–1680.

IN Hilary Term of this year (*a*) "several booksellers of the country "party were indicted for publishing seditious and scandalous "libels, as FRANCIS SMITH and LANGLEY CURTIS, besides

---

(*a*) Echard's Hist. of England, vol. iii. p. 573.

" HENRY CARE, the author; but, above all, the sentence against
" BENJAMIN HARRIS, the publisher of the Weekly Domestick
" Intelligencer, is the most observable, who, having been found
" guilty of vending the pamphlet . . . . called ' An Appeal from
" ' the country to the city,' had judgment on the last day of the
" term to stand on the pillory before the Old Exchange, to suffer
" imprisonment for one year, to find sureties for three years'
" good behaviour, and to be fined 500*l.*; and moreover, the said
" Appeal to be burnt by the common hangman," and the better
to prevent these exorbitancies, not long after, all the judges in
England, having been demanded their opinions, made their report
in Council, and declared for law, "that His Majesty may prohibit
" the printing of all news books and pamphlets of news what-
" soever not licenced by His Majesty's authority, as manifestly
" tending to the breach of the peace and disturbance of the
" kingdom; and, accordingly, the King issued a proclamation
" to suppress all news books and pamphlets of that nature."

A.D. 1686, January 9.—N° 249.

DUPIN, NICHOLAS; DE CARDONELS, ADAM; DE GRUCHY,
CHARLES REGNAULT MARINA; DE MAY, JAMES, and SHALES,
ROBERT.—"The art of makeing all sorts of writeing and printing
" paper, and to imprint our armes vpon such paper." The
Letters Patent recite a statement in the petition of the patentees, to the effect that " being encouraged by vs to improve
" the art of makeing all sorts of writeing and printing paper
" and to print our armes vpon such paper, they have lately
" brought out of France excellent workemen, and have already
" sett vp severall new invented mills and engines for makeing
" thereof not heretofore vsed in England, and made severall
" quantities of paper, haveing been at vast charges in the p̃misses,
" engageing the French artificers to instruct in the said art such
" English p̃sons as the petic̃oners shall take apprentices, and
" prayed vs to grant them Letters Patent for the sole exerciseing
" the said art."

[Extract from Letters Patent, Rolls Chapel.]

A D. 1688, February 7.—N° 258.

HOLMAN, CHARLES.—" A new art or invenc̃on of makeing a
" certaine powder, which being put into faire water, beer, ale, or

" wine, doth imediately turne the same into very good black
" writing ink, and can be afforded very cheape to the general
" advantage of our subiects, especially those in the country and
" at sea."

Sole privilege "for and dureing and to the full end and terme
" of fourteene years," to "erect, use, teach, exercise, the said new
" invenᶜon," within "our Kingdome of England, Dominion of
" Wales, and Towne of Berwick-vpon-Tweed."

[From Letters Patent, printed, 3d. No Drawing.]

### A.D. 1691, November.—Nº 284.

GIFFORD, NATHANIEL.—Grant of the sole use, exercise, and
benefit of his new invention, being a new, better, and cheaper way
of making all sorts of blew, purple, and other coloured paper, by
several ways, means, methods, engines, and instruments that never
yeat were used in England, to hold the same to him, his executors,
administrators, and assigns for fourteen years, according to the
statute, with other clauses usuall.

### A.D. 1692, October 19.—Nº 305.

GIFFORD, NATHANIEL.—Sole use of the invention of beauty-
fying, figuring, imprinting, and embellishing "all sorts of blew,
" purple, and other colored papers by the engines and instruments
" never before used."

This is a re-grant of the former privilege (Nº 284), from which
" by some neglect the words beautifying, figuring, imprinting,
" and embellishing the said papers were omitted in our warrant
" for the said Letters Patent."

[From Letters Patent, Rolls Chapel.]

### A.D. 1709 (8 Anne, c. 19).

" AN ACT for the Encouragement of Learning, by vesting the
" Copies of Printed Books in the Authors or Purchasers of such
" Copies during the Times therein mentioned." I. After the
10th April 1710, the authors of books already printed who have
not transferred their rights, and the booksellers, &c. who have
purchased copies, to have the sole right of printing them for
twenty-one years. The authors of books not printed to have the
sole right of printing for fourteen years. Penalty of forfeiture of
books and fine of 1d. per sheet for all fraudulent copies found in

possession of anyone, half the fine to the Crown, half to the prosecutor. II. Copies of books to be entered before publication in the register book of the Company of Stationers, which may be inspected at any time without fee. III. Proviso in the event of the clerk refusing to register. IV. After 25th March, the Archbishop of Canterbury, &c. to settle the prices of books upon complaint made that they are unreasonable; and if altered from the price set by the bookseller, the latter may be ordered to pay the costs to the party complaining. A fine of 5*l.* for each copy sold above the sum so settled; half to the Crown, half to the prosecutor (*a.*) V. After 10th April, nine copies of each book shall be delivered to the warehouse-keeper of the Company of Stationers for the use of the University libraries, &c., which the warehouse-keeper is to deliver ten days after demanded, under penalty of 5*l.* for each copy. VII. The Act is not to hinder the importation, &c. of books in Greek, Latin, or foreign books printed beyond sea. IX. The Act is not to prejudice the rights of the Universities. X. Actions for offences against this Act to be brought in three months. XI. After the fourteen years, the right of printing, &c. to return to the author if living for other fourteen years.

A.D. 1714, January 7.—N° 395.

MILL, HENRY.—The Letters Patent recite a statement in the petition of the patentee, to the effect "that he has by his great " study, paines, and expence lately introduced and brought to " perfection, an artificial machine or method for the impressing or " transcribing of letters, singly or progressively one after another " as in writing, whereby all writings whatsoever may be ingrossed " in paper or parchment so neat as not to be distinguished from " print; that the said machine may be of great vse in settlements " and publick recors, the impression being deeper and more lasting " than any other writing, and not to be erased or counterfeited " without manifest discovery."

[From Letters Patent, Rolls Chapel.]

A.D. 1719, February 5.—N° 423.

LE BLON, JAMES CHRISTOPHER.—"A new method of multi-" plying of pictures and draughts by a naturel colleris with im-

---

(*a*) This clause repealed by 15 Geo. II. c. 36.

" pression." Sole privilege of using an invention under this description, within England, Wales, and Berwick-upon-Tweed, for a period of 14 years. Proviso for avoiding the Letters Patent upon " signification and declaraĉon," made by the Sovereign under the Signet or Privy Seal, or by the " Lords and others " of the Privy Council, or " any six or more of them under their " hands," that the grant is " contrary to law or preiudicial or " inconvenient to our subjects in general," or not new as to public use and exercise in England, Wales, and Berwick-upon-Tweed, or not " invented and found out " by the patentee.

[From Letters Patent.]

### A.D. 1721, July 1.—Nº 432.

HARRIS, John, SENEX, John, and WILSON, Henry.—
" Making and printing globular sea charts." The petition recites that the patentees, after much labour, time, and expense, "have " invented a new method of projecting sea-charts for the vse " and improvement of navigation, which being agreeable to the " globe, as truly representing the globular surface of the sea, " they humbly apprehend may be properly called a globular sea- " chart, and that thereby all navigators may perform their voiages " with much more facility, certainty, and security than hitherto has " been done by any methodˢ of the plane or Mercator's chart;" that they had been submitted to and approved of by several able mathematicians, navigators, and astronomers, two of whom (Dr. Edmund Halley, Regis Professor of Astronomy, and Captain John Merrey) "had vouchsafed for the promoteing so publick a benefit " to certify the excellency of this chart, and to recom̄end it to all " navigators for its vse at sea in great circle sailing and other im- " ᵖrovementˢ, the which certificates or testimonials are ready to be " produced."

[From Letters Patent, Rolls Chapel.]

### A.D. 1731, May 20.—Nº 530.

POPE, Samuel.—"Marbling paper, for bank notes, cheques, &c." The Patent recites a statement in the petition to the following effect :—"That the practice of counterfeiting of bank and other " notes, &c. at this time appears very notorious, to the great " detriment of the trade and com̄erce of this kingdom, and " that the making use of paper marbled with a margent for

" merchants notes, bills of exchange, companys notes or bonds,
" receipts for subscripcons, or any other instruments that admit of
" a cheque, being generally allowed to be the most effectual remedy
" to prevent so great an evil, he [the patentee] has, by long study
" and great industry, invented and brought to perfection a new
" art of marbling paper with a margent, never practised by any
" person whatsoever before he invented it, which is performed by
" a method entirely new by taking off the colours from a body of
" water prepared after a particular manner, with a proper strength
" for supporting the said colours and make them flow upon the
" surface (*sic*) it, whereby the said colours are more easily taken off
" upon paper, which will be of very great service to the publick by
" preventing the counterfeiting of all such notes, bills, bonds,"
&c.

[From Letters Patent, Rolls Chapel.]

### A.D. 1755, July 22.—N° 702.

BÄHRE, JOACHIM ANDREAS.—"A method of printing and paint-
" ing paper, silk, cloath, and canvas in gold, silver, and brocade
" colours, which, for its beauty in colour, far excelled anything of
" that kind ever yet made, and would neither wash out, fade, nor
" tarnish, and would be of great use in the making of paper, silk,
" cloth, canvas, and all other hangings and furniture, and could
" be afforded to be sold near as cheap as the midling sort of paper
" hangings."

The paper is twice primed with glue. "For silver hangings,
" size the paper over with boiled linseed oil and white sugar, and,
" when dry, lay on the silver; for gold, size over with boiled
" linseed oil, lythargirium argenteum, lythargirium aureum, red
" lead, and ombre, and, when dry, lay on the gold; for brocade
" colours, take three quarts of linsed oyl, put into it a middle-
" sized onion, boil it until the scum turns blewish, and with this
" liquid mix the colours. With respect to linnen cloth and can-
" vas, the same method is to be persued, except that the linnen
" cloth or canvas are not to be primed, nor must the oyl be boyled;
" but instead thereof, the oyl is to be mixed with lythargirium
" argenteum in the proportion of a large spoonfull to each quart
" of oyl."

[Specification (*a*) printed, 3*d*. No Drawing. Rolls Chapel Reports, 6th
Report, p. 128. Rolls Chapel.]

(*a*) From this date the notice "Printed" refers to the Specification of the
Patent.

### A.D. 1764, April 10.—N° 810.

FRYER, Thomas, GREENOUGH, Thomas, and NEWBERY, John.—"A machine of a new construction, and in mixing and " adapting colours to the use of the said machine for printing, " staining, and colouring of silks, stuffs, linens, cottons, leather, " and paper."

The invention is performed " by means of engraved copper cylin-" ders on which the colours are laid by smaller cylinders which are " put in motion by other plain cylinders, and the whole work of " filling in, clearing off, and stamping the impressions is performed " by the joynt assistance of sundry springs and the intermediums " of coggs and rings turned by a wheel worked by either a horse, " water, or wind. The colours and stains made use of are " extracted from the different dying drugs and fixed by the help " of oyl of vitroil, aqua fortis, aqua regia, spirits of salt, allum, " cream of tartar, sal ammoniac, volatile and fixed alkalies, and " quick lime, which are used in various proportions, as the shade " of the colour is required lighter or darker."

[Printed, 3d. No Drawing. Petty Bag.]

### A.D. 1767, December 24.—N° 888.

FOUGT, Henry.—"Certain new and curious types by me in-" vented for the printing of music notes as neatly and as well " in every respect as hath been usually done by engraving." The Invention consists in the use of sectional types, " in many " respects similar to what in former ages was used in printing " offices, and known by the name of choral type." (a)

[Printed, 6d. Diagram of the sectional types. Rolls Chapel Reports, 6th Report. Rolls Chapel.]

---

(a) After noticing the points of similarity, the patentee states the difference to consist "in a new systematical drawing and division of the characters adapted to express music notes." This, he says, constitutes the second part of his narrative," which "according to the injunction laid upon him, he is going to make as circumstantially and faithfully as possible." And "the better to illustrate the nature and properties of his invention," he considers that he "must call to his aid the historical knowledge of the several improvements which have been made from time to time in the art of printing in general." There follows, accordingly, a review of the progress of the art, divided into three stages, block, wood, and letter printing. "The method of engraving music in plates of metal is the same as the primitive essays of engraving books in the same manner. The choral types, as they were called, answer to the second attempt in book printing of dividing the wooden columns; and this new method of my invention corresponds with the third and last accomplished method of printing in general," i.e. the use of separate types. In the old choral type system, "each type of every single note contains not only the whole figure of the note, but at the

A.D. 1769, November 16.—N° 939 (four).

WEDGWOOD, Josiah.—" Ornamenting earthen and porcelaine
" ware with an encaustic gold bronze, together with a peculiar
" species of encaustic painting in various colours in imitation of
" the ancient Etruscan and Roman earthenware."

The Specification describes,—1. The ingredients used in the
process ; 2. The mode of mixing them for the various colours ;
3. The application of the encaustic bronze and colours.

[Printed, 3d.    No Drawing.    Repertory of Arts, vol. 7, p. 309.    Petty Bag.

A.D. 1771, November 6.—N° 999 (four).

MOORE, Isaac, and PINE, William.—" An entirely new and
" particular method of casting cases in metal for holding and con-
" taining metallic letters or printing types of a peculiar construction
" to fix in the said cases, for marking or printing on silk, muslin,
" linnen, woollen, leather, paper, parchment, and vellum, together
" with raised letters for signs, monumental inscriptions, and other
" purposes ; and also new invented printing presses, the platens,
" whereof are made of iron and other metals as well as of wood,
" and are suspended or counteracted by a ballance or weight."
The types are set up in a metal chase, which is fitted with a
handle and can be used as a stamp. For inscriptions, they are
of metal, paper, pasteboard, &c. A hand-press in which the
platen is counterbalanced and the impression given by a screw, a
" fly " being " put on or taken off as need requires."

A " leaver printing press " in which the platen is fixed to a
lever of the second order and brought down by hand.

[Printed, 6d.   Drawings with foot notes, which furnish the entire descrip-
     tion of the invention.   Rolls Chapel Reports, 6th Report, p. 161.   Rolls
     Chapel.]

---

same time a correspondent portion of all the five lines together, whereas in this
new method a double division is introduced by dividing the figure of the note
with its tail or stalk, and the 5 lines both in the length and height of the row
so that every note, together with the 5 lines occupying the same space, is divided into 5 separate types, of which one comprehends the head of the note
alone, together with one of the lines upon or near which it is placed ; and of the
4 other types, each is for each of the rest of the lines, together with an equal
portion of the tail of the note." To render his "narrative still more compleat," the patentee adds that "what first made him think of an attempt of
this nature," was seeing prints of ornamental designs executed from separate
types, and explains the principles upon which he afterwards proceeded to put
his plan in execution.

### A.D. 1772, March 14.—N° 1007.

ADKIN, Joseph, the elder, ADKIN, Joseph, the younger, TAYLOR, Charles, and WALKER, Thomas, the younger.— " A new machine or engine for stamping and printing of paper, " silk, woollen, cotton, and linnen cloths, and other articles made " of silk, wool, cotton, whereby the printing on such materials " would be greatly facilitated and rendred much less expensive " and more perfect and exact."

The press is composed of three cylinders arranged vertically; the upper one (6½ inches in diameter) acts as a pressing cylinder; the middle one (to which the power is applied, of 3 inches), as a printing roller; and the lower one (of 7 inches), as a furnishing roller, it being partially immersed in a colour trough. The above dimensions are those in a press calculated to print a fabric 22 inches wide. The fabric passes to the impression " through two " rails fixed upon the sides of the uprights upon the level with " the middle roller, to prevent the cloth from crumping."

[Printed, 4d. No Drawing. Rolls Chapel Reports, 6th Report, p. 138. Rolls Chapel.]

### A.D. 1772, April 7.—N° 1012 (four).

ROWLEY, James.—"A method of making playing cards printed " from engravings on copper, after entire new designs, in oil " colours, with a peculiar kind of ink which will bear the leesing " or polish necessary to be given to playing cards, which no other " ink known to the printers or card makers is capable of."

The nature of the invention is said to be described and ascertained in the manner following; (that is to say,) " By the four " suits are understood the four classes of people into which the " kingdom is divided. The first, commonly called spades, means " the nobility and military, typified by the figure of an espontoon; " second, the clergy (hearts), by the chalice or communion cup; " third, the citizens and merchants, by the diamond; and, fourth " (clubbs), by the trefoil or clover grass, symbolical of the hus- " bandmen and peasants."

The ink with which these cards are printed from metal plates is compounded of the same ingredients used in painting the common cards, known to every manufacturer, but instead of water the patentee mixes them in linseed oil and allum, boiled and calcined

" to a proper crisis, which can only be ascertained by frequent
" experiments."

[Printed, 3d.   No Drawing.   Rolls Chapel Reports, 6th Report, p. 138.   Rolls Chapel.]

A.D. 1774, February 28.—N° 1066 (four).

ECKHARDT, ANTHONY GEORGE.—" A method of printing in
" designs on all manner of silks, cottons, muslins, callicoes, and
" papers."

The invention is said to be " founded on the principle of small
" squares, which compose the rul'd paper used by the pattern
" drawers in the manufacture of silk brocades and tapestry, except
" that in the present case diagonal lines are superadded.   On this
" paper, the patterns for the present purpose being neatly drawn,
" types and blanks corresponding to the respective squares of the
" pattern are to be mounted in a frame and used with the proper
" colours adapted to the design, in the same manner as is generally
" practiced in and with the common and well-known letter press,
" excepting the improvements that are introduced in the press, . . .
" and which are fully explained in the drawings and references
" thereto hereto annexed, together with the form of the types, the
" alphabet of which is formed of small squares, divers portions of
" squares, circular and other forms, suited to the nature of the
" work."

The drawings represent machines in which the fabric (in roll) is
forwarded on an endless platform passing over hexagonal drums
at each end of a long table, and the impression given by flat printing
surfaces (counterbalanced), either hinged to the side of the press or
slidden over the centre of it on rollers.

[Printed, 1s.   Drawings.   Petty Bag.]

A.D. 1778, November 9.—N° 1201 (four).

JOHNSON, HENRY.—" Method of printing with types or figures
" so connected as to prevent the possibility of error in all business
" where figures are used, particularly in taking down the numbers
" of blanks and prizes in the lottery newmerically arranged."

The invention is " performed by means of types of figures cast on
" a body, so as at one impression to form any number or numbers,
" figure or figures, without being liable to the usual errors . . . .
" which said type . . . . may be made of iron, lead, brass, copper,
" or any other metal which is capable of being melted or dissolved

" in the fire and cast into moulds proper for forming the said
" figures: or said types may be cut in wood, metal, stone, or
" cement, or any other composition fit for the purpose of making
" the impression of figures in a body as aforesaid; and when the
" said types or figures are used they are placed in a frame made of
" wood or any other substance, and placed in a common printing
" press with all such other materials, utensils, and apparatus (and
" performed in the same manner) as hath been heretofore used
" and adopted for printing and publishing in general."

[Printed, 3d. No Drawing. Petty Bag.]

A.D. 1780, February 14.—N° 1244 (four).

WATT, JAMES.—" A new method of copying letters and other
" writings expeditiously."

The writing is executed with an ink compounded of water,
Aleppo galls, green copperas or vitriol, gum arabic, and roach
allum. The sheet (which must be unsized) to receive the copy is
moistened with water or a liquor composed of distilled vinegar,
sedative salt of borax, calcined oyster shells, and the best blue
Aleppo galls. The two are laid upon a press similar to that for
copper-plate printing, and pressed " once or oftener through the
" rolls of the said press."

[Printed, 6d. Drawings. Repertory of Arts, vol. 1, p. 13; Engineers' and
Mechanics' Encyclopædia, vol. 1, p. 400; Rolls Chapel Reports, 6th
Report, p. 165. Rolls Chapel.]

A.D. 1780, October 16.—N° 1266 (four).

JOHNSON, HENRY.—" A method of casting and moulding
" types for the purpose of composing and printing by or with
" entire words, with several words combined, with sentences and
" syllables, and with figures combined, instead of the usual method
" of composing and printing with single letters, and of rendering
" the use of the said types and printing with the same easy and
" familiar to the most ordinary capacity, whereby every species of
" printing may be executed in one fourth of the time in which
" they have been usually executed, and consequently at much less
" expense.

" For moulding, casting, or cementing together entire words
" and syllables, &c., and for composing and printing with such
" intire words, with several words combined, with sentences, and
" with single and joint syllables, instead of the common method
" of composing and printing with single letters, which is performed

"by making a selection from all the words and syllables in any
"language, from those in use, and arranging the types of such
"words and syllables alphabetically; and in composing, the com-
"positor to take up such intire words, either singly or several
"words together, or in portions of the same, in single, double,
"and treble syllables, or in the different combinations of letters
"contained in such words; and also of printing, &c., in the same
"manner, with figures combined for any number, and for £ s. d.
"and f, instead of the common method of using single figures.
"And such syllables and words are formed or moulded either by
"single letters cemented together in words with the same metal,
"or else by forming matrices of such syllables and words and
"casting them therein."

[Printed, 3d.  No Drawing.  Petty Bag.]


A.D. 1781, April 21.—N° 1289 (four).

ROBERTS, WILLIAM.—"A method of cuting and preparing
"prints or moulds of whole and compleat objects and designs
"called arabesque, to the extent of from three feet seven inches
"(the largest hitherto made) to ten feet and upwards in length,
"and from two feet and a half to three and four feet wide or more,
"when occasion shall require, and of using and applying such
"prints or moulds in printing, painting, or staining of paper,
"linnen, woollen, cotton, or silk, or any manufacture made of the
"said articles, either entire or mixed in various designs and colours,
"wherewith such paper or other furniture may be done on rooms
"or apartments of any dimensions in intire and compleat impres-
"sions, without mutilation or addition."

The invention "consists in drawing and preparing patterns,
"subjects, and designs of the magnitude in the Letters Patent
"particularly mentioned," and "extends to the mode of using
"or applying the said arabesque prints or moulds, in regard
"the same from their magnitude cannot be handled about
"or dipped, or be used or applied as prints of inferior dimen-
"sions have been hitherto used in the said manufactures, and
"that the said arabesque prints or moulds must therefore
"be laid on the back, and being furnished with blacking, the
"prints may either be laid upon the cloth, paper, silk, or cotton,
"and impressed in a rolling press or with a leaver, or beaten
"with a maul, and afterwards painted, either with hand or
"with stansills or grounds, according to the usual practice; or

" the paper, cloath, silk, or cotton intended to be printed or stained
" may be laid on the arabesque prints or moulds and impressed
" thereon, or rubbed with a pad or such like thing made of cloath
" list, by either of which methods compleat and perfect impressions
" of such enlarged prints or moulds may be obtained."

[Printed, 3d. No Drawing. Petty Bag.]

A.D. 1784, April 28.—N° 1431 (four).

FOULIS, ANDREW, and TILLOCH, ALEXANDER.—" A method
" of making plates for the purpose of printing by or with plates,
" instead of the moveable types commonly used, (a) and for vend-

---

(a) Numerous attempts have been made to obtain solid printing surfaces by transfer from similar surfaces composed of movable types. The history of Stereotype printing (as such solid surface is termed), although involved in some degree of uncertainty from the secrecy observed at first by those who practised it, may be said to have originated with Vander Mey of Leyden, who, about the end of the 16th century, in conjunction with Müller, also of Leyden, prepared plates of a quarto and folio Bible, and several other works, by soldering the bottoms of common types together with melted lead and solder to the thickness of about three quires of writing paper. The costliness of the invention in this form was a bar to its adoption, and after the death of Vander Mey it was abandoned.

In 1725, Ged, a goldsmith of Edinburgh, arrived at the knowledge of the art by a series of difficult experiments. (Encyc. Lond., "Printing.") His invention was simply this; from any types of Greek, Roman, or other characters he formed a plate for every page or sheet of a book, from which he printed, instead of using a type for every letter, as is practised in the common way. In 1730, Ged and his associates in ;the enterprise obtained a privilege from the University of Cambridge, for printing Bibles and Common Prayer Books, according to their stereotype method. They sunk a large sum of money in the undertaking, but had finished only two Prayer Books when they were obliged to relinquish it. It appears that one of the partners was averse to the plan, and engaged such people for the work as he thought most likely to spoil it, for the compositors, when they corrected one fault, designedly made six more; and the pressmen aiding the combination of the compositors purposely battered the letters in the absence of their employers." (Encyc. Met., vol. xxiii., Art. Printing.) Ged died in poverty, after having refused very advantageous proposals for establishing his new art in Holland. (Encyc. Lond., "Printing.") His son James Ged published " Proposals for reviving stereotype printing " in May 1751, and Biographical Memoirs of Wm. Ged, Lond. 1781. About the same time Valleyre, a French printer, cast metal plates for printing calendars, a specimen of which may be seen in Camus' *Histoire et Procédés de Polytypage et de Stereotypie*.

In 1740, Funkter, of Erfurt, published in German a short and useful Introduction to the Cutting of Plates (or blocks) of wood and steel for the making of letters, ornaments, and other figures ; to the art of baking plaster, of preparing sand moulds, for casting letters, vignettes, tail pieces, medals, and of forming matrices for them, &c. Octavo. Camus has an account of the processes employed.

About 1775 an attempt was made at Philadelphia, by Benjamin Mecom, nephew of Benjamin Franklin. He cast plates for several pages of the New Testament, and made considerable progress towards the completion of them, but never accomplished it. Dr. Franklin himself adopted a plan of writing the subject on paper with a glutinous ink, sprinkling it with emery powder or iron filings, and passing it through a rolling press between a hard and soft metal plate, the latter of which was left with an intaglio impression, and worked as a copper-plate. The effect was rough and unsightly. M. Rochon next etched the subject direct upon a steel plate, took an impression on paper, and from this obtained,

" ing and disposing of the said printing plates, and the books or
" other publications therewith printed, whereby a much greater

---

by " set off," direct impressions on paper. This mode is said to have been used
for several works privately circulated. M. Rochon then adopted the mode of
mechanically stamping punches into soft metal, which were either used as
printing surfaces or as the matrixes for casting them. His inventions do not,
however, appear to have come into general use.

In 1780, Carez, a practical printer at Paris, started a new method, which consisted in composing the page of type in the ordinary manner, attaching it face
downwards to a heavy block of wood, which was brought down with a smart
blow upon fused type metal on the point of congealing. The sharp mould thus
produced was then made to take the place of the composed page, and being
similarly brought down upon type metal in a similar state, produced a stereotype facsimile of the composed page. Hoffman, a German, who adopted Carez's
plan, substituted for the metal matrix obtained by the first stage in the above
process, a thin layer of prepared clay, on which the subject had been impressed
by a series of punches. (See post, No. 4249; A.D. 1818.)

In 1783, Hoffman, of Alsace, endeavoured to extend the discoveries which had
been made in stereotyping. He formed two sorts of types, one for detached
letters and the other for the termination of words most frequently occurring in
the French language, such as *ais, être, eurs, ment.* He termed his art of casting
types polytypie, and that of uniting several characters into one type *logotypie.*
He printed several sheets of a *Journal Polytype* on solid plates. In 1787 he was
deprived of his printing office by a judicial decree, and in 1792 addressed a
memorial to the Minister of the Interior, to enable him to open a new channel
of industry. (Encyc. Met. Lexicog., " Printing.")

Some numbers of the *Journal Polytype* having fallen into the hands of Carez,
a printer at Toul, the latter, in 1785, made his first attempts upon works which
he called *homotyped* (to denote the union of many types in one). He printed
several works, among them an edition of the Vulgate, which is said to be very
neatly executed. (Encyc. Met., Art. " Printing.") Hoffman was followed in his
processes of polytyping and logotyping by M. Gengembre, who made his first
attempts in 1789, but relinquished them in 1794, in which year he embarked for
America.

In 1791, M. Gegembre printed the 50 sous notes of the Caisse Patriotique upon
the following plan :—He caused the whole print of the notes to be engraved
in relief upon a plate of steel, the letters and ornaments being run together in
a manner impracticable with separate punches, and this engraving he pressed
into plates of alloyed copper, from which any number of stereotype plates were
taken by Carez's method.

It is stated that in printing the first assignats of the Revolutionary Government, no less than 300 so-called facsimile engravings had to be prepared. The
result was an utter want of confidence in the Government paper. To remedy
this, the Committee of the Assignats caused many experiments to be instituted
for the production of plates which should be not only imitative and similar, but
*pro re* identical. The plan adopted was that of engraving a plate in intaglio,
from which copper punches in relief (called " mother punches") were obtained.
From these " daughters" were struck, which, when perfect, were facsimiles of
the original engraving, and were worked by the roller press in the manner of
copper-plates. Numbers of them were, however, defective, as in many cases the
air compressed in the mould of a single letter would effectually prevent the
fused metal sinking to the full depth, and thus there would be no letter at all
upon the plate. Upon the suppression of assignats the establishment was
broken up.

The most successful of the French stereotypers were Messrs. Didot the elder,
Firmin Didot, and L. H. Heran, who in 1797 obtained patents for their respective inventions. Their first productions were logarithmic tables and the
classics.

In 1798, Didot issued an edition of Virgil printed from a plate cast in a matrix
made by slow and forcible pressure of types of hard metal placed within a steel
box against a metal plate.

Héran, Didot's partner, hit upon the formation of a set of types, on which the
letter was in intaglio and direct. The spaces, quadrats, leads, &c. were of the
exact height of the type. The whole, when composed, presented the appear-

" degree of accuracy, correctness, and elegance will be introduced
" into the publication of the works both of the ancient and modern
" authors than had been hitherto obtained."

The invention is declared to be "performed by making a plate
" or plates for their page or pages of any book or other publication,
" and in printing off such book or other publication at the press.
" The plates of the pages to be arranged in their proper order, and
" the number of copies wanted thrown off, instead of throwing the
" impressions wanted from moveable types locked together in the
" common method; and such plates are made either by forming
" moulds or matrices for the page or pages of the books or other
" publications to be printed by or with plates, and filling such
" moulds or matrices with metal or with clay, or with a mixture of
" clay and earth, or by stamping or striking with these moulds or
" matrices the metal clay, earth, or mixture of clay and earth."

[Printed, 3d. No Drawing. Petty Bag.]

---

ance of a plate of copper into which the subject (direct) had been punched.
This, after the necessary corrections had been made, was used as a matrix, and
any number of printing surfaces obtained by pressing fused metal upon it.
"Works executed from such plates are of remarkable neatness, and the process
may be pronounced of very great utility, although as far as known it has never
been introduced into England." (Encyc. Brit., Art. "Printing.") For a short
time they worked in partnership, but for many years they have stereotyped
numerous works on their own account.

In 1798, some experiments in stereotyping were made at Vienna by Falka, a
Hungarian, but being refused a patent for his invention, he retired to Buda,
where he established himself in the printing-office belonging to the University.

Towards the end of the last century, Professor Wilson, of Glasgow, being
engaged in a series of experiments for making etchings upon glass with fluoric
acid for the purposes of art, thought it possible to make polytypes of glass from
engraved copper-plates. In this he in some degree succeeded, having executed
several polytypes in intaglio from moulds in copper-plates, and in relief from
woodcuts; but it cannot be said to have been practically successful, the lines
not having any degree of sharpness in either case, while the brittleness of the
material would be a decided objection. (Encyc. Brit., "Printing.")

Fifty years after the discovery of Ged, Tilloch made a similar discovery without having any knowledge of Ged's invention. (Encyc. Lond., "Printing,") and
with the assistance of Foulis, printer to the University of Glasgow, after great
labour and many experiments, overcame every difficulty, and produced plates,
the impressions from which could not be distinguished from those taken from
the types from which they were cast. A Patent was also taken out for Scotland,
but they proved unsuccessful, and after several small volumes had been stereotyped, the invention was abandoned, and Mr. Tilloch removed to London.

Some years afterwards, says Hansard (Typog. 638), "after many expensive
and tedious experiments, Lord Stanhope, aided by Mr. Walker, an ingenious
mechanist, succeeded in this important invention to the full extent of his highest
expectations." In these experiments Lord Stanhope was assisted by Mr. Wilson,
a London printer, besides receiving instructions from Mr. Tilloch, and having
the benefit of Mr. Foulis' personal attendance. (Encyc. Met. Lex., "Printing.")
The introduction of the joint letters in, an, re, se, to, of, on, attributed in No.6800,
A.D. 1835, to Lord Stanhope, date probably from the period of these experiments.
In 1804, with the approbation of his lordship, the invention was offered by Mr.
Wilson to the University of Cambridge, but some differences having arisen
between the contracting parties, the matter fell to the ground, Mr. Wilson pub-
lishing his case entitled, "Arbitration between the University of Cambridge and
Andrew Wilson," in a stereotyped pamphlet.

A.D. 1784, May 19.—N° 1435 (four).

ARNOLD, Samuel.—" Printing vocal and instrumental musick
" of all kinds with types in a neater and more expeditious manner
" than hath hitherto been used."

The invention is " described as follows :—An entire new speci-
" men of notes, together with all the characters, &c. used in
" musick, cast on purpose in types. Heretofore all the notes
" have been cast in separate pieces. Many in my new invention
" are cast together, 2, 3, 4, 5, and 6 in one piece. The breaks in
" the lines are rendered less frequent, sometimes having but one
" in a whole bar, and sometimes having no break for a whole line
" together. The musick is printed sometimes at once and some-
" times at twice, according to the nature of the composition of the
" musick. The lines are sometimes cast with the notes and
" sometimes without the notes ; this also depends on the nature
" of the composition of the musick."

[Printed, 3d. No Drawings. Rolls Chapel Reports, 6th Report. Rolls
Chapel.]

A.D. 1786, March 18.—N° 1540 (one).

BUNNETT, Jacob.—" A machine for printing of paper hangings,
" callicos, cottons, and linens in general, whereby any number of
" colours may be printed thereon at one and the same time, and
" whereby ten times as many pieces may be printed in as short a
" space of time as one piece is now printed by the common method."
Three horizontal and parallel "printing cylinders" have each a
waterproof colouring roller above them. On the top of each colouring roller is a canvas or wire-bottomed trough. The pressing
cylinders are below the printing cylinders and are thrown in and
out of gear by the action of wedges on their axles. The material
passes before being printed over six rollers " to give it friction and
" to prevent its wrinkling."

2. A similar machine with intermediate colouring rollers, the
whole motion being rendered uniform by toothed gearing.

3. A trough roller colours the paper as it passes between it and
a pressing cylinder above it. The colour is smoothed by passing
between another cylinder and a brush.

[Printed 9d. Drawings, by the foot notes to which the invention is entirely
described. Rolls Chapel Reports, 6th Report, p. 174. Rolls Chapel.]

A.D. 1786, December 9.—N° 1575 (one).

HENRY, Solomon.—" New invented instrument to stamp or
" mark with, which may be composed of various colours so as not

to be counterfeited or forged, for the better securing the property
" of His Majesty's subjects from imposition."

The face of the stamps is made in parts, each containing a part
of the design, and different " water colour stains, varnish, or oil
" colour or any other colouring " being laid on each, and the parts
united, an impression is produced of the design in any number of
colours. Various modes of dividing the design and uniting the
parts for the impression are shown, *e. g.*, plugs fitting into perforations in the face, irregular pieces confined by a collar, concentric
cylinders held together by a pin. "An instrument with pins or
" points which may be made of any shape, for the purpose of
" piercing through the back side of the impression to prevent the
" same from being erased or counterfeited; the piercing must be
" made before the impression, that the roughness which the piercing
" occasions may be flattened and smoothed by the damp ; whereas,
" should a counterfeit thereof be attempted, the colour would run
" through the holes if put on after the holes are made, and if the
" piercing is made after the impression, the same will spoil the device
" or design and cause a roughness thereon easily to be discovered."
The stamps may be of metal, "wood, ivory, horn, bone, stone,
" porcelain, wax, clay, leather, papa mache, or any composition or
" substance sufficiently hard, and the design or device thereon may
" be engraved, cut, pierced, cast, carved, struck, stamped, or etched.
" . . And in order to cause the stamp to make the impres-
" sion, device, or design, the same may be pressed, rolled, ham-
" mered, or formed by hand or anything sufficiently weighty or
" strong to impress it on the thing intended to be stampt, and
" which impression may be made on paper, parchment, leather,
" silks, stuffs, or any other commodity capable of taking up the
" same."

[Printed, 9*d*. Drawings. Petty Bag.]

### A.D. 1790, April 29.—N° 1748 (one).

NICHOLSON, WILLIAM. (*a*)—"A machine or instrument on a
" new construction for the purpose of printing on paper, linen, cotton,
" woollen, and other articles in a more neat, cheap, and accurate
" manner than is effected by the machines now in use."

Types for use by this invention are cast in the usual manner,
excepting that "instead of leaving a space in the mould for the

---

(*a*) Ante, p. 23.

" stem of one letter only," several letters are cast at once in ordi-
·nary moulds communicating " by a common groove at top."
Besides the ordinary finishing, the type is scraped on one or more
sides in a " finishing stick," whose hollowed part is less deep
at the inner than the outer side. " The purpose accomplished by
" this method of scraping is that of rendering the tail of the letter
" gradually smaller the more remote it is from the face. Such
" letter may be firmly imposed upon a cylindrical surface in the
" same manner as common letter is imposed upon a flat stone."
These types, imposed in chases of wood or metal adapted to
the surface of a cylinder, are fastened " to the said surface by screws
" or wedges, or in grooves, or by other means well known to work-
" men." " Blocks, forms, types, plates, and originals " are likewise
fastened on the surface of cylinders " for other kinds of work."

2. The ink is furnished to the printing surface by a " colouring
" cylinder," covered with " leather, or the dressed skins which
" printers call pelts or  .  .  with woollen or linen or cotton
" cloth," " and stuffed with horsehair, wool, or woollen cloth,
" defended by leather or oilskin." Distribution is effected by
two or three small rollers applied " longitudinallly against the
" coloring cylinder, so that they may be turned by the motion of
" the latter." If the color be thin, a ductor of wood or metal,
" or a strait brush, or both of these last," are applied to the colouring cylinder. Color is applied " to an engraved plate or cylin-
" der or      .    thro' the interstices of a perforated pattern (or
" cylinder) " by " a cylinder entirely covered with hair or bristles
" in the manner of a brush."

3. The material to be printed (damped if necessary) is passed
" between two cylinders or segments of cylinders in equal motion,"
one having the printing surface imposed and the other " faced
" with cloth or leather,  .  .  so as to take off an impres-
" sion of the colour previously applied."  .  .  Or the printing surface previously colored is passed in contact with the
material wrapped round a clothed cylinder, or the clothed cylinder with the material round it rolls over the printing surface
" previously coloured." Or the printing surface coloured by a
colouring cylinder, rolls along the material " spread out upon an
" even plane." The process is applicable to books, paper-hangings,
floor-cloths, cottons, linens, woollens, silks, ribbands, laces, leather,
skin, and every other flexible material.

The drawings represent :—I. A press in which which the type-table passes between an upper and lower cylinder, the former (clothed), acting upon the "table by means of cog-wheels or straps "so as to draw it backwards or forwards by the motion of its "handle." A box containing the inking roller, with its distributors above it, is supported by an arm from the press-head. On the end of the type-table is an "ink block," and upon it a vibrating roller, which, by the action of a bent lever, "dabbs against one of the "distributing rollers and gives it a small quantity of ink." The tympan (which opens sideways) with paper on it, is laid upon the form when it arrives between the inking roller and press-head. After the impression, the workman on the other side of the cylinders "takes off the sheet and leaves the tympan up."

II. A printing cylinder has (gearing with it) a pressing cylinder below and a coloring cylinder above, the latter being provided with distributors as in I., and furnished by a vibrator from a trough. A sheet of paper is applied to the surface of the pressing cylinder, where it is retained by points "in the usual manner," or by the apparatus in IV. The machine is uniformly driven in one direction by hand power applied to the printing cylinder.

III. Press for cottons, silks, paper-hangings, and other fabrics of considerable length. In this instance, the pressing cylinder is uppermost, and has the power applied to it. Coloring is effected by an intermediate roller from a trough roller below. The fabric runs off a reel on one side of the cylinder, and after the impression comes upon an endless web above the reel, which carries it away and deposits it. For printing in colors, the fabric is passed several times through the machine, or where the materials are liable to change dimensions, by applying at once to the printing cylinder several color boxes, "with their respective cylinders."

IV. A pressing cylinder and inking roller, with distributors as above, are rigidly united, and gear into a rack on a long table divided lengthwise into four parts. The sheet is laid on the former (two modes "by which the paper is taken up and laid down" are specified,) at 1; gives it the impression at 2; discharges the sheet at 3, and then returns (clearing the form by a peculiar contrivance) to 1.

V. "An instrument for printing floor-cloths, paper-hangings, "and the like, with stiff paint and a brush." The pattern is perforated on the surface of a cylinder, on the axis of which is a color

box with a hair-covered roller, which, as the cylinder revolves,
sweeps in the perforated parts of it.

" Lastly, I must take notice that in these and every other of my
" machines, as well as in every machine whatever, the power may
" be wind, water, steam, animal strength, or any other natural
" change capable of producing motion."

[Printed, 7d. Drawings. Repertory of Arts, vol. 5, p. 145; Mechanics'
Magazine, vol. 6, p. 258; Engineers' and Mechanics' Encyclopædia, vol. 2,
p. 343; Practical Mechanics' Journal, vol. 1, p. 248. Petty Bag.]

## A.D. 1790, July 26.—N° 1766 (one).

BARCLAY, ROBERT.—" A method of making punches for
" stamping and punching the matrices of printing types for letters
" and devices, and for impressing on copper cuts or other printing
" plates, and on dies, and on various metals, and on any other
" substances, which letters, devices, and marks cannot be counter-
" feited."

The method of making these punches is said to " consist of the
" following principles : —

" 1. That there is an infinite variety in all the works of nature,
" whence it will follow that any hard brittle substance broken into
" two parts will exhibit certain irregular figures, which in infinite
" repetitions of the experiment will never be exactly imitated, and
" this principle I call the accidental part of the invention. Small
" bars of steel drawn to the proper size of the punch required, and
" then broken off, will without more form a punch to punch or stamp
" matrices for types for devices, and no ingenuity will ever be able
" to imitate them with a tool so as to deceive upon a careful inspec-
" tion, and a punch so formed will serve for marking copper or any
" other printing plate or cut, or a die for milling of coin or medals,
" or for stamping paper or parchment, or for stamps for an assay
" office, or for any other private mark on any substance capable of
" an impression.

The second " principle is to combine art with nature." " Thus,
" when the grain of the steel is very fine, and the light and
" shade to be produced will not be sufficiently distinct, it may be
" rendered more so by enlarging the hollow parts with counter
" punches of a smaller size . . cutting or grinding down the
" prominent parts . . and varying them with . . cuts
" of a graver . . or other tool untill a device is . . produced

" that pleases the eye and satisfies the artist, that it is inimitable,
" and this may be infinitely varied.

The third "principle" is, that "regular, accidental, and irregular
" cuts with a graver . . or other tool . . cut or struck on a plain
" surface of either wood . . or other substance, may also produce
" an inimitable device. Drilling holes and bending the periphery of
" one into another by punches, &c. will increase the difficulty of
" imitation. This combination of art and accident may be continued
" to any given length, as punches for letter-press types may be formed
" of steel broken as above, by cutting, drilling, punching, bending
" (and all their varieties upon the same principle) parts of the letters,
" and leaving the grain of the steel, &c. to form the lines or strokes,
" with all its accidental irregularities, and in this way title letters
" and two-line letters, facs, and complex founts of types, might be
" cast, every letter of which would vary in its lines from every other,
" and in larger letters a little art might be combin'd with accident,
" so as to make the distinctions from all others obvious to a common
" observer."

[Printed, 3d. No Drawing. Repertory of Arts, vol. 2, p. 4; Rolls Chapel
Reports, 6th Report, p. 183. Rolls Chapel.]

A.D. 1793, April 30.—Nᵒ 1953 (one).

ECKHARDT, Francis Frederick.—" Invention and method
" of preparing and printing paper in different paterns, and to silver
" it over with fine silver leaves, so as to resemble damask, lace,
" and various silk stuffs, to be used for hangings and other furni-
" ture for rooms."

The invention is performed as follows :—" When the paper is
" coloured in the ordinary course, size it properly with a size of
" ising glass, parchment, or common size, so as to bear an oil or a
" varnish gold size. This being dry, lay, with a printing block or
" a brush, on those parts where the ornaments are intended to ap-
" pear, gold size, or any of the other compositions that will answer
" the same purpose; when the gold size or composition is nearly
" dry, lay on real fine silver leaves, and then size the paper well two
" or three times, and when dry varnish it over with any of the
" various sorts of varnish that will resist damp."

[Printed, 3d. No Drawing. Repertory of Arts, vol. 2, p. 87; Rolls Chapel
Reports, 6th Report, p. 187. Rolls Chapel.]

A.D. 1794, December 9.—Nᵒ 2027.

PROSSER, Thomas.—" Machine for printing of letter-press."
An ordinary hand-press, with platens, worked by a bar-handle and

screw. Two springs are introduced; the one above the press-
head, the other below the winter or base. Each spring is furnished with "regulators" at each end fixed in grooves. "By
" shifting these regulators nearer to or farther from the centre of the
" head of the press the pull is made either harder or softer." . . .
" These two springs are made to act in concert with each other,
" and thereby the impression is materially increased, and the
" labour considerably reduced, as well as the wear of the letter
" greatly saved."

[Printed, 5d. Drawing. Repertory of Arts, vol. 8, p. 368. Petty Bag.]

A.D. 1798, April 11.—N° 2305 (one).

BRUNEL, MARC ISAMBARD.—" A certain new and useful
" writing and drawing machine, by which two or more writings
" or drawings resembling each other may be made by the same
" person at the same time."

The apparatus consists of a double-motion travelling-frame,
mounted on standards fitting on to the upper part of a desk; and
carrying sockets, into which are fitted any required number of
pens, which move in a precisely similar manner by the exercise of
one manual operation. The apparatus can be folded up when not
in use, and contained within the desk.

[Printed, 10d. Drawings. Repertory of Arts, vol. 7, p. 145. Petty Bag.]

A.D. 1800, June 17.—N° 2414 (one).

WELLER, WILLIAM.—" Manufacturing, forming, making, and
" engraving copper plates for printing policies to secure persons
" from loss of property of certain descriptions."

This appears to be merely an advertisement of an Insurance Office,
" which Mr. Weller intends (if patronized by the nobility, gentry,
" and the public) establishing, . . to ensure and secure by
" these patent policies His Majesty's subjects from loss of pro-
" perty," . . and from which the following advantages were
" most evidently " to result:—1. Indemnification for the loss
of insured property; 2. The assistance of the office in bringing offenders to justice; 3. Gratuities to the widows and
orphans of those killed in the defence of insured property; and
4. " A constant reward of five guineas, over and above the usual
" rewards (upon conviction), to any watchman, patrol, or other
" person or persons who shall take into custody any one or more
" who may have robbed or shall attempt to rob any one ensured

" by these patent policies," which is to be " easily discovered by
" the office mark" being conspicuously displayed on the insured
house.

The engraving on the plate is described. At the top the royal
arms, parallel with which on one side is a figure of Justice, with
the motto " Property secured," and on the other the bust of the
patentee, with the motto " William Weller, Inventor." At the
side (to act as counterfoil) is " cut a curious schroll or check
" .   . down which will be engraved this motto, ' Property
" ' secured from Thieves and Robbers.' "

[Printed, 4d. No Drawing. Repertory of Arts, vol. 12 (second series), p. 393;
Rolls Chapel Reports, 6th Report, p. 149. Rolls Chapel.]


A.D. 1801, June 20.—N° 2518.

SENEFELDER, JOHN ALOYSIUS. (a)—"A new method and
" process of performing the various branches of the art of printing
" on paper, linen, cotton, woollen, and other articles." The invention is stated to consist of three " parts or particulars :"—1st. The
method of preparing the original from which the impression is to
be taken; 2nd. In making those originals of (in addition to those
already known) substances not hitherto employed for such purposes; 3rd. In a new method of transferring " the ink, colouring,
" or other matter (such as mordaunts thickened with gum or other
" mixtures employed in calico printing,") to the paper or other
material.

1. The parts of the original which are to receive the colouring
matter are impregnated with a substance of the same nature as
or easily combining with such colouring matter, " whilst at the
" same time the other parts of the said surface are covered with,
" impregnated by, or have affixed upon them such other sub-
" stance, simple or compound, as is different from the printing ink,
" colouring, or other matter, and of such a nature as not easily to
" combine with or be received by it." The colouring surface being
applied to the printing surface, the colouring matter will be
deposited upon such parts of it only as are covered by the design.
If the substance used be a slab of fine-grained limestone the
design may be drawn with hog's lard and lamp black, and the
rest of the slab sponged over with water. The drawing may be

(a) Ante, p. 24.

effected " with a common or a steel pen (a) or a painter's brush."
The colouring matter is applied by a " printer's ball." The substances stated to be fit for this purpose are, first, " all fattish or
" resinous matters ; " and, secondly, " all liquids that are neither
" fat nor resinous, more especially those which hold a vegetable
" gum or any acid in solution, and which either of themselves or
" in their state of combination with other matters, will in some
" manner attack or dissolve or adhere to the substance of which
" the main body of the original form, model, or printing block is
" made."

2. " Every substance is therefore suitable for a printing surface,
" if of sufficient solidity and compactness, and provided it will
" admit of being impregnated with or penetrated or dissolved,
" attacked or acted upon by certain gummous, acidulous, or other
" liquids which are not fat, at the same time that it admits any of
" the different species of fattish or resinous matters to be made
" adherent to or imbibed by certain parts of its surface."

The impression may, " in some instances," be taken by " all the
" usual and known presses and methods," " as well by themselves
" as in combination with my newly invented improvements and
" apparatus, but in general the latter will be found preferable."
In the latter " a blunt rectilinear body or cylinder of wood or metal
" or other substance of sufficient solidity (this last turning on its
" axis), is moved over the back of the paper, linen, cotton, cloth,
" woollen, silk, leather, parchment, vellum, or other article destined
" to receive the impression by means of an apparatus resembling
" that of the machines used in glazing calico, while the paper,
" linen, cotton, or other article rests on the form, which for the
" most part is fixed on the table ; or in some cases, as where an
" original form or model of little weight be employed (such as
" one made of paper, for instance), this latter may be fixed on
" the large frame, and the paper," &c., " to be printed laid on a
" thick plate . . fixed on the table, . . and rendered some-
" what elastic by placing a leather cushion under it stuffed with
" horse-hair."

" By altering the size of the blunt rectilinear body it may be
" made to pass over a large or very small surface only, in which
" latter case the power is obviously increased in proportion to the
" smallness of the space on which it is executed at any one time."

---

(a) See notice of " Pens," ante, p. 8 (n),

The impression is taken as follows. The paper (damped) is laid on a leather on a large frame, and a frisket brought down over it and fastened by a spring (as in a watch case), " upon " this the large frame itself is turned round on its hinges, " . . so that the . . article destined to receive the impres- " sion comes in contact with the surface of the stone. The " whole of this process is the same with that in book printing. " It is now time to lay hold of the pole " (by which the scraper or cylinder is suspended), " which while its knee or flexible " elbow . . is bent is placed upon the leather, so that the " printing roller . . be in a right line across the upper edge of " the leather and stone block under it; the elbow is then turned " straight, so that the whole pole with its roller and apparatus be " perpendicular and stiff in a straight line from " an elastic board on the top of the press down to the leather, " and in this situation " it is moved backwards and forwards by taking hold of the lower " part of the pole." The pressure is increased by depressing a treadle (connected by a rod with the end of the elastic board) " in " the moment that its motion forwards is begun. In this manner " a number of impressions may be taken off, with the observance " of moistening the stone well with the printing liquor each time " before the blackening ball is passed over it, and to keep it moist " during the whole process of printing." When not required for printing, the stone is " preserved by brushing over it the solution " of gum arabic in water indicated; must be washed nearly off " again when employed for a new printing." The stone may be ground again and polished for a new original printing block. Or the surface to be printed from may be thus raised : when the design is dry, " one part of single aqua fortis diluted with 20 parts " of water is poured upon the stone, which will not affect the " parts covered by the ink but only the uncovered parts. This " biting should be continued until the traces of the ink appear " raised on the surface of the stone to the thickness of thin writing " paper." The whole surface of the stone plate is then cautiously rubbed over with a fine linen rag steeped in a solution of 8 oz. of gum arabic in one quart of water, or other pure vegetable gum. The gum is then " nearly wiped off " by gently rubbing with a linen rag and water, after which another, saturated with a mixture of water (120 parts), aqua fortis (1), and gum (1), wrung nearly dry and passed over the surface of the plate.

" Metallic plates of simple or alloyed metals, or even some
" semi-metals, are likewise a fit subject to serve as original printing
" blocks," being for this purpose drawn upon with a fat ink, and
etched with a weak solution of hepar sulphuris in water, a slight
portion of which is suffered to remain on the plate. The same
process is adopted as in printing from stone, except that the
moistening liquor "must be prepared of 120 parts water, 4 parts
" gum arabic, and 15 or 20 parts potash."

" My invention also possesses this advantage, that from plates
" of copper, tin, pewter, and various metallic compounds already
" etched or engraved . . . copies may be printed off much more
" expediously than in the usual way of copper-plate printing."
The ordinary ink is rubbed into the cavities of the plate; the
surface is cleaned by a solution of potash in water, brushed over
with a weak solution of hepar sulphuris in water and wiped dry.
The printing liquor specified for metallic plates is made use of.
" The colour is then put on with the printer's ball, and the rest of
" the operation performed in the same manner as I have before
" explained with regard to the stone plates, for as long as the
" hepar sulphuris (which, if found necessary may occasionally be
" renewed) adheres to the surface of the plate.

" Even paper and such like substances may, according to the
" principles on which my invention is founded, be adapted to serve
" as forms for this new method of printing;" for instance, write or
draw with a mixture of gum mastic (1), shellac (3), tallow soap (1),
and lamp black (1), on a strong and well sized paper. When
dry "brush it over with the beard of a quill or flat brush filled
" with a mixture of equal parts of sulphuric acid and water, as
" quickly as you can to save the paper from destruction. The
" cavities then formed round the traces of the drawing by the
" swelling of the paper must be directly filled with letter-press
" printing ink, and the paper speedily cemented or fixed by means
" of a strong paste or varnish or any other means, on a plate of
" metal, stone, or wood, or any other convenient solid substance."
In printing, the surface is moistened with water, and the process
in all other respects the same as in printing from stone. The
durability of the paper will be increased by impregnating it with
linseed oil, it being, previously to use, well dried.

Directions are given for imitating "on the stone slab, metallic
" plates, &c., according to the principles of" the invention, various

styles of drawing, as "etchings," "stroke engraving or drawing," "drawings with black and red chalk," and "aquatinta."

Impressions taken from copper and other plates may be transferred to the stone by being passed with it through "a good "powerful copper-plate press," or the press mentioned above, " if sufficiently strong." A solution of gum arabic is then gently brushed over the slab, and whilst it remains there, a linen rag strongly impregnated with the colour made of linseed oil, varnish, tallow, and lamp black, is rubbed upon its surface till the transferred design appears to have taken up as much of the colour as it can. The superabundant colour and gum is then wiped off " with the printing liquor," and the slab is ready for printing.

"To print copies in the manner of handwriting." Dip common writing paper for half a minute into a solution of gum arabic and alum, "wipe the superabundant water and gum gently off the paper, let it become dry, polish it with a polishing bone, write upon it with the common ink and an ink of bees-wax, beef suet, soap, and lamp black. Thoroughly moisten the paper, and transfer its writing on to a stone covered slightly with linseed oil varnish; place stone and paper in water, when the latter may be washed away. Aqua fortis diluted with 120 parts of water is poured over the stone, and the surface thereby slightly raised.

In printing with vegetable gum colours, such colour is advantageously applied by a board the size of the stone, rendered elastic by the introduction of a layer of woollen between it and a handle, or the board "may be covered with parchment or vellum stretched " by strings over the handle like a drum."

[Printed, 1s. 2d. Drawings. Encyclopædia Metropolitana (ed. 1846), vol. 8, p. 785. Petty Bag.]


A.D. 1802, May 20.—N° 2620 (one).

RUSHER, PHILIP.—" Various improvements and alterations in " the form of printing types, and the manner in which printing " is to be performed therewith, so as to diminish the trouble and " expence of printing, and to render it much more uniform and " beautiful."

" Each capital letter, with few exceptions, should be comprised " in the compass of an oval . . Each small letter is to be " without any tail-piece or descender, and the metal . . (both " in small letters and capitals) is to extend no lower than the

" body of the letter." The letters above the line "have their
" heads shortened or lowered about one-third."

" When the whole is arranged and fixed, the printing may
" be performed in the usual manner. . . These improved types
" and characters may be adapted to stereotype printing in the
" accustomed way with greater advantage than any other."

[Printed, 5d. Diagram with specimen alphabets. Repertory of Arts, vol. 1
(*second series*), p. 91. Petty Bag.]

A.D. 1803, February 28.—N° 2683 (four).

KIRKWOOD, ROBERT.—" Certain improvements on the copper-
" plate press."

To enable the workman to return the plate to himself " through
" press," part of the upper or lower cylinder is cut away, provision
being made in the latter case for the support of the plank. Or the
same result may be obtained by raising the upper or depressing the
lower cylinder by means of levers. A clockwork apparatus is (when
required) attached to the press, for the purpose of numbering the
impressions.

[Printed, 5d. Drawings. Repertory of Arts, vol. 3 (*second series*), p. 245.
Petty Bag.]

A.D. 1804, December 19.—N° 2797.

PASQUIER, STEPHEN. — " A new manufacture, system, or
" method of writing, printing, engraving, drawing, painting,
" stamping, working, and using certain characters, figures, instru-
" ments, and machines for facilitating correspondence and other
" literary operations."

" My said invention is the contrivance of such figures . . . as
" may by presenting in their outlines and shapes an adequate or more
" than an adequate number of distinct places to the letters existing
" in the alphabet to be used, and as may also by their being the
" best calculated for expressing arithmetical numbers, furnish per-
" sons using them with an universal standard for writing, copying,
" or expressing ideas almost spontaneously, inasmuch as the per-
" son who makes use of my figures needs for writing but to fill up
" according to his want the said places marked out for such and
" such letters with mere dots or strokes or equivalent marks,
" This simple method I call œutodidactography, or self-taught
" writing, and may be used for writing and keeping accounts by
" persons who never wrote before, provided they know how to

" read. When the said figures, dots, or strokes are used in a more
" combined or perplexed way, with or without transparencies, with
" or without colours, the art is termed cryptography ; when accom-
" panied only by abbreviations it is called syntomography, and
" when conveyed by machines or instruments it is called mechan-
" ography." "Homilorgan, or machine . . . which may be of use
" to the deaf and dumb for conversation, or in being put in a large
" and conspicuous place, for speaking to the eyes of a numerous
" assembly of people by the help of letters, marks, or symbols,
" established on the general principle of my new system of writing."

A writing, reading, and tracing desk.

[Printed, 3s. 7d. Drawings. Petty Bag.]

## A.D. 1806, April 29.—Nº 2931.

BERTE, ANTHONY FRANCIS.—" A machine for casting or found-
" ing types, letters, and ornaments usually made use of in
" printing."

The casting is performed by applying the mould to one of
several apertures in the side of the metal pot, "which at that in-
" stant, by means of a lock or valve or any other well-known
" similar contrivance," is opened, when the metal suddenly flows
into the mould with a force proportionate to the height of the
surface of the type metal in the vessel. The apertures should
be "nearly horizontal, so that the fluid metal shall spout upwards
" into the mould. The easiest mode of closing the apertures is
" by a metal plate which is displaced as the mould is slidden up,
" and which, on the mould being withdrawn, is by means of a
" weight, spring, &c., made to follow it, and close the aperture
" by resuming its first situation. . . I do, in preference, form
" my vessel of the figure of a box or closed receptacle, having a
" pipe or tube rising out of the same, so that the pressure afforded
" by the statical action of the metal in the said pipe or tube
" shall produce the desired effect at the aperture or place of
" casting, or otherwise I produce or increase the said pressure by
" the statical action of water or any other fluid which may be used
" by the well-known means to compress a body of air against the
" surface of the type metal for the purposes aforesaid."

[Printed, 3d. No Drawing. Repertory of Arts, vol. 11 (second series), p. 167 ;
Rolls Chapel Reports, 7th Report, p. 192. Rolls Chapel,]

A.D. 1806, October 7.—N° 2972 (one).

WEDGWOOD, RALPH.—" An apparatus for producing dupli-
" cates of writing."

"Duplicate paper" is made by smearing thin paper with oil,
and " carbonated paper " by spreading on it carbon or other coloring matter finely levigated in oil. To write singly, a leaf of carbonated paper is placed upon a smooth metal tablet, a sheet of the
duplicate paper is laid upon this, and the writing executed on the
the latter with a style. To write doubly, a sheet of writing paper
is laid on the metal plate, a carbonated sheet upon that, a duplicate sheet, upon which the writing is performed, laid over all.
" To make a farther increase of writings from an original one,
" I use a set of types and a type tablet, and for shortening the
" handwriting the types can be reduced to one figure, namely,
" a point, but more figures may be used if seen convenient.
" These convey the idea of any letter by the ,position in which
" they may be placed in a square or other formed figure printed
" or otherwise marked on the writing paper, which square I call
" the basis of the letters, and the paper ' character paper.' . . .
" The type tablet consists of a piece of flat metal or any other mate-
" rial . . . perforated with holes or sockets to fit the types. On the
" top of the type tablet is engraved or otherwise marked squares,
" corresponding with those on the character paper upon which it
" is intended to write or print." The types are rubbed with beeswax to prevent their shifting in the sockets, and a plate placed at
the back of the tablet to regulate the distance they are to be
pressed through the sockets. " In order to fix the types previous
" to taking off impressions, melted lead or any other substance
" may be run into the tops of those sockets which are vacated by
" the depression of the types which have been used for the com-
" position of any work, the lead uniting the whole; this I call a
" stereotyped tablet." This tablet may be printed from on
" character paper " in a common press, care being taken to place
the paper so that the squares correspond with those on the tablet ;
" or leaves of thin character paper and carbonated paper may be
" laid alternately upon each other, and upon this the stereotyped
" tablet is pressed in any manner found most convenient. By
" this means, with a single pressure a multiplicity of impressions
" are formed at once. To write with the new characters, I take one,
" two, or even six layers of duplicate paper, on which is stamped

" or printed the basis of the letters. Betwixt every two leaves
" I lay a leaf of carbonated paper, and over all I lay the type
" tablet, each square of which must be exactly over the squares or
" figures in the character paper so arranged, and when thus laid,
" with the point of a metal or other hard-pointed style I press
" down each type which I may require to form a word, from which
" act six copies are produced on the paper underneath." The
lead in the sockets can be melted away and the composition of a
second page proceeded with with the same types.

[Printed, 3d. No Drawing. Repertory of Arts, vol. 11 (*second series*), p. 216 ;
Rolls Chapel Reports, 7th Report, p. 192. Rolls Chapel.]

## A.D. 1806, October 15.—N⁰ 2977 (one).

BRAMAH, JOSEPH.—" A certain machine whereby valuable im-
" provements in the art of printing will be obtained."

" First, I propose by the use of one single compound and trans-
" posable type, very simple in its nature and construction, to
" enable any person but little or not at all acquainted with the
" ordinary methods of printing, to take correct copies or to print
" off any work that ever has appeared in any language, and also
" such as may hereafter appear; and this novel and bold effect I
" mean to produce or provide for by a machine or type which will
" not, in performing to the amount of all I state, either require a
" single letter to be taken out or added; I also propose by the
" same single (a) apparatus to be enabled to print, either in whole
" lines or at intervals in arithmetical figures, any number or num-
" bers which are comprehended between an unit and a row of the
" 9th digit number, arranged in a line to the amount of twenty-six
" and more as may be required; I propose also to perform all
" that I have hitherto described by the use of engraved letters and
" figures, as well as type letters, as already mentioned, so that the
" work performed shall have the precise appearance of the finest
" copper-plate engravings that art can produce. Secondly, I
" mean also, by the help of an apparatus precisely on the same
" principle as that already mentioned, . . . to print, either in
" colours or by impression only, all kind of piece goods, or any
" other article or thing, such as leather, metals, or any other
" article on which impressions or ornaments have been usually
" made. I mean also in some instances to use my machine or

---

(a) ? Simple.

" printing apparatus in the case of printing goods, sometimes with
" prints or figures cut or raised on the usual plan, and to take the
" impression by a force periodically used, and sometimes on the
" rolling or circulating plan, and with engraved figures or lines on
" the copper-plate principle; and in the latter instance I mean to
" introduce perpetual and self-acting inking or colour boxes and
" wipers."

A series of rings or wheels, twenty-six in number, are placed side
by side on a cylinder (somewhat like a "puzzle padlock,") and
secured by a " flanch " at each end. They have at intervals on
their surfaces the letters of the alphabet, figures, stops, &c.
The mode of composing this machine is described. " When
" the whole is thus completed, the apparatus is ready to go to
" work, and the most ordinary capacity will easily discover that
" by turning these wheels on the general axis till the respective
" letters or figures (which are demanded to compose as many words
" or monosyllables in one line as the twenty-six will reach) are
" brought into unison in a straight line from one end of the roller
" to the other, that the machine will be then ready to receive the
" ink, which being put on in the common way or otherwise, and
" an impression taken by a squeeze, that then so much of the
" intended work is executed, and a line is completely printed, and
" after which the wheels may again be turned, so as to produce
" another line, and that this simple process may be carried on
" through all the changes that can be made with the number of
" wheels stated, and by the addition of more wheels upon the same
" axis, it may be continued ad infinitum.

" Secondly, in printing piece goods and other articles as stated
" in my second proposition, I mean to compose the apparatus or
" printing machinery just in the way described, only that I shall
" generally adopt the engraved plan for this purpose, and not the
" plan with raised figures used by the calico printers and paper
" stainers, except in some instances, where I shall then have sprigs,
" flowers, and other ornaments cut on the spokes or prominent
" parts, . . . and where it will be obvious that I can vary pat-
" terns endlessly, and print them by the same machine, and so
" that no two pieces shall ever be alike in pattern, notwithstanding
" the machine may be kept at work night and day for number-
" less ages, and without stopping a single instant. . . . When a
" roller for this purpose is completed, it must be mounted on a
" frame in contact with another roller like a common calendar, so

" that the piece or other article to be printed may be passed between
" just as in a calendar, the two rollers having a necessary pressure
" on each other to cause a good impression, the same as is per-
" formed by the rolling press used by those who print from copper
" plates."

The roller is surmounted by an ink or colour box without a
bottom, and consisting of a rim only, "as capacious in its largest
" dimensions as will reach from one end of the printing roller
" to the other. The under part of this box" is fitted water-
tight to the roller, against which it is continually pressed. "On
" the leaving side of this inking or colour box is fixed what I
" term a wiper, made of wood covered with leather," which clears
off the colour, and prevents the goods being smeared with it.
For printing in stripes, the colour box is fitted with partitions,
which are always "put so as to fall with their thickness (which
" must be as inconsiderable as possible) exactly equally divided
" across the joints between one wheel and its neighbour . . .
" as the roller is turned about, the engraved figures or lines, or
" whatever else may be engraved thereon, will naturally and
" unavoidably be filled with ink or colour . . . and the box
" being on the most elevated part of the roller, and the piece
" to receive the impression on the under side, it will of course
" carry the ink or colour down on the leaving side, and come up
" empty on the driving side, till it again passes its surface with the
" pattern under the inking box, which will as constantly, and with-
" out a possibility of failing, both ink or colour the mould or
" plate with certainty and a degree of equality that never can be
" attained by hand, and at the same time with great expedition
" and accuracy of effect. I have now to mention that when I print
" pieces requiring different colours, otherwise than in stripes, such
" as flowers and other figures, I have a plurality of these printing
" rollers under which the piece successively passes, and on which
" rollers each has that part engraved which is to convey the colours
" respectively to the piece, just the same as is at present done by
" shifting moulds in the common way."

The patentee observes, that he can produce all the effects
stated in the above specification "by means of flat types, moulds,
" or prints made in this compound way," and that " perhaps
" practice may evince eventually that this method of applying
" the principle may, in many instances, be preferable to the

" former." For this purpose, " the type, mould, or print will be
" composed of an equal number of sliders placed by the side of
" each other, with close joints," when " by sliding each of these
" in either direction so as to bring the required letter, figure, or
" other marks . . . into unison . . . as before directed with
" the wheels, the same effect may be produced."

At the end of the attestation clause before the signature occurs
the following:—" N.B.—I also mean to construct conversing
" machines or universal telegraphs on this principle, and by
" which not only information can be conveyed, but likewise
" ordinary conversation in any language may be carried on
" between persons stationed at hundreds or even thousands of
" miles distant, and that with incredible facility." (a)

[Printed, 4d. No Drawing. Repertory of Arts, vol. 10 (second series), p. 329.
Petty Bag.]

## A.D. 1806, October 23.—N° 2979 (one).

WHITE, Elihu.—" A machine for casting or founding types,
" letters, spaces, and quadrats usually made use of in printing."

A " slider plate," fitted with " male" and "female" sliders,
moves upon "sliding ways" in a square brass frame, which
extend nearly up to a " head-block " at (one end of the frame).
The depth of the sliders is precisely equal to the length of the
body of the letter to be cast, and the thickness of the male slider
precisely equal to its size. On the slider plate being moved (by
the action of a screw) towards the head-block, studs in the male
sliders come in contact with the front half of a " regulating bar,"
which prevents their reaching the head-block, whereas the female
sliders, having no studs, are driven home against the head-block,
by which means certain spaces are left open along the head-
block for the body of the letter. On reversing the screw the
whole is drawn back until the studs meet the after half of the
regulating bar, by which they are stopped, while the female sliders
will still move back until the letters are quite clear of the sliders,
so as to fall or be taken out. When letters are to be cast, a bar
containing a matrix box is pressed up to the under part of the
head-block and sliders, and brings the matrixes exactly under the

(a) See Bishop Wilkins' " Mercury, or the Speedy and Swift Messenger, showing how a man may with secrecy and speed communicate his thoughts to a
friend at any distance," published A.D. 1641. Natural and Philosophical Works,
Octavo, Lond., 1708.

spaces kept open by the sliders for the body of the letters, and ready to receive the metal, which is poured in through apertures in the matrix bar.

[Printed, 8d. Drawing. Repertory of Arts. vol. 11 (second series), p. 97; Rolls Chapel Reports, 7th Report, p. 196. Rolls Chapel.]

A.D. 1807, April 15.—N° 3033 (one).

BERTE, ANTHONY FRANCIS.—" Certain improvements in " casting printers' types and sorts, and other articles of metal."

The earlier part of this specification is an almost verbatim repetition of N° 2931. Where the sliding plate there mentioned for closing the aperture is inapplicable, the mould is applied " to " the said aperture, either by sliding the same to its place as " aforesaid, or by any other method of opposition."

Another mode is specified of producing pressure from the surface of the metal by the use of a piston or plug in the pipe leading from the metal pot. " And in every case of construction " wherein the said plug or piston shall be applied and used, it " will not be needful or proper to close the aperture . . . by a " cock, valve, plate, or other contrivance; but instead thereof, I " do so regulate the quantity of my metal or the position of the " parts of my apparatus, that the surface of the fused metal shall " be accurately or very nearly at the upper part or opening of the " said aperture beneath the mould."

Another improvement consists in making the body of the mould " of four adjustable pieces, instead of two. Each of " which said four pieces hath two external plane faces inclined to " each other, in the precise angle of a square or right angle, so " that all the four convex pieces when put together with their " angular edges in the same line will fit and leave no cavity; but " when the several pieces are slided upon each other face to face " at right angles to the middle line or edges, upon every one of " the touching faces a square or rectangular cavity will be left, " which, instead of being adjustable in one direction only, can be " made of any required dimensions, so as to admit of changes in " the width as well as thickness of the body of the letter; and " when the desired adjustment hath been made, the plates may " be fastened together in pairs, and used like the common " moulds. And further, I do, when required, make my moulds " without nicks or notches, or such parts as shall produce nicks

" or notches in the shank of the letter; and I do strike out or
" expel the cast letter from the mould by a punch or proper tool,
" without opening the mould as is usually done."

[Printed, 3d. No Drawing. Repertory of Arts, vol. 11 (*second series*), p. 241 ; Rolls Chapel Reports, 7th Report, p. 196. Rolls Chapel.]

## A.D. 1807, June 2.—N° 3047.

BROWN, JOHN.—" Certain improvements in the construction
" of a press for printing books and other articles, part of which
" may be applied to presses now in common use."

The " follower " (platen) is drawn down by a screw turned by a
bent lever acted on by a cord passing round a rigger on an upright
shaft, to which motion is given by bevel gearing from a winch.
After the impression the rigger is thrown out of gear, and the
platen recovers itself by means of weight or spring. A cast-iron
bed carrying the form " slides out below an inking roller. This
" roller . . . is covered with flannel, or any other proper elastic
" substance, and then is covered with parchment or vellum,
" or other proper materials, to prevent the ink from soaking
" too far in, and likewise to give it a spring, and afterwards is
" covered with superfine woollen cloth (or any other fit material)
" additionally sheared, if required, for the purpose of receiving
" the ink to supply the types." A large barrel or cylinder
having received the ink from a trough underneath it, and had
it distributed by a small roller in contact with it, supplies the
inking roller, and the latter " revolves round and feeds the types by
" the motion or movement of the spindle which moves the bed,"
*i. e.,* the rounce, from which also (" by means of a strap or any
" other convenient thing,") the large roller and its distributor are
driven. A loose moveable frisket " is connected with and slides
" in and out at the ends of the iron bed . . . for the purpose
" of conveying the paper over the types."

" I also apply the " inking apparatus " (being my principal
" improvement) to presses now in common use, by means of a
" fly wheel and traddle," which drives it. The inking roller
" may be rolled over the types to feed them with ink, either by
" the motion of the hand or fly wheel, or in various ways well
" understood by every competent workman."

[Printed, 6d. Drawing. Repertory of Arts, vol. 14 (*second series*), p. 368 ; Rolls Chapel Reports, 7th Report, p. 197. Rolls Chapel. Hansard's Typographia.]

A.D. 1808, February 22.—N° 3110 (one).

WEDGWOOD, RALPH.—" An apparatus for producing several
" original writings or drawings at one and the same time, which I
" call a pennæpolygraph, or pen and stylographic manifold
" writer."

The sheets are combined in various modes so as to admit of
being written on by a double pen " held in the hand as a pen is
" commonly held." Three modes are shown in which impressions
are obtained on two sheets. 1. The sheets are laid one upon the
other, the writing on the lower being executed through apertures cut parallel to the lines on the upper. 2. Both sheets are
endless, and so arranged as to admit of being written on with
the double pen. 3. One sheet is endless, and is laid over the
other, which is stretched in a frame. The endless sheet is constantly withdrawn as the writing progresses on the lower sheet.

[Printed, 3s. 11d. Drawings. Repertory of Arts, vol. 15 (second series),
p. 193; Rolls Chapel Reports, 7th Report, p. 199. Rolls Chapel.]

A.D. 1809, January 23.—N° 3194.

PEEK, JOHN.—" A machine for the more expeditious method of
" casting printing types, by which three motions out of five made
" in the ordinary method of casting types are saved," the first
being " performed at the same time the mould is closed, and the
" two last in the same time and almost at the same instant of
" opening it."

The invention consists in the addition of two parts to the
mould then in ordinary use. The addition to the upper part
(that usually held in the right hand) consists of a plate with a
socket, in which the matrix is suspended on pivots, and that of
the lower part (that usually held in the left hand) of a bolt which
presses the matrix to the mould, where it is kept by a spiral spring
round the bolt, and by the withdrawal of which the matrix is
tilted, another spiral spring keeping it in that position till the
mould recloses. The bolt is worked by a lever. The matrix
being drawn off the face of the type, the caster " immediately
" takes off the upper part of the mould with his right hand, and
" picks out the type as usual, continuing at the same time to
" press the end of the lever with his thumb until he recloses the
" mould."

The whole of the above machine is sometimes affixed to the
upper part of the mould " in such a manner that when the caster

" takes hold of the upper part of the mould with his right hand,
" he at the same time tilts or draws off the matrix by pressing the
" leaver."

[Printed, 7d.  No Drawing.  Rolls Chapel Reports, 7th Report, p. 203.
  Rolls Chapel.]

A.D. 1809, March 4.—Nº 3214 (one).

FÖLSCH, FREDERICK BARTHOLEMEW, and HOWARD, WIL-
LIAM.—" A certain machine, instrument, or pen, calculated to pro-
" mote facility in writing, and also a certain black writing ink or
" composition, the durability whereof is not to be affected by time
" or change of climate."

A number of sheets of thin wove writing paper are prepared, by
being smeared on one side with a composition of Frankfort black
and butter, after which they are put for forty-eight hours in a
press.   When fit for use (in about a month) they are laid alternately
(the prepared side downwards) with sheets of paper, and " a suffi-
" cient quantity of common writing ink being put into the cavity"
of a tubular pen ; "the ink flowing from the point of the tube will
" give one impression, and the other impression or impressions
" will be formed on the under sheet or sheets from the inked paper
" or composition."

[Printed, 3d.  No Drawing.  Repertory of Arts, vol 15 (second series), p. 206.
  Petty Bag.]

A.D. 1809, November 28.—Nº 3279.

BROWN, JOHN.—" Certain new improvements in a machine or
" press for letter-press printing, and also for printing various
" ornaments and figures, part of which improvements may be
" applied to presses now in use."

The form is fixed in the centre of the press.   The upper bed is
rigidly connected with a carriage which runs on a tramway above
the press, and is drawn over the form by a cord passing over a roller
turned by a hand lever.   It is confined under strong pieces of iron
fixed to the frame, and returns by means of a weighted cord.   The
impression is given (1) by the rising of a vertical rack below the
bed by motion imparted through a series of levers from a rounce
barrel ; or (2) by a screw (geared similiarly to that described in
Nº 3047 and) acting upwards ; or (3) " by a roller being fixed on the
bottom part " of the carriage where the upper bed . . . is, and by
" the same motion rolls over the tympan and types and gives the

" impression. . . I apply two tympans, one on each side, so that
" two workmen may use the same form, . . and by this mode am
" enabled to do nearly double the work in the same time."

The inking apparatus consists of three horizontal endless webs
placed one above the other, the lower part of the upper one being
on a level with the table, and the lower part of the lower one being
immediately above a trough roller; the latter " to have a true
" edge of brass, steel, iron, wood, &c., as a scraper . . . to bring
" the ink off smooth and even; and the roller to be of brass,
" pewter brass, or any other kind of mettle, made hollow inside so
" as to contain a quantity of hot water or steam to keep the ink of
" a proper thickness." The lower web is furnished by the trough
roller on the occasion of its being raised by a treadle action.
The " upper rollers" have a " soft blanket sewed round, . . . and
" on the outside a skin or skins of leather, tanned or untanned,
" superfine cloth, cotton or oil cloth, or any other fit material.
" . . . Inside the upper rollers, between the blanket, there is a
" board similar to box without cover, fixed inside the blanket for
" a bed of wool to lay on, and at the end is connected a roller
" which must be weighted on each side by rope or strap . . .
" so that the workman may with ease lift up the top feeding
" rollers . . . which will fall on the types . . . and give them a
" sufficient quantity of ink, or the types may be supplied with
" ink by rolling a roller over them," the roller returning by a
weighted cord. The endless webs are driven by a " jack . . . .
" to work either by weight or spring."

[Printed, 5d. Drawing. Rolls Chapel Reports, 7th Report, p. 207. Rolls
Chapel. Hansard's Typographia.]

## A.D. 1810, February 1.—Nº 3297 (two).

DE HEINE, AUGUSTUS FREDERICK. — " Improvements on
" printing or stamping presses."

" Instead of applying a screw for my power I apply two sectors,
" or a sector and cylinder, or a sector and roller, to move one
" against the other by a single or compound lever." (a)

---

(a) See notice of Roworth's press, ante, p. 22. In noticing this invention the
Encyclopædia Edinensis, art. " Printing," adds, " Another improvement on the
Stanhope press has been made by Mr. Keir, who has considerably altered the
lever apparatus by which the spindle is made to rise and fall, so as to equal the
descent of the great screw through a given space at the same time, and the connecting rod by this means is pulled on a horizontal plane. Mr. Midhurst has

The "plattin or dye" is under a piston, the head of which is acted on by a moveable spindle, with two opposite sectors. The lever, single or compound, is fixed to the spindle, and by its action "the piston will be depressed as in the common screw, with this "difference, that as the descent of the piston decreases in velocity, "the power must increase in the same proportion in the screw. ". . . This motion may be reversed by putting the opposite "sectors at the top of the piston and the cylinder or roller on the "moving spindle; . . . or in case this power is applied to a fly "press, it may be applied by putting the part that acts instead of "a screw . . . through the hole in the head of the press . . . "and fixing the fly lever above the head of the press. . . . "The sweep of the sector and the diameter of the moveable "spindle are made as circumstances require, and can be varied ad "infinitum."

[Printed, 5d. Drawings. Repertory of Arts, vol. 16 (second series), p. 321; Rolls Chapel Reports, 7th Report, p. 110. Rolls Chapel. Hansard's Typographia, 653, where the invention is said to have merged into that of Mr. Cogger, of which a description is given.]

## A.D. 1810, February 26.—Nº 3307 (two).

STUART, PETER.—"A method of engraving and printing maps "of countries, charts, or other plans or designs, music, mathe- "matical diagrams or figures, on wood, metal, or any other sub- "stance, so that they may be thrown off in a common printing "press or presses, either for books, newspapers, or any other "printed paper whatever."

The surface of the plate is made rough to retain ink from an ordinary inking roller, and the subject graven deeply in it. When placed in a press, level with the letter-press, an impression of the subject will be given in white on a black ground.

[Printed, 3d. No Drawing. Repertory of Arts, vol. 18 (second series), p. 332; Rolls Chapel Reports, 7th Report, p. 208. Rolls Chapel.]

---

made another improvement on this printing press, which consists in making the platen the size of a sheet, and in lieu of a screw substituting a plain spindle with a circular plate fixed on the lower extremity of it, just above the bar, and which answers as steps for the points of two iron rods which assume an inclined position when the platen is used, although the distance of both ends of them from the centre of the spindle is equal; but as the spindle is turned, the plate in which the extremities of the iron rods are made to rest moves about in a circle, while the upper extremities are stationary. In consequence of this motion, when they come towards a vertical position the spindle and platen descend; by this means the friction is greatly diminished, and when the rods come nearly parallel to the spindle the power is vastly increased."

A.D. 1810, March 29.—N° 3321.

KOENIG, FREDERICK.—"A method of printing by means of
" machinery." A table with a platen ("as in other presses") at
one end. In the centre is an inking apparatus, consisting of
several cylinders vertically arranged, above which is an ink box,
through a slit in which the ink is forced by a piston, so as to fall
upon cylinders by which it is distributed. The two middle cylinders are for this purpose of different diameters, so "that when
" they are revolving the points of contact may be constantly
" changed," and for the same purpose an alternating and opposite
endwise motion is given to the two cylinders immediately below
them, which furnish two inking cylinders revolving in opposite
directions. The latter are fitted in a moveable frame, and by the
action of spiral springs, "the one and the other cylinder is alter-
" nately applied to the form." The inking cylinders consist of
perforated tubes of brass, through axles of which (also perforated)
steam or water is introduced to moisten their felt and leather
clothing. The form is in a coffin, to which the tympan is hinged,
so as to present its back to the press-head when thrown up. The
frisket does not move upon hinges fixed at the top of the tympan,
"as is the case with the presses now in use," but has the same
centre of motion as the tympan. "In the common press the
" tympan is fixed close to the coffin; in my machine, coffin, tym-
" pan, and frisket have each two extending arms, one foot long,
" all meeting" in a common hinge. The coffin runs to and fro
along the table. On its return, after the impression, the tympan
is raised by a chain attached to the press-head until it passes the
vertical, when it falls back on and slides along a cross bar.
"When the carriage is returning to the press" the bar "will force
" the tympan to rise to the vertical line, and having passed the
" same, the tympan will sink down again upon the form by its
" own weight, guided by the end of the chain. . . ." The frisket
has counter weights on its arms, by which it has a constant tendency to be erect. When the tympan is down, its superior weight
overbalances these counterweights; "but as soon as the tympan
" rises, the counterweights begin to act by lifting the opposite part
" of the frisket and holding the same with the sheet close to the
" tympan" until it passes the vertical, when it is acted upon by a
weighted cord, which keeps it close to the tympan until the latter
has arrived at a position in which the sheet will rest by its own
weight, when the frisket rises to allow of its removal.

The impression is given by means of a compound lever, which causes a crew to make one quarter of a revolution. The motion of all parts of the machine are derived from a steam engine (a) or other first mover,—the description of the millwork occupying a great part of the specification. There is a peculiar arrangement for producing interrupted motion in the coffin and the compound levers which give the impression.

[Printed, 1s. 2d. Drawings. Mechanics' Magazine, vol. 6, p. 259; Engineers' and Mechanics' Encyclopædia, vol. 2, p. 344; Rolls Chapel Reports, 7th Report, p. 209. Rolls Chapel.]

### A.D. 1810, October 1.—N° 3385.

DYER, JOSEPH C.—(Communicated.)—" Certain improvements " in the construction and method of using plates and presses, " and for combining various species of work in the same plate, for " the kind of printing usually called copper-plate printing, de- " signed for the objects of detecting counterfeits, for multiplying " impression, and saving labour."

Plates of steel are decarbonated for the purpose of engraving them, and case-hardened for printing from. These processes are described. " Plates thus constructed are what I call ' Perkins' " ' steriographic (b) steel plates,' one of which will serve to give as " many impressions as would wear out a great number of copper- " plates." Another considerable advantage is derived from the invention in printing " bank notes, bills of exchange, lottery " tickets, or any other prints or documents wherein a part of the " impression requires changing from time to time," moveable pieces of engraved metal being for that purpose inserted, level with the plates, in holes or mortises in the same.

A compound plate is constructed of a number of pieces of decarbonated steel fitted together so as to form one plate, and then engraved. They are then separated and casehardened . . . " in " recomposing or putting together the said compound plate I do " interpose between each engraved piece another corresponding " piece or slip of cast steel, which may be polished or have any " uniform or other ground on the surface thereof. And I do then " securely fix all the said pieces so alternating with each other in

---

(a) This attempt to improve the common press proved a failure, and was abandoned for the cylindrical methods of printing adopted in Nos. 3496, 3725, and 3868.

(b) In a notice of this invention in the London Journal (Newton's), vol. 1, p. 108, the art is termed " Siderography " (σίδηρος, iron, and γράφω, I write).

" a case or frame, and the same do then . . . constitute what I
" call ' Perkins' check-plate.' "

To render counterfeiting more difficult, various lines, strokes,
letters, flourishes, or irregular chance work are marked on blocks
or pieces of steel fixed together so as to form one plane surface,
and afterwards separated in order to form the parts of a print or
impression capable of checking with each other. These parts are
used as punches for making the like lines, &c., upon parts of
another plate, being for that purpose fixed in a frame " at regular
" or irregular distances from each other," and the impression
produced upon the printing plate " by the application of a suitable
" blow or regulated pressure."

Imitations of block work are multiplied upon metallic plates by
means of hard steel cylinders called " indenting cylinders," which
are made to " revolve on and move backwards and forwards over
" the surface of the plate under a powerful pressure."

An improved table for a common copper-plate press. A cell on
the table contains a heater; a perforated plate covers this cell, and
upon this the engraved plate is laid. Instead of the " common
" dauber or rubber" a " cylindrical inker" is used, consisting of a
" number of circular pieces of cloth or felt accurately of the same
" size, which are put upon an axis and confined together with a
" cylindrical piece at each end closed against them." The ends
of the axis act as handles. The said handles are included within
cases of tin, which enable them to turn freely. The " inker " is
first run over an ink table and then applied to the printing plate,
from which the redundant ink is removed " as usual."

A copper-plate press of the usual form is shown, having the
pressing cylinder " reduced at one side in the well-known form
" called the D roler (chiefly used by calicoe printers), for the pur-
" pose of allowing the table and cushion to return, by means of
" counterweights, after the impression shall have been taken."

[Printed, 7d. Drawings. Repertory of Arts, vol. 19 (second series), p. 257
Rolls Chapel Reports, 8th Report, p. 82. Rolls Chapel.]

### A.D. 1811, October 30.—N° 3496.

KOENIG, FREDERICK.—" Further improvements on my method
" of printing by machinery," being additions to and improvements
on N° 3321. The form is fixed upon a cast-iron plate, which runs
to and fro on a table, being received at either end by strong spiral
springs. The inking apparatus is similar to that of N° 3321,

except that the ink box is a vertical cylinder with a hole at the bottom about one-eighth of an inch in diameter, and fitted with an air-tight piston (depressed by a screw), which forces the ink out on to two hard rollers, between which it is distributed, and from which it is furnished to other cylinders, " the supply of " ink not being always quite so regular and uniform as is " desirable, if the screw . . . be not mathematically true." By a peculiar arrangement of two rollers placed on excentric bearings, whatever may be the irregularities in the supply of ink from the ink box, the supply of ink will regulate itself to a great degree of uniformity. The intermediate cylinders are of different diameters, and two or more of them have endwise movement. " It is, how- " ever, not essential that the horizontal motion should be con- " fined to the middle cylinders. I claim it for the purpose of " distributing the ink." The inking rollers are similarly con- structed, and have a similar action to those of N° 3321. In the centre of the machine is a "printing (pressing) cylinder," from which, in three places, at equal intervals, a portion of the surface is removed to enable the form to pass freely beneath it on its return. Upon this cylinder are three tympans, " resembling the " inner tympans in the common press," with register points. The sheet is laid on the tympan, and lays itself round the cylinder by its own weight. Three iron frames of a peculiar construction attached to the cylinder serve the purpose of friskets, and together with straps unwound from a cross-bar convey the sheet to the im- pression. There is a peculiar arrangement for the discharge of the sheet after the return of the form. The cylinder is moved for each impression one third of a revolution and then stopped. The first start carries the sheet round and secures it by winding the frisket upon it ; with the second the impression is given and the sheet thrown off; and with the third the empty tympan is coming up for a fresh sheet.

In the case of "broadsides," a wooden cylinder "presses the " sheet to the tympan, and helps to keep it on its right place." There is a peculiar arrangement of toothed wheels and racks in the millwork by which the pressing cylinder is stopped and started gradually, and by which the printing surface and cylinder have during the impression the same velocity.

A double machine on the same principle as the above, the form alternately passing under and giving an impression at one of two cylinders at either end of the press.

A number of machines combined or brought together into a system, one machine close to the other in the form of a circle, the form continually running forward from one machine to the other, thus rendering every part of its way productive. "The " inking and printing apparatus must have, for obvious reasons, " the shape of truncated cones, tho' they," as well as the tympan and frisket, "are acting exactly in the same manner as the cylin- " drical ones." Ten machines are in the drawing, supposed to be placed round the circle, and one man for changing the sheet before each printing cone.

[Printed, 2s. Drawings. Rolls Chapel Reports, 8th Report, p. 88. Rolls Chapel.]

### A.D. 1812, July 22.—N° 3587 (two).

MOTLEY, Thomas.—"An improved method of manufacturing " letters or characters for signs and shew boards, fronts of shops, " houses, and other places, and for any other purpose of composing " or indicating names or words in relief in a conspicuous manner."

A wall of thin metal, in the form of the letters, direct or in re- verse (according as it is intended to serve as a sign or a printing surface) is let into a board or block, and forming "side plates," to the top and bottom of which other pieces of thin metal of the same form are soldered, so as to form a kind of box. To give solidity to the whole, edge bars or strengthening pieces are some- times introduced, or the box is filled with some cheap metal or other material. "And, further, I do make the said letters, par- " ticularly if of small size, by casting the back part of lead or " other metal, either solid or hollow, (instead of the side plates), " and adherent to the face or front plate or letter so cut out " as aforesaid. . . . And I do further declare that with regard to " letters intended to be fixed upon separate blocks, the nature " of the shanks, or bodies of types, I do form and make the said " letters in the manner herein-before described, or otherwise by " simple casting, and do fix or solder or rivet the same upon " blocks constructed hollow and rendered strong and solid by the " same means as are herein-before described with regard to the " said letters first mentioned; and I do use and apply the said " letters so fixed to blocks in printing by composing and imposing " the same as usual, or otherwise I do solder, attach, and connect " together a number of the said letters so as to constitute an " entire block or face, or form an instrument for printing large

" bills or inscriptions, or for marking sacks, bales, sheep, and
" other objects."

[Printed, 3d. No Drawing. Repertory of Arts, vol. 28 (*second series*), p. 7;
Rolls Chapel Reports, 8th Report, p. 90. Rolls Chapel.]

## A.D. 1812, October 31.—N° 3610.

CASLON, WILLIAM.—" An improved printing type."

" The face or letter part of the said type I make of the usual
" thickness and in the usual way, but the body . . . which
" is commonly made . . . about seven-eighths of an inch, I make
" only three-sixteenths of an inch in thickness, . . . and the
" front of the said body I make sloping or bevilling upwards
" from the outer side towards the face as well as the opposite
" side or back, by which means the upper part of the body is
" about one-eighth of an inch narrower than the under part of the
" same." Stands of iron, metal, or wood, made in parts, and fitting
exactly to the body of the types, are used to raise them to the
proper level (seven-eighths of an inch) for printing. Or the body
may, without being bevilled, be fixed by nails or otherwise upon
blocks of wood of a proper width and height. Or the stands may
be made of the whole width of the body of the type with only
one projecting part, the other being screwed on after the types are
put on the stands.

The advantage of these types is in economy of weight and space,
the former being one-half, and the latter one-third to one-seventh
only of ordinary types.

[Printed, 3d. No Drawing. Repertory of Arts, vol. 23 (*second series*),
p. 18; Rolls Chapel Reports, 8th Report, p. 94. Rolls Chapel.]

## A.D. 1813, July 23.—N° 3725.

KOENIG, FREDERICK.—" Certain additional improvements in
" my method of printing by means of machinery."

The ink box consists of a perforated tube with a spindle,
with pieces affixed to it, which, by revolving, " opens and
shuts the holes like a cock." The supply on this principle
has been found so regular as to supersede the contrivance
described in N° 3496. The types are inked as described in
N° 3496. It is not absolutely necessary that the instrument
for spreading the ink lengthways should have the shape of a
cylinder, or even that it should revolve : " any straight body . . .
" brought in slight contact with or at a very small distance from

" a revolving cylinder, and having that longitudinal motion, will
" produce the effect." The skins which form the outside cover of
the inking rollers " ought to be shaved on the flesh side to make
" them nearly of an equal thickness. . . . In most cases I use
" onehard and one soft cylinder; but sometimes, according to
" the quality of the types, or o fthe work to be produced, and the
" time allowed for it, two hard ones or two soft ones."

A contrivance for holding the sheet by endless straps, called an
" endless frisket," which " has superseded, by its greater simpli-
" city, the use of the frisket described in " N° 3496. It consists of
sets of straps passing over small rollers on each side the cylinder
and under the cylinder, which lay hold of the sheet on the margin
and on the blanks between the pages. The straps are carried along
with the printing cylinder by friction only. Beside these there is
a set of broader endless tapes, passing over one of the small rollers
which " squeezes the paper close to the printing cylinder before the
" impression."

" I have made several simplifications in the millwork. The
" machinery for producing an interrupted motion for the printing
" cylinder as described in " N° 3496 " has been superseded meerly
" by two wheels," viz., a cog wheel upon the cylinder with a peculiar form of teeth, and a continuously revolving segmental wheel
fitted also with cogs and pins. " In order to secure an absolute
" correspondence of motion between the form and the printing
" cylinder racks . . . have been added to each side of the coffin
" which meet corresponding teeth on each side of the printing
" cylinder."

" The only alteration adopted for the double machine since my
" last specification is, that I cause the two lowest inking cylinders
" to turn in the same direction, and that their motion is reversed
" for each sheet by means of a wheel, similar to those used in
" mangles." The form is thereby twice inked for each sheet.

[Printed, 9d. Drawings. Rolls Chapel Reports, 8th Report, p. 100. Rolls
Chapel.]

A.D. 1813, November 1.—N° 3746 (four).

RUTHVEN, JOHN.—" A machine or press for printing from
" types, blocks, or other surfaces."

" My printing press differs from those hitherto in use in the fol-
" lowing particulars :—1st. The types, plates, blocks, or other
" surface from which the impression is to be taken, instead of

" being situated upon a running carriage, as heretofore practised
" in printing presses, are placed upon a stationary platform or
" tablet, which is provided with the usual apparatus, known to
" printers by the name of tympan and frisket, with points, &c. to
" receive the sheet of paper and convey it to its proper situation,
" on the face of the types, after they have been inked.

" 2nd. The machinery by which the power for the pressure is
" produced is situated immediately beneath this platform or tablet,
" and the platen or surface which is opposed to the face of the
" types, to press the sheet of paper against them, can be brought
" over the types and connected to the two opposite sides or ends,
" with the machinery beneath the table. By this machinery it is
" so forcibly pressed or drawn down upon the paper which lays
" upon the types, as to give the impression, which being thus made,
" the platen can be disunited from the machinery, and removed
" from off the types by the foot or otherwise, to take out the paper
" and introduce a fresh sheet.

" 3rd. The said machinery for introducing the pressure is a
" combination of levers actuated by a crank or short lever turned
" by a winch or handle, to which the pressman applies his hand,
" or the pressure may be introduced by the tread of the foot."

The tympan of the press opens sideways. The platen recovers
itself by the elasticity of an arched bar, which connects the wheels
of the carriage, by which it is drawn over the form.

A second arrangement of the levers is shown, in which the power
is applied by a chain wound round a wheel, which for the increase
of power " may be formed like a spiral instead of circular, that the
" chain may lay upon a shorter radius when the pressure is pro-
" duced."

[Printed, 9d. Drawings. Repertory of Arts, vol. 25 (second series), p. 193;
  Engineers' and Mechanics' Encyclopædia, vol. 2, p. 342; Rolls Chapel
  Reports, 8th Report, p. 101. Rolls Chapel. Hansard's Typographia, 650.]

A.D. 1813, November 23.—N° 3757.

BACON, RICHARD MACKENZIE, and DONKIN, BRYAN.—
" Certain improvements in the implements or apparatus employed
" in printing, whether from types, from blocks, or from plates."

These consist in fixing the printing surfaces in a prismatic form
upon an axle, and applying to it a second revolving figure ("the
" platten") of such configuration that the distance between the two
shall be the same in every part of the revolution. The former may

be inked " by means of balls, such as are commonly used by " printers," or by means of a metal cylinder, covered with canvas and coated with a composition of treacle (2) and glue (1). (a) The latter is in a frame, which turns on the axle of a trough roller, furnished with a ductor, between which and the inking roller is a distributing roller. The frame is free to rise or fall upon the printing prism. The. sheet is introduced by placing it upon a blanket extended upon a feeding board, and drawn into the machine at the proper time by a small ruler affixed to it, the ends of the ruler being taken forwards by studs attached to endless chains passing from wheels at the end of the " platten " to other wheels supported in the fame of the feeding board.

A cylinder may be used for giving the impression by making it adapt its movements below to that of the prism, as the inking cylinders does above in the construction before described. Its pivots should be supported on bearings like the inking cylinder, or the bearings may be adapted to slide in grooves, so as always to have a tendency to rise up either by the action of springs or of weights acting upon levers.

Drawings are given of machines in which the prism has four and five sides respectively.

" It is perhaps proper to state here, that for ascertaining the " figures required for plattens we have no rule but repeated trials; " nor is it of much consequence, as we have ascertained that the " cylindrical platten, before described, is attended with less trouble " in construction, and answers the purpose equally well."

[Printed, 2s. 1d. Drawings. Petty Bag.]

A.D. 1814, February 8.—No 3777.

HARRIS, TIMOTHY.—" A machine or machines for ploughing, " laying on colour called grounds, flocking, and pressing, so as to " produce an even face upon paper, silk, linen, woollen, leather, " cotton, and various other articles."

1. " Ploughing." The edge of the paper is cut (" ploughed ") by a wheel knife, similar to that of a chaff-cutter.

2. " Grounding." The paper is endless, and is wound from one roller on to another. The colour is laid on it by a radiating brush,

---

(a) The casting of this composition on the canvas-covered cylinder (and no the composition itself) is claimed as new.

turned by hand in a trough, and distributed by passing under a pendant brush, and a "vertically revolving" brush, also turned by hand.

3. "Printing." The paper is forwarded through the machine on three pieces of web. The tearing cloth is first completely smeared or covered with color, and the printing block (supported on springs in a frame) slidden over it, and charged by being pressed upon it by a lever, which recovers itself by a weighted cord, and allows the block to rise. The tearing cloth is prevented following the block by flaps. The frame (with the block) is then pushed along a groove "till it comes under the pressing block and screw . . . "the paper being first put in a proper position," when the impression is given by the screw. The paper is prevented by hand levers from rising with the block.

4. "Flocking." When the material is to be flocked over its entire surface, the adhesive matter is laid on with a brush. When it is only to be partially flocked, it is brought immediately from the printing machine and laid with the flock between two canvas covered frames, the flock fixed, and what is superfluous shaken off by the action of a "beater," turned by a handle, against the frames.

5. "Finishing." The rolls of paper are pressed between a stationary "bearer" of wood and a vertically sliding box. The rack by which the latter is moved is connected with an apparatus which, by means of a bell, announces the completion of the operation. An eight-ribbed roller is shown, which "has the peculiar property "of rolling the paper more smoothly on its surface, minding "to touch the ends of the paper with a little stiff paste, in order "to connect them," so that the ribbed roller can be drawn out and a solid one introduced.

[Printed, 1s. 3d. Drawings. Rolls Chapel Reports, 8th Report, p. 101. Rolls Chapel.]

A.D. 1814, October 3.—N° 3845.

DIDOT, Ambroise Firmin.—" An improvement in the method "of making types or characters to be used in the art of printing."

" In Roman text, running hand, or any other hand consisting "more or less in hair strokes, or fine lines, from letter to "letter, I do cast my types in a mould as usual, but I do prolong "each of the projecting extremities of the letters severally and "respectively unto the body of the next succeeding letter, what-

" ever may be the angle or inclination of the said letters or ex-
" tremities with or unto the line to be formed of or by such letters,
" so that the place or point of junction shall thereby be rendered
" complete, and without any interstice upon the printed copy to
" be taken therefrom." In the case of letters which (as in common
writing) are inclined, " I do by suitable alteration in my moulds
" cast my types, and the beards and shanks or tails thereof, with
" the same or nearly the same inclination or slope of surface as afore-
" said," and to prevent such types sliding upon each other, when set
up, a " protuberance or projecting part " is cast on one face, and
a " cavity or indentation" corresponding to it in the opposite one,
" or otherwise I do, by angular or curved deviations from, in, or as
" to the strait direction of the said surfaces, render it impossible
" that any sliding should take place between the same."

Where from the variety in the direction of a hair stroke, as in
joining *a* and *n*, it cannot be " carried across the place of junction
" of the types without greatly impairing the neatness thereof, I
" do in this and the like cases . . . not only cast separate types
" for separate letters, but also for the parts of letters needful or
" expedient to be set or composed together."

[Printed, 3*d*. No Drawing. Repertory of Arts, vol. 27 (*second series*),
p. 14; Rolls Chapel Reports, 8th Report, p. 104. Rolls Chapel.]

A.D. 1814, December 24.—N° 3868.

KOENIG, FREDERICK.—" Certain further improvements (*a*) on
" my method of printing by means of machinery." (See N°ˢ
3321, 3496, and 3725.) The first improvement is a contrivance
by which the printing cylinder has a constant or uninterrupted
motion as long as the coffin moves. The sheet is laid on a
separate apparatus (the "feeder") consisting of an endless web
or cloth. The interrupted motion is applied to the comparatively light feeder, which is started and stopped gradually, but
when in its full speed moves with a velocity equal to that of
the periphery of the printing cylinder. The path of the sheet

---

(*a*) On Tuesday, November 29, 1814, The "Times" thus announced the printing
of its journal by means of this machine :—" Our Journal of this day presents to
the public the practical result of the greatest improvement connected with
printing since the discovery of the art itself. The reader of this paragraph now
holds in his hand one of many thousand impressions of ' The Times' newspaper
which were taken off last night by a mechanical apparatus. A system of machinery almost organic has been devised and arranged, which, while it relieves
the human frame of its most laborious efforts in printing, far exceeds all human
powers in rapidity and despatch."

to the impression is " so calculated that the paper meets
" the form just in time to be printed on the middle of the
" sheet."

The second improvement is the addition of an " inner frisket,"
consisting of the additional sets of straps to those mentioned in
N° 3725. " The sheet in descending to the printing cylinder is
" taken hold of by and carried along between the inner and outer
" frisket. The use of the inner frisket is to detach the sheet
" from the printing cylinder after the impression."

" The third improvement consists in the application of a
" certain principle and apparatus for printing the reiteration
" immediately after the first impression . . . so that the sheet is
" thrown out of the machine printed on both sides of the paper."
The register of the reiteration is ensured by the adjustment of
the length of the path after the " white printing."

The inking apparatus are at the ends of the press. The ink
box is placed in immediate contact with the distributing cylinders,
and " the action of the frame of the lower inking cylinders . . .
" is simplified by giving a separate frame to each cylinder, with a
" common centre for both." To fix upon a cylinder a composition such as has " been used for some years past, in order to
" cover printers' balls, instead of skins," viz., glue and treacle, the
composition is cast upon cloth (a) in a flat piece of equal thickness, and wrapped round the roller, and fixed upon it by the
edges of the cloth with nails or screws, or the composition may
be cast upon a roller in a mould. The friskets are carried along by
contact of friction with the cylinders and a " transferring cloth."
Interrupted motion is given from the mill-work to the feeder and
tapes connected with it. In the interval that the feeder is at rest,
the sheet is laid upon register points upon it, and when set in
motion the paper is carried along upon it towards tapes which
take hold of it, and it passes betwixt them and the feeder towards
the outer frisket and descending tapes, which bend the sheet
downwards, when it passes between the inner and outer frisket,
where it is printed white. It is then laid by the inner frisket on
the "transferring cloth," whence (it being turned in the mean time)
it comes under the second printing cylinder, and is printed on
the other side. The friskets of the second cylinder then detach it
from that cylinder, and throw it on a board across the machine.

---

(a) See No. 3757,

To counteract the bias which is found in almost all the straps, metal " directing pulleys" are laid upon them, which give them a strain in another direction. The printing cylinder in this machine has only one tympan, *i. e.* about one-third of it is covered with broadcloth, &c. The other parts are uncovered, and "this " inferiority in diameter gives clearance to the form when it is " repassing under the printing cylinder after the impression." A plate annexed to the specification " exhibits the plan of the " whole machine in its last stage of improvement, together with " the mill-work.'

In a "double machine on the improved plan," where two pressing cylinders are employed, the inking apparatus is in the middle, "and the form passes with a reciprocating motion " always beyond the printing cylinders, so that an impression is " obtained at each end of the machine. . . . The present im-" provements upon this machine are the same as in the single " machine, namely, the application of the feeder and the inner " frisket."

[Printed, 1s. 3d.   Drawings.   Rolls Chapel Reports, 8th Report, p. 112. Rolls Chapel.]

## A.D. 1815, March 14.—N° 3896 (two).

BELL, WILLIAM.—" New-invented improvements in the appa-" ratus for copying manuscript or other writings or designs."

The invention (to be used with N° 1244) consists in a mode of damping the sheets of a book on which copies of the writing, &c. are to be taken. The paper containing the writing to be copied (executed with a gummy or mucilaginous ink) is placed between the leaves of the book, which must be of unsized paper. On the opposite side of the leaf to the writing is placed a damping-plate of metal, pasteboard, &c. covered with thin cloth which has been damped by being previously wrapped round with wet flannels. The whole is then placed in a press, and the ink of the copy forced by the pressure through the leaf, at the back of which it may be read.

[Printed, 3d.   No Drawing.   Repertory of Arts, vol. 27 (*second series*), p. 129; Rolls Chapel Reports, 8th Report, p. 104.  Rolls Chapel.]

## A.D. 1815, March 14.—N° 3897.

RIDGWAY, JONATHAN.—"A method of casting and fixing at " the same time metallic types on the surface of metallic cylinders

" or metallic rollers, or any cylinders or rollers having metallic
" surfaces, or on blocks of metal, or blocks having metallic
" surfaces, or on flat metallic plates, for the purpose of printing
" patterns of cloth made of cotton or linen, or both." A "typing
" tool" has at its end on the upper side a cup, and on the lower
the moulds "to form the pattern or patterns required to be made
" by the type or types to be cast therein upon the cloth." There
is communication by holes between the cup and the moulds.
This typing tool works upon a slide rest above the cylinder, &c.,
and the latter having been prepared to receive solder, the typing
tool is heated and struck gently on to the cylinder, the metal
(lead two-thirds, tin one-third) is poured into the cup, and the
type formed on the cylinder, &c. ; the typing tool is raised by
gentle strokes of a hammer. The distance through which the
tool is moved for each casting is measured by an index on the
slide rest.

[Printed, 4d. Drawing. Petty Bag.]

A.D. 1816, January 10.—N° 3974.

COWPER, EDWARD.—"A method of printing paper for paper-
" hanging, and other purposes."

The invention consists in printing with curved or bent stereotype plates. "A mould is taken in plaister of Paris from the blocks
" or types used for printing paper, and the plate cast in the usual
" method practised by stereotype founders. . . . The plate is then
" heated equally," and laid "upon a level board with the face down-
" wards, interposing between the plate and the board some soft
" substance," such as flannel. "The board, the flannel, and the
" heated plate thus arranged are passed together between two
" cylinders ; a common rolling press will answer the purpose. . . .
" I sometimes curve the plates without heat, but then there is some
" danger of breaking them."

The method of printing is as follows :—" The curved stereotype
" plates are fixed upon a cylinder or part of a cylinder in the same
" manner that flat plates are fixed upon the blocks in the common
" press." As the "type cylinder" revolves, the plates come in
contact with several color or inking rollers (a) "covered with

(a) In the machines made on this principle, after the Patent No. 4194 was
obtained, the ink was distributed on a portion of the type cylinder, and the
rollers over the type cylinder took it from this portion and applied it to the
types.

" the composition of treacle and glue, frequently used for printers'
" balls." The color rollers are brought to a true surface by
" moistening the composition with water and turning them in
" a lathe." They are furnished from a metal trough roller provided with a ductor. They are inked before starting, after which
they will give and take ink from the stereotype plates, and thus
render the inking on those plates uniform. " Some of the colour
" rollers are divided, that is to say, several small rollers are placed
" on the same spindle. . . . After the plates have received the
" ink or colour from the colour rollers, they come in contact
" with another cylinder, which I call the paper cylinder, on which
" paper is laid." Three or four folds of cartridge paper should
be fixed on the paper cylinder under the paper to be printed.

" For paper-hangings, the type cylinder should be covered with
" plates, and the motion of every part of the machine con-
" tinuous."

The drawings represent a book-printing machine in which a
vibrating roller is introduced between the metal and color rollers,
and the paper is held on the paper cylinder by catches which
turn on axes. Two or three wires are bent to the curve of
the cylinder and placed underneath, and at a small distance
from it, to prevent the paper from falling. The paper may
be held by endless strings, as " in some machines for ruling
" paper." A wiper " similar to that used in Prony's condenser of
" forces," puts the paper wheel in motion, wihout any jar, and a
reverse wiper stops it as easily. All the color rollers are put
in motion by their own friction.

[Printed, 6d. Drawings. Rolls Chapel Reports, 8th Report, p. 112. Rolls
Chapel.]

A.D. 1816, September 30.—N° 4064 (two).

CLAYTON, ROBERT.—" A new method of preparing, making,
" and finishing metal and composition blocks, plates, rollers,
" types, and dies, by which various patterns, devices, and compo-
" sitions can be effectually imprinted and impressed on cotton,
" linen, silk, worsted, mohair, and woollen cloths (or any fabric
" made of a mixture of any two or more of them), also on paper,
" leather, porcelain, and earthenware, and by which the same
" effects can be produced in a shorter time and at a considerable
" less expence than by any other method now used for those
" purposes."

" I, in the first place, etch or indent upon plates or rollers of
" zinc, either in its pure metallic state or but slightly alloyed . . .
" by employing for that purpose solutions of metallic salts" (acetate
of lead, nitrate of lead, nitrate, muriate, or acetate of tin or copper,
&c.) "instead of free acids, and I defend those parts intended to
" remain untouched by following the mode generally practised by
" engravers on copper, viz., covering them with common etching
" ground or varnish, and removing the ground with the point or
" etching needle or by any other means from these parts intended
" to be corroded or bitten, by which I obtain what has hitherto been
" accomplished by etching and engraving in the old way upon
" copper . . . and also indented seals or dies. I secondly produce
" what for distinction I shall call a bass relief, in a completely
" different manner from anything heretofore attempted upon plates
" or rollers of zinc, either pure or slightly alloyed . . . by employ-
" ing solutions of metallic salts, acid salts, or acids . . . and I
" defend those parts intended to remain untouched by any of said
" solutions by drawing or covering over the said parts some
" waxy, resinous, oily, and fatty composition . . . so that the
" said parts shall stand prominent and in relief after the plates or
" rollers of zinc have been subjected to the action of such solution
" . . . and I hereby effect what has been hitherto obtained by
" engraving or cutting or brassing in wood, or by making dies
" or punches, and thus produce the varieties of wood-cut and
" cross-hatch tools or devices for impressing and ornamenting
" leather, seals in relief, &c." By combining the 1st and 2nd
process, dies can be produced, giving an impression, part intaglio
and part in relief. "Thirdly, I obtain what I shall term alto or
" high relief by producing metal castings from wooden moulds or
" matrices " punched in wood with a cross-grain, which has been
previously slightly charred or baked, " which castings may be
" used to produce impressions from sieve type press or by the
" hand." The metal is bismuth, tin, and lead in equal parts, or
tin (4), bismuth (4), lead (3), and antimony (1).

[Printed, 4*d*. No Drawing. Petty Bag.]

A.D. 1817, November 1.—N° 4174.

CLYMER, GEORGE.—" Certain improvements in printing
" presses."

The press is of iron, and derives its power multiplying principle[4] from the component parts thereof being so shaped and

arranged that they are by the moving power of the handle of the press brought from various angles of inclination which they form when the press is at rest, to parallels and right angles when the press is in motion. The principal parts connected with the impression consists of a "first or great lever," and a "second lever" connected by a rod with a "third lever or handle." The platen is hung to the lower end of a bolt sliding between vertical guides, and connected with the great lever by a pivot or trunnion. A lever with a sliding or adjusting weight acts as a counterbalance to the great lever and platen, to the former of which it is connected by a bridle. The great lever is connected to the second lever by two rods, there being unmoveably fixed to the second lever a lever carrying a sliding counterbalance weight, which commences to act when the former weight is rendered inactive from the position of its lever. A stop screw in the handle, by adjusting the length of the rod between it and the second lever, admits of the adjustment of these levers, so as to print the smallest cards on the heaviest forms. The form is on a sliding carriage, furnished in the usual manner with the tympans and frisket, and is run in and out from the press with a rounce and girths as usual.

[Printed, 1s. 3d. Drawings. Rolls Chapel Reports, 8th Report, p. 122. Rolls Chapel.]

## A.D. 1817, November 1.—Nº 4176.

HANSARD, Thomas Curson.—"Certain improvements or addi-"tions to printing presses, and also in the process of printing."

The first improvement is dividing tympans, which are capable of being added to any printing press for the purpose of printing double-sized sheets of paper, and then dividing or cutting such double-size paper to the ordinary size. These tympans consist of outer and inner tympans. The former of these has in the middle of it an iron bar perforated so as to admit a saw-like knife fitted on to the frisket. The latter is formed of two parts, having each three sides, and moving (like the leaves of a book) on pivots attached to the outer tympan. When shut down, they are fastened "in the common manner by hooks and eyes or buttons."

" For making ready a forme or sheet the tympan sheet is drawn " on the tympan, as in the ordinary mode, and the frisket pasted " and cut out, but for working the first side of the paper the knife " must be displaced," (or a frisket without the knife used), " the " whole of the paper being worked off on one side without the

" knife. The knife is then replaced, or the friskets exchanged,
" and the reiteration proceeded with. The sheet will then be
partially divided exactly along the centre, the uncut parts keeping the double sheet adhering for the pressman who may be
pulling to draw it off the tympans over the bank, where it is
finally parted by another man by a gentle pressure with each
hand on each end of the heap. " The white paper . . . is worked
" with four points opposite each other in the middle fold of each
" half of the double sheet; but for the reiteration the two lower
" points are taken off and the sheet kept in register by the two
" upper ones only. For cutting the sheet into more parts than
" two I extend the same principle by placing knives and plates in
" various positions or at right angles with each other."

The girths are recommended to be made of catgut. They are
arranged in pairs, one pair to run the table in, the other to run it
out, " with, however, a slight degree of obliquity," so that the
rounce will be in every position or turn of the wheel equally tight,
and no friction or adhesion of the lines can ever take place.

" Stereotype plate risers with holdfasts or claws." The risers
are of type metal, cast somewhat in the form of what are called
" quotations." The holdfasts are of various lengths, of brass or
hard metal, accurately adjusted in thickness to a brevier or
any other body chosen, with a projecting bevil at the top. The
height is about seven-eighths of an inch. " To prepare plates for
" working.—Form with the risers the requisite number of pages
" for the form or sheet to the nearest size they make by the various
" combinations, and add any difference wanting by reglet, leads,
" or scaleboard ; then lay on the plates, and place at the head, foot,
" and sides of each plate as many holdfasts as may, from the size
" of the plate, be deemed sufficient for proper fastening. . . . To
" change plates when worked.—Unlock the form, draw out the
" holdfast at the head or foot of the plate, slide off the done-with
" plate, replace by the new one, lock up again." If the plates
have been all cast true to one gauge the work will be in register
and equal impression.

[Printed, 7d. Drawings. Repertory of Arts, vol. 33 (second series),
p. 257; Rolls Chapel Reports, 8th Report, p. 123. Rolls Chapel.]

## A.D. 1818, January 7.—N° 4194 (two).

COWPER, EDWARD.—1. " Improved modes of distributing and
" applying the ink or colour to the surface of the types, stereotype

" plates, or wood or metal blocks used in the printing (commonly
" called letter-press printing) at or by a machine or the ordinary
" press."

1. The ink or color is distributed upon a flat "distributing
" table" by rollers covered with leather, felt, composition (treacle
and glue), &c., which either pass over the distributing table, or the
distributing table may be made to move under them, the rollers
being driven by friction from the distributing table. Some or all
of the rollers have an "end motion," which tends to the better
distribution of the ink or color. The ink or color being spread
upon the rollers, the form of types, stereotype plates, or blocks
is inked or colored by being brought into contact with the
rollers, the latter rolling over the former, or the former passing
under or in contact with the latter.

(a) The inking apparatus in a "machine" consists of three
inking rollers, which lie in fixed bearings in the framework, and
ink the form as it passes beneath them; the distributing table
(to which the form is attached) and the sides of which are slightly
indented two distributing rollers in a moveable carriage, which
lies loose on four bearings, and has affixed to it two small friction
pulleys . . . in contact with the indented sides of the distributing
table; and a vibrating roller, which, "as occasion requires," is raised
up from the distributing table and made to touch a metal roller
in an ink trough. By the action of the indented sides of the distributing table against the friction pulleys the moveable carriage
and the rollers upon it are caused to move endwise. "Sometimes
" all the rollers are caused to receive an end motion in the manner
" above described," and the form is caused to pass under them all,
" but in this case I prefer making that part of the distributing
" table which is nearest the form of type, &c. with parallel, and
" not indented sides, in order that an end motion may not be
" produced while the rollers are in contact with the type."

(b) For an "ordinary press" the distributing table " is
" furnished with an ink trough formed of a roller . . . and
" straight edge a little elevated above the distributing table.
" The roller has a winch, by which it is turned till it is covered
" with a film of ink, when a hand roller is furnished from it, and
" after being rolled backwards and forwards over the distributing
" table, is rolled once or oftener over the types. The ink trough
" is varied by forming it of two rollers in contact with each other,
" between which the ink is laid." [The mode of inking, "as

" now performed," (with balls, of which a drawing is given in the margin of the specification) is described.]

In (a) and (b) the form is provided with a slip of metal or wood at each end, called "lifts," the height of which regulates the pressure of the rollers upon the form.

(c) Another apparatus for the "ordinary press" placed at its "off-side." The distributing table slides in vertical grooves in the inner side of a frame, "after the manner of a window in its "frame." Its front part projects beyond the frame, and its sides are indented. The table is counterbalanced by a weight. Distributing rollers are placed in a moveable carriage, as in (a). A vibrating roller above them is moved by a "boss" to the trough roller at the top of the apparatus. The trough is "formed with a "roller, as in (b), and a straight edge." The hand roller is in a carriage which runs on ribs attached to the frame of the apparatus. Corresponding ribs are placed at each end of the form on the table of the press, and when the table is run out the ribs of the table are opposite to the ribs in the frame. When the table is run out and the tympan up, the pressman lays hold of the rod or handle of the hand-roller carriage and draws it over the form. " When it has reached the near side of the table, he either returns " it by his hand or suffers it to be drawn back by weights attached " to the carriage. The operation of running the table . . in and " out sets the distributing table with its rollers in motion, which " distributes the ink upon the hand roller."

(d) Another mode for an ordinary press, in which the patentee states that he has availed himself of an arrangement of rollers round a large roller, described in N° 1748. " The sides of a large "distributing roller" are indented, and the spindles of the smaller rollers in contact with it lie in a moveable carriage, which receives end motion from the indented edge of the distributing roller, and the legs of which are hinged to the frame. A vibrating roller is moved against the trough roller by a wiper on the axis of the large distributing roller. The trough, the hand roller and its carriage, and the ribs on the form, as well as the mode of using the hand roller, are as in (c). This apparatus is also put in motion by the running in and out of the table of the press by means of bevelled wheels.

"The rollers . . . may be made oval instead of circular, though " I do not recommend it." They may be of wood or any other substance, and either hollow or solid, and may be covered with

leather, with felt, with treacle and glue, &c. The distributing table
may be of wood, metal, glass, slate, marble, leather, or treacle and
glue.

2. Mode of conveying the sheet from one printing cylinder to
another in the same or another machine, by means of "con-
" veying drums," to which it is held, and over which it is carried
by two sets of endless strings, "each composed of two or more
" strings kept tight by weights or springs," or flexible wires
kept tight by means of pulleys pressing against them, the strings
being so arranged as to fall upon the margins of the form. The
printing cylinders and conveying drums are connected by toothed
wheels. There are four conveying drums, two immediately above
the pressing cylinders and level with and between them. The
sets of strings are separated by means of guide rollers where the
sheet is taken out."

[Printed, 2s. Drawings. Engineers' and Mechanics' Encyclopædia, vol. 2,
p. 345; Ure's Dict.; Encyc. Met.; Tomlinson's Cyclop.; Rolls Chapel
Reports, 8th Report, p. 122. Rolls Chapel.]

A.D. 1818, January 17.—N° 4202.

BRIGHTLY, Charles, and DONKIN, Bryan. — "An im-
" proved machine or printing press for printing from types,
" plates, or blocks."

In this case there are two forms, plates, or blocks, and one
pressing cylinder. The forms, &c. are propelled over and under
each other alternately upon an endless railway, composed of two
sets of rails united by semicircular rails, the type tables being so
connected by swing bars in the centre of the machine that the
weight of the descending form counter-balances the ascending one.
The pressing cylinder and inking apparatus are both on the
upper railway. The latter consists of a large distributing roller
supplied by a trough above it, and furnishing three inking rollers
below it. The sheets are fed in upon one of two tympans
(with steel register points), stretched over endless chains which
pass round the pressing cylinder. Three sets of endless strings
are used in connexion with the tympans, the first of which,
after taking the sheet by means of a dropping roller from a
feed board, pass along with the paper to the pressing cylinder,
oblige the paper to apply itself closely to its surface, "and,
" after the paper has received the impression and begins to

" leave the cylinder, they then detach the paper from the types
" and assist in conveying it from the cylinder towards the end of
" the wooden frame where the sheet is removed." The second
set " are employed solely for the purpose of assisting in bearing
" up the paper, after it has been printed, and in conveying it from
" the cylinder (near to which the paper is brought upon them) to "
a wooden frame. The third set " are used for the purpose of
" detaching the sheets from the tympan sheet, to which they are
" liable to adhere on the reiteration of the paper." The dropping
roller's action is caused by a cam below the press.

" During the reiteration we place two similar points . . upon
" the feeding board, . . in such a position . . relatively to the
" printing machine as that, when the two holes in each sheet are
" applied to the two points upon the feeding board, the front
" edge of the sheet when so laid will lie over the roller," below
the dropping roller, " be conducted as described before, and . .
" (in the common phrase among printers) be in register."

[Printed, 1s. 11d. Drawings. Rolls Chapel Reports, 8th Report, p. 127,
Rolls Chapel.]

## A.D. 1818, April 23.—N° 4249.

APPLEGATH, AUGUSTUS.—" Certain improvements in the art
" of casting stereotype or other plates for printing, and in the
" construction of plates for printing bank or bankers' notes, or
" other printed impressions where difficulty of imitation is a
" desideratum." (a)

(a) The page is set up " in the ordinary manner, observing
" to use the high spaces and quadrats commonly employed in
" stereotyping, as also metal furniture or bars round the page."
The chase, type, moulding frame, and a " back plate" are
attached to the lower end of a " striking rod," which is wound
up so as to be about eight inches above a wooden block. On this
block the metal is poured in a dry cartridge paper tray. " As it
" becomes cool, and just in the point between fusion and fixity,"
the workman nimbly disengages the " . . pall of a ratchet wheel,
when the striking rod instantly descends by the action of springs,
and causes the type and moulding frame to form an impression
on the semi-fluid metal " in the same manner as sealing wax
" receives the impression of the seal."

(a) Ante, p. 94.

" (b) To strike a plate from the metallic mould." The mould,
moulding frame, and back plate are attached to the striking rod,
" and the operation of striking the plate is precisely the same as
" that of striking the mould, namely, in the semi-fluid or half-
" set metal." The mould should be brushed over with dry
soap and red ochre previous to casting to prevent the stereotype
sticking to it. The back of the plate is turned true in a lathe.

" (c) I form a mould from a stereotype plate or from a
" copper plate by placing such plate upon the back plate . . .
" with the mould frame, and proceeding in the manner before set
" forth, and from such mould I cast other plates in the manner
" described in that part of my specification marked (b)."

" (d) In the application of this my invention to the construction
" of plates for printing bank or bankers' notes, or any printed
" impressions wherein difficulty of imitation is a desideratum, I
" proceed by forming an original plate or block in which I avail
" myself of both relief and creux engraving on metal, whether
" performed by hand or by machinery, such as rose engine or
" eccentric turning, and sometime I form the original of several
" or many distinct pieces of engraved metal, which I unite into
" one page or form, either by soldering at the back or by locking
" up in a chace or frame."

"The original being formed, I strike, in the manner described in
" that part of my specification marked (a), as many matrices as
" may be required, . . and from these matrices I again strike,
" in the manner represented at (b), the printing plates."

[Printed, 7d. Drawings. Repertory of Arts, vol. 36 (second series), p. 69 ;
Rolls Chapel Reports, 8th Report, p. 123. Rolls Chapel.]

### A.D. 1819, May 24.—N° 4375.

RUTT, WILLIAM.—" Certain improvements on printing ma-
" chines, which improvements do not extend to the inking
" apparatus."

The type table is driven continuously to and fro along the press
by means of a mangle wheel, or crank and rod. On each side
of the type table are racks which take into partially toothed spur
wheels on the pressing cylinder so as to drive with an interrupted
motion. It is stopped and started without jar by means of a
spring upon the pressing cylinder, and a series of peculiarly
arranged levers upon the type table, acted on by a stud on
the pressing cylinder. Portions of it (the cylinder and spur

wheel) are removed at three equal intervals to allow of the return of the type table, the pressing cylinder making one complete revolution for three impressions. The remaining parts of the cylinder are clothed with blanketing covered with a cambric and furnished with register points. The inking apparatus is also driven by the type table's motion. Composition inking rollers are used. The distributing roller has endwise motions given to it by revolving in screw bearings. The sheet is laid upon the top of the cylinder during an interval of rest, and, as the cylinder moves, is carried along with it between two sets of silk bands to the impression, after which it is discharged by two others on to a set of four ribbons, from which it is removed by hand.

[Printed, 1s. 2d. Drawings. Rolls Chapel Reports, 8th Report, p. 132. Rolls Chapel. Hansard's Typographia, p. 696.]

### A.D. 1819, October 11.—N° 4400.

PERKINS, JACOB.—(Communicated). "Certain machinery and " implements applicable to ornamental turning and engraving, " and to the transferring of engraved or other work from the sur- " face of one piece of metal to another piece of metal, and to the " forming of metallic dies and matrices; and also improvements " in the construction and method of using plates and presses for " printing bank notes and other papers, whereby the producing " and combining various species of work is effected upon the " same plates and surfaces, the difficulty of imitation increased, " and the process of printing facilitated; and also an improved " method of making and using dies and presses for coining " money, stamping medals, and other useful purposes."

The specification describes:—1. An engine lathe for engraving oval or circular geometrical figures upon flat, convex, or concave surfaces, the peculiarity in which consists in producing a lateral motion of the mandrell by means of an excentric cylinder or other shaped body upon a separate axis, and of varying the number of lateral motions of the mandril during one revolution by means of wheels of various diameters.

2. An engine lathe for engraving certain figures on the peripheries of metal and other cylinders, the novelty of which consists in producing the longitudinal motion of the mandril by a different modification of the same expedient.

3. "Horizontal vibrating lever press." On the upper surface of an adjustable bed is placed the copper or steel plate to receive

the impression. "The die or roller consists of a hollow steel
" cylinder fitted upon a steel axis, which is formed into two cylin-
" drical necks on each side of the roller. . . . A brass bearing
" box, in gaps or notches of which the necks of the roller's axis
" are received, is secured on the under-side of a vibrating lever.
" . . . Each end of the axis of the die or roller is made square,
" on which squares fit . . . square gaps made in the ends
" of the die lever or double spanner, . . . and by means of
" which the die or roller can be turned backwards and forwards
" upon the surface of the steel or copper plate." The pressure
is given by a weight below the press table, and communicated
by a combination of levers to the vibrating lever by means
of upright bars at either end of it. "The length of this press
" ought to be at least fifteen feet, in order to allow the vibrating
" lever to move sufficiently near to a straight line to answer its
" intended purpose. The difference, however, between its motion
" and a straight line is compensated for partly by the materials,
" viz., wood, of which its frame consists, but chiefly by the accom-
" modating motion of the levers, and it therefore becomes neces-
" sary in using it to place it so as to pass through the floor of the
" work-room."

4. " Improved steel or copper plate or block printing press. The
" principal improvements consist in a new method of heating the
" plate or block, in the use of a tympan for the purpose of saving
" the expence of making the plates or blocks any larger than is
" necessary to receive the engraving, as well as to save ink, and
" also time and labour in cleaning the plates or blocks." The
tympan is a wooden frame covered with copper, turning upon
hinges, " and having an aperture in it large enough to enclose the
" plate or block, the sides of which aperture are made feather-
" edged, so as to overlap the bevelled edges of the plate or block
" and prevent them from soiling the paper." The cast-iron part of
the bed of the press, with the plate or block upon it, is heated by
means of a block of cast iron, replaced from time to time. The
frame of the press is inclined. "The intention of this inclination
" is to cause the bed to return after the impression is made of its
" own accord." The roller is cut away to admit of this return of
the bed, during which it is supported in its position by a peculiar
contrivance.

5. "Cylindrical steel or copper plate printing press." The
plates are fixed on a main cylinder, below which is a small cast-iron

pressing cylinder, over which and a similar cylinder at the other end of the press passes an endless web. The plates are inked as they revolve by a roller furnished from distributing rollers, one of which "receives the ink in the usual manner of machine typo-" graphic printing presses from a trough and ductor." The ink is more uniformly distributed over the plates by a hand roller used by a workman. Another ductor is supported by brackets at each end of it to the main standards " in the usual manner of calico " printing machines," scraping or taking off the "larger portion " of the ink lying upon the surfaces of the plates, the remainder " being removed by several persons wiping it off in succession, " and finally cleaning their surfaces much in the same way as " in copper-plate printing. The paper properly moistened may " be either laid upon the revolving web in sheets," or printed in roll.

6. "Circular coining press." The upper coining die and male cutter is fixed in the circumference of a cast-iron cylinder, a cast-iron bed containing the lower coining die and female cutter. The cylinder is applied on the under side of a vibrating lever in the press described above (3). A groove is made round the cylinder to admit the slips of metal out of which the pieces are to be cut and coined to pass freely. The cylinder revolves upon the bed, the latter having a conical perforation partly through it to receive a "conical elastic wedge" and steel cylindrical ring or female cutter, and a cylindrical hole at the bottom of the conical per-foration to permit the lower die to move freely up and down in it. The slip of metal is first cut into a circular blank by the male cutter or edge of the upper coining die as it revolves passing into the female cutter "at the same time the dies give the " impression on each side of the blank, and when the cylinder " has passed," a lever, by means of a weighted cord, raises the lower die with the coin upon it a little above the top of the female cutter, "and it is carried forwards in the hole in the slip of metal " out of which it was pressed or cut and thrown off in its passage." The strip of metal is prevented from clinging to the upper die . . . by two small hooks (upon the bed), under which the slip is passed.

The part of the plate decarbonated for the purpose of trans-ferring, should not be more than three times the depth of the engraving. To decarbonate it, it should be placed vertically (covered with pure iron filings) in a close cast-iron box, and exposed for four hours to a white heat, and suffered to cool gradually. In order to re-convert the plate, &c. into steel, it is laid (in heated charcoal of leather) in a close box, and kept somewhat above a red heat from three to five hours, plunged vertically into cold water, then heated and plunged into water again.

An engraving of any sort having been made upon a decarbonated plate, and the same re-converted into steel, a transfer of such engraving is made on the decarbonated surface of a steel cylinder or circular die, in such a manner that the surface of the said cylinder becomes an exact counterpart of the aforesaid engraved plate; and this, " when hardened, may be used for " making other cylinders or circular dies almost to an indefinite " extent."

[Printed, 4s. 2d. Drawings. London Journal (Newton's), vol. 1, p. 159 ; Mechanics' Magazine, vol. 6, p. 508. Rolls Chapel.]

A.D. 1819, November 1.—N° 4404 (six).

CONGREVE, Sir WILLIAM.—" An improved mode of inlaying " or combining different metals or other hard substances, appli- " cable to various useful purposes."

A metallic or other surface capable of withstanding the heat of melted metal, " being pierced into any filagree work or pattern " intended, a metal softer than itself, when two metals are used, " or any metal where the plate is formed of corresponding " material, is then fluxed or run at the back of the principal " plate so as to form a second plate, penetrating and filling " all the filagree or interstices of the pattern." When cleaned off and polished, these surfaces in combination may be used for ornamenting furniture, &c., " or it may be made so that " the two or more plates or substances may be separated after " having been thus accurately, and as it may be termed mathe- " matically adapted, by making the filagree work so that it will " deliver the second plate after cooling; in which case it may be " applied to obtain a guage of actual identities of form, which " might be of great importance in determining the genuineness of " hard money. It might also, when made to separate, be applied " to printing in two or more colours, (a) by forming a compound " plate capable of separating after being engraved upon to " receive different colours on the different parts, and then " uniting those parts so as to print all these different combina-

(a) See ante, No. 1575, and post, No. 4521.

" tions of colour at once.    This mode may also " be success-
" fully applied to produce a new description of work, which
" could only be imitated in the way in which it was produced,
" and which, therefore, would tend to throw very great difficul-
" ties in the way of the forgery of bank notes or other docu-
" ments which it is desirable to protect."

[Printed, 3d.  No Drawing.  Repertory of Arts, vol. 42 (second series), p. 272;
London Journal (Newton's), vol. 1, p. 241.  Petty Bag.]

## A.D. 1820, January 25.—Nº 4433.

TREADWELL, DANIEL.—" Certain improvements in the con-
" struction of printing presses."   By a peculiar combination of
levers, toggle joint, &c. with "a peculiar mode of using a treadle,
" the pressman is enabled to take an impression by the weight
" of his body in descending from a certain plane of elevation,
" and " is assisted in recovering his position " by the reaction of
" all those elastic bodies which his descent had depressed."

" " The platen is of cast iron; the upper side of it is surrounded
" with ribs, and crossed by others cast with it, one piece," and
in order to diffuse the pressure as uniformly as possible, bars
of cast iron or steel are arranged in a pyramidal shape, their
lower ends resting in concavities made in the tops of the ribs
of the plattin, and their upper ends are united and surrounded
by a rim under a cap.    The cap is pressed upon for the
impression by the shorter end of a great beam in connexion
with the treadle by means of a moving arm united with the
beam by a toggle joint.    The platen is hinged to the side
of the coffin.    There is a contrivance which draws the arm out
of the way when the platen is turned back (to ink the form),
and brings it on to the cap when the impression is to be
given.    After the impression, the pressman recovers his position
by a slight exertion of the muscles of that leg which did not
sustain his weight in giving the impression, aiding the re-action
of all the elastic bodies which his descent has compressed.    The
platen is counterbalanced by weights and springs arranged in a
peculiar manner so as not to oscillate or have " any considerable
" vis inertia to oppose to a quick motion."

Revolving friskets, by means of which the sheet can be turned
over for printing on the other side in printing half-sheet wise.

[Printed, 1s. 1d.   Drawings.   London Journal (Newton's), vol. 1, p. 321.
Rolls Chapel.   Hansard's Typographia, p. 660.]

## A.D. 1820, January 25.—N° 4434.

BRUNEL, MARC ISAMBARD.— " Certain improvements in
" making stereotype plates," which consists in the means used,
(1), for taking moulds from the original plate of types or woodcuts; and (2), for obtaining the cast or the printing plate from
the said mould; the object of the invention being to multiply
" printing plates for the purpose of accelerating the printing of
" daily papers."(a)  A layer of composition [pipeclay (7), chalk

---

(a) Some persons are of opinion that the origin of newspapers is to be found in
the *Acta Diurna* of the Romans, although it was not until the sixteenth century
that any publication approaching to that character existed in modern times.
The war between the Venetian Republic and the Turks in 1536, gave rise to a
practice of communicating military and commercial news from written documents to parties assembling at a particular place and paying a coin called
*gazetta* (hence gazette). Thirty volumes of these MSS. newspapers exist in the
Magliabecchi Library at Florence.

The first English newspaper appeared in the reign of Queen Elizabeth. The
date of the earliest known (a copy is in the British Museum), relating to the
descent of the Spanish Armada, is July 23, 1558; its title is "*The English
Mercurie*, published by authoritie for the prevention of false reports, imprinted
by Christopher Barker, Her Highness's printer." From the numbers 50, 51,
and 54, found in respective early copies, it has been conjectured that there
had been earlier numbers of the same series. (Chalmers' Life of Ruddiman.)
Disraeli, in the preface to the 13th edition of the Curiosities of Literature,
treats this copy as a clearly established forgery. "In the British Museum,
indeed," he says, "George Chalmers found the printed 'English Mercurie,' but
there also, it now appears, he might have seen the *original*, with all its corrections before it was sent to the press, written on paper of modern fabric."

In the reign of James I. (1622), appeared the *London Weekly Courant*, and in
the year 1643 (the period of the civil war) were printed a variety of publications
certainly in no respect entitled to the name of newspapers. (Haydn's Dictionary
of Dates, Art. Newspapers.) "The country at this period," says a writer in the
Encyclopædia Britannica (Art. Newspapers), "overflowed with tracts of every
size and of various denominations, many of them written with great ability and
displaying uncommon courage. Mercury, however, was the prevailing title,
although generally qualified with some epithet, and the quaintness peculiar to
the age is curiously exemplified in the names of some of the 'news books,' as
The Dutch Spye, The Scots Dove, The Parliament Kite, The Secret Owle,
Heraclitus Redrus, The Parliament Vulture, The Parliament Screech Owle, The
Loyal Scout, and so forth. A catalogue of the different Mercuries would exhibit
a curious picture of those singular times; Mercurius Acheronticus brought
hebdomadal tidings from the inferior regions; Mercurius Democritus communicated marvellous intelligence from the world in the moon; the Laughing
Mercury gave exact information of proceedings at the antipodes; and the
Mercurius Mastix lashed unmercifully all other Mercuries, Scouts, Posts, Spies,
Discoverers, and Intelligencers." (See also observations in Macaulay's History
of England, vol. iv. p. 521, and 601-607.) The Restoration and the Revolution led
each to the establishment of a number of newspapers, all of which have long
disappeared. The first among them which can claim to be considered as a
vehicle of general information was the *Public Intelligencer*. It continued for
about three years, but ceased on the appearance of the *London Gazette* (still
existing), the first number of which was published at Oxford, Nov. 7, 1665, and
afterwaads in London, Feb. 5, 1666, Haydn. The printing of newspapers and
pamphlets was prohibited, 31 Charles II. 1680.  *Salmon's Chron.*

The first daily paper in England was the *Daily Courant*, published in 1709.
It appeared every day but Sunday. For a considerable time it occupied the
field alone; at length two rivals appeared in the *Daily Post* and in the *Daily
Journal*, and in 1724 we find these papers were simultaneously published.
Little change seems to have taken place during the reign of George I., but in

(12), and starch (1),] is spread on a perforated steel plate hinged to the galley of type and brought repeatedly upon the said type, a wet skin or calico being interposed at the first closing; thin sheets of paper (gradually removed) in the subsequent ones; on the last being removed the impression should be perfect. Or the composition may be spread on a cylinder, and rolled with similar interposition of substances over the galley; after which it is taken from the cylinder and unrolled so as to produce the required flat mould.

For making a casting, the mould is placed face upwards in a perforated heated tray. A " regulating plate," with overlapping edges, is laid upon it, and the metal (for expedition, an alloy of bismuth (10), lead (6), and tin (4),) poured into the tray, when it " makes its way round and under the regulating plate." Water injected through the holes in the tray cools the casting. The extra metal round the regulating plates breaks off almost of itself. The composition is washed off, and the plate is fit for the press. It is " blocked up " by the use of wax hardened with resin.

For very fine castings the mould is placed in a closed and heated cast-iron cylinder, placed horizontally. The metal is poured through a hole in the top, which is immediately afterwards closed. A communication is then opened between the cylinder and a vessel full of condensed air, " which produces the effect of " a head of metal." Water is then injected, and the metal set. The mould, when dry, retains sufficient flexibility to assume a cylindrical form, and plates of that shape may be cast by placing the mould in a box formed of parallel plates of the required radius.

---

that of George II. every kind of periodical increased abundantly. The number of newspapers annually sold in England, according to an average of three years ending with 1753, was 7,411,757, in 1760 it amounted to 9,464,790, in 1767 it rose to 11,300,980, in 1790 it was as high as 14,035,636, and in 1792 to 15,005,760.

Newspapers were first stamped in 1713.

" The word is not, as many imagine, derived from the adjective new. In former years (between the years 1595 and 1730), it was a prevalent practice to put over the periodical publications of the day the initial letters of the cardinal points of the compass, thus—

importing that those papers contained intelligence from the four quarters of the globe, and from this practice is derived the term of newspaper." Haydn's Dict. of Dates, Art. "News."

" A plate, possessing all the properties of a stereotype plate,"
may be formed by coating a thin plate of iron with shellac,
which is afterwards hardened by heat. This being immersed in
fused type metal, " comes out tinned as it were;" and being
applied to and pressed together with the mould plate while the
metal coating is fluid, a " remarkably perfect" impression is
obtained. " The same plate may be made to take another or
" several successive impressions by repeating at each time the
" immersion into type metal, and proceeding as stated above."

[Printed, 4d. No Drawing. London Journal (Newton's), vol. 1, p. 334. Rolls
Chapel.]

### A.D. 1820, January 25.—N° 4435 (two).

MOODY, John.—" An inkstand containing carbonaceous and
" extractive matter in a dry state, which, with the addition of
" water only, will supply ink."

Within an outer casing of metal is " introduced a small vessell,
" which may be made of lead, earthenware, or glass, with a hole
" to admit a pen, in which the composition is placed, and the
" whole of the interior is filled up with a cement," composed of
lamp black and melted sulphur. The " composition is made of
honey, eggs, strong extract of galls, gum arabic, sugar candy,
indigo, logwood, lamp black, charcoal, and sulphate; . . . .
" knead the whole well together in a marble mortar into stiff paste,
" which put into the stands and let it harden in the air, over which
" paste must be placed a small quantity of cotton that has pre-
" viously been soaked in vinegar, that has been well saturated
" with salt."

[Printed, 3d. No Drawing. London Journal (Newton's), vol. 1, p. 248.
Petty Bag.]

### A.D. 1820, May 15.—N° 4463 (four).

WATTS, Richard.—" Improvements in inking printing types
" with rollers, and in placing and conveying paper on types, and
" in inking with a cylinder."

A frisket frame carries two or more composition inking rollers,
which ink the types twice previous to the impression, and then
come into contact with the " inking cylinder " as the distributing
roller on the far side of the press frame is pushed across the press,
and the paper which is laid on it is kept clear of the form by

double springs beneath it. The impression is given by a loaded cylinder which travels along the press, and is received by elastic cushions at each end. All parts of this machine are united in motion.

[Printed, 1s. Drawings. London Journal (*Newton's*), vol. 2, p. 263. Rolls Chapel.]

## A.D. 1820, May 18.—Nº 4464 (four).

WINCH, ROBERT.—" A machine or press, chiefly applicable to " printing."

Two pressing cylinders roll one on each side of a double inclined plane, being driven by chains passing over a cylinder at the top of the incline. The mode of clothing the cylinders is described. The forms of type or stereotype plates are laid on plates on the faces of each plane. Elasticity of impression is obtained by means of wooden ledges raised one-sixteenth of an inch above the metal ways on which the cylinders run. Each of the pressing cylinders are fitted with a pair of metal arms, one on each side, in each of which is an inking roller and a distributor (with screw bearings) above. Toothed wheels on the ends of the pressing cylinders take into racks along the sides of the planes. At the ends of these arms are fingers or toothed pieces, which play over ratchet wheels fixed to metal trough rollers (with ductors) placed at each end of the inking roller's path. There are two distributing boards to each plane (between the forms and troughs). Four pairs of arms fixed on axes turning in holes in the sides of the frame support the feeding boards. Catches upon these arms at certain periods fall down and detain the pressing cylinders, which, by returning, draw down the feeding boards, when a sheet hanging over them is caught between seizing rollers on the pressing cylinder, which are elevated for that purpose by a peculiar arrangement. Each board is furnished with " regulating slips " and register points, withdrawn by a peculiar arrangement for laying on. Tapes (moving by friction with the pressing cylinders) convey the sheet from the seizing rollers for the impression. The sheets are discharged by the action of metal flaps upon the seizing rollers opposite to those at which they are fed in. The catches are released as soon as the paper is laid hold of by the seizing rollers, and the feeding boards recover their position by counterweights.

[Printed, 1s. 1d. Drawings. London Journal (*Newton's*), vol. 2, p. 25. Petty Bag.]

A.D. 1820, December 22.—N° 4521.

CONGREVE, Sir WILLIAM.—" Certain improvements in print-
" ing in one, two, or more colours."

1. For one color. The form is fixed on a table; the pressing
cylinder is in a carriage with three inking rollers and a messenger
roller. The latter as the carriage moves to and fro takes ink from
a trough roller (with ratchet wheel motion) at the end of the
press and distributes it upon a table, from which it is taken by
the inking rollers. The latter pass twice over the form for each
impression. The pressing cylinder prints in one direction only,
clearing the form on its return, in consequence of a portion of its
surface on one side being removed. Its motion is continuous,
owing to the action of rising and falling racks which gear with the
cylinder alternately as it comes or goes. The sheet is fed in from
endless tapes on a paper carriage (driven backwards by the printing carriage, and drawn forwards by a weight), and is conveyed to
the impression by endless tapes. The sheet is discharged on to an
endless cloth, travelling with the printing carriage, and dropped
by it on a receiving table " beyond the limits of the machine."

2. For printing in colors. The printing surface is a combination of two or more plates, (a) according to the number of colors
to be printed, forming, when united, a single printing surface. By
peculiar mechanism the surfaces separate to be coloured and descend to different levels, where they are passed over by inking
rollers connected with separate inking apparatus, on the same
principle as the above, and united on rising again so as to form a
single printing surface for the impression.

A drawing is given of a machine on this principle, " as now
" actually in use at Somerset House, for the new coloured stamps
" of the country bank notes." It differs in some trifling details
from that above described, but chiefly in having an additional set
of endless bands to discharge the sheet, and a fan roller to ensure
its quitting the cylinder.

3. " Double printing press," printing both with the forward and
backward motion of the printing carriage. Two pressing cylinders,
furnished similarly to those above described, are on a printing
carriage, with a messenger roller at each end, furnished as before,
and one set of inking rollers between the cylinders. The inking

---

(a) Ante, No. 4404.

tables are circular and horizontal, and revolve. The machine may be used for colours. Is calculated to produce forty impressions per minute.

4. " Another variation of this principle of printing press, where
" the forms or plates are at rest, and the printing cylinder in
" motion, is equally practicable by the arrangement of two printing
" cylinders, for turning paper from one cylinder to the other, so as
" to print on both sides. In this case the two forms must be at
" the extremities of the machine, and the two printing cylinders in
" the centre of it."

[Printed, 1s. 3d. Drawings. London Journal (*Newton's*), vol. 1, p. 209, and vol. 3, p. 9. Rolls Chapel.]

A.D. 1820, December 22.—N° 4522.

BRUNEL, MARC ISAMBARD.—" Pocket copying press."

The bed of the machine is of gun metal and the pressing surface of wood. The latter is backed by a steel spring plate, which is screwed to it, the ends of the plate resting on ledges, and the pressure given by two levers in combined action. Under the bottom of the press bed is a box or recess, which contains the damping apparatus, consisting of a metal cylinder wrapped round with several sheets of linen or other suitable material of the same size as the sheets of paper intended to be operated upon, and also a sponge for damping the linen. The original writing is put into a transferring book, and a blank leaf laid upon it. A sheet of the damped linen is then laid upon the blank leaf, and upon this a sheet of oiled paper. The book is then placed under the pressing surface, and the pressure given to the upper lever by hand.

[Printed, 6d. Drawings. London Journal (*Newton's*), vol. 2, p. 248. Rolls Chapel.]

A.D. 1821, July 3.—N° 4565.

CHURCH, WILLIAM.—" An improved apparatus for printing."

The invention consists:—First, in an improved mode of obtaining the pressure required for printing letter-press from types or stereotype plates. Secondly, in a new arrangement of the inking apparatus applicable thereto. And, thirdly, " in a new mode of
" raising and pulling down the frisket upon the tympan, and also
" of taking off the paper at the same time." The platen is hinged on to strong springs at the back of the coffin, which give elasticity to the impression. To the top of the platen is hinged a lever

heavily weighted at its upper end. It turns in standards at the press-head, and assumes a vertical position for the impression. The type table is run in and out by means of two chains wound on to the rounce in opposite directions. The one is fastened to the end of a steel bar hinged at its other end to one end of the type table, and the other to the other end. On the coffin receding from the press-head the platen is raised and the lever falls over. The inking apparatus (vertically disposed) is in continuous motion, and is driven from the rounce. The ductor roller is brought down at intervals by a treadle (recovering itself by a weight) on to a feeding roller, in contact with a distributing roller with double-threaded screws at one end of it, revolving in "nippers" brought into action alternately. The inking rollers are caused to rise while the table is at rest, so as to be furnished from the distributor, and when the table is run in to descend and ink the form. The frisket is raised by a convolute spring, similar to a watch spring, coiled round the joint of the tympan and frisket, and brought down by a string, connecting an excentric wheel at the joint of the frisket and tympan, with another at the joint of the platen and table. There is a contrivance for discharging the sheet, which consists of a tongue introduced between the frisket and platen.

[Printed, 10d. Drawings. London Journal (Newton's), vol. 3, p. 57. Rolls Chapel.]

## A.D. 1821, July 17.—N° 4570.

COOPER, SAMUEL, and MILLER, WILLIAM.—" Certain im-
" provements on printing machines."

The machine specified is called "The British and Foreign Press." The form is in a carriage running from end to end of the press, where it is received on spiral springs. The carriage is driven by chains passed round the pressing cylinder, the latter being driven by some first mover. At each end of the type table is a trough roller with ratchet motion and ductor. A messenger roller is brought at intervals into contact with each trough roller by the action of the machine. These messenger rollers are "pressed upon by two solid iron ink-distributing " rollers," to which endwise motion is given by their action upon annular inclined planes on each end of the pressing cylinder. The solid iron rollers are in contact with the inking rollers by the friction with which they are driven. The inking rollers are driven by catgut bands from the pressing cylinder. The sheet is fed in alternately from one of two feeding tables on standards, a register frame rising and falling at appropriate intervals by the alternate action of a lever and weight. This lever also imparts motion to a roller, which seizes the sheet from the feeding table and passes it between the tapes which conduct it to the impression. To facilitate its entrance between those tapes by which it is conveyed to the impression, "upper conductors" or knives are employed, and the paper being received between the endless types and the cylinders, is next carried between "lower "conductors" or knives; after receiving the impression, the paper meets the rounded ends of receiving bars.

[Printed, 1s. 2d. Drawings. London Journal (Newton's), vol. 3, p. 227 ; Register of Arts and Sciences, vol. 2, p. 120. Rolls Chapel.]

### A.D. 1821, July 26.—N° 4573.

BARCLAY, DAVID.—(Communicated.) — "A spiral lever or "rotary standard press."

The "rotary standard" consists of a system of inclined planes and rollers. One inclined plane ("elevated at that end which is towards the front of the press") is affixed to the top of the platen, and another with an opposite incline to the top of the frame above it. In these planes are two notches, into which are fitted rollers furnished with a flange at each end. A wedge having notches similar to and corresponding with the former ones, "the rollers will rise out of the grooves and pass along "the inclined planes, . . . while the thickest part of the wedge "coming under the rollers at the same time, the platen becomes "necessarily depressed to make room for it." The platen is raised after each operation by "spiral levers." Two modes are given of operating with the wedge, (1) with a quadrant at the end of the lever (handle), "over which passes a chain, one end of "the said chain being attached to the lever, and the other end "to" a part of the wedge; and (2) by a compound lever.

[Printed, 9d. Drawings. Repertory of Arts, vol. 46 (second series), p. 129 ; London Journal (Newton's), vol. 3, p. 175. Rolls Chapel.]

### A.D. 1821, October 18.—N° 4594 (two).

FERGUSSON, JAMES.—"Improvements upon, additions to, or "substitutes for certain materials or apparatus made use of in the "process of printing from stereotype plates."

Instead of (the practice then) using "blocks, matrix plates,
"risers, &c." or performing the operation of "underlaying" or
"overlaying" in the case of stereotype plates, the patentee applies
beneath them "cork and any other elastic substance to all kinds
"of printing apparatus and machines, with a view of remedying
"the inequalities in the thickness of stereotype plates."

[Printed, 3d. No Drawing. Repertory of Arts, vol. 42 (*second series*), p. 257;
London Journal (*Newton's*), vol. 3, p. 16. Rolls Chapel.]

A.D. 1821, November 21.—N° 4619.

PARKIN, Thomas.— "An improvement or improvements in
"printing."

The inking roller is furnished from a table on which the ink is
distributed by a peculiar arrangement of cords and pulleys.
A "furnishing roller" is caused, each time that the inking roller
is pushed in a hand frame over the form, to spread a supply of
ink at right angles to the path of the inking roller. At each side
of the press the furnishing roller comes in contact with ink boxes,
the faces of which are covered with a material through which the
ink oozes slowly, and the surfaces of which are sometimes so
shaped as to fit the "furnishing roller."

[Printed, 9d. Drawings. London Journal (*Newton's*), vol. 5, p. 128. Rolls
Chapel.]

A.D. 1821, October 24.—N° 4601.

MARTIN, Thomas, and GRAFTON, Charles. — "Making
"fine light black of very superior colour, which for distinction
"from other blacks we call spirit black, and a new apparatus for
"producing the same."

Coal tar, freed as far as possible from ammoniacal liquor and
acid held in solution, as also of mineral pitch, is poured into a
main pipe of an apparatus (heated by a flue running beneath
it) and connected with smaller pipes projecting upwards from
it about a foot. The tar being poured in till the surface is
nearly even with the top of the smaller pipes and the flue
heated to 130°, the tar can be lighted, and will burn freely in
the small tubes. The smoke arising from this combustion passes
through various pipes into canvas bags, from seventy to eighty
in number, "if more the better." The bags are occasionally
shaken; and when a sufficient quantity of black is collected,
they are untied, and the black removed for use.

[Printed, 7d. Drawings. Repertory of Arts, vol. 43 (*second series*), p. 257;
London Journal (*Newton's*), vol. 4, p. 73. Petty Bag.]

A.D. 1822, January 14.—N° 4640.

**APPLEGATH, Augustus.**—" Improvements in printing ma-
" chines."

The improvements consist, first, in applying the ink to the
form of types, plates, or blocks, " partly on one side of the
" impressing or printing cylinder and partly on the other side."
By this means " the motion of the form is lessened and the quan-
" tity of impressions taken in any given period may be increased
" in the ratio of the diminution of motion," and this not only
in those cases in which the form is caused to pass under the printing
cylinder and inking rollers, but also in those cases in which the
printing cylinder and inking rollers are caused to pass over the
form.

Secondly, in " the combination of two paper feeders with a
" printing cylinder which prints in one direction only." On
each side at the top of the pressing cylinder are two drums
equal in circumference to half that of the pressing cylinder. By
the action of a pin in a centre wheel upon arms attached to
two others symmetrically disposed, sheets are fed in above each
drum by an endless web and conducted to the impression and
discharged by endless tapes.

[Printed, 6d. Drawings. London Journal (*Newton's*), vol. 4, p. 57. Rolls
Chapel.]

A.D. 1822, January 29.—N° 4642.

**CONGREVE, Sir William.**—"Improved methods of multi-
" plying facsimile impressions to any extent."

The first has reference to letter-press work. Stereotype plates
from a form of matrix types of "brass or other such metal," such
form being "run, together with a thin sheet of prepared pewter or
" other soft metal fit for the purpose, through a rolling press
" similar to a copper-plate press, but stronger. It is evident a very
" small quantity of this letter in creux would supply the place of a
" very extensive font. Almost any number of these plates may be
" produced after the matter is set up almost as rapidly as impressions
" may be pulled on paper in a common printing press."

" The second plan for the multiplication of facsimile impressions
" applies to copper-plate work, and is not limited in dimensions
" like the plans at present in use. The original may be engraved
" on a flat surface of any size and transferred to a second flat

" surface also of any size, and from thence laid down as copies of
" the original upon any number of other flat surfaces by the use
" of plates of different gradations of hardness, as hard and soft
" steel and copper, or soft steel, copper or brass, and pewter.
" The second flat surface should be a thin plate, when a sufficient
" pressure will be obtained to produce the transfers, whatever may
" be the dimensions of the plate, by merely passing the plate
" through a rolling press . . .    such as that above mentioned
"    . . .   the rollers of which need not exceed 3 or 4 inches in
" diameter.   The size of the plates whereof the facsimiles may be
" thus multiplied is evidently not limited, as it necessarily is where
" the second impression is taken upon the outside of a cylinder."

[Printed, 3*d*.  No Drawing.  London Journal (*Newton's*), vol. 5, p. 185.  Rolls
  Chapel.]

A.D. 1822, March 24.—N⁰ 4664.

CHURCH, WILLIAM.—"An improved apparatus for printing."

1. Machine for casting the types and arranging them ready
to be transferred to the composing machinery.  A matrix bar,
containing a series of matrices, is applied to a mould bar with
a corresponding number of moulds.   At the time of casting,
the latter is applied to jets leading from the metal chest, which
is supplied from a metal fountain connected with the metal pot,
and furnished with a valve to prevent the return of the metal.
After the casting, the mould bar, drawn endways, cuts off communication with the metal, and brings the said types beneath a
series of punches, which descend and force them out at the same
time that the matrix bar is unlocked and descends clear of the
types.  The types descend into " guides," twisted one-quarter
round in order to bring the bodies of the types side by side, " in the
" same manner as when placed together in a line by a compositor."
The mould bar is kept cool during the process by a stream of water
passing through it.   The matrix bar is then locked up, and the
metal bar slidden back for another casting.  The metal is injected
by the descent of a plunger in the metal chest.  The movements
of each part of this machine are caused by the action of cams upon
the main shaft.

Modification of the above, in which several of the operations are
performed by hand.

2. The types are arranged in " files " in a case at the top of the
machine, each file being directly over a slit in a horizontal frame.

One of a " number of jacks" protrudes through each of these slits, each jack being connected with a key " in a manner somewhat " similar to the jacks and keys of an harpsichord." On the depression of any particular key, the upper part of its jack pushes forward the undermost type of the file into a " race," to the centre of which it is swept by collectors, so as to come under the beak of a lever by which it is pushed down an aperture answering the purpose of a composing stick. The mechanism for performing these various movements is moved by clockwork started by the depression of the key.

3. The inking rollers are in a frame, and are supplied from a distributing table with lateral movement, to which, at each movement of the frame, ink is transferred by the hindermost inking roller from an endless band in connexion with a trough, and having a ratchet movement consequent on that of the roller frame. The latter is driven to and fro over the form by means of an endless cord connected in a peculiar manner with the axle of a fly wheel, and having proceeded nearly over the form locks by means of a slider with the frisket frame and carries it under the platen. The impression is given by the rising of the type table by a knee lever or descent of the platen. The printed sheet is then removed by nippers on endless bands passing over and under the platen, and discharged. The register points are attached to the frisket " in a " manner similar to that by which they are attached to the tym- " pan of an ordinary press." The frisket is furnished with wedges which drop into corresponding recesses in the platen or the table, and thus ensure perfect register.

[Printed, 4s. 6d. Drawings. London Journal (*Newton's*), vol. 6, pp. 225 and 281. Rolls Chapel.]

## A.D. 1822, July 4.—N° 4690.

BOLD, JOHN.—" Certain improvements in printing."

Quadruple printing machine. The only fixed parts in this machine are the type tables and trough rollers. Of the latter there are three, one in the middle, and the others one at each end of the press. They are on a level below the type tables. Above each of these trough rollers is a furnishing roller. A carriage contains all the remaining parts of the press, consisting of two pressing cylinders (furnished with tapes), each with a double inking apparatus of two inking rollers surmounted by a distributing roller.

The cylinders are loaded or pressed down by acting against an upper rail. As the carriage moves along, the spindles of the furnishing rollers act against inclined planes, and are thus raised to supply the inking rollers, the latter being in turn raised by inclined planes into contact with distributing rollers. The feeding apparatus consists of a "horse" on one side of each cylinder and a counterbalanced delivering board on the other. The sheet is laid on register points on the latter, and hangs down over a delivering roller immediately above the pressing cylinder. The feeding table being turned down by hand, the sheet is left on the delivering roller, from which it is taken by a "seizing roller" carried round by tapes for the impression, after which it is discharged by "stripping "rollers" (called into action alternately with the seizing rollers) on to a grating beneath the horses.

A drawing is given of a "double" machine on the same principle.

[Printed, 1s. 1d. Drawings. London Journal (*Newton's*), vol. 6, p. 11. Rolls Chapel.]

## A.D. 1823, February 18.—No 4757.

APPLEGATH, Augustus.—"Certain improvements in printing "machines."

The first relates to machines having ink tables or flat surfaces, upon which the ink is distributed by means of rollers, and consists in "an improved method of giving motion endways to such "rollers by placing them diagonally across the ink table . . "instead of placing them directly across, as is usual." The distribution on this plan may be increased by allowing metal rollers to revolve on the above in the same bearings.

The second consists in making the ink table or distributing surface flexible. "It may be either endless or not, and in some "cases may be rendered inflexible one way," by thin bars of wood, &c., "but so as to permit free motion in the direction "required." Two methods of applying the principle are shown in the drawings.

The third consists in inking the form "by means of a roller "or system of rollers attached to endless revolving chains or "revolving bands or any similar contrivance." It is intended to use this method "with an interrupted as well as with a

" continued motion, and also in conjunction with a flat distri-
" buting surface, or an endless flexible distributing surface," or
any other suitable one.

The fourth consists " in using a cylinder with flattened sides,
" or a prism of any number of sides, to give the impression to
" the paper in combination with a flat type table." The impression is given by the rising of the type table or the descent of
the cylinder or prism, and the paper is confined either by a frisket
with spring hinges, or "tapes, webs, or any other convenient
" method."

The fifth consists in using a " revolving prismatic tympan
" frame " having any number of tympans thereon. The impression is given by the descent of the platen and the rising of the
type table to the level of the tympan frame.

[Printed, 1s. 4d. Drawings. London Journal (*Newton's*), vol. 7, p. 7. Rolls
Chapel.]

A.D. 1823, February 18.—N° 4760.

CHURCH, William.—"An improved apparatus for printing, to
" be used by type block and plate printers."

1. The pattern is composed on a solid cylinder by types "set
" radiantly round it," and secured by rings fitting into nicks in
their sides, the whole being locked up by a collet and screw
cap at each end of the cylinder. In printing with one colour the
cylinder is used " nearly in the same way that engraved cylinders
" are used for printing," except that it is inked by " an elastic
" roller in a similar way to letter-press printing."

2. For printing in colors, three printing cylinders are arranged
round a pressing cylinder, each being furnished with a colouring
apparatus and placed at the proper distance for register. Between
these are a series of heated tubes revolving in bearings near the
pressing cylinder, so as to dry the fabric in passing from one impression to the other, and furnished with fans or vanes to circulate
the air, and partitions which convey the damp away. Tension is
effected by the pressure of a " friction lever " upon the axis of the
roller from which it is unwound, and a multiplied motion given
by an endless band to the roller on to which it passes after the
impression.

[Printed, 9d. Drawings. London Journal (*Newton's*), vol. 7, p. 57. Rolls
Chapel.]

A.D. 1823, March 18.—N° 4767.

HOPE, WILLIAM.—" Certain improvements in the construction
" of printing presses."

These consist in adding to the system of levers in the Stanhope
press an additional connecting rod and bent lever, "whereby it
" will be seen that I bring that well-known mechanical power
" approaching to an infinite power twice into action, . . whereas,
" in the Stanhope press as hitherto made, it is employed only
" once." Instead of employing "the male and female screws
" commonly used," two portions of circular inclined planes are
made upon the bolt of the press and two corresponding planes
on the slider. The lower part of the slider is made partly of a
spherical shape, and is lodged in a corresponding cavity made in
the centre of the platen, which is hung to the slider " in the
" usual manner by four screws and nuts." The platen recovers
itself by means of a counterbalancing weight affixed to a forked
lever turning upon fulcrums resting in gaps made in the guides
of the slider.

[Printed, 1s. Drawings. London Journal (*Newton's*), vol. 6, p. 72. Rolls
Chapel.]


A.D. 1823, April 22.—N° 4783 (four).

PALMER, WILLIAM.—" Certain improvements in machinery
" for the purpose of printing or staining paper for paper-
" hangings."

The paper is coiled upon a rod at one end of a long table, and
pressure is applied to it, so that its straight or cut edge after it is
uncoiled, is continually forced against a fixed guide, the guide
being so placed that the paper does not come in contact with it
until uncoiled. The paper is passed through the machine by
means of an endless web, against which it is held by a plain
roller. While being printed it rests upon a (clothed) stone slab
adjustable in height. The printing block frame is raised and
lowered by machinery above the table, pressure being given to it
by a " driving crank," and its parallel motion ensured by a
"principal crank" and a "parallel" crank. Color is furnished
to the blocks from a color apparatus in a " parallel frame " by
means of rollers rising and falling with the block frame, and

traversing the surface of the blocks during their rise and fall. The paper is, after each impression, advanced by the movement of the endless web, regulated by a drum fitted with an adjustable stop. To prevent the paper rising with the blocks, it is for a short time after the impression held down by " pressers " acted on by cams below.   " In printing with that kind of block commonly used " for borders, which are usually half the width of the paper, they " may be used on one side of the paper first, and then " the block carriage slidden along the " principal crank " neck, the other side be printed also.   " The paper is received from the machine by " boys, and hung up to dry in the usual manner."

[Printed, 1s. 2d.   Drawings.   London Journal (Newton's), vol. 6, p. 186. Rolls Chapel.]

## A.D. 1823, June 10.—N° 4801.

COWPER, EDWARD. — " Certain improvements in machines " and apparatus for printing calico, linen, silk, wool, paper, or " other substances capable of receiving printed impressions." 1. Moveable types, blocks, stereotype plates, &c. are placed on the flattened side of a " D cylinder," around which the color is dis- tributed by a series of treacle and glue or other rollers, which also furnish the types, &c. as the D cylinder revolves.   The impression is given by causing the D cylinder to advance to the cylinder round which the fabric is passed, and roll the block, form of types, &c. against it.   The above improvements are combined with " the essen- " tial parts of the ordinary calico copper-plate printing press."   The motion of the D cylinder's carriage to and from the fabric roller is consequent on the action of " pressure plates " upon its axis against friction rollers, supported by bars linked to the spindle of the fabric cylinder.   The block, &c. on the D cylinder gives its impression simultaneously with a copper plate furnished with colour in the ordinary way, and raised for the impression by the action of a second D cylinder.   Two D cylinders, furnished as above, may be employed at the same time.

2. Two or more blocks are placed on the surface of a prism, the patterns of such blocks being those of different colours in the same design.   The prism revolves at intervals, and the impression is given by its advance towards a table, over which the fabric is passed, the uppermost block being meanwhile furnished

with its appropriate color (by hand or otherwise). The reciprocating motion of the prism is caused by a crank and connecting rod, the motion of which also drives certain peculiar mechanism, by which the several sides of the prism are made successively to deliver an impression, and when all have printed the fabric is advanced the distance requisite for the next impression.

[Printed, 9d. Drawings. London Journal (*Newton's*), vol. 8, p. 289. Rolls Chapel.]

## A.D. 1823, July 15.—N° 4813.

BRADBURY, JOHN LEIGH.—" Improvements in the art of " printing, painting, or staining silk, cottons, woollen and other " cloths, and paper, parchment, vellum, leather, and other " substances, by means of blocks or surface printing."

Instead of having "what are now called pitch points" upon the block, the table is provided with register points, which protrude through the blanket and material to be printed, the block being provided with holes corresponding with the points. The same principle is stated to be applicable to " perfect machines " for surface printing, either with rollers or blocks, by machinery, " by means known and in use."

[Printed, 8d. No Drawing. London Journal (*Newton's*), vol. 9, p. 240. Petty Bag.]

## A.D. 1823, August 5.—N° 4826.

PONCHÉE, LOUIS JOHN.—(Communicated by Didot, of Paris.) —" Certain machinery or apparatus to be employed in the casting " of metal types."

Machine calculated to cast from 150 to 200 types at each operation, the operation being repeated twice or oftener in a minute. The moulds are composed of steel bars. The first has horizontal grooves at right angles to its length, and forms the body of the letter. The second is a matrix bar screwed to the bottom of the first. The third bar forms the fourth side of the type body. The feet of the type are made by a fourth, a " break bar," with orifices communicating with each type mould. Two of these moulds are placed side by side so as to form a trough between them, in which the molten metal is poured nearly as high as the orifices on the "break bar." On pulling a trigger by a string a plunger at the end of a lever falls into the trough and injects the metal into the moulds. The lever is slightly raised after the casting by a treadle, after which the workman raises it by hand until it passes a catch, which retains it until the string is pulled again. The mould is then unclamped, the mould bars drawn asunder by wrenches, and the types are found adhering to the break bar like the teeth of a comb, when they are broken off, and dressed in the usual way.

[Printed, 2s. Drawings. London Journal (*Newton's*), vol. 7 (*conjoined series*), p. 225; Register of Arts and Sciences, vol. 1, p. 244; Engineers' and Mechanics' Encyclopædia, vol. 1, p. 562. Rolls Chapel.]

A.D. 1823, October 9.—Nº 4850 (four).

HENFREY, John, and APPLEGATH, Augustus.—" Cer-" tain machinery for casting types."

The type is cast in a space between two flanges set at right angles on a spindle, and pressed to and drawn from one another alternately by a spring and a peculiarly arranged excentric piece. A piece of steel, called the "body," adjustable to the thickness of the particular type, is screwed to one of the flanges. The matrix is on a carriage, and is run through holes in the flanges for the casting, and kept in its place by a spring. The metal is injected by the descent of a plunger, which recovers itself by a spring. After the casting the spindle begins to revolve, immediately upon which the matrix is disengaged from the type, and withdrawn clear of the flanges. The flanges are then opened, and the cast type pushed from the mould by the action of spring pins. A type is thus cast for each revolution of the spindle. The "break" is disengaged from the letter by two small pins, one of which protrudes from each jaw after the casting. Two machines, acting alternately in this principle are shown in the drawings.

[Printed, 1s. 3d. Drawings. London Journal (*Newton's*), vol. 8, p. 169. Rolls Chapel.]

A.D. 1824, February 7.—Nº 4898.

CONGREVE, Sir William.—" An improved method of stamp-" ing."

The invention "consists of a mode of stamping paper, vellum, " leather, or other suitable substance, so as in one single impression

" to unite with the embossed work usually given in stamping the
" most beautiful and delicate printed figures, either in one or more
" coloured inks or in silver or gold. . . . It may be used for the
" borders of country or other bank notes, so as to make their
" forgery very difficult, or it may be used for ornamental borders
" to tickets, cards, or papers of any sort, and also for ornamenting
" leather, vellum, and all other such materials which are combined
" in chairs, screens, or other descriptions of ornamental furniture.
" Now the difficulty involved in this process . . is that to pro-
" duce the embossed work in high perfection the paper must be
" stamped dry, which, as the fine and delicate printing used must
" be performed at the same instant as the embossing on account
" of the register . . involves the well-known difficulty of print-
" ing very fine work in perfection on dry paper sized for the pur-
" pose of being written on. To overcome this difficulty I have
" found it necessary not only to use a press of very great power,
" but to impress the paper between two metallic surfaces or other
" suitable hard substances, instead of between a metallic and
" leather surface, as in common stamping. . . Thus a steel
" die requires a copper force, which must in the first instance
" be struck as a medal from the die. . . In stamps or other
" securities of higher value, I unite the register of different colours
" with that of the embossed work, by means of my compound
" plate or die, which is already the subject of a patent, and thus
" add a further combination of difficulty to oppose the forger."
No other details of the invention are specified.

[Printed, 3d. No Drawing. Repertory of Arts, vol. 6 (*third series*), p. 141;
London Journal (*Newton's*), vol. 8, p. 121. Rolls Chapel.]

### A.D. 1824, February 19.—N° 4902.

APPLEGATH, Augustus.—" Certain improvements in printing
" machines."

The first consists " in an apparatus for distributing the ink or
" colour, and in the mode of supplying the same to the rollers
" which apply it to the form of type, &c." A large roller beneath
the press revolves in bearings of levers connected with the pressing
cylinder, so that when the impression is being given it is brought
up to furnish the inking rollers, under which the form is made
to pass. Distribution is effected by small rollers at the bottom of
the large roller in contact with it, the latter receiving its supply of

ink from an intermediate roller, which acts against the metal roller of an ink trough " of the ordinary construction." The second is chiefly applicable to machines having two pressing cylinders to impress one form, and in which great dispatch is desired It consists in diminishing the motion of the printing or type table, by causing each of the cylinders alternately to move or vibrate into the same place to give the impression, so that the distance which the type table would have to travel between two fixed cylinders is saved. The cylinders are placed in a " pendulum frame," and the type table is moved backwards in the ordinary manner, and " thus " a machine with two cylinders on a double-action machine is ob- " tained with the table motion requisite for a machine with " one cylinder only. . . The types may be inked with rollers and " inking tables in the manner usual in many printing machines, " but the carriages of the inking rollers should be moveable along " the frame of the machine, and they may be'conveniently moved " by means of rods connected with the pendulum frame." The sheets to be printed are laid on feeders of the usual construction, from which they are conveyed by tapes in the usual manner to the " drums and printing cylinders."

[Printed, 6*d*. Drawings. London Journal (*Newton's*), vol. 10, p. 14 ; Register of Arts and Sciences, vol. 1, p. 136; Patent Journal, vol. 2, pp. 484, 516, 527, and 550. Rolls Chapel.]

A.D. 1824, February 19.—N° 4903.

CHURCH, WILLIAM.— " Certain improvements in machinery " for printing."

Additions to and modifications of N° 4664 :—

1. Instead of locking up with wedges and quoins, the chase is held by " chaps," falling into notches on its sides, and moved in and out by the action of a shaft with double-threaded screw bearings passing through them and the table.

2. The " feeding tables " (square frames similar to tympans, and clothed) have a rising and falling action on pivots.

3. Register is obtained by " inserting four lines of type in holes " made for that purpose in the hedge of the chase or other part of " the form, in such positions that if continued across they would " intersect in the centre of the form, by which means joint lines at " right angles on the four edges of the paper, and these, when the " sheet is placed upon the feeding table for printing the reverse

" side, are to be brought to coincide with corresponding lines made
" upon the feeding table."

4. The frisket is furnished with "raised fingers, which come
" down at intervals upon the edge of the sheet hanging over the
" feeding table, and secure it so that the frisket carries it over the
" form. . . The inking rollers, which are connected to and move
" with the frisket carriage at every return of that carriage, rest upon
" the distributing rollers . . which are in constant rotation, and
" then receive their ink."

5. Interrupted motion is obtained by a peculiar arrangement of
moveable teeth and inclined planes, upon a wheel in continuous
motion, in connexion with a guide of a peculiar form.

6. " Supposing the sheet to be carried in ready to receive the
" impression, a bar having two or more pairs of clasps or fingers is
" brought under the edge of the platen, and made to take hold
" much in the same way as described in my former specification.
" . . These clasps are kept open by springs, but are closed
" when taking hold of the paper by "a sliding bar on which are
" inclined planes, which, as the bar slides, pass under the tails of
" the clasps, and close them. The impression being given" (by the
rising of the table), " the paper is drawn off by the rotation of"
endless chains (above the press table), " to which the clasp bar is
" attached, and is brought over" a heap of printed paper, when an
" inclined plane acting against the end of a sliding bar opens the
" clasps and lets the paper fall. The sheet of paper is prevented
" passing too far or being affected by the wind, by a check cloth
" or apron suspended over it."

7. The supply of ink from the ductor is regulated by a rod adjustable in length, "one end being connected to the ductor and
" the other to an excentric. As the excentric passes round, the
" ductor is occasionally pressed up against the distributing rollers,
" and held there for any space of time required for the supply,
" according to the length of the adjustable rod."

[Printed, 1s. 4d. Drawings. London Journal (Newton's), vol. 10, p. 169.
Rolls Chapel.]

A.D. 1824, April 15.— N° 4942.

GETHEN, THOMAS.—" Certain improvements in the machinery
" and process of making metallic rollers, paper cylinders, and
" certain other articles."

These consist, first, in causing the moulds in which such articles are cast to travel so that the metal discharged from the runner of the stationary melting pot may, by the progressive movement of the mould, produce a more extended length of casting than can be effected by the ordinary mode of running the metal, or the reservoir of fluid metal may be made to travel over the mould; secondly, in the particular construction and adaptation of a core (when hollow articles are to be cast) with a porous coating, and certain channels for conducting off the steam and other vapour from the mould, which porous coatings and air channels may also be advantageously employed in or upon the moulds or surfaces in casting other articles which are not hollow.

[Printed, 2s. 4d. Drawings.]

A.D. 1824, May 15.—N° 4958 (four).

PARKIN, THOMAS.—" Certain improvements in machinery or " apparatus applicable to or employed in printing."

A pressing cylinder is fixed in adjustable bearings between uprights, which connect an upper and lower frame of the machine. The lower part of the cylinder is covered by an endless blanket which passes over rollers above it. The type carriage (on the lower frame) is driven to and fro by a wheel which alternates in motion and takes into a rack below the carriage. A rack on its upper surface drives the pressing cylinder, and this in turn (by rack gearing) imparts to and fro motion in a direction exactly the reverse of that of the type carriage to the upper frame. The upper frame carries at each end of it an inking roller, which alternately passes over the form and a distributing table, on which the ink has been distributed in the manner specified in N° 4619. Two other inking rollers, which are stationary, also pass over the form as it passes under them for the purpose of more fully distributing the ink upon it. The sheet is fed in from a " pointing " table," which admits of a slight forward motion by the action of the upper frame, so as to feed in the sheet between two rollers, from the upper one of which a portion has been removed. By this motion the points have (in consequence of the descent of a friction roller on an inclined plane) been withdrawn, and a roller falls into such a position as to steady the sheet. The pointing table recovers its position by a weighted cord. On motion being given to the rollers between which the sheet has been introduced, the latter is passed between several series of tapes peculiarly arranged, printed and discharged on a platform above the press on the side in which it was fed in. The proper direction of the sheet after the impression is ensured by means of a peculiar arrangement of knives, which are removed by the action of the upper frame so as not to interfere with the course of the sheet on the side on which it is fed in. The press is in duplicate.

[Printed, 1s. 2d. Drawings. London Journal (*Newton's*), vol. 10, p. 57. Rolls Chapel.]

A.D. 1824, July 27.—N° 4992 (two).

CARTWRIGHT, EDWARD.—" Improvements on or additions to " roller printing presses."

These consist " in certain methods of communicating an " alternating or a backward and forward motion to them, and " also in a new construction of roller printing presses, all of " them being actuated by the powers of horses, steam engines, " or other first movers of machinery." Under the first head the patentee shows (1) a horizontal bevel wheel, partially toothed and having continuous motion, which gears alternately into two other bevel wheels ; (2) a partially-toothed bevel wheel acting alternately upon two bevel wheels mounted upon a horizontal shaft, " which may have upon it one or more " toothed spur wheels . . . working into one or more other " toothed wheels . . . affixed either upon the axis of the top or " the bottom rollers of the printing presses;" and (3) a continuously revolving shaft, which, by means of a crank or stud on the side of a wheel acting upon a connecting rod, produces the required motion in a segmental wheel immediately above a spur wheel on the axis of the upper roller. Under the second head is shown " a plan of several roller printing presses arranged " in a circular manner, and of a revolving circular table made of " cast iron or other proper material, and answering the purpose of " the planks in the usual printing presses. Here it becomes neces- " sary that the rollers, instead of being cylindrical as usual, should " be conical," and the wheels of the millwork bevelled. " The " axes of the rollers also must be inclined instead of being parallel

" to each other. The upper face of the revolving table must also
" be flat or plane, but the lower face may be made conical if
" preferred."

[Printed, 1s. Drawings. London Journal (*Newton's*), vol. 10, p. 133. Rolls
Chapel.]

## A.D. 1825, January 14.—N° 5082.

LOCKETT, JOSEPH, the elder. — " Certain improvements in
" producing or manufacturing a neb or slot in the roller, shell, or
" cylinder, made of copper or other metal, used in the printing
" of calico, muslin, cotton, or linen cloths."

The object of the invention is to prevent such roller, &c. turning
on the mandril. The mandril has a groove about one inch wide
and half an inch deep. It is introduced into the cylinder and subjected to a powerful mechanical pressure, repeated with increasing
force, until the required neb or slot is sufficiently raised or " forced
" out of the solid copper by the power applied into the said groove
" in the maundril." " The said neb or slot," it is stated, "generally
" braized or soldered upon the inside, often slacks or gets loose."

[Printed, 3d. Drawings. London Journal (*Newton's*), vol. 10, p. 364. See
Attwood's patents for improvements in cylinders for calico printing,
London Journal (*Newton's*), vol. 7, p. 285, and vol. 10, p. 307.]

## A.D. 1825, November 1.—N° 5277.

HAWKINS, JOHN ISAAC.—" Improvements on certain imple-
" ments, machines, or apparatus used in the manufacturing and
" preserving of books, whether bound or unbound."

These " implements " are (1) a printing press; (2) a book press;
(3) a copying press. In each the parts which are in contact
with and communicate pressure to the platens and tables are
of the figure known as "knife-edge bearings," and in so long a
line or in such a number of long lines across the platen and
table that only a comparatively small force is exerted on any small
portion of this line, while the aggregate force exerted on the
whole platen and table is immense. The introduction of the
knife-edge bearing renders it unnecessary to make the platens so
strong " as is requisite in the ordinary modes," where all the
pressure is given from one bearing in the middle, or from two
bearings at opposite sides of the platen, or at most from a very

few bearings at different parts of the platen and table. This arrangement reduces the friction of the moving parts and prevents any injurious wear. " In combination with the knife-" edge bearing I introduce into the printing and copying presses " certain peculiar and advantageous modifications of what is " called the infinite lever, but which I denominate the indefinitely-" increasing lever, as being a term more expressive of its opera-" tion; and I construct my printing press so that the carriage may " be run in, the pressure be given, and the carriage run out " again by the operation of a single operation of the winch." In the printing press the knife-edge surfaces which act on the table and platen are inclined outwards, and as the carriage of the press is run in they approach the vertical. A continuation of the rounce's action causes the carriage to return, and platen and table to recover their positions. "There is therefore in this press, " as thus far described, the principle of the indefinitely-increasing " lever acting upon the indefinitely-increasing lever, and the " ultimate power in the square of the indefinite or the indefinite " multiplied by itself. But when the press is made of an extra-" ordinary large size I introduce a third indefinitely-increasing " lever, . . . by which the power is augmented to the cube of the " indefinite," by putting upon the handle or winch a bar "turning " on its middle, and furnished with a handle at each end, and " also a short arm projecting from one side of the middle of the " said bar."

The press for papers or books consists of a platen working between standards (with racks on the inside), and forced down by the action of levers with the knife-edge bearing above described, a fulcrum frame above the platen being depressed with the platen by the action of palls in the racks.

In the copying press a sheet of vellum or wove paper is placed directly under the paper to be copied between two pieces of smooth metal; viz., the table having two angular grooves along the under side from end to end near the edges, and the platen having two similar angular grooves. These pieces of metal are secured by two clips with knife-edge bearings, and the impression is given by two levers, one of which is perforated to allow of the tail of the other passing through it.

An apparatus for securing " easily and without loss of time " each sheet of a book within a pair of covers united with a back,

" so that the increasing book may be preserved sheet by sheet and
" used as fast and as soon as each is printed off or written."

[Printed, 1s. 7d.  Drawings.  London Journal (*Newton's*), vol. 14, p. 298.
    Rolls Chapel.]

A.D. 1826, October 18.—N° 5417.

CHURCH, William.—" Certain improvements in printing."

1. A " set-off " sheet is wound tightly round two rollers, one on
each side of the top of the platen.  After each impression a portion
of this is drawn from one on to the other by the action of a catch
upon a ratchet wheel, with which each roller is provided.  A claw
at each end of a spring bar supports and guides the arms of these
catches, and according to the adjustment of this bar (by hand) the
set-off sheet traverses the platen in one or the other direction or
remains stationary, the latter being the case during the printing
of the first side of the sheet.  A sort of break acts upon the roller
from which the sheet is being wound.  The mechanism which
draws the set-off sheet is worked by sliding racks moved up and
down by the table rising and falling, as in N° 4903.  When the
entire length of calico has been passed in one direction the spring
bar is to be shifted and the calico worked back again, the rollers
being at each change shifted a short distance laterally.

2. Peculiar arrangement connected with the rising and falling
of the table, by which the bank or board upon which the printed
sheets are piled (as described in N° 4903) is slidden to and fro for
the purpose of drawing the sheet from the taking-off fingers.

3. The " taking-off fingers " (which in N° 4903 are attached
to bars) are here attached to cylindrical rods one within another,
and conducted, as in that Patent, by endless chains.  When the
fingers are between the table and the platen, the pressure acting
against the chaps of a " locking piece " force them together, at the
same time that a spring catch passing through a slot locks them,
and secures the end of the sheet between them.  When they have
brought the sheet on to the pile they are opened by a leaf striking
against a trigger, which forces the spring catch back and allows
springs within to throw them open.

4. Moveable bearers for supporting the ends of the inking rollers
as they pass over the inequalities of the form.  These bearers are
on springs.  When the table is up for the impression they are

below it, free from the sheet; but as the table descends, previously to the inking rollers passing over the type, pieces affixed to the frame of the machine catch the ends of the bearers and keep them up level with the surface of the type. On the table rising they again descend.

[Printed, 1s. 1d. Drawings. Repertory of Arts, vol. 5 (*third series*), p. 431 ; London Journal (*Newton's*), vol. 1 (*second series*), p. 144. Rolls Chapel.]

A.D. 1827, February 14.—N° 5463.

CHRIST, JOHN GEORGE.—(Communicated.)—"Certain improve-" ments in copper and other plate printing."

The invention consists in " putting a glazed or enamelled surface " on paper to be used for copper and other plate printing by means " of white lead and size, whereby the finer lines of the engraving are " better exhibited than heretofore; and also in a mode of polishing " the said enamel and the impression after it has been drawn from " the plate." The size is of parchment isinglass and gum. It is mixed with the purest white lead in three different proportions, for the purpose of coating it three several times. Twenty-four hours after the impression it is "placed with the impression downwards " on a plate of finely-polished steel, and passed several times through " the press with a strong pressure, which will give to the glazed or " enamelled surface of the paper its last and highest polish."

[Printed, 3d. No Drawing. Repertory of Arts, vol. 8 (*third series*), p. 51, also vol. 6 (*third series*), p. 254; London Journal (*Newton's*), vol. 1 (*second series*), p. 229 ; Register of Arts and Sciences, vol. 1 (*new series*), p. 83 ; Engineers' and Mechanics' Encyclopædia, vol. 1, p. 470; Patent Journal, vol. 2, p. 582; Webster's Reports, vol. 1, p. 83; Webster's Patent Law, pp. 27, 47, 67, 88, 108, and 132 ; Carpmael's Reports on Patent Cases, vol. 1, p. 463; Russell's Reports, vol. 5, p. 322. Rolls Chapel.]

A.D. 1827, April 5.—N° 5484.

COWPER, EDWARD.—" Certain improvements in printing " music."

The " note block " is of three layers, three-sixteenths of an inch (the " face," pear-tree, holly, &c.), half an inch (the " middle," mahogany, cedar, &c.), and one-eighth of an inch (the " back," mahogany, &c.) thick respectively, the grains of the layers crossing each other, and the middle one being sawn through, in the direction of the grain, at intervals of one inch and a half. The stave lines are cut in with a five-pointed tool. The music is then written on the block with a pen. The heads of the black notes are made of wire, and the tails of thin metal strips. " The semibreves, part " of the flats, the sharps, part of the naturals, part of the rests, " the slurs, the hooks and ties of the quavers, &c., the staccato " marks, the heads of the ledger notes, the turns, &c., are formed " of wire drawn through tapering holes in a steel plate, or in a " pair of dies, in lengths of several feet, and cut into pieces five- " sixteenths of an inch long, and driven into the block, leaving " one-sixteenth of an inch above it. The words, and sometimes the " cleffs, braces, and signatures of the key, are cast in a plate from " ordinary type, and sawn into slips of one or more words, which " are inserted in grooves in the block." The drilling apparatus with which the grooves are made in the block is described. The " stave block " is composed of a slab of mahogany, &c., five-eighths of an inch thick, with a half-inch veneer, and contains (in copper) the five stave lines with the cleffs and signatures of the key. The note and stave blocks are set up in chases, so as to register, and are then printed from by " a revolving tympan," turning on a pivot in the centre of an ordinary tympan rather "longer " than usual," and is furnished with two friskets shutting towards the centre. Two sheets of paper being placed on this revolving tympan, and the friskets buttoned down, an impression is taken on one sheet with the notes only, and the other with the staves only. The revolving tympan is then turned half round, and another impression taken, by which both sheets are perfected. For a proof an impression of the notes only is taken on transparent paper, and then laid on a sheet of which the lines only are printed.

[Printed, 9d. Drawings. London Journal (*Newton's*), vol. 3 (*second series*), p. 230. Rolls Chapel.]

A.D. 1827, September 6.—N° 5550.

CLYMER, George.—" An improvement in typographic print-" ing between plain or flat surfaces."

By this improvement the size of the sheet may be increased. " Indeed, by this new contrived press I propose to print two forms " of double royal paper at one time, being a surface of four feet six " inches by 3 feet 3 inches, which is twice the size of the largest " newspaper." This is effected by the application of jointed infinite levers connected with the platen, such levers being worked by

the bar handle.  The platen is counterbalanced.  For the impression the bar handle is swung outwards.  The press shown is
double-acting, the sheets being removed alternately at either end,
and the form (which is stationary) inked during the changing of
the sheet " by the ordinary kind of elastic rollers introduced at the
" sides of the machine."

[Printed, 6d.  Drawings.  London Journal (*Newton's*), vol. 1 (*second series*),
    p. 218.  Rolls Chapel.]


### A.D. 1828, May 22.—N° 5658.

ASPINWALL, THOMAS.— " An improved method of casting
" printing types by means of a mechanical process, which inven-
" tion I propose to call the Mechanical Type Caster."

The working parts of the machine are mounted on a table suspended so as to move to and from the melting pot.  The mould
is in two parts, mounted on two sliding " carrier pieces " on the
table, inclined to each other at a slight angle.  The matrix is
held during the casting by a spring.  On the revolution of the
crank shaft (by hand) a sliding rod on the table is made to move
towards the melting pot, and the carrier pieces being acted upon by
a cross bar attached to it by springs are drawn forward so as to
unite the two parts of the mould for the casting.  By the further
revolution of the crank shaft, a projecting piece on the end of
the sliding rod coming in contact with an adjusting screw on
one end of a bent lever, causes it to turn on its centre, and by
a friction roller at its other end forces down the plunger of a
cylinder communicating with the metal pot, so as to inject
the metal into a chamber, whence it ejects a portion previously
there through a nozzle into the mould as it is moved forward
by the forward motion of the table.  The handle of the crank
is then turned the reverse way, the table swings back from the
metal pot, the plunger rises by a spring, the parts of the mould
separate, the matrix is withdrawn from the cast type by a lever
(which overcomes the force of the spring by which it is held
during the casting), and the type itself loosened from the mould
by coming in contact with an inclined plane.

The arrangements of the machine are adapted for the usual
alterations necessary for casting different sized type.

[Printed, 1s. 1d.  Drawings.  London Journal (*Newton's*), vol. 5 (*second
    series*), p. 212.  Petty Bag.]

### A.D. 1828, October 2.—N° 5713 (two).

NAPIER, DAVID.—" Certain improvements on machinery appli-
" cable to letter-press printing."

1. Application of four-feeding apparatus to a machine with a
single pressing cylinder. The form is driven to and fro, and by
means of a rack gives motion to the pressing cylinder, which
prints in both directions. " The inking apparatuses . . . are
" the same in every respect with those adapted to my Naepeer
" machines (which machines are well known to the public),
" with the exception that in this case they are moved by . .
" wheel and pinions . . from the cylinder, and in the other
" by rack and pinion from the surface. The feeding appara-
" tuses are the same in principle with those adapted to my
" single and double imperial machines (which machines are
" equally well known), with the exception that in this case they
" are removed to a distance from the printing cylinder," and
are therefore driven by a gut band passing over a wheel on the
cylinder axle and riggers on the ends of the feeding cylinders.
Wheels are put in motion alternately. There are two feeding
tables at each end of the press, one being further from the pressing
cylinder than the other. The "feeding bars" of the feeding
tables on the same side are rigidly joined, so as to be brought
down and feed in a sheet from each at the same time, both sheets
passing into and being printed and discharged by the same tapes.
After the impression the sheet is discharged, printed side upwards,
on a board directly above the cylinder.

2. Four tables are ranged one above the other. The highest
and lowest are fixtures. The intermediate ones move against
them on vertical guides, counterbalanced and provided with flat
bearings to receive rollers at the end of arms on a shaft in the
middle of the machines, to which power is applied for the impression. The forms are laid on the second (reckoning from the
top) and the lowest, "so that two impressions will be obtained with
" the same expense of time and power as is necessary in the ordi-
" nary way to obtain one." The sheet is fed in from a board and
is carried through the machine and discharged when perfected
by endless webs and tapes, the arrangement of which is peculiar.

[Printed, 10d. Drawings. Repertory of Arts, vol. 11 (third series), p. 121;
London Journal (Newton's), vol. 4 (second series), p. 29. Rolls Chapel.]

## A.D. 1829, March 19.—N° 5776.

WAYTE, JAMES WILLS.—" Certain improvements in printing
" machines."

1. Perfecting machine with one platen. Two tables with
different forms are supported on vibrating arms, by which
they are alternately brought up to meet a descending platen,
the parallelism of the forms and platen being preserved during
their motion by an arrangement of levers and double-jointed
pieces respectively. The sheet is fed in from a board to spring
clips on a bar carried by endless chains. The sheet is thus
carried under the platen and printed white, turned over, brought
back again and perfected, and, finally (the clips opening by
contact with inclined planes), discharged on to a receiving
board. The interval of rest in the chains during the impression is owing to the omission of teeth in the gearing. The
inking apparatus is peculiar. At each end of the press table is
a trough and roller, and at the outside edge of each type table a
distributing roller, in contact (by a spring) with a messenger roller
below it. The inking rollers work loosely in pendant guides
rolling over the forms as the tables rise and fall. When the table
is at its lowest the messenger is tilted to the trough roller, and
when at its highest the distributing roller (driven by a band from
the main shaft) is in contact with the inking rollers. The sheet
is kept to the platen by "a frisket or tapes."

2. Machine in which the impression is given by a single form
of types supported on vibrating arms which bring it alternately
under two platens placed obliquely above it. The platens (suspended as in the previous machine by double-jointed pieces) are
brought down alternately by the action of the type table on two
levers connected with them, recovering themselves after the impression by counterweights. The inking apparatus is in a great
measure similar to the last, the form being inked on passing from
one platen to the other. The sheet is fed in by "a series of tapes
" passing round an endless blanket as employed in many other
" printing machines, the tapes and blanket receiving their motion
" from a rigger on the crank shaft." There are two laying-on
tables for each platen, as the machine is calculated to print with
great rapidity.

3. Inking apparatus for an ordinary press. A light carriage

contains two inking rollers and a " messenger," the latter taking
its supply at intervals from a trough roller at the back of the
machine and imparting it to a receiving roller above it when the
frame has passed over the types.   Motion is given to the carriage
by a weight connected with and wound up by the rounce, and
retained in its position when wound.   On the pressman lifting
the tympan the tail of it strikes a weighted lever, which gives a
ratchet motion to the trough roller and releases the weight, by the
action of which the carriage is suddenly projected over the form
and drawn back again by a stud in an endless chain which takes
into a slot in the carriage.   Endwise motion is given to the distributor by means of a barrel with an inclined groove, which
receives a stud on the under side of the frame of the distributing
roller, this barrel deriving motion from a lever, in which the tail
of the tympan acts.

Another method.   The inking rollers and platen are on a
carriage, the latter turning on an axle carrying a toothed segment
which takes into a rack on the table.   As the carriage is run in
(by a rounce and endless chain) the form is inked and the platen
turned over " to receive the power which gives the impression."
During the impression the inking rollers are over the distributor
and receive their supply " in the usual manner."

Mode by which the long ductor and ink trough may be
dispensed with.   A small elastic roller on a bent arm at the
tympan end is, when the tympan is thrown up, in contact with
a small "ink ductor " (trough roller); and, when the tympan
is run in, is raised so as to give its ink to blocks on a bar at the
off side of the press, so arranged as to come opposite the pages of
type, and " the inking rollers, in passing over the blocks, take up
" ink in those parts only, to avoid waste."

[Printed, 1s. 11d.   Drawings.   London Journal (*Newton's*), vol. 4 (*second
series*), p. 121; Register of Arts and Sciences, vol. 4 (*new series*), p. 67;
Engineers' and Mechanics' Encyclopædia, vol. 2, p. 319; Rolls Chapel
Reports, 7th Report, p. 129.   Rolls Chapel.]

A.D. 1830, July 19.—N° 5955.

COWPER, EDWARD, and COWPER, EBENEZER. — " Certain
" improvements on printing machines."

The improvements are applicable to those machines in which
the impression i obtained by passing the form of types under a

cylinder, "as in the former Patent of Edward Cowper" (N° 3974).
1. A distributing or travelling drum, attached to the rear of the
type table and driven by bevil gearing running along the side of
the machine, is furnished from a trough roller at the end of the
machine by a vibrator, and has the ink distributed upon it by
small rollers revolving by friction with it. It imparts a supply
to the under surface of the inking rollers, which work in fixed
bearings on the press frame, as the form passes under the cylinder
for the impression. Endwise motion is given either to the drum
(by inclined planes upon its ends acting against friction rollers) or
to the frame of the distributing rollers.

2. The blanket is wound round two rollers (furnished with
ratchet wheels) placed within a recess in and parallel to the axis of
the cylinder, and is moved from one on to the other as it begins
to set off.

[Printed, 6*d*. Drawings. Repertory of Arts, vol. 1 (*new series*), p. 92;
London Journal (*Newton's*), vol. 2 (*conjoined series*), p. 19; Mechanics'
Magazine, vol. 15, p. 61; Register of Arts and Sciences, vol. 5 (*new series*),
p. 289; Engineers' and Mechanics' Encyclopædia, vol. 2, p. 346. Rolls
Chapel.]


A.D. 1830, August 31.—N° 5988.

APPLEGATH, Augustus.—"Certain improvements in printing
machines."

The first consists "in certain contrivances by which thin copper
" or other metallic plates may receive and be printed in a curved
" or circular form." Curved plates, depressed at the margin to
avoid " bruising," are fixed to two segment beds, the one at the
side, the other below a pressing cylinder. (The plates are curved
by being passed with a slab of hard wood between the pressing
cylinder and the segment bed.) After each impression, a " draw-
" back " wheel is made to restore the plates to their original
position ready to give a fresh impression to the material, which is
brought forward for that purpose by an endless web or endless tapes.
The plates are colored and cleaned " in the usual manner."

The second relates to machines for printing with engraved plates
any material "upon which the same pattern or design has to be
" repeated *across* as well as *along* the material," and consists in
" causing the plate to move sideways across the piece of material,
" or in causing the piece of material to move sideways across the

" plate during the intervals of giving the impression, so that
" instead of engraving a plate in which the pattern is repeated to
" the whole width of the material to be printed, the plate need
" not be larger than one complete set or drawing of the pattern."
The motion of the pressing cylinder and segment beds for
printing *along* the material is the same as in the first part of the
invention. " The side motion which causes the material to be
" printed *across* is produced by the action of the angular edges "
of a " shape " (drum) against the end of the spindle of the pressing
cylinder, which it forces to move endways during the intervals of
giving the impression. While the plate is printing, the straight
parts of the shape pass the spindle without producing any side
motion. " When the plate has printed, the pressing cylinder
" becomes quiescent, and continues so for a short time until," by
the action of a " great drawback," it is " returned into the same
" position as before printing, in order that the second impression
" of the divided plate may be in the same line as the first. . .
" When the second impression has taken place, the cylinder has
" to be returned for the third. . . When the third impression
" is made, the material is printed entirely across its width, and
" the impression cylinder then only requires to be drawn back
" the small quantity of motion which continues after the plate
" was printed ; that is to say, it requires to be drawn back as
" much as is usual in the ordinary copper-plate press," this
motion being given by a " lesser drawback wheel." The rollers,
over which the endless blanket and material move, are fixed in a
frame, " which frame must move sideways with the impression
" cylinder."

[Printed, 1s. 10d. Drawings. London Journal (*Newton's*), vol. 1 (*conjoined
    series*), p. 414 ; Register of Arts and Sciences, vol. 6 (*new series*), p. 16.
    Rolls Chapel.]


A.D. 1830, October 13.—N° 6010.

NAPIER, DAVID.—" Certain improvements in printing and in
" pressing machinery, with a method of economizing the power
" applied to the same, which method of economizing power is
" applicable to other purposes."

The improvements in printing consist, " first, in keeping two
" printing cylinders revolving in one direction by their being

" acted upon by reciprocating racks, and by each other alter-
" nately." On the pressing-cylinder spindles are wheels toothed
half round their circumference, gearing into racks on the type
table, and each provided with a spring catch, by which they go
loose in one direction and fixed in the other. On the end of
the spindles are riggers connected by crossing bands. Thus each
cylinder prints while its wheel is in gear with the rack, and at
the same time drives the other cylinder. The type table is driven
by a fly wheel and crank. Secondly, in "the application of what
" is well known by the name of Boulton and Watt's parallel
" motion" to machines, "for the purpose of passing the inking
" rollers over the form." When applied to the common press,
the parallel motion is doubled.

The improvements in pressing machinery, (which are claimed
" for the use of printers alone,") consist in " passing the printed
" paper (when dried) in a similar manner to that of printing it,
" between two pressing cylinders, coated either with glazed
" board or with any other suitable medium, in place of the
" present tedious methods of either screw or hydraulic pressure."
The improvements in economizing power is " that of apply-
" ing one or more springs similar to that of a clock . . . between
" the man and the fly wheel, which spring or springs the man is
" constantly winding up by means of a lever, somewhat similar to
" the action of a pump, . . . which winding up would not be,
" as in the clock, by turning round the centre spindle on which
" the spring is wound, but rather by turning round the outer case
" in which the spring is contained." The arrangement is claimed
for " printing machines, steam and explosive engines, and espe-
" cially where it would be an object to dispense with the crank."
It would also dispense with the necessity of more than one engine,
" which is found necessary when there is no fly wheel for over-
" coming the dead points in the action of the crank."

[Printed, 7d. Drawings. London Journal (*Newton's*), vol. 8 (*conjoined
series*), p. 427 ; Register of Arts and Sciences, vol. 6 (*new series*), p. 65 ;
Engineers' and Mechanics' Encyclopædia, vol. 2, p. 350. Rolls Chapel.]

A.D. 1831, January 22.—N° 6065.

HANNINGTON, CHARLES MEPHAM.—" An improved appa-
" ratus for impressing, stamping, or printing for certain pur-
" poses."

The invention consists in indicating the number of impressions which have been struck. Four similar wheels, each with ten regular projections on their peripheries, carrying the numerals 0—9 consecutively, either in relief or sunk, are placed side by side on a hollow axis. Through each, except the fourth, passes a stud projecting on one side, and attached to a spring in a circular recess on the other. Within the hollow axis is a fixed axis carrying a circular piece of metal which lies within a cavity on the side of the first wheel, by the oscillation of which piece (by levers below the machine) the first wheel is made to advance one-tenth of a revolution. By the action of an inclined plane attached to this circular piece upon the stud of the first wheel, the second wheel is made for every complete revolution of the first to make one-tenth of a revolution, and similarly the third and fourth wheels are made to revolve by the action of the studs one-tenth of a revolution for every complete revolution of the second and third wheels respectively. A drawing is given of the various parts as placed in a " fly stamping or pressing " machine, in which the only alteration is in the parts giving the oscillating motion to the levers.

The impression is given by the descent of a clothed piece of metal (driven downwards by a handscrew) upon the printing surface, composed partly of a stationary form and partly of the projections on the type wheels. By means of guide rods connected with the screw, a sliding rod is drawn backwards and forwards so as to actuate the levers which move the wheels.

In printing with color, a plate which confines the printing surface is removed for the purpose of coloring them. No mode of coloring is given.

[Printed, 1s. 5d. Drawings. London Journal (*Newton's*), vol. 10 (*conjoined series*), p. 68; Register of Arts and Sciences, vol. 6 (*new series*), p. 170. Rolls Chapel.]

A.D. 1831, January 29.—N° 6067.

WINCH, ROBERT.—" Certain improvements in printing ma- " chines."

A cast-iron platen (in the middle of the press) is screwed to a moveable beam which moves up and down by the action of guide rods at the sides of the machine. The table beneath it

slides in and out on rails, to place upon it or remove the form.
The inking rollers are in a carriage drawn backwards and forwards
over the form for each impression by means of bands passing round
excentrics peculiarly arranged, and driven by the connecting rod's
motion. The inking roller frame passes twice over the form for
each impression. " Besides the usual crossing motion endways of
" one of the inking rollers," the inking table (at one end of the
press) " can also, by means of a handle applied underneath it,
" be traversed across backwards and forwards when it may
" be found necessary to equalize the distribution of the ink
" more perfectly." The sheet is first laid upon one or two
raised frames (at the ends of the press) fitted with tapes and
hollow register points corresponding to solid register points on the
friskets, on which the frame and sheet are thrown down, leaving
the sheet upon register points upon it. The friskets are received
upon a " rising and falling frame," which is raised by weights,
and depressed for the impression by four branches on the platen.
The friskets (connected with each other) are carried backwards
and forwards by gut bands connected with two other excentrics
driven in a peculiar manner. A " set-off sheet" of paper is
wound on two ratchet wheel rollers above the platen. For
reiteration the hollow register points are to be affixed to the
under sides of the frames in such a manner that they exactly
correspond with the solid register points of the friskets. The
sheet is then " carefully placed upon the hollow register points
" . . . and upon throwing down one of the frames . . . the
" paper will be again placed upon the solid register points . . .
" in the same holes which were originally made by the said
" solid register points."

[Printed, 1s. Drawings. Repertory of Arts, vol. 16 (*third series*), p. 257 ;
    London Journal (*Newton's*), vol. 6 (*conjoined series*), p. 31; Register of
    Arts and Sciences, vol. 6 (*new series*), p. 169; Engineers' and Mechanics'
    Encyclopædia, vol. 2, p. 352. Rolls Chapel.]


A.D. 1831, February 14.—N° 6076.

THOMSON, JAMES.—" Certain improvements in making or
" producing printing types."

" My improvements consist in making printing types by
" casting or forming a cake of metal having letters formed and
" protruding on one side of it, and in afterwards sawing this

" cake directly or transversely, so as to divide it into single
" types." The casting is effected in two ways. First, by forming
a mould from types set up, and immersing this within an iron
box in a pot of melted type metal, " as in making stereotype
" plates; with this difference, however, that in the present case
" the plate must be as thick as the length of the intended type;
" and further, that in setting up the types for the cast, proper
" spaces must be made between each letter, and between the
" lines, in order to allow for what will be taken away in the
" sawing." The second mode is, " by taking a plate of copper or
" other suitable metal, and making in it indentations or matrices
" with a punch having on it the letter for the intended type,
" taking care to make them in straight rows, direct, and trans-
" verse. This plate being so indented, is put into an iron box
" and immersed in a pot of liquid type metal, and kept there
" the proper depth and proper time, so as to enable the metal
" fully to enter into those indentations or matrices that the letter
" may be well formed. The cake thus cast or formed, after being
" taken out and cooled, is sawed as before."

[Printed, 3d. No Drawing. Repertory of Arts, vol. 12 (*third series*), p. 208;
London Journal (*Newton's*), vol. 1 (*conjoined series*), p. 417; Register of
Arts and Sciences, vol. 6 (*new series*), p. 194. Rolls Chapel.]

### A.D. 1831, May 24.—N° 6118 (four).

WOOD, Richard.—" An inking apparatus to be used with cer-
" tain descriptions of printing presses."

In flat surface presses a weight is wound up by the action of the
rounce (in running the press table in and out), and released by the
throwing back of the tympan, when by means of connecting rods
from swinging levers working in a fly wheel, a frame containing
one or two inking rollers is driven backwards and forwards over
the form once or oftener for each impression, according to the size
of certain wheels. Endwise motion is given to the distributing
roller which furnishes the inking roller by means of double-threaded
screws on its axis, the distributing apparatus being also driven
from the rounce.

[Printed, 1s. 1d. Drawings. Repertory of Arts, vol. 13 (*third series*), p. 77;
London Journal (*Newton's*), vol. 9 (*conjoined series*), p. 347; Register of
Arts and Sciences, vol. 6 (*new series*), p. 232. Rolls Chapel.]

A.D. 1831, July 6.—N° 6131.

JACQUESSON, ADOLPHE.—(Communicated.)—" Certain im-
" provements in machinery or apparatus applicable to lithogra-
" phic and other printing."

The printing surface is on a table run to and fro by the action
of a winch. The impression is given by a cylinder, also driven
(by means of an intermediate wheel) from the winch. Various
sized intermediate wheels are used, according to the speed at
which it is desired to print. The sheet is laid on by hand, or in
the case of quick printing from types or from a stone with writing
only upon it, by means of an endless felt, which passes round the
cylinder and a roller above it. For fine impressions, instead of
using the endless felt, sheets of cardboard, &c. are laid on the
paper. Pressure is given to the cylinder by means of a compound
weighted lever. No mode of inking is described.

[Printed, 10d. Drawings. Repertory of Arts, vol. 13 (*third series*), p. 40,
   and vol. 1 (*new series*), p. 7 ; London Journal (*Newton's*), vol. 4 (*conjoined
   series*), p. 131. Rolls Chapel.]

A.D. 1832, March 22.—N° 6246.

DAY, WILLIAM.—" Certain improvements in the construction
" of printing presses."

The standards or frame of the press are constructed in two
portions, the upper parts of the side standards with the cross
head in one piece, and the lower parts of the side standards
and the bed in another piece, " thus separating the frame of the
" machine about the middle in a horizontal direction. These two
" parts of the press I connect so as to form the entire frame by
" means of pins passed through sockets with powerful springs."
When the power of the press is " brought into action by running
" by running the stone in . . . the resistance causes the upper
" part of the frame to rise, which it is allowed to do by the
" compression of the springs."

[Printed, 9d. Drawings. London Journal (*Newton's*), vol. 1 (*conjoined
   series*), p. 341 ; Rolls Chapel Reports, 7th Report, p. 139. Rolls Chapel.]

A.D. 1832, April 9.—N° 6254.

BATE, JOHN.—" An improvement or improvements on machinery
" applicable to the imitation of medals, sculpture, and other works
" of art executed in relief."

The invention consists in making a tracing point move and operate upon the medal or other work of art in a plane oblique to the motion of the apparatus which is used to shift the said tracing point equal distances, whatever direction the motion of such apparatus may assume.　The tracing blade is also peculiar, and by its use " sculpture or other works of art executed in high relief may " be more advantageously traced over than could be effected by " any other instrument now in use for such a purpose."

[Printed, 1s. 1d.　Drawings.　London Journal (*Newton's*), vol. 7 (*conjoined series*), p. 33; Register of Arts and Sciences, vol. 7 (*new series*), p. 302. Petty Bag.]

## A.D. 1833, July 18.—N° 6450.

APPLEGATH, Augustus.—" Certain improvements in letter-" press and block printing, and in the machinery or apparatus used " for the same."

The invention consists in, (1) an improved method of im-posing the form " so that the said form and the table of the " printing machine may have a less distance to travel in order to " pass in contact with the impressing cylinder, whereby the pro-" duce of the machine may be augmented without increasing the " speed or rate of its various parts;" (2) a double or perfecting machine, which shows the improved form, combined with an end-less blanket or printing cloth applied to the second or perfecting cylinder as a " set off " sheet; and (3) printing with two or more colors from the same type or pattern.　According to the first, the length of the form is placed across instead of along the press.　In the second case, the pressing cylinder is " rather less in diameter " in that part which meets the type when it returns, in order that " the cloth may not rub against the surface of the type."　In the third, the subject roller (in relief) is colored by several felt rollers, from whose surface certain parts are omitted; or the subject may occupy a segment only of the roller, in which case an interrupted motion must be given to it " by any of the usual means."

[Printed, 8d.　Drawings.　London Journal (*Newton's*), vol. 15 (*conjoined series*), p. 440.　Rolls Chapel.]

## A.D. 1833, July 25.—N° 6454.

KITCHEN, John.—" Novel arrangement of the several parts and " appendages of a machine for printing from types or blocks or other " surfaces in relief, as in the operation of letter-press printing."

The printing surface is vertical, its situation being adjusted by means of racks and pinions. It is inked by an elastic roller passed up and down by means of guides and pulleys. The trough is at the bottom of the inking apparatus, and is surrounded with hollow chambers for regulating its temperature. The trough roller is driven by bands from the main shaft. There is a distributor with endwise motion, furnished by a vibrator, and this gives, by an intermediate roller, ink to a feeding roller, from which the inking roller is furnished. After the impression the cords are let loose, and as the cords are unwound the roller descends again by its weight, its descent being checked by a "flyer." The platen, with the tympan and frisket, is brought in contact with the form by vibrating upon pivots, and falls back for the removal of the printed sheet and for the supply of a fresh one. The power for giving the pressure is obtained by means of jointed levers actuated by a crank and rod.

[Printed, 7d. Drawings. London Journal (*Newton's*), vol. 4 (*conjoined series*), p. 49; Rolls Chapel Reports, 7th Report, p. 146. Rolls Chapel.]

A.D. 1833, November 23.—N° 6515.

LEGGETT, HENRY HARDINGHAM.—1. "A new printing ink " as applied to the purpose of printing in colours, the required " colour to which is given by certain chemical reagents."

The ink is made with a precipitate from a decoction of logwood, mixed with a solution of acetate of copper. The reagents are: for yellow, a weak solution of tartaric acid; for red or orange, oxalic acid; for pink or crimson, dilute sulphuric acid; for lilac or violet, nitro muriate of tin or solution of alum; for blue, bicarbonate of ammonia or other alkali; for purple, dilute solution of bitartrite of potash, and then a solution of alkali. The reagents may be applied to the impression taken with this ink, either by a block, as in paper-staining, or by a felt roller passing over a stencil plate. In the latter case the stencil plate is placed in a "lift frame," under which the impressions are successively brought on the surface of a drum, the reagent roller being passed over it, and conveyed to a trough by means of a "traversing bar." The roller is double acting, that is, colors an impression both on the going and return motion of the bar. In printing two colors at once, there are two rollers similar to the above, each with its trough and appurtenances, and these are by a peculiar arrangement made to change places continually, each bringing with it a " lift frame," with its proper stencil plate.

[Printed, 1s. 4d. Drawings. London Journal (Newton's), vol. 17 (conjoined series), p. 377. Rolls Chapel.]

A.D. 1834, September 25.—N° 6682.

SAXTON, JOSEPH.— "Improvements in printing presses and " in presses for certain other purposes."

The invention consists, (1) in the use of a flexible platen ; (2) in applying pressure to it "by means of a liquid or aeriform " fluid ;" and (3) in adapting flexible platens with such pressure " to printing presses, copying presses, and lithographic and zin-" cographic presses." The platen is of metal, varying from the thickness of foolscap to half an inch, and between it and an inflexible press-head is a water-tight bag, fitted with a cock and valve of peculiar formation. The water is admitted to the bag by means of a cock and valve of peculiar construction, the admission and discharge being effected by the action of a rod at the side of the machine. The axle of the rounce barrel is arranged to turn one-sixteenth of a revolution before engaging with the barrel, and during this motion is, by its action on a series of levers, the means of withdrawing register points from a tympan stretched above the platen. The continued revolution of the barrel runs in the type carriage, in the side of which is a stud, which coming in contact with a lever frees the rod by the action of a rack on the rod upon a toothed pinion connected with the water cock from a detaining plate, when a spiral spring pulls the rod down and admits water for the impression. The first part (also one-sixteenth of a revolution) of the barrel's return motion thrusts up the rod, thereby cutting off the supply and opening the waste pipe. The platen then recovers itself by springs and atmospheric pressure. By the further revolution of the barrel the type table is run out, a notch of the rod again caught in its detaining plate, and the register points raised again. The mode of feeding is peculiar, the tympan being fastened to a hinged frame at the press end of the type carriage, and connected with straps passing over pullies, by which it is drawn in for the impression and afterwards laid evenly on a table above the platen. The sheet is held to the tympan during its course by weighted tapes, which also perform the office of discharging the sheet. No mode of inking is shown in this press.

Modification of the invention, by fastening a flexible metallic " plate and waterproof bag to the under side of the platen of an ordinary printing press, " leaving a small space (say one-eighth of " an inch) between the ordinary plattin and the flexible bag and " plate, and filling the space with water or other liquid, the use of " which would be to equalize the pressure all over the surface of " the types when the plattin is forced down by the ordinary " screws, levers, or other means." In the lithographic press on this principle, the register points and frisket tapes are dispensed with, and if the stone be smaller than the platen, blocks are placed round it to produce an even surface. The flexible plate and bag is also sometimes placed under the stone, to afford uniform resistance in case of irregularity in its thickness, or of printing from fragile substances. In copying presses the platen is fixed under an inflexible metal plate connected with another below it, " leaving a space between the two plates underneath the flexible " platen sufficient to introduce a portfolio, with several thick- " nesses of paper placed above and below the writing, and the " damped tissue paper which is to receive the copy." This press may be employed for taking impressions from zinc plates. The bottom plate or bed "may also be provided with a flexible plate " or bag and fluid, in which case printing might be effected in this " form of press from thin glass, porcelain, and other substances." Pressure is given by connecting the platen with a column of fluid or a force pump.

[Printed, 1s. 1d. Drawings. Repertory of Arts, vol. 4 (new series), p. 121 ; London Journal (Newton's), vol. 11 (conjoined series), p. 167. Rolls Chapel.]

A.D. 1834, December 4.—N° 6728.

HUDSON, JAMES.—" Certain machinery and apparatus appli- " cable in block printing on silk, woollen, cotton, and other " fabrics, and on paper."

After describing " the process of block printing, as now com- " monly practised by calico printers," the specification proceeds : " The object of my invention is to effect the purpose before men- " tioned of presenting a renewed and uniform surface of colouring

" material or mordant to which the block may be from time to
" time applied without the intervention of the tear boy . . and
" in a more certain and uniform manner than is effected by the
" method now commonly practised." The color is spread by
a trough roller at one end of a long table upon an endless cloth
which passes along it, there being a ductor for the removal of
superfluous color. The "table" is a cistern, the top of which is
covered closely with oil-cloth, and rendered elastic by the introduction of a viscid fluid termed "swimming," with which the
cistern is filled, into a pipe extending above the level of the top.
As the endless web progresses, "the printer applies his block to
" it, as to the common sieve."

> [Printed, 10d. Drawings. Repertory of Arts, vol. 4 (new series), p. 321;
> London Journal (Newton's), vol 4 (conjoined series), p. 198. Rolls
> Chapel.]

## A.D. 1835, February 12.—Nº 6762.

HILL, ROWLAND.—" Certain improvements in certain methods
" of letter-press printing by machinery."

1. The first improvement consists in machinery for the
purpose of securely fastening side by side "a series of move-
" able printing types (with their printing surfaces in conformity
" with the whole or part of a true but supposed cylindrical
" surface), so as to form a revolving type cylinder, such type
" cylinder being somewhat similar to that which Mr. Nichol-
" son (a) aimed at constructing, but with the improvement of
" having the types so firmly fastened and retained in place
" around such type cylinder as will be suitable for letter-press
" printing . . . with machinery consisting of cylinders revolving
" continuously." The types are taper (the mould for them
is described), and are secured on the cylinder in chases by
metal binding strips which fall into a notch (b) on their sides.
For newspapers the cylinder is fitted with iron bars, fitting "like
" the staves of a cask," each bar (except those which represent
the margin) holding a column of type.

2. Gathering and taking off the ink "continually and without
" intermission from the surface of a slow revolving cylindrical
" roller, upon which surface the ink is previously spread in a thick

---

(a) Ante, A.D. 1790, Nº 1748.          (b) Nicholson's types were smooth.

" coat, by the usual means of what is called an ink trough and
" ductor," the said gathering and taking off being performed by
a quicker revolving cylindrical roller applying its quick moving
surface in contact with the slow moving surface of the ductor
roller, " and by means of that difference between the motions of
" the surfaces the said thick coat of ink is extended and spread
" out into a thin attenuated coat upon the quick moving surface."
The improvement is shown as applied to the inking apparatus
described in N° 3757.

3. Printing with paper in continuous rolls. The roll (damped)
is passed between a type and pressing cylinder, and " printed with
" a series of repetitions of the same impression in a similar manner
" to that commonly practised for printing pieces of calico in
" cylinder machinery. For the reiteration a fresh type cylinder
" must be introduced, or both forms may be on the same cylinder,
" and the roll will on each side contain alternate impressions."

4. Cutting up the aforesaid long continuous pieces or scrolls
of printed paper into separate sheets or leaves by means of
cylinders revolving continuously. The machinery in ordinary
use by paper-makers for this purpose may be employed, such
machinery being so connected with the printing machinery as to
act at the proper periods. In the mode described, the paper is
caught between nippers attached to endless chains, which hold it
during the operation of cutting (which is effected by a knife
acting against a cylinder), and then deposit it.

5. Perfecting. " For this purpose the machinery must be pro-
" vided with two type cylinders, each with its own inking appa-
" ratus, and likewise its own platten cylinder."

6. " Two impressions are respectively printed upon two distinct
" papers at one and the same time from the types which are fixed
" around the same revolving type cylinder, which must for that
" purpose be provided with two distinct inking apparatuses . . .
" at opposite sides of the circumference of the said cylinder, and
" with two platten cylinders, one situated above it and the other
" below it." One of the papers is printed at the upper, the other
at the lower pressing cylinder. Or " the improvements may be
" applied to a compound machine," as in Art. 5, in which case the
" machinery will print at the rate of two perfected impressions " for
every revolution that the cylinders make, two being either actually
perfected, or one perfected and two printed on one side only.

All the above improvements, except 1, are "applicable to the "method of letter-press printing by machinery which operates "by means of cylinders revolving continuously, with stereotype "plates bended to a cylindrical surface, and fastened around a type "cylinder after Mr. Cowper's method."

[Printed, 5s. 9d. Drawings. Repertory of Arts, vol. 6 (*new series*), pp. 129 and 219; Mechanics' Magazine, vol. 25, p. 271; Rolls Chapel Reports, 7th Report, p. 159. Rolls Chapel.]

## A.D. 1835, February 12.— N° 6763 (four).

NORRIS, Edwin. — "An improved machine for letter-press "printing."

"Double-action printing machine," in which a sheet is printed for each time the pressing cylinder passes over the form. The type table is fixed in the centre of the press. On each side of it is an inking table with traversing motion (on guides) across the press, at each end of which are fixed "inking ductors" (trough rollers). The pressing cylinder, with a double set of inking rollers and conveying rollers and tapes, is in a carriage running by the action of an oscillating lever from end to end of the press. At each end of the press are jointed tympan frames of a peculiar construction, which are periodically depressed by the action of a cam so as to come down over the cylinder, and (by the winding of a tympan cloth which recovers itself by a spring) feed in a sheet to receiving rollers near the top of the cylinder. The tympan on the right feeds in to the receiving rollers on the right of the cylinder, and *vice versâ*. From the receiving rollers it is conducted by endless tapes to the impression, it being prevented by fans from striking against the cylinder, and discharged on to a "depositor," (a travelling frame with endless bands), by which it is laid gently upon a receiving table at the end of the press. The carriage's motion is due to levers vibrating at the side of the machine on a bar at the bottom of the press.

[Printed, 1s. Drawings. Rolls Chapel.]

## A.D. 1835, March 18.—N° 6793.

SMITH, Andrew.—"A certain improvement or improvements "in printing machines."

1. The pressing cylinders have given to them by hand "the

" necessary motions to cause them to travel backwards or forwards
" in the machines, so that they can be moved any distance required
" at pleasure, to print on different sized sheets of paper, or take
" impressions from different sized forms of type."

2. Stationary delivering tables are placed at different parts of
the machines, for the purpose of supplying the sheets to the feeding apparatus by hand, the tables being adjustable to the length of
the pressing cylinder's path.

3. Apparatus for "receiving the sheets from the delivering
" tables, and giving them to the printing cylinders and guide tapes
" or bands, to be conducted through the machine and printed, and
" afterwards delivering the printed sheets from the machine."
In a machine combining the improvements in (1), (2), and (3),
the sheet comes by the motion of the cylinder over a "centre
" roller " on the top of it, when a "receiving roller " on one side of
it falls upon it by the action of a vertical rod upon an inclined
plane, and conveys the sheet to the impression. The sheet is
then discharged between the " centre roller" and an opposite
"receiving roller." When this machine is used to print in one
direction only, there is an arrangement by which the cylinder,
on its return, passes clear of the form. A machine of this kind
is shown in which the sheet is fed in between two stationary
rollers.

4. Fingers or gripers are mounted in grooves or recesses on the
cylinder, by which the sheets are laid hold of as they are presented
from the delivering tables, and carried round over the types for
the impression. Such gripers or fingers are intended to be used
when the receiving apparatus last mentioned is not applied in the
machines to take the sheets of paper from the delivering tables,
and give them to the cylinders. The gripers are on a shaft, which,
by the action of studs in the travelling frame on a weighted lever,
turns them down to seize the sheet hanging over the delivering
table, and raises them in a similar manner after the impression to
discharge it.

5. Machine which perfects " without the necessity of removing
" the sheets of paper from out of the machines during that opera-
" tion (that is to say), these machines have each two locomotive
" printing cylinders, and two forms of types, the sheets of paper
" being delivered to one of the printing cylinders from one of the
" delivering tables, and discharged from the other printing cylin-

" der after taking an impression from both forms of types, . . .
" and this operation of 'perfecting' the sheets takes place both in
" the forward and backward movements of the printing cylinders,
" . . . they both being alternately supplied from the delivering
" tables with the sheets of paper to be printed," and particularly in the " method of effecting the turning or reversing of the
" sheets . . . after being printed on one side by one printing
" cylinder, and conducting and presenting the same sheet . . .
" to the other printing cylinder to be printed on its other side,
" such improved perfecting machines having two stationary deli-
" vering tables before mentioned . . . and two forms of type
" placed in the centre . . . of the machines." The sheet is transferred from one cylinder to the other by a " reversing or transferring
" roller," mounted on the lower end of a lever in the travelling
frame, which changes its position by contact with a fixed tappet.
Each cylinder in this machine runs on a different bed, so as to
clear the other's form.

6. Application of the above improvements to machines having
two locomotive pressing cylinders and two forms, and " particu-
" larly in the improved . . . method of printing in two different
" colors from two different forms of type on one side of the sheet
" . . . without the necessity of removing the sheets of paper from
" out of the machine during this operation, which ' double print-
" 'ing' on one side of the sheet takes place both in the backward
" and forward movements of the printing cylinders ". . . the
" cylinders receiving their paper from two delivering tables."
The two forms together make up the subject, and are separately
colored, the color rollers running, as the cylinders in the former
case, in different beds. The sheet is fed in from delivering tables
in the middle of the machine between fixed rollers on one cylinder,
and after getting its impression from the first form, passes the
same side downwards by endless tapes over various rollers and
receives the remainder of the impression from the second form.
All the working parts of the above are driven from the pressing
cylinders or their framework.

A form of gripers is shown which are drawn inwards by helical
springs, and expand radially by the action of friction rollers running between guide pieces of a peculiar form.

[Printed, 3s. 6d. Drawings. London Journal (Newton's), vol. 8 (conjoined
    series), p. 201; Rolls Chapel Reports, 7th Report, p. 161. Rolls Chapel.]

## A.D. 1835, March 25.—N° 6800.

HOUSTOUN, WILLIAM.—" Certain improvements in tools,
" implements, or apparatus which are either used in or are sub-
" servient to the art of letter-press printing." Types of words or
parts of words of frequent occurrence (as *ac, all, am, and . . .
yet, yes, you, wn*) are cast together, the combined letters being cut
on one punch, in order to ensure uniformity in the matrix.

The patentee states that he does "not claim the combinations of
" letters in type which have been long in use, namely, *ff, fi, fl, ffi,*
" *ffl, æ, œ,* nor those which are attempted to be introduced by Lord
" Stanhope, namely, *th, in, an, re, se, to, of, on.*"

[Printed, 6*d.* Diagram plan of the " case" used with the above. Rolls
Chapel.]

## A.D. 1835, April 9.—N° 6809.

BERRY, MILES.—(Communicated.)—" Certain improvements in
" the construction of printing machinery or presses."

The principal feature of the invention is the mode in which two
friskets are worked at one end of the press, the one receiving the
impression, while the sheet is being changed in the other. The
friskets move in an upper and lower parallel groove, and pass
over each other alternately, being successively raised from the
lower groove for the impression by moveable plates, into which
they pass on arriving under the platen.

[Printed, 11*d.* Drawings. Rolls Chapel Reports, 7th Report, p. 162. Rolls
Chapel.]

## A.D. 1835, May 13.—N° 6834.

BUCHANAN, JOHN.—" Certain improvements in the construc-
" tion of cylendar printing machines, used for printing paper,
" calico, and other fabrics."

These " consist in the new arrangement of certain parts of an
" ordinary cylender printing machine, together with the construc-
" tion and adaptation of certain additional parts to such machine,
" by means of which I am enabled to print calicos and other
" fabrics usually printed in such machines, without the interven-
" tion of the endless woollen cloth or blanket required in ordinary
" machines of this nature, and also obtain other advantages."
They include, first, the adaptation of a revolving drying cylinder

to a cylinder printing or padding machine; and, secondly, a peculiar
mode of arranging the lapping on the boll, and certain appendages
for governing the course of the tapes.

[Printed, 2s. 4d. Drawings. Repertory of Arts, vol. 5 (*new series*), p. 80;
London Journal (*Newton's*), vol. 10 (*conjoined series*), p. 15. Rolls
Chapel.]

## A.D. 1835, October 23.—Nº 6916.

BAXTER, GEORGE.—"Improvements in producing coloured
" steel-plate, copper-plate, and other impressions."

The invention consists in coloring impressions of steel and
copper-plate engravings, and lithographic and zincographic
printing by means of block printing, in place of coloring such
impressions by hand " as heretofore practised." " In order
" to produce a number of ornamental prints resembling a highly
" coloured painting, whether in oil or water colours . . . I
" proceed, first, to have the design engraved on a copper or steel
" plate, or on stone or zinc, as is well understood, observing, how-
" ever, that I make several spots or points on the plate or stone from
" which the impressions are taken, in order to serve as register
" marks." Such points are very minute, and are so placed as to
be hidden by the color when laid on. Impressions of the print
having been taken, they are transferred to the coloring blocks,
each of which is cut away so as to leave only its own coloured part
in relief. " Having taken the number of impressions . . . and
" having the necessary block in the press for the first colour on
" the tympan, there are four or other number of fine points to
" receive the impression, which is to be coloured by a series of
" blocks, the fine points receiving each engraving at the four
" points . . . before mentioned; and on such tympan there
" are a number of points which are caused to strike through the
" paper in pulling the first printing of colour, and the point holes
" thus produced are those which are used for the purpose of secur-
" ing a correct register in all the future impressions from the
" wooden blocks, the holes which were marked on the original
" impression not being used after the first time." Metal blocks
will answer the same purpose as the wooden. Various specimens
of the invention were filed with the specification:—No. 1, steel-
plate engraving; Nos. 2-17, the same in various stages of colouring; Nos. 18–20, finished steel-plate coloured engravings; No. 21,

steel-plate engraving; No. 22, the same coloured with ten blocks; No. 23, print from the same blocks, illustrating "the old plan, "that of block printing alone;" No. 24, coloured copper-plate engraving; No. 25, lithographic print; No. 26, the same coloured. No impressions from zinc are given, "seeing that they resemble "lithographic impressions."

[Printed. Specimen Drawings (not published). London Journal (*Newton's*), vol. 34 (*conjoined series*), p. 434; Repertory of Arts, vol. 14 (*enlarged series*), p. 155; Patent Journal, vol. 7, p. 124. Rolls Chapel.]

A.D. 1835, November 10.—N° 6927.

GREIG, Thomas.—"A mode of embossing and printing at one "and the same time, by means of a cylinder or roller, on goods or "fabrics made of or from cotton, silk, flax, hemp, and wool, or any "one or more of these materials, or on paper and other fibrous "substances."

"My invention consists in a novel adaptation and arrangement "of machinery for embossing and printing silk, cotton, woollen, "paper, and other fabrics or goods in one or more colours at one "operation, either simultaneously or consecutively, by means of "revolving cylinders." The machine, as shown, consists of a pressing cylinder, with "three distinct printing cylinders of copper "or other suitable material" with their necessary appendages for printing three different colors upon the fabric, as it passes through the machine. The cylinders, having either engraved or raised surfaces, are furnished by trough rollers, "or endless felts "called sieves may be employed, as in ordinary printing machines," when the device is in relief. "The cylinders may be furnished "with doctors or scrapers when required, or the same may be "applied to the endless felts." The "doctors" are kept in their bearings by weighted levers and screws, and receive a slight endwise movement by the rotation of an excentric. If a back cloth be required between the paper bowl and the fabric, it must, for printing and embossing cotton, silk, or paper, be of linen or cotton, but if woollen goods are to be operated upon, of felt, "or "some such material." An iron roller above the pressing cylinder is used to obliterate from it the marks of the embossing roller. For embossing paper a counter roller is required, with a circumference which is some exact multiple of the embossing cylinder. The pattern cylinders are hollow; and there are hollow chambers under the color boxes, in order to regulate their temperature by the introduction of steam. The fabric being wound tightly on a roller at the back of the machine, is conducted between tension rails to the impression, after which it proceeds over a carrier roller and steam boxes, or into a hot room to be dried.

[Printed, 1s. 1d. Drawings. London Journal (*Newton's*), vol. 10 (*conjoined series*), p. 57; Rolls Chapel Reports, 7th Report, p. 167. Rolls Chapel.]

## A.D. 1837, April 18.—N° 7343.

NAPIER, DAVID.—" Improvements in letter-press printing."

1. Obtaining from a continuously revolving shaft reciprocating action, and appropriate periods of rest for the frisket frame, by the action of a " guide " (a wheel with excentric and concentric grooves upon the revolving shaft), upon a compound lever connected with the frisket frame. The frisket frame is double; and the sheet is thus changed at each end alternately while at rest for the impression, which is given by a platen in " any of the ordinary " ways."

2. Part of the type cylinder (stereotype) is made into a distributing surface for the ink, and the number of pressing cylinders is increased. A " feeding " (vibrating) roller takes ink in " the common way " from a " duct " roller, and communicates in two or three revolutions to the distributing surface, " so that " each set of inking rollers . . . will pass over the whole length " of distributing surface . . . before they come into contact with " the type, there being one set of inking rollers . . . for each " impressing cylinder." The paper may be supplied " in any of " the usual ways." A mode is represented, described as that " adopted by some of the most rapid machines at present in " use."

[Printed, 9d. Drawings. Repertory of Arts, vol. 9 (*new series*), p. 18; London Journal (*Newton's*), vol. 13 (*conjoined series*), p. 15. Rolls Chapel.]

## A.D. 1837, June 12.—N° 7389.

WOONE, GODFREY.—" An improved method of forming plates " with raised surfaces thereon, for printing impressions on different " substances."

" For the finer patterns used in calico or other printing, or

" paper-staining, or for engravings, such as are usually cut on box
" wood and printed at a type press," a coating (varying from one-
eighth to one-twenty-fourth of an inch in thickness) of white
lead (2) and plaster of Paris (1) is laid upon a block, and the design
scratched completely through it. For coarser patterns a slab of
metal, wood, pasteboard, or stone is substituted for the composition. From this block a cast is taken with stereotype metal,
papier maché, &c., and used as a printing surface.

Castings to be used upon a cylinder may either be cast in that
form, or " the plate may be cast level, and the required circular
" direction given by pressure."

[Printed, 4d. No Drawing. Repertory of Arts, vol. 9 (*new series*), p. 95:
London Journal (*Newton's*), vol. 13 (*conjoined series*), p. 162; Mechanics'
Magazine, vol. 29, pp. 163, 210, and 230. Rolls Chapel.]

## A.D. 1837, July 20.—N° 7411.

PALMER, WILLIAM.—" Improvements in printing paper-hang-
" ings."

The block is in a frame, by the motion of which it is alternately brought into contact with a color table (at the side of the
machine) and the paper, a " parallel frame" keeping it horizontal
during such motion. The coloring table is furnished by hand.
The impression is given by the action of a pressing lever, which,
when not engaged for the printing, is drawn back by a spring to
allow of the blocks passing to and from the color table. The
paper (in roll) is passed through the machine upon an endless
cloth. The register points are fixed on the sides of the table.
The axis to which the power is applied is hollow, and has two
handles, which, at a certain point, lock and act as one. The
machine is worked by three boys ; (1) furnishes the color surface,
(2) works the handle, and (3) moves the paper to register. After
the handles have locked, the block is raised from the color surface
and brought on to the paper, (3) then moves the pressing lever
inwards till it rests in a position for the impression, which is given
by the further revolution of the handle, (3) then pushes off the
pressing lever, (1) moves back the handles by which the block
returns to the color surface, and (3) brings forward a further surface of paper for the next impression.

[Printed, 1s. 3d. Drawings. Repertory of Arts, vol. 10 (*new series*), p. 31:
London Journal (*Newton's*), vol. 14 (*conjoined series*), p. 327. Rolls
Chapel.]

LOCKETT, Joseph.—(Communicated.)—" A new arrangement
" of machinery for the purpose of printing one, two, or more
" colours on cloth, paper, or other goods, by means of engraved
" blocks, or what is sometimes called surface printing."

1. Machine constructed to print on a continuous length of
cloth by means of three separate blocks or surfaces. The blocks
are attached to holders which are placed in grooves in carriages
moved by the action of cranks against "pronged pieces," jointed
to the carriages at the proper periods for the impression. Of these
carriages two work horizontally, the third vertically. The former
recover themselves by a spring, the latter " has a constant ten-
" dency to retire by its own weight, which is in part counter-
" balanced." The rollers of the printing table are furnished with
small needle points for preventing the slipping of the blanket or
goods to be printed, and forwarding the fabric through the
machine. The blocks are colored by sieves moving in grooves
in the printing table, the color being supplied to the sieves by
furnishing rollers, " similarly arranged to those used in ordinary
" printing machines " in connexion with a trough. " The alternate
" traverse is effected by a series of levers connected to each other,
" and receiving motion at the proper period . . . by means of
" an excentric scroll guide . . . placed on the driving shaft of
" the machine."

A machine similar to the above, for printing goods such as
handkerchiefs which require a border, with additional parts for
changing the movements of the carriages which require to be
interrupted in consequence of the borders, the period of this interruption varying with the width of the goods. " This machine
" prints three colours, as in that already described, two on the
" middle or filling of the handkerchief, and one on the border,
" the second colour when required in the border being blocked in
" by hand." The working of the carriage, and consequently the
printing of the block, is determined by the position of projections
upon a " face plate " in connexion with it. An arrangement is
shown for giving two strokes of the blocks in the same place.
" This requires that the driving apparatus should be so dis-
" posed that the cloth cannot move forward except once in two
" revolutions of the machine; and in many cases it is found useful

" that the second stroke of the block should be much lighter than
" the first," which is effected by varying the form and number of
teeth of the " face plate."

To print paper by this machine, modifications are required in
the position of the tables (which are placed horizontally), the
principal parts and mode of action being the same. The blocks
are colored by sieves furnished by " tear boys," with large
brushes from a tub. The paper is rolled upon a cylinder, from
which it is taken by claws or clamps which advance it periodically.
The color sieves stop when underneath the blocks, the latter then
descending upon them and taking color. The carriages then re-
ascend, the sieves are withdrawn, and the carriages a second time
descend and give the impression. The tear boys spread the color,
the clamps open by the action of pallets slipping forward a quantity equal to the width of the blocks, and immediately close. " At
" this moment the carriages re-ascend, and at the same time the
" clamps again take the place they occupied, and again bring the
" proper length of paper under the blocks." The printed paper is
dried in a stove.

[Printed, 3s. 1d. Drawings. Rolls Chapel.]

A.D. 1837, December 5.—N° 7499.

POOLE, Moses.—(Communicated.)—" Improvements in print-
" ing."

The object of the invention is " to construct the wedges em-
" ployed for the affixing and setting up forms of type of cast
" iron, rendered malleable by ordinary well-known means, such
" wedges being made according to one uniform system, by which,
" on bringing two wedges together, their outer sides will at all
" times offer parallel surfaces, whatever be the difference of size
" of such two wedges."

[Printed, 5d. Drawings. Repertory of Arts, vol. 10 (new series), p. 85;
London Journal (Newton's), vol. 14 (conjoined series), p. 320. Rolls
Chapel.]

A.D. 1838, March 8.—N° 7585.

BESSEMER, Henry.—" Certain improvements in machinery or
" apparatus for casting printing types, spaces, and quadrats, and
" the means of breaking off and counting the same."

These consist in,—1. Placing the metal pot vertically over the mould and the use of cylindrical plugs for closing and clearing the nipples. 2. Forming one side of the mould by a pusher, the adjustment of which varies the thickness of the type, and which pushes out the type when cast. 3. Forming another side of the mould by sliding doors, the other two sides of the mould being fixed. 4. Exhausting the air from the mould in the process of casting. 5. Applying a blast of cold air, externally or internally, to· cool the mould. 6. The use of a breaking-off apparatus or " separator," or vibrating plate, which clears the " breaks " from the types, and guides them as they fall into a receptacle. 7. The use of " intercepting plates " attached to the sliding doors to prevent any metal accidentally entering the mould. 8. A counting machine indicating the number of types cast.

[Printed, 7s. Drawings. Rolls Chapel.]

A.D. 1838, June 7.—Nº 7673.

KNIGHT, CHARLES.—" Improvements in the process and in " the apparatus used in the production of coloured impressions " on paper, vellum, parchment, and pasteboard by surface " printing," stated to be " applicable to the cheap multiplication " of colored maps, prints, pictures, drawings, and other works of " graphic art on sheets of paper, vellum, parchment, and paste- " board."

The improvements in the process consist,—1. In reversing the usual order of proceeding, by first printing the coloring or tinting, " and I finish by printing the outlines upon the colored " or tinted ground, by which means I obtain clearness and pre- " cision in the minutiæ of the impression, and thus I ensure a " brilliant and harmonious effect, which I call illuminated print- " ing or illuminated surface printing." Secondly, in printing several colors at the same time upon as many different sheets, " the position of the printing surfaces and the sheets with respect " to each being so changed after every impression that each " printing surface shall successively be applied to each sheet until " all the colors have been printed upon the corresponding parts " of all the sheets, and thus every sheet has become a fac-simile of " each of the other sheets. For convenience during the opera- " tion, one large sheet may receive all the impression, and after- " wards be cut up into as many small sheets as there are colors." Thirdly, in producing a compound tint by printing one color over the other in so short a time as not to allow the color first printed to become dry before the second is added, " thereby " affording an opportunity for the two colors to mix and form the " new tint;" and fourthly, in blending one color with another, by gradually bevelling the surface of each plate, so that at the boundary the depression is such as to receive the least possible quantity of color.

The improvements on the apparatus consist, first, "in certain " additions to the common printing press, by which I can print " various tints, shadings, and outlines successively upon one " sheet without removing the sheet from its tympan. Secondly, " in certain other additions to the common printing press . . . " by which I can print various colors or tints at one and the same " time upon as many different sheets as there are colors employed, " and by which I can shift the position of the printing surfaces " in respect of the sheets, so as to print successively all the colors " upon all the sheets."

The drawings represent:—1. A press for printing four colors in succession. The blocks are fixed on four beds hinged to the sides of a square table which are turned backwards to be colored, and downwards for the impression, which is given by the rising of the table, caused "by any ordinary system of levers or " screws." Each bed, with its appendages, is counterbalanced. 2. A rising table, carrying the tympan and frisket, acts in succession against the printing surfaces affixed to the sides of an octagonal prism. The inking is performed by hand at the top of the prism. "This octagonal or polygonal prism may be " used in combination with the Ruthven press, made deep " enough to receive the revolving prism, so that its upper surface " shall be held in the situation which the bed usually occupies." 3. " Press for printing four colors at the same time upon four " different sheets, . . . or upon four places on one large sheet " to be afterwards cut into four small sheets." Upon a " pri- " mary bed " (that of the common press) is a "secondary bed " turned by a key, and held by a catch in four different positions (somewhat like a railway turntable). The printing surfaces are fixed on four " tertiary beds " or discs, revolving on the " secondary "bed," by the revolution of which they are successively brought over four different sheets on the " primary bed." A centre wheel is so arranged that the tertiary beds revolve so as to be in the same relative position to the different parts of the press. In the case of a wood engraving of large size to be printed in three colors, three of the printing surfaces contain the portion to be in color, the fourth the outline. Register is obtained in the case of transferring a frisket from one press to another by the frame of the tympan falling between guides on the corners of the table.

In making printing surfaces for maps, where the words run in a curve or diagonally, types are let into a wooden block, and a stereotype taken from the block and types combined. Where the words occur parallel to the top or bottom, they are set up in the ordinary way, stereotyped, and printed from, either before or after the outline plate.

[Printed, 1s. 8d. Drawings. Rolls Chapel.]

### A.D. 1838, August 30.—N° 7786.

DOLIER, WILLIAM.—"A certain durable substance or tablet for " the purpose of receiving writings, drawings, or impressions of " engravings, or other devices capable of being printed, which sur- " face may be applied for roads or pavements, and part of which " invention may also be used as the means of strengthening and " beautifying glass."

1. The tablet consists of a slab of common glass enamel (flint glass, borax, and arsenic) ground with emery powder.

2. Flexible surface for maps, &c. A piece of linen has a coat of size laid on the back of it, and on the other side (having been rubbed smooth with pumice stone) three coats of flaked white, lin- seed oil, and turpentine. The back may be ornamented either by flocking or sprinkling it with gold, silver, or bronze powder, over a coating of buffalo size.

3. A pavement is made of "tablets," with designs on the under side, or Bath tiles of different colors, and the seams coated with glass enamel.

4. The glass is fused over a design in metal work. This is suit- able for ornamental windows, ships, dead-lights, &c.

[Printed, 3d. No Drawing. London Journal (Newton's), vol. 14 (conjoined series), p. 150. Rolls Chapel.]

### A.D. 1838, December 20.—N° 7918.

HOLM, CARL AUGUSTUS, and BARRETT, JOHN.—"Certain " improvements in printing."

1. The " distribution and feeding rollers " in a platen press are in the frisket frame, and " every time that this moveable frame " is pushed forward and backward the ink is supplied and distri- " buted over an inking table . . . at one or both ends of the type " table." A " setting off " sheet is wound on two small rollers on the platen. The sheet of paper is supported by a blanket till " flappers or dropping pieces " have time to catch the edges of the sheet in order to hold it extended during the printing opera- tion. The platen is brought down by a double-knee lever.

2. Two fixed platens, with type tables beneath them, are placed one above the other. The type tables rise by the action of a double- knee lever, and give the impression. Inking apparatus, as in 1, the inking rollers passing over the forms during the depression of the tables. The paper in roll is printed white at the upper platen, turned by a cylinder, and receives reiteration from the lower one, after which it is brought to scissors and cut to any dimensions required.

3. Inking apparatus :—(a) The " distribution rollers " laid at an angle across the press, have one bearing fixed, and the other moveable.˙ " On that end of the rollers where they lay in the fixed " bearing, there is adapted a spring . . . or counterpoise, which " pushes the rollers from one to two inches longitudinally every " time that the rollers leave the inking table." (b) Modifica- tion of the same, in which the distributing rollers are supported on two double-armed levers, one longer than the other, and have a vibrating and traversing motion, the former being given by a counterpoise put in motion by the action of the machine.

4. " Printing by means of an alternating moveable form against " one or more cylinders laying in fixed bearings, whereby it is " possible to print both during the forward and backward motion " of this form." The drawings show machines with one, two, three, and four cylinders on the same principle. In each the type table is provided with two inking tables, and has a rack from which the cylinder is driven. The sheet is fed in from a feed table, seized by a drop-down roller, and carried to the impression and discharged on to a receiving table by endless tapes.

5. Modes of combining apparatus to supply color to blocks in block printing. The blocks are in a rising and falling frame.

Three modes are shown in the drawings in which "elastic rollers
" take the colour from cylinders or surfaces on which it has been
" spread, and passing under the blocks communicate the colour
" to them," and a fourth, in which "elastic rollers by the motion
" given to them by the frame in which they are fixed press a web
" to which colour has been supplied in the usual manner against
" the blocks."

A drawing is given, showing "how it is possible, by adding
" another printing cylinder and another set of engraved rollers to
" the modern cylindrical calico-printing machine, to print on both
" sides of the stuff."

[Printed, 2s. 1d. Drawings. Rolls Chapel.]

## A.D. 1839, January 15.—Nº 7937.

BURCH, JOSEPH.—" Certain improvements in printing cotton,
" woollen, paper, and other fabrics and materials.'

" The invention consists in a mode of printing and grounding
" by blocks any number of colors or shades of colors at one and
" the same time; also in a mode of printing on damped calico or
" other suitable fabrics, and the means of drying, which pro-
" duces an effect not before shewn;" in printing and grounding
a number of pieces with separate patterns in one machine at the
same time; and in improvements in the mode of supplying
the tiering brushes, cleansing the backing, and drying and
collecting the cloth after it is printed; also in applying a long
moveable table to the machine, by which, when the first colors are
dried, the piece can be replaced, to be grounded again if required
" also grounding fine shades on blotch grounds, which is essential
" where the first colors have been worked thin, as the fine shades
" are liable to mix on a large body of color while it is wet."

The improvements consist in causing the perpendicular descent of
the printing and dipping beams, and spring pressers and mauls, by
mechanical arrangement, in separating the table from the printed
piece before the time the piece is moved on to prevent the colour
slurring the back of the piece and to allow the oilskin to move
simultaneously to the cleansing apparatus, and in heating the
printing table by steam, hot air, &c.; also " in tinting natural
" flowers on the surface of the printing block, and printing by
" means of my traversing frame on various materials. By this

" method, with a double frame to work two blocks, I am enabled
" to print a dozen or more shades of colours to a pattern, giving
" flowers and landscapes their natural hues, and producing effects
" superior by far to the old method of rainbowing."

[Printed, 3s. 8d. Drawings. Rolls Chapel.]

### A.D. 1839, June 26.—N° 8133.

DUCÔTÉ, PIERRE AUGUSTE.—" Certain improvements in the
" art of printing on paper, calicoes, silks, and other fabrics."

The first is the application of stone rollers or cylinders as printing surfaces. To produce the subject in relief, the drawing is
made on it with white wax (2), asphaltum (4), Burgundy pitch (2),
and soap (2), and (the ends and axle being protected with the
same composition) turned in a trough of nitric acid. The composition is then washed off with spirits of turpentine. For intaglio
patterns the portions of the surface eaten away would be the design
or pattern. The next is a mode of printing paper, calicoes, silks,
and other fabrics twice or oftener with the same device, drawing,
or pattern, or parts thereof in register, " whatever be the number
" of impression or printing rollers." Cog wheels on the ends of
the subject roller take into chains carring a series of " clamps or
" holders," which hold the fabric securely for the requisite number
of impressions. These clamps consist of an upper and lower plate,
and are peculiarly constructed to facilitate their opening and
closing. Paper, particularly when weak, is conducted through the
machine on an endless cloth.

[Printed, 7d. Drawings. Inventors' Advocate, vol. 1, p. 243. Rolls Chapel.]

### A.D. 1839, July 20.—N° 8159.

POOLE, MOSES.—(Communicated.)—" Improvements in casting
" for printing purposes."

The invention consists of a mode of obtaining castings of
surfaces for printing purposes by means of flexible moulds,
" whereby I am enabled to obtain flat plates or curved surfaces
" or forms, to be employed in printing with flat or cylindrical
" printing presses." Upon a sheet of paper are placed successively a coating of glue, a layer of paste and potters' earth,
and " on to this a sheet of tissue paper, and then another

" layer of the composition, until the whole assumes the required
" thickness (about one-eighth of an inch). The last sheet of
" paper should have applied to it a coating of sweet oil. With
" this flexible material (before it is dry) an impression is taken
" from types or other printing surface by pressure in any convenient manner." If for immediate use the mould may be
dried by heat. When dry it is placed between plates of the
form required for the stereotype to be cast, and the casting
performed in the usual manner.

[Printed, 3d. No Drawing. Inventors' Advocate, vol. 2, p. 133. Enrolment
Office.]

### A.D. 1839, August 14.—Nº 8,194.

BERRY, MILES. — (Communicated.) (a)—" A new or improved
" method of obtaining the spontaneous reproduction of all the
" images received in the focus of the camera obscura."

A plate of copper, the thickness of a card, is coated thinly with
silver. It is polished by sprinkling it with pounce powder, and
rubbing it with oiled cotton, and, when perfectly polished, with
dry cotton. A uniform tint is then produced upon it by the
application of nitric acid dissolved in water. The plate is finally
cleaned by sprinkling it with powdered pounce, or pumice powder,
or calcined venetian tripoli, and slightly rubbing it with carded
cotton. It is then exposed to heat until the silver surface becomes
of a whitish tint, when it is cooled rapidly and polished again. It
is then rubbed again with acid dissolved in water, sprinkled
with pounce powder, and rubbed with cotton. " The acid is then
to be laid upon the plate, say three different times, care being
taken to sprinkle each time the plate with powder, and to rub it
" dry and very lightly with clean cotton. . . . When the plate is
" not intended for immediate use or operation the acid may be
" used only twice upon its surface after being exposed to the
" heat." Before using the plates in the camera it is "indispen-
" sable" to put "at least once more some acid on the plate, and
" to rub it lightly with pounce, as before stated."

The second operation is that of applying a sensitive layer to the
silver surface. For this purpose the plate is fastened (silver side

(a) Ante, p. 35.

outwards) to a board, which is then laid upon a ledge in a well-closed box, so that the plate is exposed to the exhalation of iodine, by which means the silver receives a coating of fine golden yellow. The colour deepens with the length of exposure. If too deep, the deposit must be removed, and the polishing repeated. The vapour of iodine may either be applied by placing some of it in a cup, covered with gauze, at the bottom of the box, or by laying it parallel to a board saturated with iodine, which will serve for coating " several plates during a whole day, or even several days." This operation should be performed in a dark room.

The third operation consists " in submitting in the camera " obscura the prepared surface or plate to the action of the light, " so that it may receive the images." The position to be occupied by the plate is ascertained by the insertion of a ground glass plate, on which the object appears distinct when at a proper focal distance. The glass is then removed, and the prepared plate put in its place. The transference of the plate should be effected in the dark, or by the light of a wax taper. The camera is then closed, obscuring shutters are then opened, and the plate is ready to receive the impression. " Nothing more need be done but to " open the aperture of the camera obscura, and to consult a watch, " to reckon the minutes the prepared surface shall be under " the action of the light " which may vary from three to thirty minutes, depending upon the intensity of the light. The second and third operations should be conducted with as short an interval as possible.

The fourth operation, which must follow at not more than one hour's interval upon the third, consists in " bringing out " the picture, which is not visible when the plate is taken out of the camera. For this purpose it is exposed in the closed box, at an angle of 45°, to vapour of mercury. When a thermometer immersed in the mercury indicates 60° centigrade, the spirit lamp, by which the evaporation has been produced, is removed. When the thermometer has fallen 45° the plate is taken out, and the operation is complete. This stage of the process is performed by candle light. The box has a glass side, for the purpose of observation.

The plate may be kept in this state for several months without undergoing any alteration, provided it be not frequently exposed in the open daylight.

" The fifth and last operation is that of removing the sensitive
" layer or coating." The plate is immersed in pure water and
drawn out again immediately, it is then, without allowing it to
dry, plunged into pure salt water or a solution of hyposulphite of
pure soda, the plate being moved about in it by a small hooked
instrument. It is then placed on an incline, and hot but not
boiling distilled water poured gently over it, so as to carry away
the salt or hydrosulphite. When this washing is completed the
picture is finished, and requires only to be protected by glass from
friction, dust, and vapours which tarnish silver.

> [Printed 11*d*. Drawings. Repertory of Arts, vol. 13 (*new series*), p. 176,
> vol. 6 (*enlarged series*), p. 256, vol. 8 (*enlarged series*), p. 67, and vol. 14
> (*enlarged series*), p. 293; London Journal (*Newton's*), vol. 16 (*conjoined
> series*), p. 1, vol. 21 (*conjoined series*), p. 57, vol. 28 (*conjoined series*),
> p. 368, vol. 31 (*conjoined series*), p. 64, and vol. 34 (*conjoined series*),
> p. 438; Mechanics' Magazine, vol. 32, p. 77, vol. 31, p. 464, and vol. 47,
> p. 45; Patent Journal, vol. 3, p. 157, also vol. 7, p. 125; Inventors' Advo-
> cate, vol. 2, p. 163; Common Bench Reports, vol. 3, p. 97, also vol. 8,
> p. 165; Carrington and Kirwan's Reports, vol. 2, p. 667. Rolls Chapel.]

### A.D. 1839, November 21.—N° 8278.

DUCÔTÉ, Pierre Auguste.—" Improvements in printing
" china, porcelain, earthenware, and other like wares, and for
" printing on paper, calicoes, silks, woollens, oilcloths, leather,
" and other fabrics, and for an improved material to be used in
" printing."

[The then obtaining mode of printing on china is stated, and
the costliness of the " stippling" requisite for " bat printing"
pointed out.] 1. An impression is taken with linseed oil from
an etched stone upon a surface of glue, india-rubber, or glue
and treacle, and transferred by pressing the oil out with a
" dossill"(*a*) to the ware, which is then " dusted over with the
" color powder, in like manner to what is now practised when
" impressions from sunken engravings on copper are employed
" and transferred on to glazed surfaces of ware." Zincographic
impressions may be treated in the same way. For printing on
biscuit ware, before glazing the stone is prepared as described in
N° 8133, (the etching ground being white wax (2), asphaltum
(4), Burgundy pitch (2), and soap (2) ), and the impression taken
on pottery tissue paper, and transferred to the ware. For sunk

---

(*a*) From the old French *dosil*, a stopple, and not as Johnson thinks from
dorsel. (Todd.)

chalk, or granulated designs, the drawing (reversed in respect of light and shade) is made with " lithographic chalk, ink, or other " material, as is well understood," a soft etching ground spread over the rest of the stone, and the design etched in. Slabs thus prepared may be used in the same way as wood blocks, in the printing of paper, calicoes, silk, woollens, oilcloth, leather, &c.

A block of biscuit in the state known as " printing body," may be substituted for the stone for coarse designs.

Substitution of birdlime or vegetable gluten (liquified with spirits of turpentine or naphtha) for potters' varnish. " When " applying it the surfaces do not require heat, and by mixing it " with the color and with it about 1-6th part by weight of " burnt borax ground to a fine powder, decreasing the quantity " of silex used with the color by a quantity equal to the borax " added, and the impressions transferred to the wares will at once " take the glaze, having previously dipped the article so printed " into a caustic alkaline ley."

[Printed, 5d. No Drawing. Inventors' Advocate, vol. 2, p. 355. Enrolment Office.]

A.D. 1839, December 16.—No 8316.

MORISON, David.—" Improvements in printing."

The general principle of this invention is, " that of establishing " perfectly equalized motion between contiguous parts of printing " machinery, making them mutually act upon each other, inde- " pendent of any pressure or contact subsequently applied."

1. An inking apparatus on this principle is shown, in which the arrangement of the rollers is vertical, the trough being at the top, fitting over the trough roller. The whole is driven by a rack on the type table gearing with the inking rollers. Endwise motion is given to one or more of the rollers in it by means of a spring at one end, and an inclined pivot or bearer at the other.

2. The principle is applied to cylinder printing in two ways; first, " when quick printing is required, a stereotype plate is laid " on the main cylinder (horizontal), and around this are placed " as many pressing cylinders and inking apparatus alternately as " the size of the respective rollers will admit of, or rapidity " requires." The power is in this case applied to the main cylinder. The sheets are fed in by tapes at each pressing cylinder

as rapidly as the centre cylinder turns.   Secondly, for printing in colors, the centre cylinder acts as a pressing cylinder, the printing rollers for the various colors, with their respective coloring apparatus, being arranged around it so as to print in register. The material is also fed in by tapes.

3. In a " vibrating printing machine."   The type table is here the segment of a cylinder, the form being on its upper surface, and the pressing and inking apparatus so arranged as to act as the form passes beneath them in vibrating about the cylinder axle.   The sheet is fed in by tapes, and an impression obtained for each vibration.   " And I find when the section of a large " cylinder is thus used, good and equal impressions may be taken " from very large surfaces of the types in common use," by giving a slight bevel to the furniture in which the form is locked. " In this way newspapers may be printed, placing the columns " parallel to the axle of the cylinder, " and giving a slight bevel to " the rules between the columns."

Among the advantages of this principle is mentioned " the " capability of printing from any kind of raised figures, even of " comparatively soft materials . . . thus rendering the process " peculiarly applicable to paper-hangings."   Good sharp impressions, it is stated, have been obtained in this way from leather, paper, cork, &c.

4. " Machine for printing upon substances of unequal thick- " nesses, such as letters or newspapers," consisting of two cylinders, the one having a spring or otherwise elastic surface, and the other carrying the requisite stamps, which are inked as it evolves.   The article to be printed on is passed between them.

5. Machine for printing or stamping.   The stamp is on the outside of a circular surface, part of which forms a small inking table.   By the action of a hand lever the stamp is alternately drawn down for the impression, a small inking roller (furnished from the inking table) passing over it as it moves.

[Printed, 6d.   Drawings.   Inventors' Advocate, vol. 2, p. 415.   Enrolment Office.]

A.D. 1840, March 13.—No 8427.

GAUBERT, Etienne Robert. — " Certain improvements in " machinery or apparatus for distributing types or other typo-

" graphical characters into proper receptacles, and placing the
" same in order for setting up after being used in printing."

Machine for distributing, which " will, in three minutes, do
" what would occupy a workman two or three hours." The
types (108 in number) are divided into two equal " classes,"
each containing three " divisions," with " subdivisions" of six.
The " classes " are determined by having or not having a notch
on the foot of the type; the " divisions" by the absence or position of a nick on one side of the type; and the " subdivisions " by
its absence or position on the other. The separation is effected by
passing them ever holes furnished with pins corresponding to their
form, and finally under bridges which select them according to
thickness. The plane, on which types and spaces are promis-
cuously laid, is inclined and made to oscillate slightly " by any
" suitable mechanical contrivance." The types pass hence to a
" directing plane," and thence in a row by oblique bars into
" directing passages," the sides of which are high enough to allow
of the passage of one type only at a time, consequently if one letter
is on the top of the other " the upper one would be shaken off and
" fall down into a receptacle." In each passage are two bolts,
raised and lowered alternately so as to prevent more than one
type passing down at the same time. From these passages they
pass to a " sifting or separating plate," furnished with " apertures
" sufficiently long to admit of the 'spaces' passing through them,
" but not long enough to allow letters or other characters to pass."
The spaces are thus separated and conveyed away. The types may
fall on to the separating plate in four different positions " before it
" is allowed to escape into compartments to undergo a similar
" sifting." The positions are " upon one or other of its faces, and
" also with the head to the right or left." The falling type is, by
means of obstacles in its path, turned round and shot foot foremost
down " diagonal ways," which direct it into the lower compartments of a plate below and parallel to the separating plate, where it
is caused to turn round and fall against oblique guides which
direct it into its compartment, " but always keeping the foot or
" end of the type to the right." Those types which do not fall
properly, so as to pass through apertures in this last plate, are
replaced on the original inclined plane; the rest fall on to a
second plate, called " the plate for separating the classes." Hence
the types of the same subdivision pass to a " common conductor,"

at the end of which is an apparatus called the "plane for sepa-
"rating by thickness," furnished for that purpose with a series
of bridges of decreasing height. The spaces are similarly sorted,
according to their thickness.

[Printed, 1s. 5d. Drawings. London Journal (*Newton's*), vol. 19 (*conjoined
series*), p. 233; Inventors' Advocate, vol. 3, p. 213. Petty Bag.]

## A.D. 1840, March 13.—N° 8428.

YOUNG, JAMES HADDEN, and DELCAMBRE, ADRIEN.—"An
" improved mode of setting up printing types."

The invention consists in a set of elevated chambers containing
types, "which are pushed out of the said chambers, in the order
" required, by levers, and what we call pushers, acted upon by
" keys somewhat similar to pianoforte keys, touched for that
" purpose by the fingers and thumbs, and when pushed out of
" their respective chambers the types fall upon an inclined plane
" grooved and set at so steep an inclination that the type, on
" being pushed out of its chamber, instantly slides down the
" groove adapted to receive it (this groove leading to one point at
" the lower end of the inclined plane, where all the grooves on
" the inclined plane meet immediately over a small box), and
" drops into the said box," which answers the purpose of a
composing stick. The pushers recover themselves by a spring.
There are provisions for preventing breakage of the type by its
sticking in the channel leading to the composing box (by means
of a hinged piece and spring), and for preventing its jumping out
from the cross grooves (by means of a "shield"). For each additional letter that falls into the composing box the part of the line
already formed is, by the same action of the key, moved on. When
a line is complete it is moved sideways (by a winch) to make room
for the next. The completion of the line is notified to the workman by a rod entering a loop. On the completion of a page the
types are placed in the ordinary chase for printing.

[Printed, 1s. 4d. Drawings. London Journal (*Newton's*), vol. 19 (*conjoined
series*), p. 174; Mechanics' Magazine, vol. 33, p. 317; vol. 36, p. 497; and
vol. 37, p. 401; Artizan, vol. 9, p. 77; Inventors' Advocate, vol. 3, p. 196;
Transactions of the Society of Arts, vol. 54, p. 168. Enrolment Office.]

## A.D. 1840, March 17.—N° 8434.

BAGGS, ISHAM.—" Improvements in engraving, which improve-
" ments are applicable to lithography."

A mode of combining a swinging frame, capable of engraving several plates at one time, of the same or different sizes, with a pentagraph " or other such like instrument for reducing or " enlarging drawings." The plates to be engraved are clamped to horizontal tables affixed at different points to two vertical bars, suspended so as to form a sort of universal joint. The tracing or cutting points are suspended by cords from an "ex- " centric bar " in an iron frame, which is also suspended from centre carriages. The pentagraph is at the foot of the vertical rods. Motion is given to the swinging frame by a handle. The subject may be engraved on the enlarged or reduced scale, either immediately from the original, or by first obtaining the enlarged or reduced drawing, and thence executing the engraving.

In applying this apparatus to the purposes of lithography, " unxious or other suitable points" are substituted for the tracing points.

[Printed, 1s. 7d. Drawings. Repertory of Arts, vol. 15 (new series), p. 65 ;
Mechanics' Magazine, vol. 33, p. 348; Inventors' Advocate, vol. 3, p. 227.
Enrolment Office.]

A.D. 1840, March 30.—N° 8458.

MARTIN, HENRY.—" Improvements in preparing surfaces of " paper."

1. " By combining thereon a coating of oil paint with subsequent " embossing." To obtain a coating of oil paint, (a) the paper (sized or not) has the color worked upon it as evenly as possible with a " common paint brush," scoured over lightly with a clothes or shoe brush, and smoothed over with a " softener " (brush of badger's hair); (b) the oil paint is laid on by passing the paper between two rollers, together with an endless felt or other fabric supplied with oil color as it passes through a trough and under a roller partly immersed in the oil paint or color, a scraper being placed to act upon the felt as it ascends. " Having obtained paper coated with oil paint by the above or " such like means, I submit it, when dry, to the operation of " embossing, by passing it between properly engraved rollers, or " I use dies, as is well understood."

2. By combining thereon a coating of oil paint, and afterwards printing or producing thereon the required pattern for paper-hangings. The paper having received its coating of oil paint, is

printed by blocks or other surfaces, " as is now generally practised."
When making paper-hangings in imitation of marble, I prefer to
" resort to that mode wherein the design is produced, or a liquid, as
" is well understood; and I prefer to take the impression on to the
" printed surface of the paper before that printed surface is dry.
" By this means the effect will be improved, as it allows of soften-
" ing off by a brush."

3. By " combining thereon a coating of oil paint, and subse-
" quent glazing or planishing." The paper being coated with oil
paint, " I use plain or tinted or water-color under grounds, . . .
" the oil-color surface being laid on by the above or other
" suitable means, the oil paint being such as is used for flatting."
After the turpentine, with which the color is thinned, has
evaporated, " the color becomes set, and will allow a smooth
" knife to be passed over without injuring the surface, and when
" it is in such state, it is to be glazed as early as possible. For
" this purpose I lay the paper upon a . . . soft material. . . . I
" then take a pallet knife or a trowel having a good smooth
" or polished surface, and lay it flat on the painted surface of
" the paper, and pass it along with a slight pressure, the color
" being set it yields to the pressure, and glaze is thereby pro-
" duced; or other means may be resorted to for glazing. When
" the surface is dry it may be heightened by the well-known means
" used for glazing and planishing, or the paint on the paper may
" be dry before planishing." Paper thus planished is stated to be
suitable for " copper and other plate engravings, as also for paper-
" hangings and other purposes."

4. " Laying on a coating of oil paint on paper by means of
" rollers."

[Printed, 4d. No Drawing. Repertory of Arts, vol. 16 (new series), p. 50 ;
London Journal (Newton's), vol. 23 (conjoined series), p. 17 ; Mechanics'
Magazine, vol. 33, p. 382 ; Inventors' Advocate, vol. 3, p. 229 ; Engineers'
and Architects' Journal, vol. 3, p. 396, and vol. 6, pp. 305 and 400. Enrolment Office.]

A.D. 1840, June 9.—N° 8538.

EDMONDSON, Thomas.—" Certain improvements in printing
" presses."

The invention consists, firstly, in " a certain novel arrangement
" of mechanism " for printing a set form of type in one part of

the press, and a varying form, as a regularly progressive number, letter, or other character, in another part.

On depressing a hand lever below the table, a vibrating lever sweeps a card from a box or chamber at the back of the machine, and thereby pushes forward those already printed along the table, so as to bring them one by one under the type wheels. The same action of the lever brings up the table, so as to give the impression from the fixed type and type wheels. There are two type wheels numbered from 0—99. Each stroke of the lever advances the first one figure, by means of a rod carrying a click. The ribbon is, by the mechanism of the machine, drawn backwards and forwards, so as to intervene between the type wheel and the card.

2. Machine " put into complete operation by merely pushing " the end of a cardboard ticket into the apparatus." A saturated ribbon on two ratchet wheels passes over a form on a table. The ticket being inserted, the impression is given by pressing lightly against the front of a receiving lever. The ribbon at the same time is moved upon the ratchet wheels.

3. Portable apparatus for office use. The elementary parts and inking ribbon are the same as (2). The types are in a frame on a bed plate, while another frame of parallel bars carries the printing table. On pressing a lever handle backwards the types are held down, while the impression is given by the pressure of a cam.

[Printed, 1s. 4d. Drawings. Mechanics' Magazine, vol. 34, p. 13. Petty Bag.]

## A.D. 1840, August 27.—N° 8610.

LOCKETT, Joseph.—" Certain improvements in manufacturing, " preparing, and engraving cylinders, rollers, or other surfaces for " printing or embossing calicoes or other fabrics."

These consist, first, " in the employment or application of the force " or power usually termed galvanic or voltaic electricity, and by " means of the same force or power recoating, covering, or thicken- " ing those cylinders, rollers, or other surfaces which have been " manufactured by this or any other process, the engraving or " etching upon which is required to be obliterated, or which may " have been reduced by former use, or to manufacture a new roller " or cylinder by the same process." Secondly, "in a peculiar method " of preparing surfaces by galvanic or voltaic electricity, appli-

" cable to cylinders, plates, or blocks for printing or embossing
" calicoes and other fabrics." The parts of the engraved roller,
&c., to be retained are coated with an etching ground; those to be
obliterated are left bare, and are consequently filled up by the
electro deposit. "Thirdly, in a simple mechanical contrivance"
(a revolving cutting or filing tool) "to be applied either to the
" ordinary slide lathe or the engraving machine commonly used
" for cylindrical engraving, for the purpose of cleaning, filing, or
" turning off the superfluous portions of the copper thus de-
" posited."

[Printed, 10d. Drawings. London Journal (Newton's), vol. 19 (conjoined
series), p. 89; Mechanics' Magazine, vol. 34, p. 221; Inventors' Advocate,
vol. 4, p. 150. Petty Bag.]

## A.D. 1840. September 17.—Nº 8633.

POOLE, MOSES. — (Communicated.)--" Improvements in pre-
" paring materials to facilitate the teaching of writing."

This process consists in producing copies of letters and of hair
strokes, by which children are to be taught to trace, by the application of typography and with colored ink, or with one of a pale tint,
of whatever shade it may be, but capable of being passed over
again with writing ink. In order to make the formation of
MSS. letters, when printed, "correspond with the principles
" of caligraphy, . . . I have employed every means of joining
" letters, . . . giving the preference to the shape of the letter
" which afforded the greatest regularity in the direction of the
" different hair strokes; indeed, for every hair stroke that could
" belong to a letter, I have had a type of the letter cast. The ink
" suitable for printing these copies is made by dissolving in water
" the most suitable vegetable or mineral colours. . . . A cer-
" tain quantity of this liquid is mixed with white lead until it
" becomes perfectly coloured; the mixture is then dried and after-
" wards made use of in the composition of ink by grinding it on a
" marble slab with" as little unboiled linseed oil as possible.

[Printed, 3d. No Drawing. Mechanics' Magazine, vol. 34, p. 251; Inventors'
Advocate, vol. 4, p. 197. Enrolment Office.]

## A.D. 1840, November 5.—Nº 8683.

HULLMANDEL, CHARLES JOSEPH.—" A new effect of light
" and shadow, imitating a brush or stump drawing, or both com-

" bined, produced on paper, being an impression from a plate or
" stone prepared in a particular manner for that purpose ; as also
" the mode of preparing the said plate or stone for that object."
The drawing being made upon the plate or stone "with ordinary
" lithographic ink dissolved in water, and with the use of a brush
" or a hair pencil, or with the stump, or with any of these styles
" mixed, it is prepared with acid, as is usually done with chalk
" drawings." As soon as dry, a " solution of resin in a volatile
" solvent, such as is generally used in aquatinting," is poured
over the drawing. On the solvent evaporating, the resin cracks
and exposes certain portions of the plate or stone. The resin is
then well fixed on the drawing by heat, and a strong mixture of
nitric or muriatic acid (1) and gum water (6) thrown over the
whole, by which the unprotected parts are etched or bitten in.
" The ground and the drawing are then washed off with spirits
" of turpentine, and the plate or stone is ready for printing . . .
" it is evident that the new preparation aforesaid of the said plate
" or stone may be performed before or after the ordinary process
" of washing off the drawing is accomplished."

*Note.*—By a disclaimer and memorandum of alteration, enrolled
May 25, 1842, the patentee disclaims the use of the word "plate,"
and confines himself to " stone." He states that the " new pre-
" paration " can only be performed before the washing off of the
drawing, and qualifies the words " etching and biting " by prefixing to them the words "what I call."

[Printed (with Disclaimer), 4d. No Drawing. Mechanics' Magazine,
vol. 34, p. 207; Inventors' Advocate, vol. 4, p. 164; Transactions of the
Society of Arts, vol. 54, p. 174. Enrolment Office.]

## A.D. 1840, November 27.—N° 8726.

CLAY, JOHN, and ROSENBORG, FREDERICK. — " Improve-
" ments in arranging and setting up types for printing."

Composing machine. The types are arranged in a series of
grooves in vertical plates at the top of the machine, the upper
case being in front and the lower case at the back. On depressing
one of a series of keys, the upper part of a weighted lever by its
action on a slider pushes the particular type from its compartment on to a horizontal groove, while, by the action of the same

lever upon a snail-formed bar in the machine, a "conductor" sweeps them one by one into a "receiver" or rectangular chamber immediately below it, where they accumulate upon the upper edge of a vertical sliding plate, which, being balanced by a weight, descends as each is successively deposited, so as to bring it below the level of the plane and make room for the next. The length of the conductor's path is regulated by the length of the sliders which push out the type. The pressure of an upper slider acting upon the type at every stroke forces down both type and plate a distance equal to the thickness of the deposited type, and the plate is held in its depressed positions by spring clicks acting upon a ratchet wheel. The length of the composed line is shown by an index upon an axle turning against a graduated dial plate. In order to compose a second line, the first is lowered to the bottom of the composing chamber and deposited there, while the sliding plate is raised again to receive another line. "In this way "the several lines of type are composed and forced back into the "chamber in the form of a page or column, a graduated dial and "index showing the progress made in its formation." To prevent the type being thrown off the plane by the rapid action of the conductor, the latter is furnished with two smal 'spring latches," which, "when the conductor comes up to the type, pass over it "and hold the type securely and in its right position as it slides "along the plane, and when the type has arrived immediately "over the recess . . . the latches are raised by two small plates, "which leaves the type free in the recess, and the conductor is "allowed to return without touching the type."

A modification of the above machine, in which the types are conveyed upon an endless band as a substitute for the action of the conductor.

[Printed, 3s. 3d. Drawings. London Journal (*Newton's*), vol. 20 (*conjoined series*), p. 233; Mechanics' Magazine, vol. 34, p. 462; Artizan, vol. 9, p. 77; Inventors' Advocate, vol. 4, p. 373. Petty Bag.]

A.D. 1840, December 17.—N° 8743.

MABLEY, WILLIAM TUDOR.—" Certain improvements to be " used in printing, embossing, or impressing."

The invention " consists in certain modifications or applica-" tions of the art known as electrography or electro-metallurgy." If the design be symmetrical, one portion of it is executed " by

" any of the ordinary means," and the rest obtained by compression, casting, or electro deposit on a mould taken from it. The portions " are then placed together so as to form the " entire design in relief, and soldered or otherwise held in this " position." The whole is then placed in connection with a battery, when one consolidated plate is produced, possessing the entire design. In some cases a mould of the whole design may be formed in one piece by successively impressing one portion upon a sheet of soft metal. Various modes are given of dividing irregular patterns. " Before placing the electrotype copy " of the portion of the design in connection with the battery, I affix, " by means of clamps or otherwise, bars or ribs (by preference of " metal) along those edges . . . which are intended to be joined . . . " and then varnish or otherwise insulate certain parts, so that the " metal shall be precipitated " so as to form flanges. " By this " means I am enabled to get a more extensive surface to join the ⸽ portions with, and can dispense with solder or other adhesive " matter." Against the back of the flanges are placed stiff bars of metal, tightly pressed together by clamps. If "desired, the " finished plates or blocks may be subsequently coiled around a " drum or mandril, in order to print from a cylindrical surface."

2. " A mode of joining together engraved or otherwise executed " metallic plates." A groove is made along the edges to be joined, and the parts clamped together. All parts are then insulated, except the grooves, which are washed with dilute nitric acid. The whole is then placed in connection with the battery, and the parts united by the deposit.

3. Obtaining an extended surface to an engraved plate by taking a mould of such engraved plate and attaching thereto a plain metallic or other surface, and then submitting the whole to the action of the battery.

4. Producing surfaces suitable for printing or embossing without the aid of ordinary original engraving, (a) by drawing the design on a metal plate, coated with beeswax, turpentine, and lamp black, and obtaining a reverse by the battery, when the composition is melted away; similarly for embossing surfaces and cylinders, the latter being formed in segments; (b) by etching a stone roller so as to produce a relief surface, and coating it with an electro deposit. (c) The design is punched in sheet lead, which is soldered to a metal

plate, or the inside of a cylinder. The whole is then connected with the battery, and the lead melted from the precipitated metal.

5. Obtaining metallic surfaces suitable for printing in two or more colors. As many moulds as there are colors having been obtained from a sunk engraving, all portions, except one particular color, are removed by hand from each, and printing surfaces obtained from them by the battery.

6. Forming dies to be used in embossing or impressing buttons of hoof, horn, or tortoiseshell, " by precipitating metal through the " agency of voltaic electricity upon suitably formed moulds." Various modes of mounting a plate or block of such dies are shown.

7. Mode of mounting seals, bookbinders' tools, " and other " such instruments " by " causing the precipitated copy of the " design to attach itself in the act of depositing upon the holder of " such precipitated copy, instead of being attached thereto by sub- " sequent soldering."

8. Producing seals by setting up portions of them similar to ordinary type, and precipitating metal on them.

[Printed, 1s. 3d. Drawings. London Journal (*Newton's*), vol. 19 (*conjoined series*), p. 94; Mechanics' Magazine, vol. 34, p. 476; Inventors' Advocate, vol. 4, p. 406. Rolls Chapel.]

## A.D. 1841, January 23.—N° 8809.

BAGGS, Isham.—1. " Improvements in printing."

The pattern is stamped in different metals, according to the colors to be produced, and soldered on to a metal plate, or it may be woven in wires of different metals, and fixed on a block. For instance, for a yellow flower, green leaves, and a brown stalk, iron, copper, and silver are employed respectively. The impression is given by placing a sheet of paper, moistened with a solution of carbonate of soda, on the negative pole of the battery, laying the metal pattern upon the sheet, and completing the circuit. The colors are varied by varying either the metals or solutions.

2. The design is formed with fine platinum wire upon a glass plate, and laid upon a sheet moistened with a solution of iodide of potassium and starch, and being subjected to a current of electricity of high tension, an impression is produced in purple. " After the electricity has traversed one plate it may be conducted " to a second, from that to a third, and so on, and thus, with a

" single discharge, a hundred or more impressions, from as many
" different plates, may be simultaneously produced."

3. A circular copper tube, plugged at one end with plaster, is
filled with a solution of cochineal and potassa, by the percolation
of which through the plaster, and its reaction upon the acetate of
alumina, with which the paper is moistened, a pink circle, with
green rim, is produced on the completion of the circuit, caused by
the copper tube being in contact with the positive pole of the battery

In printing with electrical eels, &c. the saddle collectors are to be
those " introduced by Dr. Farraday." Each alternate wave is to
be cut off or reversed, " or the anions and cations will be mingled
" together, and the effect destroyed."

4. Tests for printing. " The plan to be adopted in this case is
" to make a mixture of different tests, with a due regard to the
" play of affinities which will be called into action." Thus, while
iodide of potassium produces, with lead, a beautiful yellow, no
metal will, with this reageant, form a blue at the same time, but a
mixture of protosalts of iron with sesque-ferrocyanuret of potassium, substituted for the simple iodide, will produce the required
blue and yellow.

[Printed, 4d. No Drawing. Repertory of Arts, vol. 16 (*new series*), p. 180 ;
Mechanics' Magazine, vol. 35, p. 143; Inventors' Advocate, vol. 5, p. 71.
Enrolment Office.]

## A.D. 1841, February 8.—N° 8842.

TALBOT, WILLIAM HENRY FOX (*a*).—"Improvements in obtain-
" pictures or representations of objects."

The first part of the preparation of the paper consists in washing
one side of it with a solution of crystallized nitrate of silver (100
grains) in distilled water (6 oz.), drying it, and then dipping it in
a solution of iodide of potassium (500 grains) in water (one pint),
keeping it there a minute or two, then dipping it in water and
afterwards drying it. Paper thus prepared will keep (if not exposed
to the light) "any length of time."

The second stage, which is best left until the paper is required for
use, consists in washing the iodized paper with gallo-nitrate of
silver (the mode of preparing this mixture is described) by candle-
light. The paper is then dipped in water, and, when dried, is ready
for use. The paper thus prepared, termed "calotype paper" is
placed in a camera, so as to receive an image from the lens, the paper

(*a*) Ante, p. 35.

being screened until it is secured in its place. On the screen being withdrawn, an image is formed on the paper, which is subsequently developed by washing the paper with gallo-nitrate of silver, and drying it before a gentle fire. The "fixing process" consists in dipping the picture into water, partly drying it with blotting paper, and washing it with a solution of bromide of potassium (100 grains) or common salt in water (8 or 10 ozs.) The picture is then washed with water, and finally dried. "The picture thus obtained is a " 'negative' one, that is, it has its lights and shades reversed with " respect to natural objects, viz., the lights of the objects are repre- " sented by shades, and vice versâ." A copy of this, with the natural lights and shades, is obtained by placing a second sheet of sensitive calotype paper, or "common photographic paper," (a) in close contact with the paper containing the picture, putting a board below them and a sheet of glass above, and pressing the whole together by screws. The papers thus arranged are exposed to the sun, when a picture with natural lights (a "positive" picture) is produced on the second sheet, and developed in the same way as the first.

The negative picture, when rendered faint by having furnished several copies, may be revived by washing it by candlelight with gallo-nitrate of silver, and then warming it. The revived picture must then be "fixed" as before.

2. To produce a "positive" picture by a single process. A sheet of calotype paper is slightly discoloured by exposure for a few seconds to daylight. It is then dipped in a solution (as above) of iodide of potassium and afterwards in water, lightly dried with blotting paper, and placed in the camera. "After five or ten minutes the " paper is withdrawn, and washed with gallo-nitrate of silver, and " warmed as before directed. An image will then appear of a " positive kind. . . . Engravings may be copied in the same way," but the pictures will be inverted. The copy may be strengthened with gallo-nitrate of silver.

For taking portraits, the focal length of the lens should be only three or four times greater than the diameter of the aperture. The process should be conducted "in the open air under a serene sky, " but without sunshine." The portrait on the calotype paper will be a "negative."

---

(a) "This paper," the patentee observes, " is made by washing good writing paper, first, with a weak solution of common salt, and next, with a solution of nitrate of silver," and had been freely communicated by him to the public in 1839.

3. [" Obtaining photogenic images upon copper." A plate of polished copper is rendered sensitive by exposure to the vapour of iodine or bromine, or both, or either in union with chlorine, or by immersing "a solution of some of the above-mentioned substances " in alcohol, ether, or other convenient solvent. A photogenic " image is then to be formed in the usual manner. The plate is " then exposed to the vapor of sulphuretted hydrogen or of some " of the liquid hydro-sulphurets," or (but with less advantage) vapours or liquid solutions of iodine, bromine, or chlorine. No further fixing is required.

4. "A smooth surface of steel, platina, or other suitable metal " is coated with an extremely thin layer of silver. The silver is " then made sensitive to light by the methods now well known, " and a photogenic image is received upon it. The plate, with " the image, is then placed in a horizontal position, and a solution " of acetate of lead in water is poured upon it. A galvanic cur-" rent is then made to pass through the plate and the solution " which causes a colored film to precipitate upon the plate."

5. A method of "obtaining very thin silver plates or surfaces" for economy and convenience of transport. A thin electro-deposit of copper is made on a polished plate, and a sheet of paper or card glued to the back of the layer of copper, and, when dry, removed with the layer of copper adhering. The copper is then silvered by immersion in "any suitable solution of silver."

"The last part of my invention consists in transferring photo-" genic images from paper to metal. In order to do this, the " metallic surface is made sensitive to light; the paper photograph " is then placed on it, with a sheet of glass in front, and the whole " is pressed into firm contact by screws or otherwise, and exposed, " sunshine. A photograph on metal is thus obtained, which is " afterwards to be fixed, and to be otherwise treated according to " the effect to be obtained."]

By a Disclaimer, enrolled August 7, 1841, the parts of the Specification included between brackets were disclaimed.

[Printed, with Disclaimer, 5d. No Drawing. Repertory of Arts, vol. 16 (*new series*), p. 165; London Journal (*Newton's*), vol. 19 (*conjoined series*), p. 189, and vol. 44 (*conjoined series*) p. 457; Mechanics' Magazine, vol. 35, p. 188; Inventors' Advocate, vol. 5, p. 99; Engineers' and Architects' Journal, vol. 4, p. 429. Enrolment Office.]

A.D. 1841, June 12.—N° 8984.

WAYTE, James Wills.—" Certain improvements in machinery " or apparatus for letter-press printing."

The invention consists, first, in the mode of bringing the platen and the table together to produce the impression, those two surfaces being both flat; secondly, in mechanism for working the frisket frame, as applied to the same machine; thirdly, in a novel arrangement of the inking apparatus, also applicable to the same; and, fourthly, in mechanism by which a machine having only one pressing cylinder is made " perfecting."

1. The platen and type table are counterbalanced. The impression is given by the engagement of two tappet pins upon a main shaft below the table with toggle pieces; the one acting on a short stem on which the type table is supported, causes it to rise, the other simultaneously drawing the platen down by means of rods. By the continued rotation of the shaft the pins escape and adjust themselves for re-engaging.

2. The movements of the frisket frame are produced by the action of a tumbling shaft upon a mangle wheel, by which two endless chains are made to travel to and fro with a reciprocating action. Studs in these endless chains act against slotted guides in the frisket frame, so constructed that the studs pass out of them at intervals and leave the frame at rest, "which takes place at the " time that the impression is being given. This interval of rest " allows time for laying on a fresh sheet, and when the contrary " rotary movement of the mangle wheel . . . takes place the frisket " will in like manner be conducted back again and the fresh sheet " receive its impression."

3. The endless chains also carry the inking rollers, which ink the form in the lower part of their circuit, and receive their supply from an inking surface over which they pass in the upper part of it, the ink being distributed by rollers running on horizontal rails.

4. The two forms come alternately by the action of a tumbling shaft pinion on a horizontal mangle rack under a pressing cylinder in spring bearings, driven by a rack on the type table, and consequently alternating in motion and drawn down for each impression by a knee joint worked by a cam. The sheet is fed in to gripers on the cylinder, and printed successively by each form, it being in the interval between the impressions delivered from the cylinder to endless tapes, which reverse its direction and feed it in again. The inking in this machine is " effected as in all other cylinder " machines."

[Printed, 1s. 7d.  Drawings.  London Journal (Newton's), vol. 20 (conjoined series), p. 244.  Petty Bag.]

A.D. 1841, June 12.—N° 8987.

PALMER, EDWARD.—" Improvements in producing printing
" surfaces, and printing china, pottery ware, music, maps, and
" portraits."

The invention consists, first, of a mode of obtaining printing
surfaces by drawing and printing on metallic or conducting
surfaces, or by painting or drawing on other surfaces made conducting after painting or drawing thereon, "in such manner
" as to enable me, by the use of the known process of electrotype
" or electrography, to obtain copper or other metallic plates or
" other surfaces with sunken surfaces, from which prints may
" be taken as from engraved copper or steel plates or rollers."
The surface is whitened, and the painting or drawing performed with white wax (1), lard (2), and lamp black (1), ground
with olive oil. Various styles of "handling" are described to
produce particular effects in the printing surfaces. A soft brush
containing plumbago passed over the surface renders it conducting,
after which it is connected with the battery, and a plate obtained
by electro deposit.

Secondly, the invention consists in a mode of drawing or
painting on metallic or conducting surfaces, or on surfaces made
conducting after painting or drawing thereon, " so as to enable
" me, by the use of the aforesaid process . . . to produce or obtain
" . . . metallic plates with raised surfaces, from which prints may
" be taken as from engraved wood blocks or stereotype plates."
The surface is dark, and the painting or drawing performed
with sulphate of lead (2), lard (9), and wax (2). Various directions as to handling are given. The dark parts in the drawing are
left bare upon the plate, and the broad lights obtained by
laying the composition on thickly. The light parts are lowered
by means of sheets of paper pasted on flaps of millboard and
pressed against the composition. When the painting or drawing
is finished, "an electro-tint surface is to be obtained as before de-
" scribed. In some instances the drawing can be made upon a
" flat ground, and the electrotype block entrusted to the wood-
" cut prover, who would prepare it for the ordinary printing
" press."

[Printed, 4d. No Drawings. Repertory of Arts, vol. 17 (new series), p. 101 ;
London Journal (Newton's), vol. 20 (conjoined series), p. 172; Mechanics'
Magazine, vol. 36, p. 28. Enrolment Office.]

A.D. 1841, June 28.—Nº 9010.

BENJAMIN, NATHANIEL.—(Communicated.)—" Machine for
" manufacturing many pieces of type at one operation."

A series (in the drawings 19) of "angular grooves," in a long
" bed plate," form two sides of the moulds, the other two, including the "nick" part, being formed in a bar (adjustable for different
sizes of type), moving on an axis at the end of the bed plate. A
matrix plate containing a matrix for each mould is also hinged to
the bed plate. The mould bar and matrix bar being adjusted and
clamped down, the metal is poured into a channel on the bed plate,
whence it is forced by a " presser bar" (worked by hand) into
the several moulds. The handle of the presser bar is then turned
down, the matrix and mould bars unclamped, when the series of
cast types " will be found all connected together, which may
" readily be removed."

[Printed, 1s. 7d. Drawings. Enrolment Office.]

A.D. 1841. September 8.—Nº 9076.

BERRY, MILES.—" A new or improved method or means of and
" apparatus for cleansing typographical characters or forms of type
" after being used in printing."

Instead of cleansing type (the mode then obtaining) by brushes
wetted with a solution of ordinary potash or carbonate of potash,
and other alkaline matters, a solution of common potash or soda
is poured on quick-lime, and the mixture thrown by a double-
action pump over the surface of the types. If filtered through
quick-lime, the liquid will be cleared of the dirt arising from the
ink, and used for cleansing the types again and again.

[Printed, 7d. Drawings. London Journal (Newton's), vol. 21 (conjoined
series), p. 323. Petty Bag.]

A.D. 1841, December 21.—Nº 9204.

WRIGHT, THOMAS, and BAIN, ALEXANDER.—" Improvements
" in applying electricity to control railway engines and carriages,
" to mark time, to give signals, and print intelligence at distant
" places."

1. A "pilot" engine and locomotive are connected by metallic
conductors. On the former is a governor, by the rising and falling
of whose arms the contact is made or broken. The governor is

dependent for its motion on the pilot's progress. On the latter being arrested, and the current thereby broken, certain mechanism on the locomotive is started, which shuts off the steam, blows the whistle, and gives notice by an indicator that the pilot has stopped.

2. Printing. Eight magnets are fixed in the circumference of a circular plate. In connexion with each is a type lever, which, on the current being sent to its magnet by depressing a key in the composing machine, is brought with its type end in the centre of the plate, where it is acted on by a magnet so as to be drawn down upon a saturated ribbon and paper roll, the latter being then mechanically advanced for another impression. The composition on the ribbon is oil (2), lamp black (4), and spirits of turpentine (1).

3. Another machine in which a type wheel is forced against a ribbon and roll. The machinery is actuated by clockwork, and started by the breaking of the circuit (consequent on the depression of a key in the composing machine). The impression is given by the type wheel against a saturated ribbon and paper roll.

4. The correspondence of the machines at any two stations is ascertained by the deflection of a coil by the return current.

5. Application of the deflection of the coil to timepieces.

6. Imbedding the conducting wires in asphalte.

7. Two coils are made "to work two ratchets for working clocks, " or giving signals, or printing."

8. Using a body of natural water to complete an electric circuit.

[Printed, 2s. 5d. Drawings. Mechanics' Magazine, vol. 36, p. 97. Petty Bag.]

A.D. 1842, January 15.—N° 9227.

PALMER, EDWARD.—" Improvements in producing printing and " embossing surfaces."

The invention relates, first, to a mode of obtaining surfaces for relief printing by means of the electrotype process or by casting, " by causing the subject to be etched or engraved through a white " or light-colored composition, placed on a blackened or darkened " surface." Secondly, to a mode of obtaining metallic printing surfaces with the design thereon to be printed from " in the " ordinary manner of line or sunk engraved surfaces." Thirdly, to a mode of obtaining printing surfaces for relief printing from engraved plates or surfaces " by repeated applications of a com- " position, in a similar manner to the ordinary inking process, to " build up surfaces partaking of the etched or engraved subject on

" the plate." And fourthly, to a mode of obtaining embossing surfaces by the electrotype process, " or by casting from engraved " or sunk surfaces produced on a prepared surface of plaster of " Paris."

For the first process, the plate is blackened with a solution of chloride of platinum or hydrosulphuret of ammonia, and the composition is of Burgundy pitch (1), resin (1), white wax (2), and spermaceti (1), whitened with sulphate of lead. The printing surface is then obtained, either by electro deposit or by metal casting in a plaster mou cast from another plaster mould taken from the composition.

The second part consists in making the drawings upon prepared surfaces of plaster of Paris, or any other suitable soft composition. In the case of composition, a layer of sulphate of lead and white wax, and of white wax colored with black lead, &c., are successively laid upon a metal plate, and, when cold, removed from it, and the design as before traced through to the black background. Or the tablet of plaster is cast on a plate of metal or glass, and the drawing etched in with a needle, the effect being seen as it proceeds by rubbing in powdered charcoal. " From this a cast in wax (or in a " composition consisting of five parts rosin and one part white " wax) may be taken, which cast by means of the electrotype will " furnish a metallic plate which will be a printing surface ; or a " metallic cast may be obtained by electrotype, from which any " number of printing metal surfaces may be obtained by the elec- " trotype process."

In the third process the ordinary engraved plate has a letter-press printer's composition roller, with a small quantity of ink well compounded with driers passed over it, and very fine oxide of iron and litharge sifted over it. The plate is warmed, and the process repeated " until the ground is of sufficient thickness above " the surface of the plate to form a proper and sufficient depth in " the reverse for being printed from as a raised surface." The iron and litharge is then brushed out, the "lights" built up, and the whole black-leaded, to render the surface conducting. An electrotype matrix is then produced, from which " all that part of " the surface which filled up the engraved work of the original " plate " is rubbed off. Or the matrix plate may be made in plaster, and the printing plate in stereotype.

Under the fourth head, " the artist having sunk or engraved the " subject on such surface of plaster of Paris, a cast is to be ob-

" tained in wax if it is intended to be electrotyped, and the wax
" impression is to be rendered conductive of electricity, and elec-
" trotyped as is well understood; or if the embossing block is to
" be made by stereotype or casting, then the cast is to be made in
" plaster of Paris, and cast or stereotyped as is well understood."

[Printed, 4d. No Drawing. London Journal (*Newton's*), vol. 22 (*conjoined series*), p. 279. Enrolment Office.]

A.D. 1842, March 25.—Nº 9300.

CLAY, JOHN, and ROSENBORG, FREDERICK.—" Improve-
" ments in arranging and setting up types for printing."

1. *Distributing.* A page of types, in a galley, is slidden along a bracket (by hand) until it comes under a vertical slider, which depresses the first line of it through a slot in the galley into a sliding frame, where, by the action of a spring pusher, it is constantly forced against a " stop plate " at the end, so that the first letter of the line is directly over a row of vertical grooves arranged at right angles to the sliding frame. The sliding frame is drawn (by hand) over the groove to which the first type corresponds, where it is arrested by a stop which rises on the depression of the corresponding key by the workman, and is at the same moment pushed by a pendant lever out of the sliding frame. It falls into a recess formed in a peculiar manner, whence it descends the groove, at the bottom of which it is pressed back by a cam bar into a horizontal groove, in which the files of type accumulate. Or the types may be distributed by hand into the grooves or cases communicating with them, and arranged by the cam bar : or the grooves may be inclined instead of vertical, and arranged in a double row, for the convenience of hand distributing, and forced back as before.

2. *Composing.* The types are arranged in a double row of vertical grooves, between which at the bottom is an endless band in continuous motion. The lowest type of a file being forced out from its groove by a pusher connected with a key below, one end is supported by a pin, and the other resting on the endless band, by the motion of which it is drawn off and conducted, right end foremost, towards a vertical slider, on which it is deposited, and where the types accumulate. On the completion of a line (an index notifies the progress) the slider is lowered by a winch into a receiver, whence the line of types is pushed by a slider into an adjusting stick at the end of it, from which, on withdrawing another slider, it is deposited in a galley placed under it.

Variation of the above, in which the band is widened and receives two types abreast.

A " feeding stick " for transferring a grooveful of type from the distributing to the composing machine.

[Printed, 3s. 3d. Drawings. London Journal (*Newton's*), vol. 22 (*conjoined series*), p. 417 ; Record of Patent Inventions, vol. 1, p. 152. Petty Bag.]

### A.D. 1842, March 23.—N° 9308.

BEACH, MOSES SPERRY.—(Communicated.)—" Improvements in " machinery used for printing with type, and in the construction " of type for printing."

In the press in which the paper (damped and in roll) is conducted successively between two pairs of cylinders, the type cylinder being uppermost in the first, and the pressing cylinder in the second pair, from which the paper receives the reiteration. An ordinary inking apparatus is attached to each type cylinder. After the impression the paper is led over rollers and between converging plates which fold it. It then passes between vertical cylinders, and is cut into sheets by a revolving knife.

The types are tapering (the degree of taper varying with the size of the cylinder), and they, as well as the column rules, ring, cross rules, &c., have alternate indents and projections on their sides, the spaces between the lines having them on their ends. An apparatus, called a " grab," is used for placing a column of type upon the cylinder. The types are secured by plates at the ends of the cylinder. Margins are made across the columns by tapering blocks, with indents and projections, and in the other direction by rings on the cylinder.

Proof press for the above, in which the form is inked and the paper laid on by hand. The pressing cylinder turns in the arms of parallel levers hinged to the frame, and is drawn over the form by a handle.

A machine for damping and packing the paper for the above. The roller on which the paper is to be wound for printing is placed in connexion with a first mover, and thus winds the paper from another roller. As it is thus wound, it is damped by a clothed roller in contact with a roller revolving in a water trough. The trough is upon wheels, and is kept in its position by a weight, which enables it to adjust itself as the roll of damped paper increases. Several intermediate rollers may be used between the trough roller and the roller in contact with the roll.

[Printed, 1s. 7d. Drawings. Repertory of Arts, vol. 18 (*new series*), p. 257 ; Mechanics' Magazine, vol. 37, p. 476; Record of Patent Inventions, vol. 1, p. 159. Enrolment Office.]

### A.D. 1842, April 21.—N° 9327.

DE TROISBRIOUX, ALPHONSE.—" Improvements in litho-" graphic and other presses."

The invention consists in a peculiar arrangement of apparatus for obtaining impressions from cylinders of stone and " other suit-" able materials, as, for instance, a metal cylinder or a cylinder " covered with metallic plates, the pattern or device being drawn " and arranged on the surface of the cylinder by any of the known " methods."

In the " double-acting lithographic press," each subject roller has under it an endless belt, and above it a damping cylinder, which latter, as well as the inking apparatus (at the side), is driven by contact with the subject roller. The inking apparatus consists of an endless band passing over rollers (by three of which it is at intervals brought into contact with the stone) and furnished from a trough roller by a vibrating roller, and scraped by a ductor. Distribution is effected by a roller drawn endwise by cords, connecting its axle with pins on wheels at either side of the machine. The sheet is fed in between a dropping roller and the endless belt, when by the rising of the scraper the endless belt, which is in motion, is pressed against the stone roller, and produces the impression. The sheet is conducted by endless tapes for the " verso " to a second stone cylinder, whose action and arrangement is similar to the first. The arrangement is applicable to a single press or printing in colours. " The general arrangements and prin-" ciple of the said improvements will also serve as a press for " printing from engraved cylinders, the damper cylinder being " removed, and the well-known apparatus for inking and cleaning " the cylinder according to the process of calico and other printing " being supplied."

[Printed, 1s. 8d. Drawings. Record of Patent Inventions, vol. 1, p. 206. Enrolment Office.]

### A.D. 1842, December 29.—N° 9577.

BOURLIER, JOHN STEPHEN.—" Certain improvements in ma-" chinery used in printing calicoes, silks, paper-hangings, and other " fabrics."

The improvements are shown as applied to Lockett's Patent (Nº 7455).

1. Apparatus which moves the frame which carries the engraved plates or blocks. The frame in which they are fixed has two steady movements independent of each other, obtained by using two crank shafts in combination. (In Nº 7455 only one crank shaft is used, and the machine works in consequence by jerks.) The first movement carries the frame towards the colour sieve placed between it and the table above it, and the second carries it as far as the fabric upon the table after the colour sieve is withdrawn. Each of these movements is caused by sliding pieces in a compound connecting rod, the adjustment of which regulates the pressure of the plates or blocks on the colour sieve and fabric.

Apparatus " to prevent at different times the application of the " engraved plate or block to the colour sieve and upon the fabric to " be printed." The action of this arrangement is founded upon periodically shortening the connecting rods moved by the crank which turns more slowly. The effect of this shortening of the connecting rod is that the blocks cannot come in contact with the colour sieve and with the fabric. The shortening of the rod is caused by discs of an " intermittent apparatus" attached to the frame carriage, which act upon the arms of alternately revolving " excentric pieces," in connection with the sliding pieces of the connecting rod. The intermittent apparatus is employed in the following manner when printing handkerchiefs with borders :—
" Suppose, with a machine of six plates or blocks, it is desired to
" print handkerchiefs of three colors, the same on the border as
" the other part, I then employ three plates or blocks for the middle
" or ground part, each . . . of about four or five inches in width,
" and of a length equal to the width of the fabric to be printed,
" and at each of their extremities a portion is engraved to produce
" the longitudinal border : the three other plates or blocks are use
" for the border transversely. . . The discs . . of the carriages
" supplied for the groundwork of the handkerchief will be formed
" in such a manner that the printing will go on without interruption
" for each of these plates or blocks, until that part of the fabric
" which should be worked with the transverse border presents itself.
" The discs of the carriages which carry the plates or blocks of the
" transverse border should be, on the contrary, so arranged as to
" prevent the printing during the time that that part of the fabric
" reserved for the middle presents itself, and they determine the

" application of the plate or block at the moment when will be
" presented the interval left by the blocks which have printed the
" middle or ground. These intermittent apparatus are again em-
" ployed when the machine is so arranged as to print several
" times with each plate or block upon the same part of the fabric.
" If it be desired that some only of the blocks print a second time,
" then those which are not so required are so arranged with the
" discs . . as to prevent them doing so."

" Machinery by which six plates or blocks may be moved simul-
" taneously." The only point in which this differs from the machine described in N° 7455 is in the mode of moving the carriage
of the plates or blocks. The fabric is conducted through the machine by rollers driven by a rack. There is a peculiar arrangement
by which the fresh fabric is prevented from being brought forward
whilst the plates or blocks are printing a second time in the same
places.

" Apparatus for regulating the stretching of the fabric." A
weighted break is applied to the roller on which it is wound; after
leaving which it descends between " holding jaws," which press
the fabric the whole of its width with a force regulated by a
spring.

The fabric is dried by passing it through a metal box or case
heated with steam.

[Printed, 2s. 6d. Drawings. Mechanics' Magazine, vol. 39, p. 45. Enrolment Office.]

### A.D. 1843, May 16.—N° 9728.

BURCH, JOSEPH.—" Improvements in machinery for printing on
" cotton, silk, woollen, paper, oil-cloth, and other fabrics and ma-
" terials, and certain apparatus to be used in preparing the moulds
" and casting surfaces for printing, and for certain modes of pre-
" paring surfaces previous to the design being delineated upon
" them."

" This invention consists in certain improved modes of print-
" ing by surface blocks with any reasonable number of colours
" at one and the same time, and may be called an improved block-
" printing machine. The main principle of this part of the inven-
" tion is based upon my original Patent (N° 7937), as far as regards
" the application of the printing blocks upon the tissue, and the
" traversing frame in which the blocks are carried from the coloring
" apparatus to the piece, and in the mode of furnishing the color to

" the surface of the blocks, the movement of the tissue by means
" of one drum, the color boxes, and in the general combination it
" is different. It also consists in an easy manner of correcting the
" register of the design by the improved block plate and back. It
" also consists in a mode of producing the moulds for casting sur-
" faces, by means of a machine and heated punches, which I have
" herein called a mould-making machine. It also consists in a
" certain apparatus for casting surfaces, which I have herein called
" a casting frame. It also consists in a certain mode for cutting
" and preparing surfaces for a particular style of design, and the
" novelty of this part of the invention is that the surfaces are first
" cut, and the designs afterwards drawn upon them."

A six-color printing machine is shown. The color is supplied
by rollers revolving on the same axis as the friction rollers which
carry the traversing frame (described in N° 7937), and furnished
from trough rollers below them, and cleaned off by brushes and
ductors. The fabric is passed through the machine (having an
under cloth to carry off superfluous color) on an endless foundation cloth, kept stretched. The impression is given by pressers
acted on by cams above them, and the fabric disengaged from the
blocks, after the impression, by a light frame between the table and
traversing frame. The distance moved by the fabric after each impression is regulated by observing a graduated ring on the side of
a drum, over which it passes.

Mould-making machine. Eight punches are (by the action of
treadles) drawn down, with " heaters " which pass through a fire
box, upon a cross-grain wood block, the elasticity of which is destroyed by the heat.

Casting frame. A trough with six compartments has, at the
bottom of each, a mould on a mould plate. The top of each compartment is filled with thin pieces of wood, set edgewise, each
of which has a channel or groove down its side to allow of the passage of the metal. The mould is screwed up to the channelled
leaves, the metal poured in, the waste metal poured off by tilting
the trough, the mould plate withdrawn by the screw, and the
casting is found adhering to the bottom of the channelled leaves.

Surfaces for printing carpets, oil-cloths, paper-hangings, &c.,
are prepared by cutting parallel lines in them, in a machine similar
to an iron planing machine, about one-eighth or one-fourth of an
inch deep, then turning the plate so as to produce, by other parallel

lines, checks or diamonds. The design is then drawn upon those parts required to form the pattern, each color upon a different block, and "the intermediate parts are easily removed."

[Printed, 1s. 6d. Drawings. Practical Mechanics' Journal, vol. 3, p. 198. Enrolment Office.]

A.D. 1843, May 16.—N° 9731.

MAZZINI, JOSEPH.—(Partly communicated.)—" Improvements " in typographical, combining the advantages of moveable types " with the stereotype process, by substituting for distribution a " special font for each new work, by means of a pneumatic machine " for casting, and a uniplane machine for composing."

The inventor proposes to do away with " distribution," and to substitute therefor a "special font for each new work, and in order " that this method may not be more expensive than distribution, " and may be as expeditiously performed, he has invented a " machine by means of which type may be cast in a very expe- " ditious manner. He also intends to diminish the length of " the stem of the type from one-half to two-thirds, so that a page " when composed will not be much thicker than stereotype."

1. " Pneumatic type-founding machine." The casting is effected in vacuo. By means of vertical sliding racks an upper and lower cylinder are made to rise and fall, so that the former slides over the latter, and it being concentric with and fitted tightly to it a vacuum is produced between the two cylinders on its rising. The lower cylinder "is made hollow, but is hermetically sealed and " encloses some light substance, such as coal dust, so that the " specific gravity of this lower cylinder is less than the mixture of " lead and antimony in the boiler. It is therefore supported by " this mixture when in the state of fusion, and floats therein." The mould is placed upon the lower cylinder, and the upper cylinder made to descend so as to meet the lower. An airhole in the upper cylinder is then shut by a screw, " and on the upper cylinder being " raised, the operation is performed. . . Now the proportions " are arranged in such a manner that the separation of the two " cylinders takes place below the surface of the melted metal, and " the air enclosed within the moulds is then at the moment of " separation dilated . . to the whole extent of the large cylinder, " in the same manner as a pneumatic pump. . . At the same time " that the upper cylinder is raised the lower . . one rises of itself

" from its own lightness. The mould is then taken away, and
" replaced by another."

Machine for forming the matrices. "The body of the matrix is
" first drawn through a draw-plate and cut to the required height
" or length. Thus prepared it is placed between two jaws," screwed
into a carriage, the carriage being conducted along grooves under a
piston, at the end of which a punch is attached. " It will only be
" necessary to strike the top of the piston with a hammer to stamp
" or form the matrices." (a)

Description of the mould. When formed and justified the
matrices serve to form the mould. " For this purpose they are
" perforated laterally, so as to allow a steel wire to pass through
" them, and by separating them by means of oblong pieces . .
" they are formed into lines strung together on the wire, and which
" lines are separated from each other by means of steel plates." A
square frame with a circular projection at its base holds these
matrices (arranged in families of letters, viz., one of several rows of
a, b, &c.), "in such a manner that they cannot be disarranged."
This frame when placed upon the lower cylinder "is surrounded
" by a bed or cup of metal . . hollowed out at the sides coni-
" cally. It is this bed or cup which affords the necessary support
" or fulcrum for drawing out the letters. When the letters are
" cast and have been thus separated from the mould, the body of
" metal to which they are affixed is carried under a sort of cutter,
" by which the types are divided into lines and removed from the
" superfluous metal by cutting through the same in such a manner
" that the letters of each line only are united. . . It now only
" remains to smooth the bottom as usual."

"Uniplane machine for composing." A square plate of wood
fitted with grooves for the lines of type is mounted upon an axle
fixed to the framework. To the lower end of this plate metal
pieces are attached, and form a prolongation of the grooves, the
lower parts of which are closed by a hinged shutter. In a square
piece of wood, &c. secured on the upper part of the ends of the
grooves are apertures corresponding with the grooves of the plate.
These apertures are furnished with pistons, which carry on their
inner ends small pushers, for the purpose of forcing out the types
from the grooves on the plate. Near the outer ends of the pistons

---

(a) This the patentee describes as "applying in a novel manner the old process
of Heran, which is not in use at the present day, for making copper matrices for
stereotype."

small cams or excentric pieces are fastened. On depressing one of the pistons its pusher forces out a type which is received in a groove formed by the meeting of two plates, even with the metal pieces above mentioned. The piston recovers itself by a spring, and another type then drops down on the shutter ready to be acted upon on the next occasion. A further arrangement of the mechanism releases the type, which slides down into the composing stick. The grooved plate is vertical, and in order to prevent the falling out of the types and allow of the types being easily arranged and inspected, a " shutter " is affixed to it, made of a piece of wire, having at each end a cross piece which takes into grooves made in the sides of the wooden plate. In this machine the workman has to stand. Another machine is shown which allows the workmen to sit down. The arrangement is very similar; the pistons, however, are depressed by the action of bell-cranked levers. "The principal features of " these composing machines is the use of two planes inclined in " opposite directions, but at the same angle in relation to the " horizon." The same movement which causes the letters to fall causes them to advance in the composing stick. A small spring which acts each time the inclined plane rises, and which pushes the letter just descended to a distance equal to the thickness of an $m$, effects this object, and the line thus "becomes " sufficiently long to form one or more pages." It is, therefore, necessary from time to time to divide the line by moving that part of it previously formed from the other by hand.

Justification is thus effected. " At the extremity of the long " composing stick, composed of two bands or raised pieces, dis- " tant from each other the thickness of the body of the letter, is " a moveable carriage on the same plane. On this carriage is a " frame of the size of the intended page." The carriage is placed so that its extremity corresponds with the composing stick, and the end of the line is introduced into it. The way in which the line falls must then be noticed, and by means of an indicator which descends upon the carriage on a level with the line, it will be seen how many points are required to fill the line.

Another mode of justification, by means of a moveable carriage, is shown.

" If instead of making the types one-half they are made one- " third the usual size, steps must be taken to prevent such small " types from being carried away or disarranged while under the

" press." This is done by making nicks on each side of the type
" deeper and more of a square form than ordinary. The spaces
" between the lines will have projections corresponding to these
" nicks, and will also have a projection at their extremities, with a
" hole in the middle. Very thin rods of iron passing through
" these holes will serve to keep them in their places."

[Printed, 2s. 6d. Drawings. Rolls Chapel.]

## A.D. 1843, May 27.—N° 9745.

BAIN, ALEXANDER.—" Certain improvements in producing and
" regulating electric currents, and improvements in electric time-
" pieces, and in electric printing and signal telegraphs."

1. Producing electric currents by positive and negative substances placed in the earth, or in natural bodies of water when
connected by insulated conducting wires.

2. Mode of regulating the same, (a) by varying the distance of
the magnet from its keeper, (b) by clockwork, the plates acting as
the weight.

3. The attraction and repulsion of the multiplied electric conductor by fixed permanent magnets and of permanent magnets by
fixed electric conductors, when produced by the action of the
currents at or near right angles to the poles of the magnets, are
substituted in timepieces, printing, and signal telegraphs, for the
deflection of the needle. Various arrangements of the magnets
are shown with a view to gaining power by the current.

4. Mode of working electric timepieces by currents passing
through secondary conducting wires.

5. Printing telegraph. The machines at each end of the circuit
are similar, and the hand of a dial plate being moved in the one, a
corresponding motion takes place in the other. The current is
made and broken by a screw, through the hand. The current being
broken by the release of the screw, the machinery is permitted (by
the deflection of a coil of insulated wire) to work; and on the
arrest of the hand at a particular signal, a type cylinder is made
(by means of a saturated ribbon interposed) to mark the corresponding type upon a roll of paper on a cylinder. This cylinder
has endwise motion, so that the message is continuously printed
in spiral lines.

6. Means of enabling the operator to know when the distant
instruments are in unison with his own; and if not correct, giving
him power to adjust them.

7. Copying telegraph (a). The machines at both stations are similar. In each a frame contains a number of short wires bedded in sealing wax, both surfaces being ground smooth. The types to be copied are set up in one machine in contact with these wires ; and in the other, two thicknesses of paper, saturated with prussiate of potash and nitrate of soda, are pressed against them by a metal plate. The impression is produced in a series of dots by the traversing of a steel spring attached to a pendulum in the former instrument over the other side of the wires. By using a number of conducting wires and springs, a whole line can be printed at once.

8. Method of securing the conducting wires in wood pavement, or in the longitudinal sleepers of railways.

9. Arrangement of signal telegraphs, by which, with one conducting wire and two characters, assisted by an explanatory table, numerous signals may be given. The instruments at each end are similar. On one side of each is a stud, marked I, and on the other a stud, marked V. The current is made or broken by the depression of these studs, a "pointer" indicating in the far machine which of the two has been depressed. The signals consist of repetition of I. for the first four numerals, V. for five, and combination for subsequent ones up to eleven, which indicates a stop.

[Printed, 3s. 5d. Drawings. Mechanics' Magazine, vol. 52, p. 101; Artizan, vol. 2, pp. 82 and 99. Enrolment Office.]

A.D. 1843, June 1.—No 9753.

TALBOT, WILLIAM HENRY FOX.—"Improvements in photo-"graphy."

These are contained under nine heads. 1. Since the yellowish tint of some calotype pictures impedes the process of taking copies from them, such picture is plunged into a bath of some soluble hyposulphite, whereby it is rendered white and permanent. Transparency is imparted to the picture after this process by "causing "melted wax to penetrate into the pores of the paper." 2. During the process of taking a calotype picture I place a warm plate of iron behind the paper holder to communicate warmth to the prepared paper. This makes it more sensitive, and consequently the picture is obtained more rapidly. 3. "Io-gallic" paper is prepared

(a) See Lardner's Electric Telegraph, § 9. Museum of Science and Art, 8vo. Lond., 1855.

by washing a sheet of iodized paper with a solution of gallic acid water and dried. It will keep for a considerable time in a press or portfolio. When required for use it is rendered sensitive by a solution of nitrate of silver, and fit to be used in the camera. The separate use of the nitrate of silver and gallic acid " removes the " great inconvenience arising from the speedy decomposition of " the gallo-nitrate of silver." 4. A sheet of iodized paper is washed over with the mixture of gallic acid and nitrate of silver " usually employed in the calotype (a) process," and dried at a gentle fire. It will keep in a press a considerable time. " It is " less sensitive than ordinary calotype paper." " This paper is as " convenient to use in a copying frame as the ordinary photogra- " phic drawing paper, it being used quite dry, and it has the " advantage of being much more sensitive." 5. A copy or reversed impression of a photographic picture is taken " in the " usual way," but allowed to remain in the light twice the usual or necessary time, " in consequence of which it comes out with " its shadows too black, and with its lights not sufficiently white " to give a pleasant effect." It is then washed and plunged for one or two minutes into a bath of iodide of potassium (500 grains to one pint of water), when the picture becomes brighter, and its lights a pale yellow tint. The effect may be increased by exposure to the light. The picture is then washed and plunged into hot hyposulphite, as in (1). The pale yellow tint is then discharged, and the lights remain of a white colour. The picture is permanent, and " has a pleasing and peculiar effect of light and shade not " easily attainable." 6. A photographic picture is rendered trans- parent by waxing it, and a sheet of white or coloured paper placed behind it, so as to produce a " very pleasing artistical effect," or " various beautiful tones of color." 7. A magnified negative or reversed copy of a daguerreotype or calotype portrait, " or other " small photographic picture, whose details are minute, is taken " by means of lenses on calotype paper." From this negative positive copies are obtained " in the usual manner." The advantage of this method consists in the economy of the sitter's time. 8. " A kind of photographic printing." A page of printed matter is set up (direct) on a sheet of white paper

---

(a) This term, as well as the term "iodized," are stated to have been ex- plained in No. 8842.

by fixing waxed paper letters upon it; a negative (inverted) photographic copy of this is taken, and from the negative the requisite number of positive (direct) copies obtained. Or the pages may be composed by sliding letters into grooves in a rectangular board, and placed before a camera, when a reduced image of it, of the size desired, is thrown upon the sensitive paper.

9. " Photographic publication. . . . I take writing paper of a " good quality, destitute of paper mark, and dip it into a salt " water bath containing 3 or 4 ounces of salt dissolved in a gallon " of water, it is then wiped and dried. I then take a solution of " 100 grains nitrate silver dissolved in 2 oz. of distilled water, and " add to it just enough ammonia to form a precipitate, and re-" dissolve the same, leaving the solution clear. With this solution " I wash the salted paper above described, and then dry it. Such " paper may be preserved in a press, but should be used within " one or two days. This paper may be called ' copying paper.' " To obtain on such paper a negative or reversed copy of any " print, map, photograph, or other original on paper, it is placed " in contact with the original in a copying frame, and placed in " the daylight until the copy is effected. The copy is then washed " with warm water, kept afterwards for 2 or 3 minutes in a solu-" tion of hyposulphite of soda dissolved in 10 times its weight of " water, and then plunged into 2 or 3 baths of warm water con-" secutively, in order to remove all that is soluble in water." It is then dried, and may be waxed, if thought proper, for greater transparency. " A good negative picture is obtained with a " camera upon calotype paper, which is then cleaned by boiling in " hyposulphite of soda," and " waxed, if thought necessary." The negative being thus prepared, either on copying or calotype paper, is placed in contact with a second sheet of copying paper in a copying frame, and a positive copy obtained. The other positive copies are similarly obtained. They are then fixed with hyposulphite of soda in the same way as the negative copy was. The hyposulphite should be quite free from sulphurous acid, and the copies, both before fixation and afterwards, should be dipped into two or three warm water baths consecutively, to remove every trace of soluble matter from them.

[Printed, 4d. No Drawing. Repertory of Arts, vol. 3 (*enlarged series*), p. 47; London Journal (*Newton's*), vol. 23 (*conjoined series*), p. 430; Artizan, vol. 2, p. 23. Enrolment Office.]

A.D. 1843, June 26.—N° 9802.

DUNCAN, JOHN.—" Improvements in the casting or construc-
" tion of types for printing."

The object of the invention is "to perform by means of a ma-
" chine the motions required in casting type, and in smoothing
" the same, and in setting it up for examination, which motions
" have chiefly been hitherto performed by hand." Between the
nozzle of the jet pipe and the mould comes at each casting one of
a series of radiating arms perforated to allow of the metal passing
through. The metal is injected by a spring depressing a plunger
in a cylinder. After the casting, the matrix is withdrawn and
the mould opened, when the cast type is carried away by the
radiating arm. It is broken from the jet at a " separator " (plate),
drawn between smoothing dies by a " sliding catch," and finally
deposited in a setting-up box. The mould then closes, the matrix
is brought up, the mould arm and jet pipe again brought together,
the piston is raised, and the whole is ready for another casting.
The necessary movements of the various parts of this machine
are given by a shaft and the cams which it carries, the shaft
being turned by hand with a winch, or by any other suitable
power and apparatus. Or the radiating arm, smoothing and
setting-up apparatus may be dispensed with, the mould being so
placed that on its opening the type slides away by its gravity
towards the separator. The flue through which the jet pipe
passes is peculiarly divided for the purpose of heating the jet pipe.
The mould is attached to a large bar for the purpose of carrying
away the heat caused by rapid casting. The mode of tilting the
matrix is peculiar, as is also the construction of the plunger and
valve of the pump. ;The parts of the machine exposed to the
metal are covered with smoke of substances free from resin.
The best speed for the machine is from 60 to 100 revolutions
per minute.

[Printed, 2s. 4d. Drawings. Enrolment Office.]

A.D. 1844, January 16.—N° 10,018.

NICHOL, WILLIAM.—" Improvements in lithographic and
" other printing presses."

1. The stone has a reciprocating motion by rack and pinion,
the latter deriving its alternating movement through the medium of a mangle wheel, from a continuously rotating shaft.

2. A " self-acting presser bar " forms one arm of a bent lever, the other being weighted and tending to keep the bar always in an inclined position. On the stone being run in, a " lifter " on the stone carriage engages the weighted end, and brings the presser bar down vertical, where it is kept by its flanges coming against the press standards. 3. " Press designed to " act at both ends." The stone has alternating movement by means of a rack and pinion, the latter being on a vertical shaft driven by a bevel wheel in different directions by the engaging and disengaging of a clutch. 4. In place of the " comparatively " rigid" wood scraper, an elastic presser bar of steel " at a " spring temper" is employed, the edge of which is " so formed " as to present to the surface of the tympan the same angle in one " direction horizontally as the length of the presser or scraper " does in the other, and then rounded so as to prevent injury to " the tympan." 5. The tympan frame rests in sockets at either end of the stone carriage, and is gradually raised and lowered at each end alternately by the action of double hooks in the standards upon studs in the tympan frame, the other end being kept in its socket as a hinge by the action of friction rollers connected with it against an inverted rail. After each impression the machine is thrown out of gear for the purpose of changing the sheet.

[Printed, 1s. Drawings. London Journal (*Newton's*), vol. 25 (*conjoined series*), p. 103. Rolls Chapel.]

A.D. 1844, March 28.—N° 10,129.

DUMONTIER, CHARLES HECTOR FRANÇOIS.—(Partly communicated.)—" Improvements in the construction of lithographic " and autographic (a) presses."

The stone bed has a come and go movement (varying with the size of the stone) by means of a crank and connecting rod. The inking rollers and wetting apparatus are in a frame suspended by a chain fastened to an " excentric cam," the action of which cam causes it to rise to supply the inking rollers from distributors above them, and fall to ink and damp it. The inking apparatus consists of three rows of rollers, one below the other, the trough rollers being uppermost, and the distributors before mentioned below. The wetting appa-

(a) Explained as meaning "presses for taking off impressions from autograph written with suitable materials on stone."

ratus is supplied with water by a perforated roller above it. An " obsorbing roller" is placed between the inking and wetting apparatus. The impression is given by a roller revolving in a fork at the bottom of the lower joint of a knee lever, which is periodically straightened by the action of the " excentric cam," and assumes an acute position after the impression by the action of a spring. During the impression the roller revolves by friction with the stone, thereby drawing the paper as required from a roll on which it is wound. After the impression, the printed part is wound upon a roller driven by an endless band from the pressing roller. The machine shown is calculated to produce seven impressions per minute.

[Printed, 1s. Drawings. Petty Bag.]

A.D. 1844, June 6.—N° 10,219.

WOODS, JOSEPH.—(Communicated.)—"Improvements in pro-" ducing designs and copies, and in multiplying impressions " either of printed or written surfaces." (a)

These consist, first, " in the process termed anastatic (b) " printing, or obtaining reversed facsimiles on metallic surfaces " from designs, writings, &c. ;" and secondly " in the presses for " obtaining impressions from the said " metallic surfaces." The metal preferred is zinc, used in the form of plates or cylinders, and polished by grinding with emery in parallel lines. The design may be drawn on any clean well-sized paper with ink of a saponaceous or fatty nature. An " original" is charged with nitric or other " convenient " acid. If freshly printed, so as to yield a set-off, it is saturated with the acid, applied on the wrong side. It is then laid with its printed side upon the prepared plate, and passed with the plate under considerable rolling pressure, the reverse side being covered with blotting paper. Or the paper may be laid between two prepared plates, and an impression taken on both in the same way.

Originals " of more than two months old " are laid to soak for a period varying from twelve hours to seven days, according to the length of time they have been printed, (c) in the acid. The strength

---

(a) By a Memorandum of Alteration enrolled the 6th December 1844, the title was varied to " Improvements in producing and multiplying copies of designs and impressions of printed or written surfaces."

(b) See introductory notice, p. 24.

(c) Books ten years old require, it is stated, about 24 hours, those 30 or 40 years " some days, but after that age no material difference appears to have taken place in the chemical condition of the printing ink."

of the acid in which they are immersed is reduced by the addition of water to such a degree as not to taste strongly. The papers are partially dried by blotting paper laid on the polished surface, and subjected with the plate "to much greater rolling pressure than " before." " If saving of time is an object, and when the originals " have been very much indurated and dried, as in engraving, &c.," the latter are placed in a solution of caustic potash, and afterwards face uppermost in a solution of tartaric acid, which leaves the imprinted parts covered with crystals of cream of tartar. The " back lines " are then revived, either by passing a hard litho- graphic roller charged with ink over the original, and cleaning off with an uncharged roller, or by means of the vapour of " con- " venient volatile oils," such as oil of turpentine, after which the crystals of cream of tartar are dissolved by immersing the original in dilute nitric acid. " When I wish to draw on the plate, I do so " with lithographic transfer ink while in its clean state, and wash " it over lightly with gum water containing a small quantity of " phosphatic acid, then rub in ink, and protect the blank surfaces " as next described; or I first treat the metallic surface with " phosphatic acid and gum, wash it clean, scrape away the parts " intended to carry ink, and rub them up as hereafter described." The original having been removed, the plate is washed over with thick gum and rubbed up with a mixture of lithographic ink and gum water wherever it has been protected from the action of the acid. In the transfer of " old work, this process should be repeated " at intervals of one hour or more." The plate is then washed with water and charged with ink with a soft leather roller. Spots of dirt are ground out with slate pencil and water. A "few " hundred copies " could be printed " in the usual mode " from the plate as thus prepared ; but as the fine lines have a tendency to thicken, the plate is washed over with a " solution of the " substance called by Dulong phosphatic acid, or, as termed by " Davy, a mixture of phosphorous and phosphoric acids mixed " with gum water." The surface is thus slightly etched so as to reject the ink, or by continuing the process with stronger acid, may be transformed into a printing surface similar to stereotype. The mode of preparing the phosphatic acid is described.

2. (a) Hand press shown for printing from flat plates, consisting of a driving roller below the bed of the press turned by hand,

and a pressing cylinder above it. An endless web of silk passes round the latter, and a roller immediately above it.

(b) "Self-acting power printing press," consisting of an iron cylinder carrying the prepared zinc plate, and surrounded by a double (or, if for finer work, a treble) set of washing and inking apparatus. The washing rollers are composed of linen in the form of a rope wound spirally round a cylinder, and are damped by contact with trough rollers. They move at double the circumferential velocity of and in the same direction as the printing surface. The washing rollers have also an endwise motion, thus producing on the plate a compound washing in serpentine curves crossing each other, which is similar to the circular action produced by hand washing. After passing the washing rollers, the plate passes beneath. The inking apparatus are very similar, consisting of an ink trough, a "wandering" (vibrating) roller, a distributing and two or more inking rollers, the ink in each "system" increasing in consistency.

The paper is placed on a moveable table, where it is retained by a catch lever until the latter is lifted by a pin on a moveable segment with a cam, which acts on a second lever carrying a feeding roller. On this lifting of the catch lever the table is released and drawn towards the feeding roller by a weight, directly after which the feeding roller is pressed into contact with the paper between an endless cloth roller and ribbons on the other side. At the same moment a register pin and lever is pressed up, and allows the tapes and endless cloth of strong silk to draw the sheet forward. The action of the segment cam at this moment draws the table back for a fresh sheet. The impression is given by a roller above the printing surface, the former being "driven by contact "only." Or endless paper may be used. The press may, by the addition of a second cylinder, be worked as a perfecting machine.

[Printed, with Memorandum of Alteration, 2s. 2d. Drawings. Petty Bag; Memorandum of Alteration also in Petty Bag.]

A.D. 1844, July 29.—No 10,275.

KRONHEIM, JOSEPH MARTIN.—(Communicated.)—" Im-" provements in stereotyping."

1. A mould is made by pressing " a flanc," (alternate layers of tissue paper and paste on a foundation of brown paper), when moist,

upon á form of types, and leaving it to dry under pressure. 2. The apparatus for holding the said matrices and performing the operation of casting, composed of metal plates hinged together like a portfolio. It turns on an axle beneath one of the sides (the "lower "plate "). Both plates are turned horizontal, and the matrix powdered with talc, having been laid on the lower plate, and metal strips to regulate the thickness of the casting having been laid on its margin, the upper one is brought down and clamped to it. The mould is then turned vertical, and the metal poured into the mould at the mouth formed by the bevelled edges of the plates. The upper plate is covered with a sheet of paper to ensure the parallelism of the stereotype plate at the back by allowing the escape of air.

[Printed, 10d. Drawings. London Journal (Newton's), vol. 26 (conjoined series), p. 161. Petty Bag.]

A.D. 1844, August 2.—N° 10,284.

HILL, JOHN REED. — "Improvements in a press or presses, " machine or machines for letter-press printing."

The invention consists in " the construction of a machine " which shall place within the reach of the general hand or " jobbing printer the means of printing with the rapidity " of the steam press." To and fro motion is given to the type table (there are springs at each end to check it) by the action of a pendulous frame, set in motion by connecting rods of peculiar construction, which works in flat grooved wheels at the ends of the pressing cylinder. The pressing cylinder (counterbalanced) is driven by a band passing round the axis of a fly wheel. The form is inked by two fixed rollers furnished from an inking table (attached to the type table) on which the ink laid on by a trough roller is distributed by·rollers placed at an angle across the machine. The sheet is laid (to a register mark) on a feeding plate, which (by the action of a spring roller on the cylinder axle upon a depressing frame) is brought down at the moment that spring nippers on the cylinder close and secure the paper to the front edge of the cylinder, and carry it round to meet the type. On one or both edges of the type table, and outside the form, there is a narrow slip of (clothed) metal or wood supported on a spring so adjusted as to cause the table to move with the cylinder " by the resistance of contact, and

" which will be the only communication of motion between the
" table and cylinder at the time that an impression is being taken."
After the impression, the sheet is laid hold of by spring jaws of
nippers on a rod vibrating on a spindle at the bottom of the press.
The vibration draws it from the cylinder, and on the opening of
the nippers it is discharged into a suitable receptacle.

[Printed, 1s. 4d. Drawings. Mechanics' Magazine, vol. 44, p. 401; Engineers'
and Architects' Journal, vol. 9, p. 219. Rolls Chapel.]

### A.D. 1844, December 12.—N° 10,432.

LOCKETT, JOSEPH. — " Certain improvements in apparatus
" for preparing to be engraved or turned such copper or other
" metal cylinders or rollers as are to be used for printing or
" embossing or callendering calico or other fabrics."

The invention consists in constructing the machine so that " it
" may be worked by steam or other power, and that the anvil, which
" is made in the form of a cylinder, and which revolves, has the
" copper or other metal cylinder or roller parallel to and resting its
" whole length upon the upper surface of the anvil, which is made
" so long as to allow of the cylinder or roller being traversed a
" short distance on its surface if required." A series of hammers,
worked by cams, are placed over the copper cylinder so as to
act upon it; both hammers and cams are made to traverse
a short distance sideways if required. There is a provision for
adjusting the height of the hammers' fall, as also for stopping any
one of them.

The apparatus in use previous to this invention is described as
consisting of " a fixed swage or anvil with a concave opening on
" its surface, in which the cylinder or roller was placed to be struck
" by hammers wielded by men."

[Printed, 1s. 4d. Drawings. Enrolment Office.]

### A.D. 1845, January 21.—N° 10,488.

SCHNEBLY, WILLIAM.—" Certain improvements in machinery
" for letter-press or surface printing."

The platen is fixed. The impression is given by the rising
of the type table under the action of a knee lever below it.
The type table and tympan (the latter of which slides in and
out from under the platen) are so constructed as to admit of

their being readily removed. Two inking rollers in a travelling frame pass over the form when at its lowest. They are
supplied from a large roller (on the main shaft), to which ink
has been furnished by a vibrator from an ink trough below it.
Appropriate motion is communicated to the various working parts
of the machine by means of a pinion taking into a toothed wheel,
with an excentric groove in connection with large vibrating levers.
The feeding table is placed either above the platen or at the end
of the press. It is laid hold of and carried down for the impression
by nippers (the construction varying slightly for the two feeding
tables) on a slight rod connected to endless bands, and is supported
against the under side of the platen "by means of strings or tapes,
" as is well understood." The sheet returns after the impression,
and on the nippers opening (by coming in contact with inclined
pieces in the framing), is discharged on to a light lath framing,
called a "vibrating frame," mounted on a sector which turns
over and deposits the sheets in a pile upon a table, which,
by a ratchet wheel, is made to descend as the pile increases.
Endwise motion is given to a distributing roller above the large
cylinder by means of an arm extending horizontally from a vertical
shaft. "Shogging the distributing rollers sideways for the purpose
" of effecting a more equal distribution of the ink has been long
" known and in use, but I consider the above-described mode a
" preferable one to any of those now in use."

The press is worked either by hand or steam. The whole of the
millwork is on one side of it.

[Printed, 10d. Drawings. London Journal (Newton's), vol 27 (conjoined
series), p. 305. Petty Bag.].

## A.D. 1845, March 3.—Nº 10,543.

SHAW, WILLIAM.—"A machine for paging books and number-
" ing documents consecutively and otherwise, and for printing
" dates, words, marks, numbers, and impressions in an expeditious
" manner."

Six type wheels, with the numerals 0—9 on them, are placed
side by side on a small drum revolving in a fork at the lower
end of a vertical bar. The last wheel may have "any words
" or letters that may be required." The bar is brought down by a
hand lever for the impression, which is given upon a small bracket
traversed by an endless "setting-off" cloth, and recovers itself by
a counterweight and springs. The type wheels are all provided
with eleven notches into which the wedge-shaped heads of pins are

pressed by spiral springs round the pins. A stationary click takes at each rise of the bar into a ratchet wheel connected with the unit's wheel which thereby makes one-tenth of a revolution. The ten's wheel is moved by one of several moveable clicks before supported upon the projecting rib of the ten's wheel coming opposite to a recess and being pushed forwards by a spring until a pin enters a recess in the ten's wheel, and moves it one stage in advance. In paging books, the odd numbers are printed first, which requires the unit's wheel to have 1, 3, 5, 7, 9, twice over. The inking is performed mechanically. A "feeding roller," which lays the ink upon the types, takes it from the under side of a brass piece fixed to the fork of the bar, in the corner of which piece the ink trough is placed. The depression of the bar causes the elevation of certain "side plates," and the consequent rotation of the trough roller; a "working" roller, during the downward motion of the plates, distributing the ink. A modification of the above for railway ticket printing. The material is propelled at regular intervals by pressure rollers in connexion with the numbering machines, after which it is cut by a knife, the whole machinery being moved by a handle similar to that above mentioned.

[Printed, 10d. Drawings. Repertory of Arts, vol. 6 (enlarged series), p. 212; Mechanics' Magazine, vol. 57, p. 411; Law Journal (Exchequer), vol. 22, pp. 26 and 210. Enrolment Office.]

A.D. 1845, March 13.—N° 10,554.

POOLE, MOSES.—(Communicated.)—" Improvements in litho-" graphic presses."

1. " So arranging a lithographic press as to cause the scraper " or presser to move over the stone." 2. "So applying inking " apparatus to a lithographic press that ink may be applied " to an inking roller or rollers, and the surface of the stone " inked by the working of the press." The scraper is in a carriage which runs upon rails on the machine, the flanges of its wheels being also in contact with a rail above it, to resist the impression. Its motion is given by a crank and connecting rod. A rack on the carriage drives a pinion on the axle of a pair of rollers over which an endless felt passes, receiving ink from a roller in contact with a trough roller, the inking roller receiving its supply from the lower side of the band. The bearings of the inking roller are in a carriage running on the same rails as the scraper carriage, and driven by crank axles set in motion by endless chains. If the stone be moveable and the scraper fixed,

the inking roller need not move over the stone, but the stone can be made to move under the inking roller, the latter being supplied with ink by the motion of the machinery. No mention is made of the wetting apparatus.

[Printed, 2s. 2d. Drawings. Enrolment Office.]

A.D. 1845, April 22.—N° 10,633.

MOSS, THOMAS.—" Improvements in printing and preparing " bankers' notes, cheques, and other papers for the better preven- " tion of fraud."

The object of this invention is stated to be " to place further " difficulties in the way of persons desirous of forging bankers' " notes, cheques, and other like documents, the efficacy of the " mode hitherto resorted to by intricate and elaborate engraving, " having been more or less impaired by the recent discovery of " means of obtaining impressions or copies from printed surfaces, " so as closely to resemble the original documents." It consists " in so impressing patterns on the surface of paper used as " bankers' cheques, notes, and other documents liable to for- " gery, on which designs or letters are or are intended to be " printed in the ordinary way, that the paper so treated is " caused to be smooth or level on one side, whilst the other " side thereof is indented in patterns so as to produce to the " eye the appearance of a reticulate surface, but the indentations " do not pass through the paper. . . I also sometimes obtain " a further protection against fraud by causing the surface of " the paper, on the side on which it is indented, to be printed, by " inking the surface which causes the impression or indentation. " In carrying out this invention I employ two steel rollers, one " being smooth and the other having engraved in relief the pattern " the reverse of that which I wish to obtain in the paper; such " engraving I prefer to perform in a lathe, as is well understood ; " . . . between these rollers I pass the paper, . . . the upper " roller (the engraved roller) being pressed heavily down on " to the lower roller; and it will be found that paper passed " between such rollers will be indented with the pattern or design, " and if this roller is inked (as for surface printing) the pattern " thereof indented into the paper will at the same time be colored."

[Printed, 3d. No Drawing. Repertory of Arts, vol. 7 (*enlarged series*), p. 110; London Journal (*Newton's*), vol. 27 (*conjoined series*), p. 348; Engineers' and Architects' Journal, vol. 9, p. 16. Enrolment Office.]

A.D. 1845, May 6.—N° 10,657.

BURCH, JOSEPH.—"Improvements in machinery for printing
" calico and other fabrics, part of which improvements is appli-
" cable to other purposes where resistance to heat is required."

1. " Rainbowing or shading apparatus." The sieve roller has
small rollers around it to distribute the color, which is laid on it
by a furnishing roller at the bottom, to which the color is supplied by a " feeding roller," composed of flanges on a mandril,
each working in a separate compartment of the color trough.

2. Color box, in which the color is distributed on the sieve
roller by small rollers, " instead of the brushes as described in my
" former Patent (N° 9728), and furnished with a lever and screw
" for adjusting the feeding roller." The presser described in
N° 7937 is improved by the introduction of a slide which prevents
friction, and keeps the main shaft from wearing. The color
sieve rollers are driven by means of a tooth rack fixed to one
side of the traversing frame of the block printing machine.

3. " Wax printing machine." Parallel with each other are (arranged from left to right) a pattern roller, a backing drum, and a
receiving drum. The fabric passes from a piece roller above the
press through " stretcher bars," partly round an entering drum,
and over a " compensating rail," (where by the action of a lever
it is moved to or from the printing cylinder) and then printed,
after which, if it does not require padding, it is carried under the
backing drum, and passes up with the backing. But when padding is required it is led under a roller in a padding trough, carried to the receiving drum, and rolled on a gathering roller. The
printing roller is furnished by a roller below it, revolving in a
heated trough of hot wax. The backing cloth is rubbed with sand
or chalk to prevent the wax sticking to it. " This machine is also
" applicable for other styles of printing, such as discharging
" mordaunts, &c., and its novelty is in delivering the design
" upon the cloth without the aid of an underneath foundation.
" The combination and arrangement of this machine are also
" new."

4. Application to the punching machine of a cold-water guard
or shield, for the purpose of protecting the workman from the
heat of the fire-box, the same being applicable to steam boats, or
elsewhere.

5. Application of a similar shield or guard having a constant stream of cold water, regulated by cocks, turned through it. A fixed guide is introduced above the fire-box and the heaters are lengthened. (See Nº 9728.)

[Printed, 1s. 4d. Drawings. Enrolment Office.]

## A.D. 1845, May 22.—Nº 10,677.

LEWIS, JAMES HEATH.—" Certain improvements in printing." The object of the invention is "to obtain, by means of the " ordinary constructions of platten printing presses, impressions " from steel, copper, or other engraved plates, containing invoice " heads, labels, address cards, and such other plates as are " employed by mercantile houses generally; but the superior " kinds of printing, such as proving and obtaining impressions " from large plates, may be also performed in the letter-press " printing machine if required." This is effected by substituting, for the ordinary woollen cloth lining of the tympans, a sheet of some elastic substance, such as galvanized india-rubber, gutta percha, &c., which forms a cushion capable of entering into the lines of the plate. The plate is blocked liked a stereotype plate, "inked and " cleaned off in the ordinary manner, and placed beneath the platten, " and the wet paper or card being laid over the engraving, the " tympan is brought over it and the platten depressed as usual."

[Printed, 3d. No Drawing. London Journal (Newton's), vol. 27 (conjoined series), p. 394. Petty Bag.]

## A.D. 1845, July 1.—Nº 10,746.

POIRRIER DE, St. CHARLES PHILIPPE. (a)—" Certain im- " provements in the production of type for printing, and in the " machinery employed for the same." These consist, first, " in a new and peculiar mode of pro- " ducing type for printing, by arranging or disposing a consi- " derable length of a wrought or cast metallic bar, or bar formed " of a metallic alloy or alloys, and in passing the same in its cold " state around a cylinder or pulley, . . . " and secondly, "in a " new and mechanical combination and arrangement of parts, " constituting a machine wherein the said metallic bar is operated " upon and the type are formed."

---

(a) See post, No. 14,309, A.D. 1852.

"The metallic bar is passed round pulleys having grooves "corresponding with the width of the bar, which determine the "direction of the bar's motion." A "conductor," consisting of a carriage containing an upper and lower "bill," which approach each other on depressing a lever so as to secure the bar, advances the bar so as to place it between an upper and a lower "prop." A sliding block containing a flat punch, varying in form according to the letter to be formed, and a rounded punch, descends at this juncture by mechanism, the straight side of the former cutting the bar perfectly square with the sides and of the precise length of the body of the type, and the latter forming the "nick," while its notched side prepares the bar to enter into the matrix, and the rounded punch by pressing with half its circumference upon the bar forms the "nick." The punches remain fixed in this position until the matrix, by mechanism connected with the first mover, has impressed the letter upon the end of the cut bar. Density is given to the type thus formed by prongs or projections on the props, proportionate in size to the character of the letter formed. (In the case of concave letters the prongs have corresponding recesses). A retrograde movement of the carriage then takes place (the sliding block rising at the same time), and on its return a fresh portion of the bar pushes out the formed type. The machine shown is capable of forming two types at each operation.

[Printed, 2s. 2d. Drawings. Rolls Chapel.]

A.D. 1845, November 4.—N° 10,924.

SCHOLEFIELD, GEORGE.—"Certain improvements in machi- "nery or apparatus to be employed for lithographic printing." "Entirely novel arrangement of revolving or rotary mechanism," for lithographic printing. Power is applied to the subject roller ("stone, zinc, or other suitable material,") which drives the pressing cylinder (immediately below it) by friction, and an endless band carrying the inking rollers by means of gearing. The inking rollers are furnished by a trough roller as they ascend, and distribute the ink in passing over a table above the subject roller. The latter is damped by a revolving linen wiper (in opposed motion), "set edgewise upon a roller in a longitudinal "and slightly oblique direction," damped by a brush revolving in a water trough, and having a reciprocating lateral motion, caused by a disc set obliquely upon its shaft, working in the forked end of a lever fixed to the framing. The paper (either in sheet or roll) is fed in upon an endless tympan cloth, and discharged by delivering rollers into a suitable receptacle.

[Printed, 8*d.* Drawings. London Journal (*Newton's*), vol. 29 (*conjoined series*), p. 395. Petty Bag.]

## A.D. 1845, November 13.—N° 10,939.

BRETT, JACOB.—(Communicated.)—" Improvements in printing " communications made by electric telegraphs."

At one station is a "composing machine," and at the other a "printing machine," the two being connected by electric conductors. Both parts are " chiefly propelled by the power of weights, the electric " or galvanic force being applied or used only to regulate the mo- " tion of the printing machine by means of an escapement which " it moves, and which requires much less power than is necessary " to propel the machinery." The principal part of the composing machine is a shaft with keys corresponding to various symbols arranged spirally round it, and at the end of the shaft a cogged " circuit wheel," the cogs and hollows of which correspond with the keys upon the shaft. The circuit is made and broken by the sliding of a spring over the cogs and hollows as the circuit wheel revolves when the shaft is turned by the keys. When the key shaft is at rest the motion of the rest of the machine is continued by the action of a governor. The printing machine consists of mechanism so arranged that as often as the circuit is broken and made a shaft is turned backwards and forwards. On the shaft is an escapement, and on an axis parallel to the shaft the type wheel. Pins on the side of the type wheel (driven by clock-work) take alternately into two arms on the escapement (which vibrates with the shaft), and the type wheel's motion is thus regulated by the current. A paper cylinder revolving with a ratchet motion is carried by the action of excentrics and levers in connection with a " hydraulic regulator " of peculiar con- struction to and from the type wheel, a cloth furnished with plumbago being interposed for the impression. The cylinder has either lateral motion by moving in screw bearings, in which case the message is printed "in a helix," or if its axle is plain, revolves so that the printing takes place in parallel lines. So long as the " key shaft " is in motion no printing takes places, the type wheel merely adjusting itself to correspond with the circuit wheel. The printing machine is fitted with a bell alarum.

Printing machine, in which the electric power is used. A considerable portion of the mechanism used in the above printing machine is discarded, and a "second circuit" is introduced, extending only a short distance from the machine, and broken or made by the "first circuit," that is, the circuit extending the whole distance the message has to travel. By this means the power required to make or close the second circuit is very small, and as the second circuit may be connected with a battery, the power of a short circuit may be brought to bear so as to regulate the motion of the shaft connected with the type wheel.

*Oceanic Telegraphic Apparatus.*—Wires coated with copal varnish, and bound with wax cloth or twine, are "platted by "machinery in the manner of a riding whip," with waxed or greased cord or twine. Over the whole of these wires is platted a cable of hemp, saturated with tar or grease, and within these materials one, two, or more wires of communication are enclosed. This cable is designed to extend from one station to the other. The connections of this "oceeanic line" with the shore are protected by tubes coated with bituminous substances. The line itself has, at intervals of a mile, metallic floats or buoys, ballasted with concrete.

[Printed, 1s. 5½d. Drawings. Artizan, vol. 5, p. 110. Enrolment Office.]

A.D. 1845, November 17.—N° 10,947.

NEWTON, WILLIAM.—(Communicated.)—" Improvements in " manufacturing types and other similar raised surfaces for print- " ing."

A pan or vessel containing type metal is placed over a furnace, " contiguous to which the mould with the matrice is " mounted with certain appendages, whereby the melted metal is " forced into the mould for the purpose of casting a type, and " when such type has been cast the mould is thrown open for " the discharge of the type, and closed again ready for a second " operation." In the centre of the metal pan is a "receptacle" and plunger, and a pipe rising towards the "lever frame" carrying the type mould (in two parts, hinged to each other), and mounted upon adjustable centres in the upper part of a stationary inclined standard fixed to the platform. The power is applied to a rotary shaft by a winch in front, and its motion is governed by a fly wheel at the reverse end. Upon this shaft are three cams. The first coming against the under part of a lever occasions (through the medium of a vertical rod and spring lever) the closing of the communication between the pan and the receptacle. Immediately after, the falling of a lever into a notch in the second cam brings down the plunger (by means of a vertical rod and lever) and forces the metal up the pipe into the mould, which is brought down to the jet for this purpose by means of a sliding rod (worked by the third cam) which raises a "lever frame." The further rotation of the shaft lifts the plunger and re-establishes the communication. The "lever frame" is then raised by the sliding rod. A strong helical spring is coiled round the sliding rod to prevent any strain arising from a portion of hard type metal intervening between the mould and the jet. When the lever frame is raised a tension rod forces the mould to open by its bracket frame turning on centres, and on its falling, forces it to close by the same means. The type having been cast, the opening of the mould causes a small hook to take hold of the type and pick it out of the opening half of the mould to which it is attached, previously to which the matrice is tilted by a "tilting lever," acted on by a sliding wedge. As the lever frame rises the sliding wedge is pushed under the tail of a tilting lever, by which a small "beak" presses on the end of the matrice and tilts it. On the descent of the lever frame the sliding wedge retires, and a large spring "attached in the ordinary way to the mould and matrice" causes the matrice to assume its operating position. For keeping the mould cool, the lever frame is made hollow, and a current of cold water made to pass through it continuously.

[Printed, 1s. 2d. Drawings. London Journal (*Newton's*), vol. 30 (*conjoined series*), p. 8. Petty Bag.]

## A.D. 1846, April 1.—N° 11,157.

POTTER, HAROLD.—" Improvements in printing or staining of " paper."

The pattern roller is furnished by an endless blanket or sieve cloth, on which various colors are laid by a hand block, with several rows of studs or projections, which enter into the color trough, which, in the case shown, is divided into seven compartments, into which seven different colors may be placed. The color so laid on is spread by a bar covered with woollen cloth pressed slightly against the sieve surface, and any excess of color is scraped off by a doctor.

[Printed, 5d. Drawing. Repertory of Arts, vol. 8 (*enlarged series*), p. 200; London Journal (*Newton's*), vol. 29 (*conjoined series*), p. 415; Patent Journal, vol. 1, p. 325; Engineers' and Architects' Journal, vol. 9, p. 356. Enrolment Office.]

### A.D. 1846, May 12.—No 11,202.

SIEVIER, ROBERT WILLIAM.—" Improvements in printing."

1. " Mode of making a block in separate pieces so as to give " to the face of such block any pattern that its arrangement " may be capable of." The block is composed of small blocks or types, supported by springs on their stems, in square (or in the case of terry fabrics oblong rectangular) compartments of a frame. Those representing the particular colours are successively inserted in the frame, and printed by it.

2. " Mode of arranging and also of applying color to a block." Wires are attached to the back of the small blocks, and by connecting these with a jacquard apparatus, those to be coloured by the several colours are successively selected and coloured by a trough roller, which runs on rails below it. The blocks having thus received each its colour, the whole of them are let down, and the pattern printed in colours by the rising of the table (which is elastic,) " in any convenient manner."

3. Mode of arranging a pattern on a block composed of many similar pieces, so that when any suitable material is cast, moulded, or pressed into it, a block or printing surface, or such pattern surface, may be employed to obtain a casting, which is to be used as a mould. The blocks, arranged as before, are rubbed with tallow, and used as a matrix with metal, gutta percha, &c.

4. Another mode of making a mould for a printing surface, to be used " for printing patterns on (*a*) letter-press." Small blocks or types with intaglio designs are arranged as above in a frame, " in the form of any device or pattern, with the blank types or " blocks between them ; but if for letter-press they must be " arranged as when read after printing, . . . and the blank types " or spaces must be longer than the lettered types. From this " surface a cast is taken in any suitable metal, (in this case the

(*a*) (?) " or."

" types must be of copper,) plaister, cement, gutta percha, &c.,"
and printed with "in the ordinary manner of block printing."

[Printed, 1s. 3d. Drawings. Repertory of Arts, vol. 9 (*enlarged series*), p. 4. Patent Journal, vol. 2, p. 460. Enrolment Office.]

A.D. 1846, May 12,—Nº 11,203.

LITTLE, WILLIAM.—"Improvements in machinery for printing."
  The invention has for its object " to obtain greater speed or more
" numerous impressions in the same time than other printing
" machines using the like number of printing cylinders." It is
stated that in "the fast machines now in use for printing the daily
" newspapers " four cylinders are employed, "two of which con-
" stantly revolve in one direction and the other two in the opposite
" direction, so that in the passing of the form of type in one direc-
" tion two impressions only are obtained (by two of the cylinders)
" and two more impressions are obtained (by means of the other
" two cylinders) on the passage back of the form of type, . . so
" that four impressions (that is, one impression by means of each
" of the four printing cylinders) requires that the form of type
" should pass to and fro.  Now such is the peculiar character of
" my invention, that when four cylinders are used in a printing
" machine three impressions are obtained from each movement of
" the form of type under the four printing cylinders, thus obtaining
" one half more impressions by the use of a like number of print-
" ing cylinders ; and such also is the nature of my invention, that
" when using three printing cylinders in a machine twice as many
" impressions could be obtained at each movement of the form of
" type as could be obtained by two cylinders when arranged accord-
" ing to the old construction of printing machinery.  And further,
" such is the nature of the principle on which printing machines
" have been heretofore arranged, that only half as many impres-
" sions can be obtained from each movement of the form of type
" as there are cylinders used in a machine, and the number of
" cylinders cannot with any great advantage be extended beyond
" four, but according to my invention many cylinders may be em-
" ployed, and there will be as many impressions, less one, obtained
" from the form of type at each of its movements as there are
" printing cylinders employed in the machine.  In the former
" construction of printing machines each pair of the printing
" cylinders constantly revolved in opposite directions, and the
" feeding tapes are so arranged as to pass under the cylinders, in

" such manner that they never part with the paper after receiving
" it, till they have conducted it under the respective printing
" cylinders. Now, according to my improvements, only each of
" the outer cylinders continuously revolves in one direction, and
" the direction of their motion is opposite to each other, as hereto-
" fore, all the other cylinders, or intermediate of the two outer
" ones, first revolving in one direction and then in the other, by
" which each of the intermediate cylinders prints an impression
" with each movement of the form of type, in whichever direction
" the form may be passing, so that all the cylinders but one (of
" the two outer ones) will produce its impression with each move-
" ment of the form of type. And in order to accomplish the
" feeding and taking away of the sheets of paper into and from
" the machine, the feeding tapes (of the intermediate cylinders
" which first receive the sheets of paper), in place of descending
" under the printing cylinders, only carry the paper down to such
" a position as to be taken by other feeding tapes, and then such
" feeding tapes, acting with the intermediate cylinders, move in
" such a manner, that having fed a sheet of paper so that it may
" pass under their printing cylinder in one direction, they may
" feed the next sheet of paper so that it may pass under their
" printing cylinder in an opposite direction, and at the same time
" they will perform their part in carrying away the sheets of paper
" as they receive their impressions."

The drawings represent a machine having four printing cylinders,
the four outermost ones of which act with their tapes " in a similar
" manner to those heretofore used in a four-cylinder machine; but
" the two intermediate cylinders are so arranged and worked that
" they alternately produce their impression by first being caused
" to revolve in one direction and then in the other direction."
The feeding and discharging apparatus of the intermediate cylinders has a to and fro motion (to enable them to feed and discharge on either side alternately), by means of a cam or "excentric
" track." Each of the outer cylinders are driven independently,
and each rises out of the way of the form of type when it is travelling in the opposite direction to which they are moving, as is
well understood. The intermediate cylinders are driven. One
set of the tapes is not endless, but wound up on spring or
weighted rollers. The feeding places are "of the ordinary con-
" struction," and the sheets are fed in to dropping rollers. "The
" inking tables receive ink at either end of their motion in the

" ordinary manner, and ink is supplied from the inking tables to
" the type after each impression is taken, by proper inking rollers
" placed between the printing cylinders."

[Printed, 3s. 4d. Drawings. Repertory of Arts, vol. 9 (*enlarged series*),
p. 65; Mechanics' Magazine, vol. 45, p. 540; Artizan, vol. 1, p. 17; Patent
Journal, vol. 2, pp. 441 and 550. Enrolment Office.]

A.D. 1846, November 17.—N° 11,451.

BENIOWSKI, BARTHOLEMEW.—" Certain improvements in
" the apparatus for and process of printing."

1. To facilitate composing and distributing the types and correcting the composition, the four sides and lower surface of each type
have its particular letter (direct) written, painted, engraved, etched,
&c., upon them (different colours being used for upper and lower
case).

2. To prevent the effects of the lead and antimony upon the
compositors' hands and lungs, the whole of the types, except their
faces, are covered with varnish.

3. The spaces and quadrats are made of either iron or wood, or
both, painted of various colours and varnished.

4. An apparatus, called a "type store," formed by a number of
vertical tubes about one foot long, the lower ends of these tubes
being closed and their horizontal sections such as to prevent the types
tumbling over in them. To distribute, a page of types, blocks, and
spaces is unlocked and placed in a tray. " I then spread the types
" loosely, separating them, and causing them to lay upon their . . .
" sides by pressing with the hand in such a manner as that they shall
" form an even layer upon the tray." A magnet is then passed over
the whole, and all the iron spaces extracted. The "logotypes" and
" phrasotypes " are then selected by hand and placed "upon a
" board in alphabetical order in vertical columns. Water is then
" poured in, and the wooden spaces and quadrats rise to the sur-
" face, and are removed." The water is then poured off, and the
types dried, " I then select the several types and place them, with
" their faces upwards, in their respective tubes of the type store,"
where they slide down and arrange themselves side by side and
one above another, all being erect and face uppermost.

5. An "authoriton," or "apparatus for the purpose of facilitating
" composition," consisting of a number of tubes, about one foot
and a half long and half an inch square, each marked with the
letter it contains. They are filled from the type store, the faces
of the types being towards the compositor. In the back part of

each tube is a pusher for "the purpose of pushing the types for-
"ward until their faces reach exactly the front end of the tube.
"When the types visible at this portion of the tube are exhausted
"by composition, a new supply is forwarded by pressing on the
"pusher." The types are selected by tweezers and placed in
compartments formed by some elastic substance in a "copying
"stick" about ten inches long. "In placing the types in this
"copying stick, I care not on which of their sides they happen to
"fall from the tweezers, provided they lay with their faces towards
"me. At the end of each word I do not place any spaces; I
"merely leave one or more of the compartments empty. When-
"ever double letters occur, I pick up the two letters together and
"place them both in the same compartment. Whenever logotypes
"and phrasotypes occur, I place them upon the elastic partitions.
"This will naturally cover several compartments, and so I con-
"tinue to the end of the stick. I put nothing into the large
"right-hand compartment, which is merely for the purpose of
"allowing room in case of a logotype or phrasotype ending the
"stick; I proceed filling one stick after another, which I place one
"before another, the back of each stick touching the faces of the
"types in the adjoining stick behind it." The sticks being filled
and read over are handed to "a justifying boy, who puts one type
"after another into the usual composing stick, and exactly in the
"usual manner," placing "spaces whenever he meets with empty
"compartments of the copying stick, which spaces are placed before
"him in a few ordinary boxes." The under surface of the form
can be read "as easily as a printed page."

6. "Polycomposing." If, for instance, several compositions of
the word "London" are required, several L's are taken from the
authoriton and placed in one compartment of the copying stick,
several o's in another, and so on. The copying sticks are then
passed to justifying boys, each of whom takes one set for his
composing stick.

7. "Logotypes" and "phrasotypes," formed by uniting the
separate types of words and phrases by gum, glue, &c., or binding
them with tinfoil. A boy, it is stated, may make easily 200 per hour.

8. To economize room, spaces are omitted ("in imitation of the
"Hebrew language") after the article "the," and any preposition,
conjunction, or pronoun.

9. Inking balls or rollers are made of inflated gut, bladders,
Macintosh's impervious cloth, or sheet india-rubber.

10. Printing for the blind. (a) "I lay upon the form of types a
" well-wetted stout paper, and apply a greater pressure than usual.
" Columbian press answers my purpose best."

[Printed, 11d. Drawings. London Journal (*Newton's*), vol. 31 (*conjoined
series*), p. 166 ; Patent Journal, vol. 3, p. 27. Petty Bag.]

## A.D. 1846, November 19.—No 11,455.

BROCKEDON, WILLIAM, and HANCOCK, THOMAS.—" Im-
" provements in the manufacture of articles where india-rubber or
" gutta percha is used."

The processes enumerated in this Patent produce certain
changes in the qualities of caoutchouc and gutta percha, some
of them similar to those produced by sulphur and heat in the
process now termed "vulcanizing," in others, purifying and
colouring those substances, and " by these means rendering them
" suitable to a great variety of surfaces."

Among the articles which may be made of the material, as improved by the patent process, are mentioned " printers' blankets,"
" sieve cloths," "printer's furnishers," "covering and lapping
" rollers, bowls, and other similar articles," and finally, "forms
" and impressions to print from type."

" Other articles variously compounded, such as of treacle and
" glue, or the like matters, after being made of the required form,
" may be dipped into the solutions of caoutchouc or gutta percha,
" or their compounds above mentioned, and thereby rendered
" impermeable, and then immersed " in solvents "to produce the
" change."

[Printed, 5d. No Drawing. Repertory of Arts, vol. 10 (*enlarged series*),
p. 103 ; Mechanics' Magazine, vol. 46, p. 504. Enrolment Office.]

## A.D. 1846, December 15.—No 11,495.

BINGLEY, MARK. — " Improvements in bookbinding and in
" weaving materials used in bookbinding, applicable also to other
" weavings, and in preparing for and making alphabets for
" accounts and other books, and in inking type therefor, and
" other purposes ; and in preparing sprinkled, granulated, or
" mottled paper for bookbinders and others ; applicable also to
" the edges of books, and in graining or chequering Russia and
" other leather."

The invention relates, first, to a mode of applying sides or lids
and backs to books ; secondly, to weaving suitable fabrics with

---

(a) A history of the art of printing for the blind will be found in the Poly-
technic Journal for March 1840.

beads, for what are called head bands of books; thirdly, to a mode of applying inking apparatus to printing presses; and fourthly, to apparatus to be used in preparing sprinkled, granulated, or mottled paper.

As regards the third head, the patentee states, that " by sepa- " rating the mechanical operation of laying the ink on to the type " from that which goes to work the press (which constitutes the " novelty of this part of my invention), I have succeeded in " arranging parts in connection with a printing press, so that " the operations of working the press, changing the paper, and " inking the type may readily and easily be performed by one " person." The type table is worked backwards and forwards by a rounce. Below the level of the press is an ink trough and roller with a ductor. The roller has a ratchet wheel driven by the action of a plate furnished with a spring raised by means of a cord, the other end of which is fastened to a bar handle. In contact with and above the trough roller is a vibrating (" distributing ") roller, which is tilted by hand, so as to furnish a roller above it, from which latter roller (driven by a cord from the rounce) the inking roller receives its supply. The inking roller is in a frame, which, by the action of a treadle and cords, is drawn over the form while the sheet is being changed.

The fourth part is performed by an apparatus (strapped in front of the workman) in which rollers " bring up color to a revolving " sprinkling brush or brushes."

[Printed, 2s. 8d. Drawings. Enrolment Office.]

A.D. 1846, December 21.—No 11,497.

SMART, WALTER.—" A new or improved lithographic printing " press."

The invention consists in " the whole of the presswork, with " the exception of the operation of laying on and taking off " the paper, being performed by a series of movements, all " resulting from the first motion given to the machine, and not " requiring the intervention of any hand labour." The stone is " backed " as usual on a slate bed, the latter being bolted to a wooden bed which fits into a cast-iron traversing frame, to the under side of which, at the centre, there is attached a rack. A " secondary framework " at one end of the stone carries the wetting, inking, and cleaning parts of the machine, while another at the other end carries the tympan and scraper and their appendages. In working the press, the stone is moved on the traversing frame, first towards one end to be wetted and inked, and then back to the centre to have the paper laid on, after which it is moved towards the opposite end to have the requisite pressure brought upon the paper and stone, " when it returns to the centre " in order to have the paper, which has now been printed, taken " off; and the motive parts of the machinery are so adjusted as " to produce successively the exact pauses required for the " accomplishment of each of the said operations," the intermittent motion in the millwork being caused by the engagement and disengagement of a main wheel with a ring. The inking apparatus consists of a ductor roller attached to the bearings of a drum, "with two endless threads on it (similar " to the " one used in Brown's well-known letter-printing machines)," and caused by its rotation to move on the faces of " supply "rollers" below, "in a direction at right angles to their line " of rotation. Three inking rollers below and in contact with " the supply rollers " are kept to their work by springs coiled on their respective shafts, " and have the ink distributed by small " rollers on each side of them." Attached to the front of the machine is a water trough having " a row of vertical tubes open at " both ends, which rise above the level of the water, and project " a little way through the bottom of the trough. These tubes are " each filled with threads of worsted or cotton, the upper ends of " which drop over the tops of the tubes into the water; thence " they draw up by the force of capillary attraction a continuous " supply of water, which they deliver at their lower ends to the " sponge box." . . . When the stone is moved towards the wetting and inking apparatus, it passes under and in immediate contact with the sponge, whereby it is wetted, but on its return, after being inked, the sponge box is raised by the action of . . . cams quite clear of the stone." The " doctor " and supply rollers are hollow tubes of seamless gutta percha or vulcanized india-rubber brought at the end over discs distended and kept cool by the admission of " water or any other refrigerating liquid." " Rollers made of brass " as usual may be constructed in the same manner as the preced- " ing, in so far as regards the provision made for introducing cold " water into the interior."

A tympan leather is fastened at one end to a rod, while at its other it is wound round a drum. Clasps rising from the end of the traversing frame lay hold of this rod, and unwind the tympan leather, while weighted simultaneously winding-on pulleys keep the tympan tight during the pull. The length or duration of this pull depends on the time which a pressure roller is kept pressed up against the stone, and this again is regulated by cams, on which the roller rests. When by the revolution of these cams the pressure roller is lowered from under the stone, the tympan begins to be wound upon the drum, and the cords to be unwound, when the descending weights attached to the cords reacting on the traversing frame cause it to recede towards the centre of the machine.

A metal roller covered with gutta percha or vulcanized caoutchouc, which runs in bearings in a sliding box, may be substituted for the tympan and scraper. The roller is kept cool by the admission of water. The tympan leather being thus superseded, the tympan rod is connected by cords to the drum, on the ends of which are the pulleys of the weighted cords.

[Printed, 1s. 9d. Drawings. Mechanics' Magazine, vol. 47, p. 587; Patent Journal, vol. 3, p. 98. Enrolment Office.]

A.D. 1846, December 21.—Nº 11,502.

GONIN, Louis Sylvain.—"Improvements in printing stuffs, " papers, and other matters," by hand.

" The particular characters of my invention are, first, the " arrangement of guides for the workman for laying on the block " to the fabric, by which the practice and knowledge of a good " workman is rendered not so indispensable as is the case with the " ordinary system of printing, and at the same time, by this new " arrangement, I am enabled to perform the work with regularity, " precision, and great rapidity.

" The second part of the invention is a system of keeping the " fabric to be printed at a continuous tension, which is brought in " the piece over a roller, and caused to unrol in proportion as is " required, according to the will of the workman.

" And the third part of my invention is in the mode of arrang- " ing the printing table combined with the guides above alluded " to, and also with the mode of stretching the fabrics."

The "guide" (placed across the machine) is perforated with small holes, into which pins upon the block successively fall as the block is shifted. The progress of the fabric through the machine (upon an endless cloth) is regulated by a ratchet wheel under the control of the workman.

[Printed, 9d. Drawings. Repertory of Arts, vol. 10 (*enlarged series*), p. 21; London Journal (*Newton's*), vol. 30 (*conjoined series*), p. 430; Patent Journal, vol. 3, p. 176. Enrolment Office.]

A.D. 1846, December 21.—Nº 11,505.

APPLEGATH, Augustus.—" Improvements (*a*) in machines for " printing paper and other fabrics."

The general disposition of this machine is that of a vertical cylinder 200 inches in circumference, holding on it the type and distributing surfaces, and surrounded alternately by inking rollers and pressing cylinders, each of the latter being furnished with an apparatus for feeding, which radiates from the centre cylinder, the

(*a*) The following remarks are made in this Specification :—
" In the machine contrived for the 'Times' by me in 1827," (see Nº 4902,) " the form of type, its iron supporting bed, the rack, and other necessary appendages, weigh more than 10 cwt., and when working at its quickest speed, in order to print 6,000 sheets per hour, this heavy mass travels 76 inches backwards and forwards 3,000 times, at the rate of 255,000 inches per hour, and the concussions attendant upon such rapid changes of motion are very considerable. In the vertical system, the path of the form, &c. being circular, these concussions are entirely avoided. I therefore estimate that the rate of motion may be advanced from 255,000 to 300,000 inches per hour, in which case the machine herein-before described with eight cylinders, and having a circular type path of 200 inches, will make 1,500 revolutions per hour, and as it prints a sheet of each of the eight cylinders as it passes them, the quantity of sheets printed will be 12,000 per hour. This machine, with tangential planes, has been expressly contrived to meet the exigencies of a printing office for a journal of very large circulation, where the columns of matter must be composed so as to be capable of printing either at flat machines, or on the vertical system, but a still greater production can be obtained in cases where the vertical machine is employed exclusively, for by making the leads, the transverse metal rules, . . . . . and the engraved arms and heads of a slightly curved shape, the ordinary letter or type which is cast with parallel sides can be imposed upon a type holder, such as before shown, but having a true circular face, and can be retained therein by the angular or wedge-shaped column rules made to act as tension bars, in the manner before described, the type forming itself, by almost imperceptible gradations, into a circular surface. . . . . The advantage of this extremely near approach to a true circular surface is, that much smaller printing cylinders may be employed to give the impression than can be used with tangential planes, and by having only two inking rollers for each impression, the printing cylinders may be put at 15 inches distance from each other, measuring from centre to centre, or even less, and thus a type cylinder . . . . having a circuit of 200 inches, may have 12 printing cylinders around it, leaving a space of 35 inches for putting on the type holders. Such a machine moving at the rate of 300,000 inches per hour will make 1,500 revolutions, and print a sheet of each cylinder, or 18,000 per hour, without sacrificing good inking, or any practical convenience in working the machine."
" It is possible that a still greater production and more economy may be obtained by " a machine (shown in the drawings) " in which the paper is supplied in rolls containing 500 or more sheets in one length, in which case the paper must have an interrupted motion; and I describe this machine only as a possible variety of my invention, in case a suitable ink shall be made, and in case an apparatus by which damp paper can be rapidly cut, and provided Her Majesty's Honourable Commissioners of Stamps shall think fit to grant the necessary concession as to the stamping."

whole being driven from the centre cylinder shaft. The form is placed upon three cast-iron rings, secured to a vertical shaft. On the upper and lower rings are circular pieces of wood called " lifts" and " bearers," the former (of the same shape as the form) are placed above and below the form to produce an even impression, the latter projecting so as at the proper periods to force the inking rollers into contact with ink boxes behind them. The distributing surface has an up and down movement consequent on a conical pulley attached to it, running on an undulating railway on the upper side of the bottom frame. The surface of the type holder is a series of tangential planes " so nearly approaching a " circle, that by underlaying the lower printing cloth [on the " pressing cylinder] in the centre of the columns equal to the " depression of the tangent from a true circle, and gradually dimi-" nishing the underlay as it approaches the column rules, an im-" pression will be obtained not discernible from that given by flat " type, or the printing [pressing] cylinder itself may be shaped " into the proper form." By means of screw holders at the bottom of the type holder the column rules are converted into ten-sion bars, and " in all cases where possible, the central column rule " should be a fixture. The form is locked up by set screws in " the sides and at the ends of the type holder." The inking rollers are kept in their places sideways by notched bearings, and are caused to press against the form and distributing surface by coiled springs, the lifts forcing them outwards as the type cylinder revolves, so that they come in contact with the rollers of the ink boxes immediately behind them. The laying on is per-formed at ordinary tables (a) above the level of the press, and arried downwards by a drop roller and endless tapes till it is on a level with the pressing cylinders, when by the opening and closing of vertical drawing rollers and endless tapes it is conveyed hori-zontally to the pressing cylinder, where it receives its impression as the type cylinder comes round, is carried away again by horizontal tapes almost on parallel line to that of its approach, and received by a " taker off."

A machine with an " upright spindle, with its rings, type holders, " distributing table, and inking rollers, as before described." The

(a) " The intention of retaining these old parts being that the layer on may have no new difficulty    ncounter in working at this machine."

pressing cylinders, "(which may be from twelve to thirteen in
"number,)" are clothed with woollen "in the usual manner."
The type holder "is made with a circular face, as in the last ma-
"chine described, having the transverse leads and metal rules, &c.
"made of a curved form to suit the surface of the type holder,
"and ordinary type may be used. The acts of distributing and
"applying the ink are similar to what has been already described."
The bearings of the pressing cylinders are made so as to slide in
order to draw them back a quarter of an inch from the line of
pressure, the teeth of the connecting wheels being made long to
prevent their getting out of gear. During the printing, a "pres-
"sure quadrant" presses friction pulleys, "which revolve freely
"upon the spindle of the printing cylinder, which is thereby forced
"on to the line of pressure and contact with the forms and bearers
". . . tapes . . . being between the bearers and ends of the
"cylinder, as is the paper between the form and the cylinder; the
"paper therefore moves on as it receives the impression, and the
"tapes being forced to move also, give motion to" a drum, around
which they pass, and which is connected by cross bands to another
drum, "against which (so as to move by friction) the rolls of paper
". . . are pressed by the coiled springs, . . . and thus during
"the printing the paper and drums and tapes move. When the
"impression is made, the quadrant passes on from the friction
"rollers, and thus the cylinder is permitted to be forced back by
"the full part of the bearer in the manner of cam wheels, and the
"paper and drums stop and wait for the next impression."

"Paper in rolls may be conveniently wetted by the ordinary
"padding machine in use in calico printing." . . . "The stamping
"may be quickly and economically performed by" passing over a
cylinder (the exact circumference of a newspaper), at the under
part of which it receives a "damp impression" from a wetting
pad (a little larger than the stamp) on an arm attached to a roller
spindle. It then comes in contact with a stamp on a roller, round
which red ink is "distributed by the inking rollers," and which is
"furnished with a vibrating roller and ink trough in the usual
"manner." Lastly, it comes in contact with a blotting pad, which
occasionally presses an endless roll of calico against the stamped
impression, to absorb the superfluous colour, and is then wound
upon a drum. "By enlarging the wetting trough, and substi-
"tuting a roller or cylinder for the pad, the damping of the paper
"for printing may be performed, as well as for the stamping."

Perfecting machine, consisting of two machines such as are above described, there being, however, a slight difference in the vertical drums and tapes of the feeding apparatus, and in the details of the inking apparatus.

Two modes of imposing eight pages of 8vo., in one of which " the type holder may be dispensed with, and an open chase made " of a curved shape used, while the locking up may be obtained " by the ordinary wedges or quoins."

Perfecting machine with pressing cylinders of thirty inches diameter, printing two double forms of 8vo. at each revolution. "The " paper is supplied from two sets of feeding apparatus similar to " those already described, . . . and there are two sets of marginal " types by which the sheets of each form are kept distant from the " other. Such machine having a type path of about ninety-four " inches may make 1,000 revolutions per hour, and perfect in good " register 2,000 sheets of double or 4,000 sheets of single demy or " royal per hour."

Among the claims is the following:—"And inasmuch as the " powerful means contained in the type holder for locking up the " type will in some cases permit it to be used in a horizontal posi- " tion, I claim the type holder, whether used vertically, as here " shown, or whether attached to a type cylinder placed horizon- " tally."

[Printed, 4s. 9d. Drawings. Practical Mechanics' Journal, vol. 1, p. 248; Artizan, vol. 7, p. 265. Patent Journal, vol. 3, p. 150. Enrolment Office. See Weale's "London and its Vicinity," where this and Applegath and Cowper's previous machine for the "Times" are described.]

## A.D. 1847, January 12.—N° 11,526.

BRITTEN, JOHN.—" Certain improvements in machinery or " apparatus for printing, ruling, and damping paper for various " purposes."

1. In a single machine for letter-press printing, the main driving shaft carries a large distributing roller and two cranks (one on each side of the machine), which by means of connecting rods move the frisket and inking roller carriage backwards and forwards. The form is stationary. The platen rises and falls (in slots in the framing) by means of a peculiar arrangement of cranks and jointed rods, acted on by the driving shaft. The frisket is furnished with a rod " having gripers attached to it in the usual manner." It is kept forward by a spring, and, on its coming under the platen, a

projecting piece in the framing acts upon the griper bar, and the frisket is held stationary during the impression without the necessity of bringing the carriage to a dead pause. The gripers are opened and closed (so as to secure and discharge the sheet) by a finger connected with the bar coming in contact with a pendant catch.

Another arrangement is shown by which " as the frisket and " type table both slide in separate guides in different directions, " the platen need not be raised much higher than in the common " hand press."

Perfecting machine. Two platens are fixed to the framework, one above another, each having below it a type table. The type tables are fixed together by rods sliding through the lower platen. The sheets are forwarded through the machine by gripers on bars stretched across endless chains which pass under each platen. When the sheets have arrived beneath the platens they remain stationary, by the stopping of the rollers, consequent on the engagement of a stud and catch. The impression is given by the type tables rising " in any convenient manner." The discharge is effected by part of the "griper rod" coming against a curved guide.

Paper-hangings. The printing block slides in slots in a framing raised and lowered by a cam, by the rotation of which a pad upon which colour is distributed is pushed, which descends upon it for a supply. The block then rises, the pad is withdrawn by a weight, and the block again descends and gives the impression. A second cam driven from the axis of the first causes a lever to push a colour pad beneath the block when it descends. The pad is withdrawn by a weighted cord.

Mechanism for printing progressive numbers in the process called "reading-in" patterns, which is a modification of the apparatus " now in use " for numbering railway tickets. The pointer is moved to and fro over the pattern by the attendant, and the squares in the pattern being numbered, the type wheels "must be " so arranged that when the pointer is over a certain square they " will print the corresponding number."

Apparatus for holding the pens in ruling machines " both " parallel and perpendicular, and also enabling them to be varied " in their relative distances, at the option of the attendant." The

pens are attached to the lower rivets of levers similar to " lazy-
" tongs," the upper levers sliding in slots.

Small apparatus for damping paper, stamps, or labels, on the
principle of capillary attraction.

[Printed, 10d. Drawings. Petty Bag.]

A.D. 1847, May 4.—N° 11,688.

NEWTON, WILLIAM. — (Communicated.) — Improvements in
that class of printing machines in which a series of pressing
cylinders and inking apparatus are placed alternately round the
type cylinder.

1. The form occupies a part (about one-fourth) of the cylinder
surface, the rest, which is of less radius than the form to clear the
pressing cylinders, being a distributing table. The ink is taken
from a " fountain" by a ductor roller, communicated to a
" taking " roller, and thence transferred by means of " vibrating
" distributing " and " transferring " rollers to the distributing
table, one or more small distributing rollers being applied to the
surface of the " vibrating distributor," and between the " taking "
and " transferring " rollers. The " vibrating distributing " roller
has independent motion equal to that of the distributing table, and
has endwise motion by a double worm at the end of the arbor which
travels on a small swivel " feather." The " taking-up" roller, the
" transferring " roller, and the " small distributing " roller are
carried round by the rotary motion of the vibrating distributing
roller by contact of their surfaces.

2. " A vibratory motion " is given to the inking rollers, arranged
in sets around the large cylinder, and also to the transferring roller
of the inking apparatus, by means of a cam and springs acting
alternately, so that they may press on the distributing table as it
passes under them to distribute the ink and " be thrown out suffi-
" ciently far from the centre to transfer the ink to the form of
" types when it comes round." Separate inking apparatus may be
placed in each space between the impression cylinders, in which
case the distributing surface may be dispensed with. If required,
a second form of type may be added opposite to the first, " and
" then the paper must be fed in twice as quickly."

3. A slow continuous rotary, " instead of an intermitting motion
" as heretofore," is given to the ductor or fountain roller, so that
the ink is regularly transmitted to the taking-up roller and thence

to the distributing roller and table. The arbor of this ductor is connected with mechanism that gives to it slow rotary motion by means of a ratchet, " so that it may be turned forward when " desired to alter the supply of ink."

4. Securing and retaining the types on a cylindrical bed by means of column rules that are thicker at the outer than at the inner part, so that the sides of any two of them shall be parallel with each other, or so nearly so as to hold the column of types as tight at the top as at the base, the said rules being made with projections from the lower edge, so that they may be held down from below in such a manner that the columns of types with the rules separating them may be afterwards pressed together laterally by screws, or by wedges or quoins at the side of the bed, in the usual manner, without the risk of breaking or bending the rules. Various methods are shown of securing these types, which taper, and have on one side a projection, and on the other a corresponding " nick " on a curved surface.

In the machine described the pressing cylinders (four in number) are furnished either with tapes or grippers. Their bearings are in sliding boxes capable of every adjustment. The sheet is fed in on one side above, on the other below, the cylinders, and in order to facilitate this operation a slight vibrating lifting motion is communicated to the inner end of the feeding table, which is hinged. A " proving press" is described, " in which the pressing roller is " made concave on part of its surface, to correspond to the convex " form of the type, and is cylindrical the other portion of its " surface, in order to suit a flat form."

[Printed, 2s. 1d. Drawings. Petty Bag.]

## A.D. 1847, July 10.—Nº 11,789.

STOKES, SAMUEL.—" An improved machine for tracing or " engraving from solid bodies or subjects in relief."

This machine consists in a framework or stand fitted with an universal joint, and carrying a long hollow bar. Attached to this is a " secting and dividing apparatus," which determines the plane in which a " tracing blade " moves. This apparatus consists of an arrangement of cones, with centres or axes, universal joints, and balance weights, which have rising and falling motions on a prism-shaped standard. The tracing blade is carried by a sliding rod, which moves in the hollow bar, through which bar the line of projection of the instrument is determined. The sliding rod is moved by the hand of the operator against the surface of the solid body or subject in relief. The required engraving is produced by diamond point on a fixed plane opposite to and at a distance from the tracing blade.

[Printed, 9d. Drawings. Patent Journal, vol. 4, p. 200. Enrolment Office.]

A.D. 1847, July 19.—Nº 11,805.

CHIDLEY, JOHN JAMES.—" Improvements in printing presses."

The invention consists in, 1, a mode " of working the platten and " mounting the inking rollers only on the same frame which carries " the frisket." 2, an arrangement of machinery, by which the patentee is " enabled to deliver the printed sheets of paper without " being obliged to lift up the frisket by hand, as is usually done, the " paper being delivered by the motion which withdraws the frame " and frisket from under the platten." It is shown as applied to a " demy folio Columbian press," in which, among other altera- " tions, a second table is introduced, and the piston of the platen " staple shortened. A frisket frame carries two inking rollers, which " are furnished at the far end of the frame from a large wooden cylinder below the level of the form. This wooden cylinder is fed by a vibrator from a trough roller, and has the ink distributed by a concave roller, which by means of cords traverses along it from end to end, the trough roller having a ratchet wheel movement given by a treadle. " The tympans are the same as are usually " used, but on the near end of the outer tympan are fixed two " hinges. By two screws passing through these hinges, the " tympans are attached to the frame of the frisket." After the impression, the platen recovers itself by a weight. The frisket frame being run out by the turning of the rounce, a cross piece on the frame acts upon a lever, and a curved rod in the frisket on a " semicircular piece " at the near end of the press, and " pulls over the semicircular piece and the frisket until the frisket " is about four inches from the wooden table." When the lever is passed, a weight brings back the frisket and semicircular piece to their former position, leaving the printed sheet of paper on the wooden table the printed side upwards.

[Printed, 6d. Drawings. Repertory of Arts, vol. 11 (enlarged series), p. 197; Patent Journal, vol. 4, p. 320. Rolls Chapel.]

A.D. 1847, July 23.—N° 11,812.

LEWTHWAITE, JOHN.—" Certain improvements in numbering
" machines."

"Figure wheels," having on their cogs the numerals 0–9 in
sequence, are placed on an axis so as to revolve independently
of each other. The number of these wheels varies with the
range of the notation required. On another shaft are a similar number of "driving wheels," also with ten cogs gearing into
the figure wheels, and driving them. An annular portion is
removed at the side of each driving wheel (where the cypher cog
gears), so as to leave in each a complete rim, with the exception of
a small part, which is removed in each, equal to the space between
one cog and another. Each driving wheel is acted on by a corresponding spring "key stop." These key stops are attached to a
bar, on which they rise and fall freely, independent of each other,
and so placed that at each period of mutual action with the
driving wheels the latter are driven the distance of one cog. The
key stop corresponding to the unit figure wheel having caused
that wheel to print the numbers up to 9, the cypher cog of that
wheel, and simultaneously the notch on the rim of the first driving
wheel, comes opposite the pointed key stop of the ten series,
whereby the 10 driving wheel, and consequently the 10 figure
wheel, is advanced one cog; after which it remains stationary
until the unit figure wheel has made another complete revolution.
The action of the hundred, thousand, &c., wheels are similar to
that of the ten wheel. There is an arrangement for holding the
wheels firm when it is not desired to change them.

A mode is shown "in which any number of figure wheels and
" key stops, such as" those before described, "may be made to
" act in unison," that is, one set of key stops to several numbering
apparatus. The paper is supplied to the machine by feeding
tubes, and printed by a roller, as the whole numbering apparatus, with its stops, is run to and fro by rack and pinion. The
inking of the figures is done by rollers set in motion from the
same wheel as gives the rack and pinion movement. But the
specification continues :—" I find it preferable in practice to use
" ten sets, and to arrange the unit wheels in a sequence from
" 0 to 9. With the figure 1 on each of the ten wheels I get
" numbers from 10 to 19; with the next change the numbers from
" 20 to 29, and so on, the figure wheel always remaining station-

" ary. But in order to effect this (supposing the numbers are to
" be printed in their natural consecutive order), it is necessary
" that the key stops should be moved laterally till the unit key
" stop is withdrawn from acting on the unit driving wheel, and
" made to act on the ten driving wheel, which then becomes the
" unit driving wheel in respect of all consequent changes. But
" should it be required that each figure wheel shall commence
" with a different number from the others, or that separate por-
" tions of the series of natural numbers shall be exhibited simul-
" taneously, then the ten stops must preserve their original posi-
" tion, and this rule will hold" whatever the number of wheels in
the machine. For paging books, in which case it is necessary to
use alternate numbers, a "supplementary prong" is added to the
unit key stop, so that for each action the unit driving wheel is
moved the distance of two cogs.

[Printed, 10d. Drawings. Mechanics' Magazine, vol. 48, p. 193. Enrolment
Office.]

A.D. 1847, October 7.—N° 11,883.

TAYLOR, NATHANIEL FORTESCUE.—" Improvements in ma-
" chinery for printing and staining paper and other fabrics."

At each end of a table is a hexagonal drum. These drums
carry an " endless chain of plates," with register points upon
them, the upper part of the chain resting on the table, and the
under part " hanging down below, the outer edges being sup-
" ported by longitudinal bars, so as to keep the plates off the floor."
Ribs formed in the back of the plates slide in an opening in the
table. There are notches in the ribs, into which a "driver " takes
at proper intervals, and moves the chain " so as to bring fresh
" surfaces of the paper or other material on the plates under the
" printing surface." The printing block is placed in a rectangular
frame, which by means of a crank and connecting rod travels in a
line perpendicular to the table's length from the middle of the table
to a sieve at the side of it. The colour sieve is arranged so as to
rise and fall. When at its lowest point, a brush is, by apparatus
affixed to the machine, " raised up and moved to and fro over the
" sieve ;" after which it descends into the colour trough to be out of
the way of the sieve rising. Pressure is given to the block for the
impression by a heart-shaped cam, which, when the block frame is
over the sieve, raises the end of the frame which, is next to it, and
thus depresses the block so as to touch the sieve,

Instead of the endless chain of plates, a long table, on which the fabric to be printed is laid and accurately held by pins or otherwise, may be used, such table being moved at intervals, "in like manner " to that described in respect to the endless chain of plates." This arrangement "will be found useful when printing fabrics requiring " to be evenly and carefully spread." It requires more room than the endless chain of plates, "and it will be evident to a mechanic " that the apparatus for moving the long table may . . . be so " arranged as at any time to move the table backwards or forwards " like distances; and in place of having the bearing surfaces, "whether an endless chain of plates or a long table, capable of " movement, I can so arrange apparatus that the paper only may " be moved proper distances at intervals."

In the case of a fixed table the paper (wound, as in the previous case, off a roll,) is held down by bars across the table during the operation of printing, and drawn forwards after it by means of " clampiug levers " and other gearing of a peculiar construction.

Machinery so arranged "that two sets of blocks or printing " surfaces may be simultaneously worked in such manner that one " block or set of blocks may be receiving color from the sieve, " and the other block or set of blocks be giving off color to one " of the pieces of paper or other fabric." The blocks are kept horizontally in their frame by means of springs, which allow, however, of their being depressed on to the fabric or sieve. The frame is worked to and fro by hand. The sieve is divided into four compartments, in order to use four colours, and is placed between the two printing tables. Each of the rollers on to which the printed fabric is rolled "is so arranged" (by means of a prop drawn by a spring under a projection in a side plate) "as to correctly measure " off a length equal to the length of one of the four surfaces of which "a set of blocks" consists. On the descent of a plate connected with four "mallets" above the block frame, "the whole of the mallets " will descend, one set of blocks being thereby pressed on to the " sieve, and the other set . . . simultaneously pressed on to one " of the pieces of . . . fabric on the tables."

" . . . a mode of constructing and working blocks or printing " surfaces in sets, so that several colors may be simultaneously " applied, and by the successive impressions to cause the different " colors of a pattern to register . . . This part of the invention " consists in so arranging the pattern on the different blocks or " surfaces of a set that by having movement of the . . . fabric

" equal to the length of one of the surfaces . . . after each impres-
" sion the pattern may be made to register, . . . and this is accom-
" plished by removing from one end of the second, third, and
" other block or blocks of a set, parts of the pattern, and placing
" such quantity of the pattern on the other end thereof."

[Printed, 4s. Drawings. Patent Journal, vol. 4, p. 521. Enrolment Office.]

### A.D. 1847, October 14.—N° 11,905.

BENIOWSKI, BARTHOLEMEW.—" Certain improvements in the
" apparatus for and process of printing." The invention consists,
1, in various improvements upon N° 11,451. The letters on the sides
and foot of the type are cast (in intaglio) with it, (a mould with the
alterations requisite for this purpose is shown,) or being "first made
" thereon in intaglio," are electrotyped. Electroplating is substituted for the varnishing of the types. "Final letters," consisting
of a letter and space cast in one, are used. The reverse of the
type surface can be read off and used as a mould for stereotype.
The pushers in the "authoriton" are dispensed with, and the tubes
closed, the types being taken from the top. Using the ordinary
case for "polycomposing." Modification of the "type store," the
tubes being placed in a box attached to a small table. 2. A new or
" improved machine for letter-press printing, which is constructed
" upon the continuous rotary principle, the type being secured to
" the internal or concave surface of a large cylinder, and made to
" pass in alternate succession in contact, first with suitable inking
" rollers, and then with conveniently arranged impression cylin-
" ders."

The large type cylinder has the part of its surface not occupied
by the form disposed for an inking table, supplied by a vibrator
from a fountain roller. The inking and distributing rollers are
pressed to this inking table by coiled springs. Distribution is
effected by friction pulleys with conical face, at the ends of
the rollers, running on the waved edges of the large cylinder.
It is driven from the outside, and is not attached to anything
within. Within are any number of pressing cylinders, with feeding
and delivering tables. The sheets are fed in by drop-down bars.
The type used is of the ordinary kind. The chases and imposing
table must be of the required curve, and in newspaper printing
wedge-formed column rules and furniture are employed.

[Printed, 1s. 10d. Drawings. London Journal (*Newton's*), vol. 34 (*conjoined series*), p. 320. Petty Bag.]

A.D. 1848, January 13.—Nº 12,022.

MORSE, Sidney Edwards.—"Improvements in the manufac-
" ture of plates or surfaces for printing or embossing."

These consist, first, " in making the plate or surface by a new
" mode of combining two substances, one of which is afterwards
" partially destroyed or removed; and, secondly, in a new mode
" of forming the cavities or sunken parts of the surface." The
subject is etched (direct) upon a copper plate, having a ground
on both sides of it. The subject part is then immersed in a
weak solution of pernitrate of mercury, rinsed with water, then
immersed in a solution of sulphate of copper, and connected
with the battery. When the copper begins to be deposited
on other parts, the plate is taken out, rinsed, immersed in the
mercurial solution, rinsed again, and dried. It is then placed
between two pasteboard " flasks " and wooden blocks, and a
mixture of bismuth, tin, and lead poured first into the back
cavity to heat the plate, and next into the cavity in front of the
plate. The deposited copper will, when cool, be found firmly
united with the alloy, and forming a surface which, on the
removal of the intervening alloy to a sufficient depth (by dilute
nitric acid), " will print every letter and line of the drawing which
" was made in the etching ground."

The second part of the invention is performed exactly similarly
to the first down to the drying of the plate. The plate is then
heated, and a thin coating of chloride of zinc (exposed to the air
so long that " it is deliquescing freely on the surface " of a copper
plate or in a thin copper cup) is spread over the whole of the etched
surface with a camel's hair brush. " Allow it to set, but as soon as
" it is in this condition withdraw the plate from the . . . heat,
" and continue to move the brush, as in the act of painting, until
" the fluid is revived on every part of the surface. . . . Take
" now the pasteboard flasks and mahogany blocks described under
" the first head, . . . and cast into them the melted alloy of
" bismuth, tin, and lead, just as described under the first head.
" When cool, open the mould, and . . . a plate will be found
" with a surface of copper lines in the most projecting parts, and
" between the copper lines, cavities formed in the process of
" casting by the accumulations of the chloride of zinc, and the
" evaporation of the water united with it, . . . it is possible to
" make a plate having the requisite cavities for printing or emboss-

" ing with the alloy alone, the copper exposed in the lines of the
" etching ground being used merely to attract the melted metal,
" and hold it loosely until it cools."

[Printed, 4d. No Drawing. London Journal (*Newton's*), vol. 34 (*conjoined series*), p. 257; Artizan, vol. 6, p. 250; Patent Journal, vol. 5, p. 235. Enrolment Office.]

## A.D. 1848, July 18.—N° 12,216.

NEWTON, WILLIAM EDWARD.—(Communicated.)—" Certain
" improvements in machinery for letter-press printing."

The first part of this invention relates to N° 11,688, and consists,
" first, in various modes of giving to each set of inking rollers
" an equal quantity of ink, and in dispensing (if required) with
" the use of the distributing surface on the large cylinder, and
" also the stationary inking apparatus, and in employing in place
" thereof what the inventor calls a revolving ink fountain; second,
" in a novel arrangement of apparatus whereby the sheet may be
" printed on both sides by the same impression cylinder before it
" is delivered from the machine," such impression cylinders revolving constantly in one direction. By the action of a cam on
the axis of the large cylinder a " service roller " is made at
intervals to move in to the distributing table, or segments of the
distributing table are made to move out to the " service roller,"
the same cam causing the several inking rollers to take their
supply from different parts of the same table. The revolving fountain is fed from a reservoir by means of pipes passing through the
shaft of the large cylinder; and by means of small distributing
rollers in connection with it, the distributing surface may be
entirely dispensed with. In the second part, the two forms
are on the main cylinder. The sheet is fed in as usual, and
printed white, after which it passes on tapes to certain rollers,
by which its motion is reversed, and which convey it again to
the pressing cylinder at the right period for reiteration, when it
is deposited by the turning of a light fly frame upon a table.

2. " Improvement in the hand printing press," consisting in a
combination of a toggle joint and lever called the " standard and
" lever," with the bar handle and connecting rod, which " makes
" a compound leverage and toggle joint with immense power."

3. " Self-inking machine," consisting of " mechanism which by
" the action of the workman in running the bed of a common hand
" letter-printing press in and out, takes and distributes the ink,"

and while he is changing the sheet, " causes the inking roller to
" roll over and back once or twice as desired, thereby inking the
" types on the press." The inking roller, when at rest, is in contact with a distributor from which the rest of the inking apparatus
derives its motion. By cords wound round screws on its axis, and
the action of counterweights, the requisite motion is given to the
inking-roller frame. The action of a vibrating roller is given by
the tympan frame, the motions of which also regulate the period
of the inking roller's action.

A similar machine, with independent motive power, the period
of action in the inking roller being also dependent on the movements of the tympan. In both of the above there is an arrangement by which the inking rollers may be passed any number of
times over the form for each impression.

4. Machine " for printing with rapidity from a form of types
" cards of address or business." The machine is driven by foot.
The form is vertical. The impression is given by the type surface
being driven against a platen by a cam recovering itself by a spring.
The form is inked by two composition rollers in a frame, drawn up
and down by connecting rods in contact, after each impression
with a distributor which has endwise motion by the action of an
oblique cam upon its shaft against a friction roller held against it
by a spring. The cards are in an adjustable box with grooves. On
one of them being struck through an aperture in the box by a
" feeder " on the inking frame, it falls until arrested by a " stop
" piece " in a position for the impression, after which the stop-piece
is mechanically withdrawn, and the printed card drops into a box.

[Printed, 2s. 9d. Drawings. London Journal (*Newton's*), vol. 34 (*conjoined
series*), p. 377 ; Mechanics' Magazine, vol. 50, p. 91, and vol. 49, p. 193;
Artizan, vol. 7, p. 153 ; Patent Journal, vol. 6. pp. 154 and 164. Enrolment
Office.]

## A.D. 1848, July 29.—No 12,226.

PRATT, GEORGE WALTER.—" Improvements in the manufac-
" ture of printing ink."

" The invention consists of employing rosin oil in the manufac-
" ture of printing ink" as a cheap substitute for linseed oil. Rosin
oil (1 lb.), rosin (13 oz.), and yellow soap (5 oz.) are heated and mixed
together. When cold the mixture is ground with pigments, " in
" like manner to that heretofore practised when using linseed oil."

[Printed, 3d. No Drawing. Repertory of Arts, vol. 13 (*enlarged series*),
p. 185 ; London Journal (*Newton's*), vol. 34 (*conjoined series*), p. 34;
Mechanics' Magazine, vol. 50, p. 116; Artizan, vol. 7, p.155; Patent Journal,
vol. 6, p. 177. Enrolment Office.]

A.D. 1848, August 5.—N° 12,229.

MACKENZIE, DUNCAN.—" Certain improvements in Jacquard
" machinery for figuring fabrics and tissues generally, and appa-
" ratus for transmission of designs to said Jacquard machinery,
" parts of which are applicable to playing musical instruments, and
" composing printing types, and other like purposes."

1 and 2. Substitutes for the ordinary revolving bar and cards.

3. Application of the same to musical instruments.

4. A " reading apparatus," in which the punches are selected,
and the material pierced by depressing keys similar to those of a
pianoforte.

The application of the invention to the purpose of composing
types is not noticed in the body of the specification.

[Printed, 3s. 6d. Drawings. Mechanics' Magazine, vol. 50, p. 138 ; Artizan,
vol. 7, p. 155 ; Patent Journal, vol. 6, p. 184. Enrolment Office.]

A.D. 1848, August 21.—N° 12,248.

TAYLOR, ISAAC.—" Improvements in preparing and engraving
" surfaces, and in the construction of cylinders adapted for en-
" graving, and also in machinery for printing and ornamenting
" surfaces."

The first part of the invention consists of machinery which
includes and brings into combined operation, in a superior manner to any hitherto adopted, three principal elements of " the
" well-known principle of the hinged rhomboidal frame or
" pentagraph." The first is " that by means of which the
" highest perfection of work is secured, and which is not attain-
" able except by what is in this specification called a high diminu-
" tion, i.e. such a ratio or proportion between the tracing point of
" the instrument and the working point as cannot be usefully or
" for any practical purpose obtained by the means of a single
" rhomboidal frame." This is effected by placing several penta-
graphs in a continuous series, the first imparting its movement
to a second frame, or to a pair of such frames, and these to a
third, or to a third pair, and so on, if requisite, to a fourth, or
more. The second is " the means of bringing a number of
" working points or tools to operate simultaneously, and in perfect
" unison upon one continuous surface, or upon several continuous
" surfaces," so as to ensure a multiplied repetition of the same
pattern and " a perfect fusion of the work on all its sides with its

" fellows." This is effected by placing rhomboidal frames in pairs, " or, as it might be said, back to back, in contrary positions " one to the other, and yet so that the two take on to one " axis of movement at the extremity of the longer bar. The pair " being so adjusted, a bar of some kind is carried across from " the working point of the one frame to that of the other." " By means of this bar we . . . may take as many points " around and between the two diagonal points as the bar or board " will offer to our use, and as this may be done indeterminately, " large ample scope is afforded, as well as to the number of points " as to the application of mechanical adjustments to them." . . . Either the points or the surface to be operated upon may be affixed to the connecting bar, and " inasmuch as the working points " attach to one surface and are fixed in juxtaposition, they may " easily be so arranged as that the work of each shall flow into that " of its neighbour. A machine of this construction covers a large " surface with work in the same time that would be required to " execute a single compartment of the whole."

The third " principal element " is in an apparatus for engraving on the surface of a cylinder such that " each tool, and how many " soever that may be brought to bear upon any part of the cylin- " der, operates always in the line of the radius of the cylinder, and " therefore the work it performs is liable to no deflection." The cylinder rests upon blocks or sleepers attached to the connecting bar or yoke of a working pair of frames, and " taking this bearing " upon the bar, is carried with it, or if unconfined, would be car- " ried in all directions, laterally, or from side to side in the direc- " tion of its own axis. It is carried in obedience to the movement " of the tracing point. But what is wanted is also to give it a " rotatory movement, and so by the combination of the two move- " ments at right angles to obtain a diagonal or any other required " movement. To effect this the axis or mandril of the cylinder is " made to work freely, and yet exactly at each end in sockets, which " themselves are adjusted in the grooves of standards or brackets. " When, therefore, the moving bar takes its direction longitu- " dinally, or in any direction not precisely lateral, the cylinder " receives a corresponding rotatory movement, equivalent in peri- " pheral extent to the longitudinal movement of the bar on which " it rests. . . . If for the sake of the beauty and perfection " of the work it is done at a high diminution," the design is executed in parts, and a shaft of the cylinder effected " according

" to a dial and index, or by any similar means." The mode of etching the cylinder is described.

" If a large plane surface or a cylinder be covered with paper of
" any sort or thickness required, over this may be placed a thin
" undersized paper, the inner surface of which, to the surface in
" contact with the paper first named, is coated more or less thickly
" with any pigment mixed with an unctuous medium." . . .
The carriages are furnished with " points somewhat obtuse," which,
acting upon the exterior of the upper and transfer paper, transfer
to the other paper the color it is charged with, the effect produced
being merely that of a pencil or crayon, " and thus one colour after
" another is transferred." " For the decoration of paper, such as
" paper-hangings and other surfaces, as also for the adding those
" colours that are ordinarily produced upon them by the means of
" what is called block printing, the following method is appli-
" cable :—In place of the blunted points above mentioned, and
" of the carriages, . . . a swing carriage is used, at the extre-
" mity of which is a small conical tube loosely filled with a roll of
" soft leather or sponge; near to this tube is a small cistern hold-
" ing a small quantity of the colour required. . . . From the
" cistern to the head of the tube there is to be a communication,
" either by a groove or pipe, or by a thread or two of worsted.
" When the spring carriage falls to impart its colour to the surface
" beneath, the fluid passes forward also, but returns or ceases to
" flow when the carriage tilts upwards. The requisite number of
" these carriages being planted upon cross bars over the surface to
" be figured or printed, the machine operates in its usual manner,
" the small aperture of each tube conveying its contents at a regu-
" lated rate to the surface, whether of paper or other material."

[Printed, 4s.  Drawings.  Mechanics' Magazine, vol. 50, p. 187; Artizan, vol. 7, p. 184; Patent Journal, vol. 6, p. 203.  Enrolment Office.]


A.D. 1848, November 2.—N° 12,306.

HARRIS, JOHN.—"A mode or modes of founding type and of
" casting in metal, plaster, and certain other materials."

After noticing the frequent unsoundness of type and other casting
the imperfect displacement of air by the metal in the mould, the
patentee says : " Now my invention has for its object the removal
" of this objection to the modes hitherto ordinarily practised,
" either completely or to a very considerable extent, and consists,

" firstly, in causing the metal or other material (in a molten or
" fluid or analogous state,) to run, pass, or flow through the
" mould in a continuous stream, carrying with it the air, scum,
" dirt, sand, &c., and (when the mould is completely filled with
" the metal or other material, in shutting or cutting off the flow of
" the said metal or other material whilst it is so running, passing,
" or flowing; secondly, in causing the said metal or other material
" in condition as aforesaid) to run, pass, or flow through the
" mould, and in shutting or cutting off the flow before that the
" whole of the mould is filled, thus driving the air from the lower
" portions of the mould (or that nearest the exit), and together
" with the air, the scoria, dirt, sand, &c. also, leaving the remaining
" portion of the mould to be filled after .that such shutting or
" cutting off is effected." The first of these modes is "the more
" applicable to type founding (including . . . . quadrates, blanks,
" spaces, stereotype plates, or other forms commonly in use
" amongst printers), and also to the casting of small articles or
" objects."

The type-casting apparatus consists of two parts (A & B) hinged
together and secured for the casting by a catch. B is fixed to
the bed plate. Connected with these parts are an upper, a middle,
and a lower slide, the upper and lower slides being worked by a
lever, and moving in grooves, formed half in either of the halves
of the apparatus. The middle slide moves (by the action of a
pin in the upper slide) in a groove wholly in B. A & B, when
secured together, form at the top a long groove, and below a series
(in the drawing 11) of rectangular passages, the size of the
required type. The upper and lower slides have "ports" or openings corresponding with the passages. A beading on the under
part of the upper slide forms the feet of the type; similar bead-
ings on the middle slide form the nicks. The lower slide contains
the matrices. A and B being secured, and the slides arranged so
as to leave a series of vertical passages through the apparatus,
metal is poured into the trough, whence it flows through the passages and expels the air. While the metal is flowing (time being
given for the passage of the dross, scum, &c. through the passages), the position of the slides is to be reversed, the lower slide
carrying the matrices under the passages, and stopping the flow of
metal, the upper one cutting off and slightly compressing the
metal, at the same time that it forms the foot of the type, and the

middle one immediately afterwards forming the nicks on the type, and also slightly compressing the metal. The type thus cast is free from "jet." The catch is then thrown back, and A swung round on its hinge, "when the type will either fall out or may be "readily removed." The types "require finishing in the ordinary "manner." "It is necessary, . . . in order to save the trouble "and expense of sorting, to have the same letter on each matrix "of a series employed at one and the same time or operation of "casting."

The second mode described is "more applicable to the casting "of large articles and subjects," and the illustrations given of it are casting bullets and cylinders.

[Printed, 2s. Drawings. Mechanics' Magazine, vol. 50, p. 430; Patent Journal, vol. 7, p. 94. Enrolment Office.]

A.D. 1848, November 25.—N° 12,342.

DE FONTAINE MOREAU, PIERRE ARMAND le Comte.— "Certain improvements in the process of and in the apparatus "for treating fatty bodies, and in the application of the products "thereof to various useful purposes."

The invention consists, "firstly, in improvements in the process "and apparatus for treating fatty bodies in general; secondly, in "the application of the several products obtained by the said "improved process and apparatus to the manufacturing of candles "and other similar luminaries, and also to various other useful "purposes."

"Typographical ink" is mentioned as one of the substances produced from the refuse of vegetable wax and tallow, manufactured according to the patent.

[Printed, 11d. Drawings. London Journal (Newton's), vol. 35 (conjoined series), p. 240; Mechanics' Magazine, vol. 50, p. 525; Patent Journal, vol. 9, p. 92. Enrolment Office.]

A.D. 1848, December 11.—N° 12,366.

LEE, GEORGE LAWRENCE.—"Improvements in producing orna- "mental designs."

These consist, first, "of certain means of obtaining ornamental "designs by the use of gelatine, printed or painted with opaque "colors, in combination with glass;" secondly, of a mode of manu- "facturing ornamental designs, in the form of letters and figures, "for shop fronts and other places;" and, thirdly, "of producing

" ornamental designs of marbled surfaces on plaster and other
" materials."

The " quicking " of the gelatine, when required in the first
process, is conducted in the same manner as the silvering of glass.

The second part consists of printing on paper, which is then
rendered waterproof by size and varnish.

By the third, colours are put in a trough of water, and stirred
about till they produce the required pattern. A plaster surface is
then dipped in, instantly withdrawn, and washed by throwing
water over it. The process may be repeated.

[Printed, 3d. No Drawings. Repertory of Arts, vol. 14 (*enlarged series*),
p. 25 ; Mechanics' Magazine, vol. 50, p. 574; Patent Journal, vol. 7, p. 120.
Enrolment Office.]

A.D. 1848, December 16.—N° 12,372.

NEWTON, ALFRED VINCENT.—(Communicated.)—" Improve-
" ments in casting printing types and other similar raised surfaces,
" and also in casting quadrats and spaces."

By the first of these the supply of metal is regulated ; and by the
second, increased accuracy and speed are obtained. The mould is in
two parts, and the matrix applied to it by a circular spring. It is
locked up by a " tension bar " (adjustable in length for the changes
in the size of the mould), which constitutes the principal feature of
the invention. When ready for casting, the mould rests about one-
eighth of an inch above a nipple on a vertical pipe connected with
the metal pot. The action of friction roller on an " excentric slot "
brings down the orifice of the mould upon the nipple, at the same
time that the piston (a pecularity in the valve of which regulates
the supply) is forced down by a spiral spring, and propels the
metal into the mould. The piston is then raised by a lever, and,
owing to the action of the friction roller upon the inner surface of
the excentric slot, two arms are raised carrying with them the
mould. A " tilting lever " on one of these arms frees the matrice,
which still adheres to the side of the mould carried by that arm.

At this particular time " ejectors " or pushers come in contact
with the type, by means of the coupling tension rod extending
outwards, and are drawn over the face and jet of the part of the
mould on the arm, and thus discharges the type.

The motion of the whole machine is uniform, and results from various contrivances connected with a main shaft, revolving by hand or other power.

[Printed, 1s. 7d. Drawings. London Journal (*Newton's*), vol. 35 (*conjoined series*), p. 150; Mechanics' Magazine, vol. 50, p. 598. Enrolment Office.]

## A.D. 1848, December 21.—N° 12,382.

HOLM, CHARLES AUGUSTUS.—"Improvements in printing."
1. Machinery for letter-press printing, in which the pecularities are:—(a) the application of a moving surface or surfaces for the distribution of the ink, in combination with one or two tympans, in a moveable carriage, or with the peculiar cam motions for working the frisket or inking-roller carriage, or with a cam crank, or cams upon a shaft placed longitudinally in the machine, and under the printing table, for giving the pressure, or with blankets placed within a double printing table, or so otherwise placed as to obtain elasticity; (b) the fixing of an inking apparatus to a printing table, in such a manner that it may be disengaged from the framing, to allow the printing table to be drawn out to one end of the machine when required; (c) the combination of an inking drum or cylinder with one or more intermediate rollers, by means of which the ink is supplied to a greater number of inking rollers than could be charged from an inking drum of a limited diameter; (d) an intermittent and reciprocating movement of a frisket carriage, obtained by the combination of two concentric and excentric flanges on a plate; (e) the taking of the ink from a revolving drum or surface by inking rollers, fixed in or moved by a sliding carriage, working independently of the movement of the frisket carriage; (f) the causing the inking rollers to remain for a certain time stationary on a revolving drum or surface to receive ink.

2. Machinery for block printing (six blocks shown), in which the peculiarities are:—(a) a double cam motion for working the block or blocks; (b) an intermittent excentric motion for moving the teerer or colouring rollers; (c) supplying colour to the blocks by elastic rollers working in colour boxes, and gearing into fixed racks, by which a rotary motion is given to the colouring rollers for the purpose of distributing the colour thereon as it moves under the surface of the block or blocks; (d) a feeding apparatus, such that several impressions may be taken from the blocks in the same places of the pattern, for the purpose of producing shaded

and other printing; (e) regulating the tension of the cloth by means of a break applied to independent or separate tension rollers; (f) printing or discharging colours on a vacuum table, for the purpose of drawing the colours or other liquids through the fabric.

3. Machinery for producing shaded ("rainbow") or other printing, in which the peculiarities are:—(a) that the printing is performed on one or both sides of the fabric, by rollers geared together by an intermediate wheel or wheels, or a registering chain, and that whether the fabric be moved in a horizontal or perpendicular direction between the printing rollers, whereby spots, plaids, waving lines, or other configurations may be produced, either by printing the colours on the fabric, or by discharging on a dyed ground, or discharging and printing colours in the part so discharged, or by printing the colours first, and then covering the printed part with a protecting wax or paste; (b) applying to the last-mentioned machines a washing apparatus, a protecting blanket, or a steam drying apparatus, as circumstances may require; (c) the combination of the same machines with separate tension rollers, and also with pin rollers, whereby a superior register of the pattern may be obtained; (d) packing pattern wheels, bars, or surface rollers with wool or other absorbing substance, within hollow parts of the pattern wheels, bars, or printing surfaces, and covering such packing with flannel, whereby the printing surface will absorb a greater quantity of colour than otherwise, and whereby the shaded effect or depth of colour may be produced with a less number of printing rollers; (e) mounting or supporting the printing rollers on friction wheels, when used for such purposes; (f) the manner of making, forming, and combining parts for surface rollers; (g) the supporting or guiding the fabric between rollers with indentations in their surfaces, so as to admit the shaded or printed part of the fabric to pass between the rollers without touching them; and also the covering the supporting or guiding rollers with an endless blanket, the lower part of which works in water, whereby the indentations or cavities in the supporting or guiding rollers may be dispensed with; (h) the use of a colour box, so divided that colour can be supplied at each end to all the different compartments across the machine; (i) the giving a backward and forward motion to a frame in which the fabric is kept stretched, and in which it is moved between printing rollers revolving on their shafts by means of an endless chain fixed to the moveable frame,

and so arranged as to register the colours and advance the fabric by a motion considerably slower than the backward and forward motion of the chain and of the moving frame, whereby the printing rollers will print several times in the same places, according to the adjustment of the velocities of the two combined motions, and thus produce a shaded effect or intensity of colour on the fabric, (j) the use of a printing table in combination with a registering chain, for advancing the fabric on the table, over which a backward and forward motion is given to printing rollers geared into the chain, at the same time as the fabric advances at a slower rate than the motion of the printing rollers; (k) the heating of the colours by placing the colour box or boxes on a hollow plate or plates, into which heated air or other gases are admitted.

[Printed, 6s. Drawings. Mechanics' Magazine, vol. 50, p. 621. Enrolment Office.]

## A.D. 1849, January 16.—N° 12,421.

MARTIN, WILLIAM.—" Certain improvements in machinery for
" figuring fabrics, parts of which improvements are applicable to
" playing certain musical instruments, and also to printing and
" other like purposes."

The invention is described as applied to N° 9300. A band perforated with a pattern passes between a barrel with moveable pins and a slotted plate, when a pin corresponding to the perforation enters, and is kept extended by a "guide ring" until it acts on a bell-crank lever so as to push a type on to the endless band, which in N° 9300 carries it to the composing stick, when the pin recovers itself by a spring. Or the type may be pushed into an inclined channel, down which it will slide, as in N° 8428.

[Printed, 4s. 3d. Drawings. Mechanics' Magazine, vol. 51, p. 67. Enrolment Office.]

## A.D. 1849, April 16.—N° 12,569.

RUTHVEN, JOHN.—" Improvements in preserving lives and
" property from water and fire, and in producing pressure for
" various useful purposes."

1. Screw coupling stopcock for pipes.
2. Stopcock for the nozzle of a fire-engine hose.
3. Pipe and valve for inflating air bags, hats, &c.

4. Hand press for copying letters, letter-press, or woodcut printing, &c. A beam having its fulcrum in standards at the near end of the press brings down a rod attached to it upon the platen. The pressure is given to the near end of the beam by a compound lever worked by the handle which moves in a pivot in the near standards.

[Printed, 6d. Drawings. Repertory of Arts, vol. 15 (*enlarged series*), p. 21; Mechanics' Magazine, vol. 51, p. 381; Patent Journal, vol. 8, p. 58. Enrolment Office.]

## A.D. 1849, April 26.—N° 12,589.

BENIOWSKI, BARTHOLEMEW.—" Improvements in the appa-
" ratus for and process of printing."

The invention includes, first, " improvements relating to types
" for letter-press printing; 2ndly, improvements in apparatus for
" composing type; 3rdly, improvements in apparatus for inking
" printing surfaces, or supplying them with colouring matter; and
" 4thly, improvements in machinery for printing." Under 1, types
for use in the press, described in N° 11,905, are made taper by different coatings of varnish. They must be cleaned with turpentine
instead of the solution of potash. A mould is " so constructed as
" to receive the type metal at the side instead of at the top," by
which the " mouth pieces and a great portion of the back plates "
are dispensed with, and the " blowing " occurring at the " break "
when casting with the pump, " being at the side instead of at the
" foot of the types, is less injurious."

The second head comprises an improved " authorition " (see
N° 11,451 and N° 11,905) in which notches are cut in the partitions between the types for the introduction of tweezers, and a
" revoling composing stick," consisting of an ordinary composing
stick attached to an " angular piece " mounted on a vertical rod.
The latter can " only be conveniently used " when composing
from the authoriton.

The third head comprises inking rollers of vulcanized india-
rubber, either solid or filled with water.

The fourth consists of improvements to the " concave cylindrical
" printing machine," described in N° 11,905. The sheet is fed in
by an endless blanket, on which are strips of some sticky substance, and which by the action of a vibrating frame comes down
upon and picks up the sheet from a feeding board. It is carried
to the impression by " margin pieces " (of india-rubber, &c.), and

the pressing cylinder. It afterwards slides upon hooked wires, becomes detached from the printing surface, and guided round the cylinder until it is caught between " skating pieces," (loops of india-rubber, &c.), and a polished " skating rail," the former of which " cause the advancing corners of the paper to " slide forward until they leave the rail and allow the sheet to fall " down."

[Printed, 2s. 2d. Drawings. London Journal (Newton's), vol. 36 (conjoined series), p. 153; Mechanics' Magazine, vol. 51, p. 426. Enrolment Office.]

## A.D. 1849, June 7.—No 12,653.

KNIGHT, HENRY.—" Certain improvements in apparatus for " printing, embossing, pressing, and perforating."

1. Machine, by the operation of which numbers may be printed " either consecutively, as 1, 2, 3, &c., or alternately, as " 1, 3, 5, 7, &c.; and which is also capable of printing duplicate " or triplicate numbers of both series, as 1, 1, 2, 2, 3, 3, &c., 111, " 222, 333, &c., 11, 33, 55, &c., 1, 1, 1; 3, 3, 3; 5, 5, 5, &c., which " machine is also applicable to the printing of other characters " besides figures." A character disc (composed of wheels placed side by side) is placed in a frame, which is turned over by the action of a pedal, and brings down the disc so as to print upon a pad in front of the machine. The frame recovers itself by a spring. The variations of the disc surface are consequent on the action of two " clicks " upon mechanism in the wheels. When both are in action the printing is alternate; when one only, it is consecutive; and when one is suspended from operation during one or more operations, the printing is duplicate, triplicate, &c. The arrangement of these clicks is effected by a bolt moveable by a " thumb piece." A frame and appendages are shown for use with the above, with which by means of sliding guides the disc will print upon any particular part of a sheet of paper. A substitute for the character disc to be used in printing labels, &c., consists of a carriage containing character plates, and retained in any required position by a click and ratchet on one of its axes.

2. Machine for effecting the combined processes of printing or colouring and embossing. A vertical circular bolt carrying the force is immediately above the die. The latter is coloured by a roller drawn forward by a chain, and recovering itself by a weight. By the action of a pedal a cam forces down the bolt, and the

inking roller is brought into contact with a reservoir. The bolt recovers itself by a spiral spring.

3. Lever press for pressing, perforating, and embossing. The bolt is polygonal, and recovers itself by a weight.

Improved hand-lever press.

Press which " is moved by means of a rack and pinion, and " provides a larger stroke than would be obtained by lever or screw " press."

4. Apparatus for " pressing into required forms covers for " notes or letters, and other similar purposes," and adaptation of " differential pullies " for conveying and regulating motion to such apparatus by foot.

[Printed, 2s. Drawings. Mechanics' Magazine, vol. 51, p. 573; Patent Journal, vol. 8, p. 297. Enrolment Office.]

## A.D. 1849, June 14.—N° 12,658.

BURCH, JOSEPH.—"Improvements in printing on cotton, woollen, " silk, paper, and other fabrics and materials."

The improvements in block printing are divided into four parts :—First, " the mode of constructing a machine which shall " consist of a series of block-printing machines joined together at " equal distances, . . giving the whole a simultaneous movement, " so that each machine shall print a different colour of the same " design." Secondly, "the mode of conveying the carpet or fabric " to be printed through a machine or machines upon an endless " cloth or material having short pin points projecting from the " upper or outer surface, and metal or non-elastic bands affixed to " each edge, having a series of holes at exact distances . . to " ensure its movement in a direct line." Thirdly, " the mode of " repeating the impressions of the blocks by mechanical contrivances, " each time varying the . . pressure; . . by using a heavy " pressure with the first impressions, I force the color into the cloth, " and by reducing the pressure with the last impressions, I leave the " color merely on the surface, which in consequence finishes with " great brilliancy and effect " (particularly applicable to carpets). Fourthly, " the mode of bringing the furnishing rollers alternately " in contact with the sieve rollers every time the action of the sieve " roller is reversed, in order to prevent any flush of color on its " upper surface, and thereby ensure even furnishing."

The improvements in roller printing consist in two parts :— First, " the mode of constructing a drum or wheel of sufficient " dimensions that the whole length of the tissue or piece of cloth

" to be printed may be exposed on its surface without any portion
" of its length overlapping to one side. Round its whole circum-
" ference is fixed a continuous row of cogs or teeth, and the tooth
" wheel on the end of the print roller is an exact division of its
" whole circumference, so that the same teeth, on repeating its
" revolutions, always work together." Secondly, " the mode of
" fixing pin points on its outer surface to prevent the derange-
" ment of the cloth." Thirdly, " the mode of cutting the surfaces
" of printing rollers by the aid of machinery in squares or checks
" previous to the design or parts of the design being marked upon
" them."

The improvements in ticket printing consist in " a mode of
" constructing machines and printing by mechanical contrivances
" both sides of the ticket at the same time and changing a figure
" on the reverse side to correspond with the unit of the progressive
" number." The blank cards are laid in a trough, the lowest
resting on a guide, whence it is swept by the vibration of a lever
above a cylinder, from which it receives the entire impression on
one side, and upon which it rests while the reverse (except the
changing numbers) is printed with two different colours successively
by presses (furnished by colour rollers below them) with a reciprocating movement. The cylinder has ten sides, all alike, except a
small figure in the centre, varying 0—9. The cylinder descends to
receive colour from a roller in contact with a trough roller. The
ticket being thus far printed is pushed on by the blank tickets
until it comes under a type wheel, also coloured by a roller, where
the number is printed.

The improvements in printing piled fabrics consist in " having
" them wetted or damped for the purpose of causing the colour
" to sink to the foundation of velvet or terry surfaces. . . The
" process has the same advantages as dying, as the fibre—wet
" from the preparation or mordaunt, and softened by the applica-
" tion of the usual preparing liquors—is more easily stained with
" the colouring matter, and is a far better absorbent while wet than
" it is in a dry state."

[Printed, 1s. 8d. Drawings. Mechanics' Magazine, vol. 51, p. 596; Patent
Journal, vol. 8, p. 151. Enrolment Office.]

A.D. 1849, July 24.—N° 12,715.

ROSE, ALEXANDER FERRIER. — "A certain improvement or
" certain improvements in the process or operation of printing, and
" in the machinery or apparatus employed therein."

The improvements introduced by this invention are thus enumerated by the patentee. 1. The combination of two letter-press printing machines, set angularly with respect to each other, forming a duplex machine. 2. The use of reversing bars and rollers, separately or in combination, for the purpose of reversing or turning the surfaces of the paper for obtaining reverse or second impressions. 3. The use of elastic bands or fabrics as the means of obtaining a correct register in double printed sheets or webs of paper. 4. The system of obtaining a correct register of the two impressions by means of an adjustment of the height of one or more of the blank spaces across the form of type in the cylinder. 5. The formation of one or both ends of the type cylinders with separate loose pieces combined to form one whole surface, so as to allow of putting in or taking out the separate columns of type. 6. The mode of fastening or adjusting types upon cylinders by means of wedge-shaped column rules or division pieces, arranged so that each pair gives a parallel wedging action to compress the types laterally. 7. The use or application of radiated types upon cylinders of various diameters by means of galleys with curved surfaces. 8. The adaptation and use of type cylinders with a surface equal to the size of the required form of type, with angular surfaces adapted for holding parallel types of the ordinary form. When used for newspapers, the last-mentioned machine has seventeen sides : the opposite pressing cylinders and inking rollers (the latter held by springs to the cylinder) act always the one on an angle and the other on a side of the prism. The pressing cylinders are under-laid. Distribution is effected by a bar traversing the inking roller under the action of a worm wheel and connecting rod.

[Printed, 11d. Drawings. Mechanics' Magazine, vol. 52, p. 90; Practical Mechanics' Journal, vol. 3, p. 15; Patent Journal, vol. 8, p. 235. Enrolment Office.]

A.D. 1849, August 16, N° 12,741.

BODMER, FREDERICK WILLIAM.—" Certain improvements in " machinery or apparatus for letter-press printing."

" By my said invention of improvements in machinery for letter-
" press printing I can damp, print, and partially dry two continuous
" lengths or rolls of paper on both sides during their passage through
" my printing press, without the aid of any tapes or other stays to

" keep them in their places. Each row of paper is independent
" of the other, and is entered and removed at opposite sides of the
" machinery." There are three type cylinders, G, C, and P, of
which the first two have similar type surfaces, and are furnished
each with a single inking apparatus, and have one pressing
cylinder between them. P has the reiteration surface, and is furnished with a double inking apparatus and two pressing cylinders.
The type is attached to the cylinders by a series of collets or flat
rings, having a groove or channel on each side, with a corresponding groove or notch in the tail of each letter. The letters
are connected with these collets and with each other by fillets
which fall or fit into the notches and into the grooves in the
collets. Distribution is effected by cams at the ends of the axes
of small rollers. The two rolls of paper are wound upon drums.
All parts of the machine are united in motion. The one roll
entering on the left is damped between clothed cylinders and
printed white by G. It then passes over a roller to P, where it
receives the reiteration, having in its course the first impression
set by an upper fan. After passing P, the reiteration is set by
another fan, and the roll is delivered by rollers, " and, being cut
" into equal portions by cutters or shears worked by the ma-
" chinery, the journal or printed paper is ready for use." In a
similar manner, the second roll enters on the right, is damped,
printed white at P, and receives reiteration from C, the impressions being severally set, and the paper delivered and cut in the
same manner as in the case of the former roll. Register is attained
by the adjustment of the rollers in the path of the paper.

[Printed, 1s. 3d. Drawings. Mechanics' Magazine, vol. 52, p. 158; Patent
Journal, vol. 8, p. 271. Enrolment Office.]

A.D. 1849, October 12.—N° 12,800.

LE BASTIER, JULES.—" Certain improvements in machinery
" or apparatus for printing."

The invention consists,—First, " in printing mechanically one
" or more colours on the upper surface of a moveable cylindrical
" table by means of one or more printing rollers engraved in
" relievo."

Secondly, " in the mode of disposing the moveable cylindrical
" table to cause its approaching or receding from the printing

" rollers, and in the means of having the cogs by which these last
" are put in motion constantly catching, whatever may be the ap-
" proaching or receding motion of the said moveable cylindrical
" table."

Thirdly, " in constructing printing rollers engraved in relievo,
" and in the suitable mechanism or apparatus regulating their
" respective positions relatively to the moveable cylindrical
" table."

" Fourthly, in the apparatus for tracing or marking the engraving
" or designs on the printing rollers, and in the application of steel
" stamps, drawing points, scrapers, and carriage supporters for the
" purpose of cutting certain engravings, and for scraping, divid-
" ing, and turning the said printing rollers.

" Fifthly, in replacing the sieve rollers for feeding the printing
" rollers by endless cloth, felt, or any other suitable material."

The " table " is of cast iron, and clothed. The relief rollers are
furnished by endless cloths, which are supplied by intermediate
rollers, which revolve more slowly than the cloths, and which are
fed from trough rollers. The printing rollers are so contrived as
to continue their motion when the table is at rest. Pressure is
given by levers on the axles of the printing rollers. The tissue intended to be printed (wound on a roller) is brought on to the surface of the cylindrical table, and " drawn on in the rotative motion
" according to the momentum given to it by means of" endless
cloths which keep it pressed on the table. " It will be very easy
" by any convenient means to dispose two machines similar for
" one or more colours, and to have them to work together by the
" same motive power."

Apparatus for tracing on the surface of the rollers the required
lines or divisions, and for perforating, turning, flushing, and marking them. Two rollers " composed of a thin and cylindrically-
" shaped sheet of iron or brass fixed on two cast-iron discs . . .
" having their edges lapping over," have their axes united by a joint-
ing and placed in a lathe furnished with a " carriage bearer" fitted
with " steel stamps, drawing points, or scoopers." The surface of
the iron or brass tube is covered with a layer of plaster of Paris,
&c., which is turned true. Into this composite layer either metallic
stereotype designs are set round by means of matrices, having a
circular form, and impressed on the surface by excentrics, "or I fix on

" the said layer a thin wood surface, shaped cylindrically by steam
" or other convenient means, and inlaid with glue insoluble in cold
" water.  I delineate afterwards on that wood the design which I
" intend to engrave on the external surface of the cylinder; or if
" the kind of design allows it, I cut it at once, by using drawing
" points . . or scoopers, to which a continuous rotative move-
" ment is given by means of grooved pulleys. . .  Instead of
" wood or metallic designs I can also employ . . . beeswax,
" rosin, stearine, or marine glue, which forms in conjunction with
" sawdust a kind of pasty composition like putty.  I turn this
" paste cylindrically when laid out, and I engrave on it the re-
" quired designs."

[Printed, 2s. 5d.  Drawings.  Mechanics' Magazine, vol. 52, p. 316; Patent
Journal, vol. 9, p. 44.  Enrolment Office.]

A.D. 1849, December 19.—Nº 12,906.

TALBOT, WILLIAM HENRY FOX, and MALONE, THOMAS
AUGUSTINE.—" Improvements in photography."

1. A coating of white of egg is laid evenly on thin plates of un-
glazed porcelain, and dried.  The plate is then rendered sensitive
in the manner described for " the calotype, since called the Talbo-
" type, process upon paper, as described in" Nº 8842.  A solution
of nitrate of silver (25 gr.) in water (1 oz.) is spread over the plate,
which is then dried and dipped in a solution of iodide of potassium
(25 gr.) in water (1 oz.)  It is dried again, and its surface rubbed
clear and smooth with cotton.  The plate is now of a pale yellow
colour, and is kept in that state until required for use, when it is
rendered sensitive by washing it over with a solution of gallo-
nitrate of silver.  It is then placed in the camera, and the image
developed and strengthened by another wash of the same liquid
aided by gentle warmth.  The picture (a negative one) " is fixed
" by washing it with water, then with bromide of potassium, or
" better, with hyposulphite of soda, and again several times with
" water.  The process and manipulation do not differ from that
" described as applicable to photography on paper " in Nº 8842.
Positive pictures can be obtained from the negatives by copying
them in a copying frame.

[" The next part of] the invention consists in converting nega-
" tive into positive pictures.  A coating of gelatine or other

" animal or vegetable substance is laid on a glass plate and
" dried. The glass is then placed coated side downwards hori-
" zontally over iodine till it has a yellow tinge, then dipped into a
solution of nitrate of silver, dried and placed on the camera. The
picture is developed by pouring over it a saturated solution of gallic
acid in water. " The gallic acid being poured off the plate, a solu-
" tion of nitrate of silver of about 30 grains to    (sic) ounce of
" water is poured on the plate, and after standing for some time it
" effects a very remarkable change upon the picture, by converting
" the lights of the picture into shades, and vice versâ, or in other
" words, it changes the picture from a negative to a positive one."
It must " be fixed as usual by washing it with water, then with
" hyposulphite of soda, and finally again with water." For the
picture to be well seen, the glass should be placed on a dark surface. [Talc, varnished paper, oiled paper, porcelain of a black or
dark colour, and other black or dark coloured surfaces may be treated
in the same way, provided they admit of being uniformly coated
with albumen, gelatine, or other animal and vegetable substances
capable of giving transparent films.]

[The next improvement consists in the use of transparent
waterproof paper, impervious to water, as a substitute for glass.
It is coated on one side with albumen or albumen and gelatine,
and rendered sensitive by exposure to vapour of iodine, " and by
" following the rest of the process indicated in the preceding
" section of this specification." Besides the advantages of
portability possessed by paper over glass, " there is a well-known
" kind of photographic pictures, giving panoramic views of
" scenery, which are produced upon a curved surface by a move-
" ment of the object-glass of the camera. To the production of
" these images glass is hardly applicable, since it cannot readily
" be bent into the required curve and again strengthened ; but the
" case is met by employing as a substitute for glass, talc, var-
" nished paper, or oiled paper. . ."

The next improvement consists in fixing pictures on paper by
dipping it, after the usual fixing process, into a boiling solution of
strong caustic potash. " The picture is then well washed and
" dried, and if the tint acquired by it is not pleasing to the eye,
" a short exposure of it to the vapors of sulphuretted hydrogen
" restores an agreeable brown or sepii tint."

" The next improvement consists in forming pictures on polished
" steel plates.    One part by measure of a saturated solution of
" iodide of potassium is mixed with 20 parts of albumen, and
" spread as uniformly as possible upon the surface of the plate,
" and then dried by heat.    The plate is then taken, and while still
" warm is washed over with an alcoholic solution of gallo-nitrate
" of silver of moderate strength.    It then becomes very sensitive.
" If the plate is cold the sensibility is considerably lower.    The
" image obtained is fixed by washing with hyposulphite of soda,
" and finally with water."]

---

By a Disclaimer, filed 1st May 1855, the parts within brackets
were disclaimed, and the substitutes for albumen limited to such
substances as gave films " adhering to the surface of glass."

[Printed, with Disclaimer, 5d.   No Drawing.   Repertory of Arts, vol. 16
     (enlarged series), p. 97 ; Mechanics' Magazine, vol. 52, p. 518 ; Patent
     Journal, vol. 9, p. 518 ; Patent Journal, vol. 9, p. 143.   Enrolment Office.]

A.D. 1850, January 3.—Nº 12,913.

WATERLOW, ALBERT CRAKELL. — " Improvements in the
" means and apparatus for obtaining copies of writings, drawings,
" and other designs."    " The invention consists of modes of
" arranging apparatus, by means of which copies of writings,
" such as letters and other documents, and by which also impres-
" sions of stone or plate, of drawings or other designs, in like
" manner to which lithographic drawings and designs are now
" produced, may be obtained."
    A damp sheet of paper is laid over the subject to be copied, and
the copy taken by drawing over it a frame containing a pressing
cylinder in spring bearings or a scraper bar.    When the subject is
paper the damp sheet is covered with a sheet of felt.
    A modification of the above, in which the stone or plate is on a
bed, which, by means of a rack, is passed between two cylinders.
    Arrangement of a very simple nature for obtaining copies
according to lithographic or zincographic process.    The paper to
be printed is placed upon the subject (stone, plate, litho, or zinco-
graph), and covered with a tympan.    The impression is given by

**a** piece of wood or roller passed over by hand. An ink box to be used with this machine is shown in the Drawings."

[Printed, 1s. 5d. Drawings. Repertory of Arts, vol. 16 (*enlarged series*), p. 80; London Journal (*Newton's*), vol. 38 (*conjoined series*), p. 24; Mechanics' Magazine, vol. 53, p. 18; Practical Mechanics' Journal, vol. 3, p. 175; Patent Journal, vol. 9, p. 176. Enrolment Office.]

A.D. 1850, March 7.—N⁰ 12,994.

CHURCH, WILLIAM.—" Certain improvements in machinery or " apparatus to be employed in manufacturing cards and other " articles composed wholly or in part of paper or pasteboard, " part or parts of the said machinery being applicable to printing " the same, and parts to other purposes where pressure is re- " quired."

1. Apparatus attached to the hydraulic press used in the manu- facture of pasteboard, which assists the workman by gradually increasing his leverage as the pumping operation proceeds.

2. An arrangement of rollers with circular knives for cutting up pasteboard to form railway tickets and cards. The board is first cut into strips by one set of knives, and then crosswise by another set, after which they fall into a box.

3. Machinery for cutting pasteboard to form boxes, in which the above cutting rollers are combined with apparatus for indenting or marking the lines where parts of the pasteboard are to be bent up to form the sides.

4. Machinery for printing, numbering, and cutting railway tickets and other cards, in which the types, a numbering apparatus, and a moveable knive are mounted on the same table, so that they " rise together and simultaneously effect the several operations " which they are designed to perform." The inking is performed by a traversing roller. An indicator announces by a bell the com- pletion of each 100 tickets. A similar machine enabling the workman to print upon the whole width of a sheet of pasteboard " intended to manufacture ten tickets or cards simultaneously." The numbering apparatus in this is peculiar.

5. Machine for dating railway tickets. The printing table and chase (with the date) are jointed to the upper end of a crank rod, which is driven by the action of a treadle. The " ink reservoir " " consists of a roller having a lip or flange on each end," which by mechanism passes at intervals over an inking plate, and inks the type in the chase. The ticket is held by hand in a guide

beneath the platen. A counting or registering apparatus applicable to this machine is described.

6. Adaptation of the last-mentioned apparatus to the purpose of paging books, and to other purposes where the printing of progressive numbers is required. The pages to be numbered are placed one by one on a bed-piece immediately under the numbering wheels, and the printing performed by the depression of a hand lever.

[Printed, 4s. Drawings. Mechanics' Magazine, vol. 53, p. 217; Patent Journal, vol 9, p. 281. Enrolment Office.]

## A.D. 1850, March 7.—No 12,995.

BROOMAN, RICHARD ARCHIBALD.—(Communicated.)—" Im-
" provements in types, stereotype plates, and other figured surfaces
" for printing from."

The invention consists in covering, coating, or plating the types, stereotype plates, &c. " with some protecting metal which will " increase their durability without impairing their sharpness." " The types and other printing surfaces have the required cover- " ing or coating precipitated upon them by the action of galvanic " electricity, and the metal that I find to answer best for the pur- " pose is copper." A number of types being made up into parcels are tied together, and immersed in the solution of salt of copper " to the depth only of the shoulder."

[Printed, 5d. Drawing of the type. London Journal (*Newton's*), vol. 37 (*conjoined series*), p. 179; Mechanics' Magazine, vol. 53, p. 219; Patent Journal, vol. 9, p. 274. Enrolment Office.]

## A.D. 1850, March 7.—No 12,998.

DE WITTE, GERARD JOHN. — "Improvements in machinery, " apparatus, metallic and other substances, for the purposes of " letter-press and other printing."

This invention has for its object the " manufacturing cylindrical " stereotype (clichage cylindrique), by which newspapers, journals, " or other works or papers are printed on both sides at once by a " continuous movement, and cut and folded when required; and " also the printing of painted papers (commonly called paper- " hangings), and woven and other fabrics, by a similar continuous " movement." The casting is conducted similarly to flat stereotyping from paper moulds (lead 85, antimony 13, and tin 2).

For typographical printing the machine consists of four horizontal cylinders placed parallel, the outer ones containing the cylindrical type surface, and the inner ones being clothed and acting as pressing cylinders and conveying drums. " Above each " stereotype cylinder is fixed a cast-iron cylinder . . . of the same " diameter. It is on this cylinder that the operation of spreading " the ink is performed. At each extremity of the machine is a third " cylinder . . . designed by the name of the inking table or " cylinder" (trough cylinder). The ink is taken from the trough cylinder by a vibrating roller (of gelatine), and deposited on the distributing cylinder. Above the distributing cylinder are "two " other rollers . . . of gelatine, animated or set in motion by two " persons, (a) the one of rotation by the rubbing of their weight " (gravity), the other the come-and-go already mentioned, by an " excentric system aided by levers; and lastly, two other . . . . " rollers of gelatine taking up the ink from " the distributing cylinder, "deposit it on the projecting faces of the stereotype . . . " The paper is printed in roll. After the reiteration it is pierced by passing between a cylinder with a " saw blade" and a slotted cylinder, and severed by the tension of rollers revolving at a greater speed than the paper. These cutting cylinders are further employed in folding the paper, being for that purpose "furnished with sides " or portions of sides parallel and perpendicular to the axis, and " hollowed in the parts corresponding to the sides (côtés), which " . . . causes the paper to leave the cylinder folded in two. The " other folds are formed at pleasure, but the most convenient method " has been found to fold newspapers in the form the stuff . . . in " a lady's fan is folded. It is then only required to pick up each " paper, approach (fan-like) the folds together, and the operation " of folding is complete." The sheets, when severed, are conducted between tapes into directing tunnels, from which they pass into a wheel with radiating compartments formed of thread or cardboard. The wheel, in its rotation, either deposits the sheets one upon another or presents them at the side . . in such a manner that a person . . . there placed may easily catch and arrange them."

Printing woven fabrics or paper-hangings. The drawings represent a machine for printing in five colours. In general the printing surface for each colour is on a separate cylinder, " but it is evident " that for designs of a certain nature a single cylinder will serve

---

(a) (?) Motions.

" for many colours. Designs of parallel or longitudinal lines, for
" example, may be printed in a great number of colours by the use
" of very few cylinders. The number of colours possible to be
" used at once is unlimited. The application of each of them is
" obtained by the aid of an apparatus composed in the same
" fashion or form for all, and analogous to that which serves in
" typographical printing as herein-before described." The fabric
is passed between two " superposed cylinders " (the upper one
having the printing surface) pressed firmly against each other, with
india-rubber between the screws and cushions for a spring." The
" stereotype cylinder is surmounted by two cylinders composed of
" gelatine covered with a thin coating of " some colour-proof substance. " Above these is a metal cylinder . . . . against which
" presses a hopper " (trough). " A circular brush situated below
" this hopper lightly brushes the last-named cylinder," the brush
having " a come-and-go " movement. The motion of the whole is
uniform by cog wheel. The fabric passes over a double-threaded
screw, for the purpose of straightening out creases.

The cylinders may be arranged vertically, or " might be placed
" circularly."

[Printed, 2s. 11d. Drawings. Mechanics' Magazine, vol. 53, p. 215; Patent
Journal, vol. 9, p. 185. Enrolment Office.]

A.D. 1850, April 23.—No 13,058.

NEWTON, WILLIAM EDWARD. — (Communicated.) — " Im-
" provements in casting type."

The mould is in two parts hinged together, and the matrix is held
to it by a spring. It is mounted (at an angle of 45°) upon a horizontal slide, by the motion of which it is alternately carried to and
from the nozzle of the melting pot. The same motion operates also
upon levers which open and close the mould, and withdraw or secure
the matrix at the proper periods. In consequence of the mould's
position the type falls immediately on the opening of the mould.
The metal pot is peculiarly constructed, the metal running down
past the nipple (into which a stopper is thrust) into a well below
the plunger, by the descent of which (the stopper being withdrawn
for the purpose) it is injected into the mould. The machine is
worked by three cams on a main shaft, the first giving the moving
the horizontal slide (which recovers itself by a spring), the second
thrusting the stopper into the nipple (the stopper being withdrawn

by a spring), and the third raising the plunger, the descent of which is also given by a spring.

[Printed, 10d. Drawings. London Journal (*Newton's*), vol. 40 (*conjoined series*), p. 458; Mechanics' Magazine, vol. 53, p. 333; Patent Journal, vol. 10, p. 45. Enrolment Office.]

### A.D. 1850, August 29.—N° 13,239.

NEWTON, ALFRED VINCENT.— (Communicated.)—Improve-
" ments in cutting types and other irregular figures."

A block, slab, &c., is placed beneath a cutter mounted in stationary bearings, and driven from some first mover. " All the
" requisite motions are communicated to the bed by a rectangular
" frame constructed upon the principle of the pentagraph, and
" consisting of four or more bars jointed together, and connected
" at one corner to the bed, and carrying at the opposite end a
" tracer or point, which, when moved over the surface of the pat-
" tern, communicates a corresponding motion to the bed and
" block at the opposite end of the pentagraph. In addition to the
" horizontal pentagraph above mentioned, there is also a second
" pentagraph, which being placed vertically and connected to the
" same centre and same part of the bed as the horizontal penta-
" graph, will communicate to the bed and block a vertical motion
" corresponding to the motion of the tracing point at the opposite
" end of the pentagraph. . . . . It has been found by expe-
" rience, that in cutting out letters or flat surfaces, it is most con-
" venient to follow the outline of the pattern, but for bas-reliefs or
" irregular carving it will be found advisable to trace straight
" across the pattern in horizontal parallel lines."

[Printed, 10d. Drawings. London Journal (*Newton's*), vol. 38 (*conjoined series*), p. 325; Mechanics' Magazine, vol. 54, p. 197. Enrolment Office.]

### A.D. 1850, September 28.—N° 13,266.

BURCH, JOSEPH.—"Improvements in printing terry and pile
" carpets, woollen, silk, and other materials."

1. " A new method of preparing by a machine surface-printing
" blocks or rollers which supersedes the work of the block cutter,
" and the necessity of colouring the block surfaces with those
" parts of the design their impressions have to represent."
The design having been transferred to squared or point paper,
is fixed on the table surface under a pointer, and a plain block is
fixed on the table surface under a drill slide connected by a

horizontal bar with the pointer. The pointer is then adjusted over the centre of each square of the same color in the design, and the drill (which is driven by a band) depressed by a lever, drills a corresponding hole in the block; and this is repeated until the number of holes in the block corresponds with that of the squares of the particular color in this design, when the block is replaced by another to be drilled for another colour. The printing surface is made by square pegs rounded at the other end, and fitted into the drilled holes. In preparing surface rollers on this plan, such rollers are placed in bearings below the drill, and all the holes in one line drilled before turning it.

2. " Mode of furnishing surface blocks for printing on very " thick materials, such as carpets, rugs, &c., without the use of a " colour sieve or furnisher, and where a great quantity of colour is " required." The printing surfaces are immersed in different colours in compartments of a sliding trough, and are brought up for the impression (which is given against the under side of the table) by a lever and bolts which pass through the bottom of each compartment. The compartments are successively brought under the table until their respective blocks have completed the design.

3. " Method of constructing a printing surface with moveable " vertical slides, with which I am enabled to print any design " from the same surface." The printing surface and presser surface are each composed of a series of pins in a frame, kept in their places by springs. A plate perforated with the pattern being introduced between them, and the presser surface depressed, those pins only of the printing surface which are proper for the particular colour descend and take color from a sieve which is slidden under it upon the bed of the press. The color sieve being removed, the impression is given by the action of a lever on the printing frame.

4. " Mode of printing from surfaces formed into distinct colour " chambers or compartments, each one representing a different " colour or tint of the design to be produced, the divisions being " made by thin boundaries projecting from the surface a sufficient " height to hold the required quantity of colour, and prevent the " colours from mixing. These chambers are to be fed by small " pipes underneath channels from one to another of the same " colours, or poured in from a feeding pot." This mode of printing is only suitable for terry and velvet fabrics, rugs, &c.

5. " Method of producing the high lights or pale shades of a
" design, or reducing other colours to produce lighter shades by
" the impression of one block or roller (worked in a reducing liquid,
" or in some instances by mere pressure,) having parts on its sur-
" face corresponding with all the different colours and shades to
" be reduced."

6. Mode of bending metal plates to form the surfaces of printing rollers, by passing it between a roller and a concentric surface,
the printing surface being protected from friction with the latter
by a thin steel plate which accompanies it.

[Printed, 4s. 5d. Drawings. Mechanics' Magazine, vol. 54, p. 278; Patent
Journal, vol. 11, p. 27. Enrolment Office.]

A.D. 1850, October 24.—Nº 13,300.

JACOBS, SAMUEL. — " Certain improvements in printing on
" woollen, cotton, paper, and other substances, parts of which im-
" provements are applicable also to the purposes of coloring,
" shading, tinting, or varnishing such substances."

" The principal feature in this invention consists in a new and
" peculiar arrangement and construction of the color trough or
" vessel wherein the several different colors are placed, to be after-
" wards taken up separately or collectively by a roller which re-
" volves in such said trough, the said roller giving off the color or
" colors so taken up to the cut or engraved patterns or cast type
" with which the said roller is in forced contact ; and it is proposed
" by this invention to employ several of these color rollers and
" troughs when the design or pattern to be printed is elaborate."

1. The machine used consists of three similar tiers of rollers, the
subject rollers in the centre, the pressing cylinders above, and
trough rollers below. The fabric is varnished by hair-covered
rollers revolving in a trough of varnish after it has received a
coating of size in a similar manner.

2. Various " mechanisms and appliances " for " cross-printing,
" shading, tinting, &c." The trough runs on rails of a peculiar
form below the colour roller, thereby " throwing in the cross
" colors, tints, and shades, which are then taken up by the print
" roller and transferred to the fabric."

3. In hand block printing the roller is turned by hand in the
trough, and then applied to the surface of a table in a " direction
" to suit pattern, leaving thereon the colors for the block to take
" up by being pressed thereon by the printer."

4. Modes of stopping the cells of the color trough, and forcing the colour on to the server.    Color guage for regulating the supply.

Apparatus for conveying cut sheets or squares of paper, &c. through the machine, consisting of catches on an endless band which draw the sheets one by one beneath a panel.

" Graining apparatus for imitating certain woods in colors," by means of combs, brushes, &c., travelling in serpentine guides at the end of rollers above them, round which the fabric passes.  Embossing patterns in various substances by passing them between rollers, the one in relief, the other in intaglio.

Preparing wood for wood printing by gluing veneers of valuable kinds to thicker pieces of inferior quality, and varnishing them with glass cylinders.

Improved mill for grinding colors or pigments.

Printing by means of a perforated cylinder or endless band.  The color and cleansing rollers are placed inside them, and a ductor is applied outwardly on the rising side.  The color roller is at the top (opposite the pressing cylinder) and the cleansing roller at the bottom.

Extra coloring by means of segments of cylinders forming the color rollers, in place of entire cylindrical color rollers.

" Poppet," or pin coloring, in which the colour is laid on the server by the pattern in pin work.

Apparatus called a " color shuttle," consisting of a trough divided into cells with one or more ranges of color rollers.  In this the shuttle has by mechanism " a swift oscillating motion, " carrying it from end to end of the color trough and printing " the fabric  .  .  .  .  as it passes a bed placed directly above " in the machine."

Pronged or pointed servers.

Mechanism for forcing the color from the cisterns to the color troughs.

" Circular printing machine," the diagram of which represents the adaptation of the before-described color troughs, cisterns, forces, &c. and printing rollers to the surface of a large cylinder or drum, whereby the size of the color trough may be reduced to " the small segment of a small circle," as also " the method of " increasing the number of printing rollers around the drum."

" Two single-cylinder printing machines," (an " over printer "
and an " under printer,") " so constructed as to be used singly,
" or joined at the sides opposite each other, forming a double or
" two-cylinder machine."

" Machine for performing the operation of lithographic, faber-
" graphic [printing from a belt of linen, &c.], threadgraphic [from
" a stitched pattern], and verergraphic [from a wire pattern] print-
" ing by an entirely new mode, that is to say, by a stone cylinder,
" and also by a travelling cloth or band on which is the drawing
" to be printed from."

Anti-damp and anti-oil compositions for the colour belts.

Metal varnish of naphtha, resin, and gutta percha for the troughs
and pipe joints.

Modes of setting up taper type on cylinders, (a) by a " ring
" key," running through them, " to receive which . . . one
" side of the type has a square notch . . . . in lieu of the
" circular ones now used ;" (b) a circular plate with cross arms and
collar fits on the axle and has upon it a flange, through which
any number of taper keys are fastened by nuts.

" A new type table for ornamental printing," illustrating the
mode of applying segments of circles, angles, and straight lines,
by moveable type, to printing purposes in horizontal or cylindrical
forms.

A " wheel dealer " (furnished with spring catches on cross arms)
which delivers the articles to be printed between the pressing and
pattern roller.

[Printed, 3s. 10d. Drawings. Mechanics' Magazine, vol. 54, p. 359 ; Practical
Mechanics' Journal, vol. 5, pp. 32 and 124 ; Patent Journal, vol. 12, p. 47.
Enrolment Office.]

## A.D. 1850, November 7.—N° 13,326.

LUCAS, ROBERT.—(Communicated.) — " Improvements in tele-
" graphic and printing apparatus."

The invention consists in the use of sheet gutta percha (pure or
mixed with caoutchouc sawdust, &c.) for printing surfaces. A
matrix is formed by pressing a piece of thin but strong linen coated
with prepared gutta percha by passing it through hot rollers upon
a form of types, &c., and from this matrix an impression is taken
upon a similar band pressed against it, which, when cooled, " is
" fastened by means of steel springs, or otherwise, upon the printing
" cylinder." The preparation of the gutta percha consists in im-

mersing it (in a divided state) in nitric acid, until it becomes soft, and then placing it for an hour or two in a solution of carbonate of soda or other alkali.

No reference is made in the body of the specification to the use of the invention for telegraphic purposes.

[Printed, 3d. No Drawing. Mechanics' Magazine, vol. 54, p. 398. Enrolment Office.]

A.D. 1850, November 8.—N° 13,327.

MAIN, THOMAS.— " Improvements in printing machinery."

The invention consists of a reciprocating roller and table so connected that their surfaces move equably, various modes of communicating such motion from a rotating shaft, eccentric bearings for the pressing cylinder to depress and raise it in its forward and backward movements respectively, and in grippers on the cylinder and register points. Reciprocating motion is obtained by (1) a circular cogged rack on the end of a connecting rod leading from the crank, gearing with a pinion on the axis of the pressing cylinder. When the shaft and crank rotate, the centre of the circular rack being retained by slings at a constant distance from the axis, receives reciprocating rotary motion through an arc determined by the crank throw, and the pinion receives from it reciprocating rotary motion through an arc, increased in proportion as the radius or number of teeth of the circle of which the rack is a portion exceeds the radius or number of teeth of the pinion. (2) the connecting rod has at its end a cogged wheel and two cogged pinions on the same axis. The latter gear into a fixed rack below them, and thus give reciprocating motion to the axis, and the former gearing into a rack on the under side of the type table, imparts to it a like motion, the increase of throw being greater in proportion as the radius or number of teeth in the wheel exceeds the radius or number of teeth of the pinions. (3) by the connecting rod acting upon parallel jointed bars (like lazy tongs), one joint of which is fixed to the table. At the end of the type table is an inking table. On the forward stroke the type table passes under inking rollers "arranged and fed as in other printing machines." On the return the cylinder clears the form by means of its excentric bearings, which depress it also for the impression. The sheet is fed into " grippers" upon the cylinder by endless tapes reaching to the lower part of it and alternating in motion. The arrangement for register points on a bar extending across endless tapes is peculiar. The sheet may also be carried to the impression in this machine by endless tapes in "a mode similar to that followed in "other printing machines." The printed sheet is discharged upon a board.

[Printed, 10d. Drawings. Mechanics' Magazine, vol. 54, p. 398; Patent Journal, vol. 11, p. 75. Enrolment Office.]

A.D. 1851, January 16.—N° 13,453.

BUCHHOLZ, GUSTAV ADOLPH.—" Improvements in printing, " and in the manufacture of printing apparatus, and also in fold- " ing and cutting apparatus."

1. A cylindrical gutta percha printing surface in relief is obtained as follows :—A gutta percha mould is taken from a printing surface, and placed upon the inner surface of a cylinder, within which is a concentric drum. Upon this mould as a matrix is laid a sheet of plain gutta percha, the latter being forced into contact with it, so as to take an impression in relief by means of warm gutta percha introduced, under pressure, between it and the drum.

2. Press, the parts of which are so arranged as to admit of as many sheets (less one) being perfected as there are printing rollers employed. The machine shown has three rollers perfecting two sheets (in roll). The outer rollers (which have the same type surface) printing one side, and the middle one giving two impressions, and being for that purpose provided with a double inking and pressing apparatus. The whole machine is united in motion. Register is obtained by regulating the distance between the rollers. There is a peculiarity about the printing roller's shaft which admits of its being easily changed. The inking apparatus consists of four rollers (of gutta percha turned by hot tools in a lathe) peculiarly disposed, there being a roller in each disconnected from the rest, whose duty it is to "distribute the ink more equally over " the surface of the printing roller." The ink drops out of the ink box from holes opened and closed by the revolution of a screw.

3. Folding apparatus, in which the paper is carried between two plates backwards and forwards by vibrating levers, depositing one edge of the paper, at each vibration, beneath "valves," which are lifted by tongue pieces on one of the plates as the levers approach, and close upon and secure it as they retire. "This process " is continued until the whole roll of printed paper is folded up."

[Printed, 6s. 7d. Drawings. Mechanics' Magazine, vol. 55, p. 77; Patent Journal, vol. 11, p. 263. Enrolment Office.]

## A.D. 1851, February 12.—N° 13,511.

ULLMER, EDWIN.—"Certain improvements in printing presses."

The object of this invention is to cause the motion of the type table to ink the form, thus economizing time in the process of printing, and space in the construction of the press. An ink table and trough are attached to the type table. Two inking and two or more distributing rollers work in upright open slots in the press frame. The type table, in addition to moving to and from the press head, has likewise a lateral motion, for the purpose of distributing the ink upon the inking table. The latter motion is produced either by pulleys on the table running against guides in the press frame, or by a screw spindle working in a nut on the under side of the table, and having at one end a friction wheel which runs on a ledge of the press. The trough roller has a ratchet motion given to it by the free end of a lever, which is raised as the table returns by sliding upon a ledge in the framework. The tympan and frisket are jointed at the lower edge, and open like the leaves of a book. They are raised on coming out of the press by a guide (in large presses by two) on the framework, and slide down the same as they are run into the press. The press should be so disposed "that the length of the sheet instead " of the breadth may lay across the press," to shorten the path of the bed. In small presses the rounce should be such, as to take the bed in or out by an entire revolution; in large presses it may be increased, so as to perform the same work " by one half or any " other portion of a turn."

[Printed, 10d. Drawings. Mechanics' Magazine, vol. 55, p. 142; Patent Journal, vol. 11, p. 241. Enrolment Office.]

## A.D. 1851, May 14.—N° 13,633.

SMITH, LUKE, SMITH, MARK, and SMITH, MATTHEW.— " Improvements in fabrics in weaving, and in machinery for " winding, weaving, cutting, and printing."

The invention comprises twenty-one heads, the first nineteen of which refer exclusively to the manufacture of textile fabrics. The twentieth consists of improved machinery or apparatus applicable co printing carpets and other fabrics or materials, " for lifting " the blocks from the color cloth or tier cloth to the fabric or " material to be printed, and *vice versâ*, and for giving the requi-

" site motion to the fabric or material under operation," and lastly, " in the construction of printing tables."

The drawings show a " machine applicable to printing paper. " One side of the table contains the color, the other, over which the fabric passes, is heated with steam. The fabric is passed round a steam-heated roller, pressed against by a second roller (on which the fabric is wound), under the action of a weighted lever, along the table, and then round a similar heated cylinder at the other end of the press, on to a roller pressed against the heated cylinder, as in the former case. The blocks are brought by parallel motion from one side of the table, where they are furnished to the fabric where they print, intermittent motion being given to the steam cylinders and rollers at the proper period for advancing fresh lengths of the fabrics.

[Printed, 2s. 11d. Drawings. Mechanics' Magazine, vol. 55, p. 419 ; Patent Journal, vol. 12. pp. 107 and 118; Enrolment Office.]

### A.D. 1851, June 12.—Nº 13,664.

TALBOT, WILLIAM . HENRY Fox.—" Improvements in photo-" graphy."

The first part of the invention consists in a new method of producing the picture on glass. The operations (which may be carried on in moderate daylight) are,—1. Spreading a layer of equal parts of white of egg and water on the plate and drying it. 2. Mixing an aqueous solution of nitrate of silver with alcohol. 3. Dipping the plate into this solution for a few seconds, and then withdrawing and drying it. 4. Dipping the plate into water to remove the superfluous nitrate. 5. Spreading a second coating of albumen as in (1), and drying it with gentle heat. 6. Taking an aqueous solution of protiodide of iron, and colouring the solution yellow with free iodine, mixing together one measured portion of this solution, one of acetic acid, and ten of alcohol. 7. Covering the plate with this solution of protiodide of iron, and drying it with gentle warmth. 8. To produce a picture, dip the plate once or twice for a few seconds into a mixture of a solution of nitrate of silver in water, and acetic acid and water, by candle-light or in a dark room. Remove the picture when taken into the dark room. 9. Develope by dipping the plate into a mixture of a solution of sulphate of iron and water. 10. Wash the plate with a strong solution of hydrosulphite of soda in water, then with distilled water, and clean with cotton and water. To preserve it, coat with transparent varnish or extra coat of albumen.

The pictures thus obtained are called amphitypes. They are either positive or negative, according to the light in which they are held; the latter if held against a bright surface, the former if against a dark ground, or seen by obliquely reflected light. The negative pictures may be copied "upon paper in the usual way." Positive pictures may be secured by pouring black paint upon the pictured side of the glass, then turning the glass the picture is seen non-inverted.

[Where the facilities afforded by a dark chamber are not obtainable the following arrangement is recommended :—A plate glass cell, having one of its sides of ground glass, and furnished with a funnel at one of its upper corners, and a cock or waste pipe of caoutchouc below, is placed in the under part of the camera, the ground glass of the cell serving to fix the position of the plate in the camera. Four bottles, the contents of which are nearly sufficient to fill the cell when holding the plate, are filled as follows :— The first with nitrate of silver, as in (8); the 2nd with sulphate of iron, as in (9); the 3rd with water; and the 4th with a strong solution of hydrosulphite of soda. The plates are prepared as above, from (1) to (7) inclusive. The plate is thus placed in the empty cell, and the focus of the camera being adjusted, the operator "lets fall a curtain which covers and conceals the glass cell, "allowing only the mouth of the funnel to be seen above and the "waste pipe below it." The nitrate of silver is then poured in and the plate rendered sensitive. The picture is taken either while the cell is filled with the solution or after the latter has been run off. If the former, the solution is run off after the picture is formed and the cock closed. The sulphate of iron is then poured in, and in half a minute run off, and the cock closed. The water is then poured in and run off, and the cock closed again. Lastly, the hydrosulphite of soda is poured in, and after a minute or two the plate removed. The plate is now fixed. It should be washed with distilled water, finished, and varnished. Another arrangement of the apparatus, in which the contents of the bottles are measured out in tubes with stopcocks terminating at the cell, is described.

The second part of the invention consists in obtaining, in a darkened room, pictures of objects, for instance, a wheel in rapid motion. A plate prepared as above is placed in the camera, and a sudden flash caused by the discharge of an electrical battery. The image on the glass plate is then rendered visible, and the whole process finished also in the way above described.]

---

By a Disclaimer, enrolled 8th March 1854, the part of the specification included between brackets was disclaimed.

[Printed, with Disclaimer, 5d. No Drawing. Repertory of Arts, vol. 19 (*enlarged series*), p. 41; Mechanics' Magazine, vol. 55, p. 497. Enrolment Office.]

## A.D. 1851, July 7.—N° 13,688.

BAILDON, HENRY CRAVEN.—" Improvements in writing, " printing, or marking letters, characters, or figures upon paper, " parchment, or other material properly prepared for that pur- " pose."

The object of the invention is the prevention of fraudulent alterations in bankers' letters of credit and other documents. " It consists in the employment of colored paper, parchment, or " other proper material, upon which I write, print, or mark all " or a part of the letters, characters, or figures of the intended " document, by means of a chemical fluid or mixture, of such " a nature as will discharge or change the color of those parts " of the paper or other material upon which I so write, print, " or mark, and thus cause the letters, characters, or figures to " be white, or to be of a color different from the paper, parch- " ment, or other material upon which they shall have been written, " printed, or marked." The fluid chiefly used is a solution of caustic potash or soda. " Some of the colored papers frequently " sold by stationers are colored by means of Prussian blue or " some other color, which may be discharged or changed by the " action of caustic or partially caustic alkali . . ."

The solution is applied to printing types by means of gutta percha rollers, the sides and cavities of the types being " slightly " oiled, to prevent the solution from wetting them, and so render- " ing the impression indistinct."

[Printed, 4d. No Drawing. Mechanics' Magazine, vol. 56, p. 59. Enrolment Office.]

A.D. 1851, December 19.—N° 13,866.

BURCH, JOSEPH.—"Improvements in printing cut pile and
" other fabrics and yarns."

The first part of the invention consists in "a mode of producing
" designs upon velvet, piled and other fabrics, by combining the
" processes of printing and embossing, the result of each process
" forming part of the same design, and together perfecting it."
Opaque colours are used, " or colors which require no after process
" to fix or cleanse them. . . . The ordinary modes of printing
" are used in the process . . . the effect being produced in the
" usual way by pressure."

The second consists " in a mode of passing the fabrics, before
" they come under embossing surfaces, through a steam chamber
" or box filled with steam, of a sufficient heat to soften the fibres
" of the material, which, by this mode, is made to yield to the
" embossing surfaces with a lesser amount of pressure than by
" ordinary methods, and a softer and more agreeable effect upon
" the fabric is the result."

The third consists " in the adaptation of the principle of my
" patent block-printing machine to a mode or apparatus for hand
" block printing, and by this means I ensure the perfect registering
" of the different colors without depending upon the skill of the
" workman. It also consists in a mode of fixing the fabric on an
" endless cloth by means of pin points and clasps, and moving it
" from block to block, or from workman to workman; and in
" order to ensure its passing under each block in a direct line, the
" attaching to each side of the endless cloth a non-elastic band,
" having guide rollers at suitable distances through its whole length,
" and by means of holes in the bands and corresponding studs on
" the entering drum, move it forward by such stages that the head
" joinings of each impression are not made in a line across the
" piece, but fall half the length of the sketch. It also consists in
" the mode of adapting sliding frames for carrying the printing
" blocks, and which, being actuated by hand labor, are passed over
" furnishing rollers, instead of, as heretofore, the block being
" carried by the workman, and furnished with color by being
" dipped upon the color sieve."

[Printed, 1s. 10d. Drawings. Mechanics' Magazine, vol. 56, p. 515. Enrolment Office.]

## A.D. 1851, December 24.—N° 13,879.

APPLEGATH, AUGUSTUS. — " Printing machine, adapted for " newspapers," called " a Victoria machine."

The form is divided, and placed in alternate columns upon two cylinders in contact with the same pressing cylinder. The types are thus held more securely, and cylinders of small diameter may be employed, and placed horizontally as well as vertically. " In " the machinery used at the 'Times,' to which this patent is in-" tended to be a sequel, the type cylinder is 200 inches in circum-" ference, and being made to revolve vertically, expensive feeding " apparatus is required for the conveyance of the sheets from the " flat to the vertical position. Now, on the principle of dividing " the form into columns, the cylinder for ordinary types need not " be more than 70 inches in circumference; and when taper or ' wedge-sided type is employed, the cylinder need not be more in " circumference than the size of the sheet of paper (measuring " across the columns), which permits the printing of long con-" tinuous paper, as indicated by Nicholson's Patent of 1792." (a) Part of each type cylinder is formed into a distributing table, with indented sides, which give endwise motion to inking rollers placed in a light iron frame, and held to the cylinder surface by springs. The ink is furnished by a vibrating roller from an ink trough to the distributing table. The sheet is fed in by a " feed drum " and dropping roller, receives a complete impression from the two cylin-ders, and is then discharged by tapes on a receiving board.

" Double-action Victoria machine" for a journal. The type is divided on cylinders as before, their circumference being seventy inches. Each type cylinder is furnished with a double inking apparatus, so as to give an impression both at an upper and lower pressing cylinder. " This machine, with ordinary type and dis-" tributing surfaces, can safely be worked up to the supply of " paper afforded by 6 layers on, or from 8,000 to 9,000 per hour. " But if taper type is used, the circumference of the type cylinder " need not be more than 36 inches, or the dimensions of the paper " upon which the journal is printed, in which case a different " arrangement of inking apparatus would be required, and the " produce nearly double."

---

(a) (?) 1790, see ante, No. 1748.

Two diagrams are given of perfecting machines on this principle, the one with ordinary the other with taper type, the paper being printed in the first instance in sheets, and in the other in rolls.

[Printed, 1s. 11d. Drawings. Repertory of Arts, vol. 20 (*enlarged series*), p. 124; Mechanics' Magazine, vol. 57, pp. 19 and 22. Enrolment Office.]

A.D. 1852, January 24.—N° 13,916.

DE FONTAINE MOREAU, Peter Armand le Comte.—(Communicated.)—" Certain improvements in lithographic, typo-" graphic, and other printing presses, which improvements are " also applicable with certain modifications to extracting saccha-" rine, oleaginous, and other matters, and to compressing in " general."

1. Lithographic press. The stone moves to and fro beneath a " rubber " (prismatic scraper), which by a peculiar arrangement is tilted so as to clear the stone on the return, and brought down by the action of a cam into a vertical position for the impression. It is wetted either by a buckskin bag full of wet sponges, or a cloth perforated double cylinder. The inking apparatus consists of two inking rollers covered with leather, a large roller above them, to which the ink is supplied by a vibrator from a trough roller, and on which it is distributed by small rollers on the top of it. The " rubber " is fixed within a sort of cylinder. A thin leather stretched over a segment of the open cylinder acts as a tympan against which the sheet, fed in from a table above the cylinder, is held (between two rows of pincers) by springs, during the revolution of the cylinder for the impression, after which it is discharged between delivering rollers on to a receiving board.

2. The cylinder containing the rubber can, with a slight modification, be used for typographical printing, the arrangement of the pincers and leather being the same.

The rest of the specification relates to the extraction of saccharine, oily, and other matters.

[Printed, 1s. 7d. Drawings. Mechanics' Magazine, vol. 57, p. 115. Enrolment Office.]

A.D. 1852, May 8.—N° 14,113.

NEWTON, Alfred Vincent.—(Communicated.)—" Improve-" ments in the manufacture of printing surfaces."

The invention consists " in producing plates of letters, signs,
" figures, &c., arranged in any suitable manner, by moulding or
" pressing a substance or compound whilst in the plastic state,
" so as to receive from the mould the configuration, letters, signs,
" figures, &c., required, and then permitting such substance or
" compound to become sufficiently hard to resist the force re-
" quired for giving the impressions by a press, but still so elastic
" and pliable as to admit of being bent around the cylinder of
" a press." The compound recommended for this purpose consists of caoutchouc or gutta percha (two to three parts), mixed
with finely pulverized graphite or soapstone, or plaster of Paris, or
peroxide of manganese (one to three parts).

The second part of the invention "relates to the making of elastic
" printing plates, for printing on irregular or smooth but hard
" surfaces, such as glass, wood, oil-cloth, and a variety of other
" surfaces, and consists in producing such printing plates by
" moulding or pressing in suitable moulds, having the letters or
" figures, &c., in reverse, some highly elastic substance or com-
" pound, such for instance, as that used for making the inking
" rollers of printing presses."

[Printed, 4d. No Drawing. London Journal (*Newton's*), vol. 42 (*conjoined
series*), p. 230. Enrolment Office.]

A.D. 1852, June 24.—No. 14,180.

SWAN, JOSEPH.—"Improvements in the production of figured
" surfaces and in printing, and in the machinery or apparatus used
" therein."

The invention relates, first, to "a mode of engraving metal
" plates, or of producing figured surfaces on various substances
" by the use of a species of pentagraphic apparatus, worked in
" connection with guide figures or surfaces, so as to enable an un-
" skilled operator to produce an engraving or figured surface of
" great accuracy, and in a much shorter time than has hitherto
" been required for the execution of a similar work by the hand of
" a skilled engraver." Secondly, to "a mode of increasing the
" efficiency of the ordinary lithographic press, or modification
" thereof, by actuating it from some continual mover, as the shaft
" of a steam engine or water wheel, instead of working it by hand
" as at present, such connection being effected by suitable engaging

" and disengaging apparatus, actuated by simple self-acting me-
" chanism." The pattern is on a talbe at the bottom, and the
plate to be engraved on a table at the top of an upright pentagraphic rod. In the case of letters, engraved metal plates are used,
capable of being combined at pleasure to form words and sentences. A tracer being passed over the former, the latter has a
copy engraved on it by a cutter, to a scale depending upon the
relative distance of the copy and the plate from the rod's centre of
motion. If the copy contain heavy lines, the plate is covered with
an etching ground, and the lines cut with a cutter and etched in
the plate, then cleaned and re-placed for the finer lines. By
making one or more of the parallel motions duplex, several copies
may be engraved at the same time. There is an arrangement for
giving a periodical traverse to the copy in the case of line ruling.
For flat tinting, a glass plate ruled with lines is laid on the design,
and the tracer passed over the lines "only at such parts as
" are over the spaces between the figures of the device," . . . or
" the edge of the glass plate may be used instead of the guide
" lines ruled upon its surface."

In the lithographic press a continuously rotating shaft has
at its end a duplex armed engaging piece, arranged to act as a
driver upon the corresponding arms of the sliding half of a loose
ratchet clutch piece, which is bored to fit the cylindrical end of the
shaft, the engaging and disengaging being effected by a hand
lever. The stone being run in under the scraper, a pressing roller
beneath it rises by the action of cams, and gives the impression.
The stone (which is bevilled so as to release it after the impression)
is returned by a counterweight.

[Printed, 1s. 3d. Drawings. Mechanics' Magazine, vol. 58, p. 37. Enrolment
Office.]

A.D. 1852, September 23.—No 14,302.

TARDIEU, Jaques Leon. — " Certain improvements in the
" coloring of photographical images."

The manner of coloring them "now in practice" is stated to
" necessarily efface or take away from the truthfulness" of this
picture, "since the colors are spread over the lines and shades."
If the picture be not positive and on glass, it requires to be made
transparent. This is effected, in the case of a positive picture on
paper and other suitable material, by varnishing or sticking it on
a sheet of glass or other transparent substance. " The colors I

" prefer employing are the same as those used for oil painting ;
" they are prepared and applied by brushes. In the same manner,
" however, I may use colors prepared by any known process, be
" it with gum, paste, wax, &c. &c. When the colors I use are not
" oil colors, I pass over them several coats of any suitable var-
" nish, if deemed suitable. The laying on of the colours is the
" most difficult and delicate part of Tardeochromy (name which I
" give to my process). The image must be so placed on an easel
" so that the light may show its transparency, and enable the
" artist to see perfectly at the *back* of the image the lines and
" shades that appear on the front, and the colours are to be laid
" on the *back* of the image," which, being transparent, admits of
their appearing "in all their brightness on the paper side." . . .
" None but an artist, and even a talented artist," it is observed,
" can make the colouring with proper discrimination." The " final
" operation for the preservation of the images :"—Paper, thin
tissue, pasteboard, wood, metal, or other suitable substance of
slight thickness is stuck on the colour. " This operation being
" accomplished, I pare off the edges of the image, and pass on
" its surface one or two coats of varnish used for oil paintings,
" and I let it dry."

[Printed, 3½d. No Drawing. Mechanics' Magazine, vol. 58, p. 296. Enrolment Office.]

A.D. 1852, September 13.—N° 14,309.

JUDE, HENRY GARDINER GUION.—(Communicated.)—" Im-
" provements in the manufacture of type. "

These refer to N° 10,746, to remedy the defects in which :—1. In
respect of the want of means to compress the metal in the event of
the blank containing a slight excess of it, a longitudinal groove
or indentation is formed on one or both sides of the wire or strip
of metal from which the blank is cut, or it may be formed in the
blank subsequently. Blanks thus produced have a sufficient area
in cross section to fill the angles of the chamber in which they are
compressed. In the case of the blanks containing an excess of
metal, it is compressed into the space occupied by the grooves.

The second part of the invention consists in the manufacture of
type partly by pressure and partly by casting or other means, the
letter, vignette, or ornament forming the type face by pressure,
and the body attached to such face by casting, soldering, or other-

wise. The strip of copper or other metal is wound on a drum from which it is delivered between two "feed rollers" which communicate to it periodic motion towards a pair of knives, one of which is fixed to the stationary bed and the other to a cylinder which moves vertically, severing a portion of the metal strip, which falls on the face of the bed between "fingers," and is then caught hold of and traversed sideways by a sliding frame so as to be deposited on the matrix into which it is to be struck. The slide is returned by a spring. A force fixed to a cylinder descends and forces the piece of metal into the matrix, which is on the stationary bed, at the same time that a fresh strip of metal is cut off for the succeeding operation. The stamped piece is discharged by means of a helical spring upon the force on to a shovel which is brought forward by mechanism to receive it. The shovel being on the next descent of the cylinder, tilted by a prong, deposits the stamped piece in a drawer or other suitable receptacle below. The stamped pieces are then trimmed to shapes suitable for the body of the type to which they are to be attached.

[Printed, 1s. 1d. Drawings. Repertory of Arts, vol. 21 (enlarged series), p. 267. Enrolment Office.]

## A.D. 1852, October 14.—No 14,324.

FIELD, JOHN.—(Communicated.)—"Improvements in trans-"ferring and printing."

"A lithographic stone or a plate of zinc or other suitable metal "or material is to be coated over with bitumen dissolved in ether "(or other matter which is known to have the property of being "soluble in any solvent, and which, on being spread out into a thin "film and subjected to light, is rendered insoluble) is spread on in "a thin film, taking care that daylight or rays of light which are "capable of changing the nature of the substance do not come on "it till the process of transferring is to be performed; when this "thin film is set, a photographic negative picture or representation "is placed therein and covered with a glass, and then the light of "the sun is to be allowed to act, which will cause the parts of the "prepared surface where the light comes freely to be rendered "insoluble in the solvent previously used to dissolve the matter; "and I would state, that for this purpose it is preferred to employ "the bitumen of Judea, dissolved in ether; I do not, however, "confine myself thereto. The stone, plate, or surface thus treated "is then in a condition to have the parts not acted on by the light

" removed by washing with the solvent, by which means those parts
" of the prepared surface which were covered by the dark parts of
" the photographic negative picture will still remain soluble, and
" they will wash off by the use of the solvent, and thus leave the
" parts of the surface of the lithographic stone (or it may be of
" metal) uncovered and unprotected, whilst those parts which were
" covered by the light parts of the photographic picture will be
" rendered insoluble, and they will not be washed off by the use of
" the solvent. The uncovered parts of the surface may then be
" bit in by acid, or otherwise treated, as is well understood by
" engravers, or the surface thus obtained may be used as a print-
" ing surface as when printing by the processes of lithography or
" zincography."

[Printed, 3d. No Drawing. Enrolment Office.]

# PATENT LAW AMENDMENT ACT, 1852.

## 1852.

### A.D. 1852, October 1.—N° 77.

SOULBY, STEPHEN.—" Improvements in machinery for letter-
" press printing."

The table and form are fixed on a stationary frame which supports the whole of the machinery, and a pressing cylinder with an
inking apparatus attached to it is mounted in a travelling frame
which runs on V guides, and is furnished with a hand-rail, by
which it is drawn to and fro over the form, thereby producing an
impression on the paper, which is drawn in by the cylinder from a
table at one end of the press. Endwise motion is given to the
inking rollers as they run over the type. A pair of additional
rollers pass over the form before and after the inking roller for
the purpose of more evenly distributing the ink, and also removing any dust. The bearings of the pressing cylinder are at
the end of a pair of levers, which lift it clear of the form as it
passes to the feed table. Pressure is obtained by the weight of the

cylinder, and the employment of levers connected with the moving frame of the machine. The machine is capable of printing in colors, by dividing the ink trough into partitions, but in this case the zig-zag motion must not be given to the inking rollers.

[Printed, 1s. 0½d. Drawings.]

### A.D. 1852, October 1.—N° 118.

STEWART, ALEXANDER. — (Provisional Protection only.)— " Improvements in the manufacture or production of orna- " mental fabrics."

The invention relates to an improved mode of figuring or orna- menting woven fabrics, by a peculiar application of the "dis- " charge " process, by printing or applying a suitable discharging medium, such as an alkali, chloride of lime, or acidulous solutions to a colored fabric.

[Printed, 2½d. No Drawing.]

### A.D. 1852, October 2.—N° 164.

JOHNSON, JOHN ROBERT.—" Improvements in fixing colour- " ing matter of madder in printing and dyeing."

The invention consists in employing casein, albumen, or some one of the nitrogenous organic substances soluble in alkalis, known as the "protein compounds," for fixing alizurine (the coloring matter of madder), upon the textile fibres.

[Printed, 2½d.]

### A.D. 1852, October 5.—N° 273.

JÄGER, HERM.—(Communicated.) — " Improvements in the " treatment of cotton and other similar fabrics, by the introduc- " tion of chemical agents to supersede the use of dung in the " dunging process."

The invention relates to calico printed with aluminia or iron mordants, and consists in applying silicates, especially the silicates of soda and potash, as substitutes for the dung after the mordant or colors have been applied to the fabric.

[Printed, 3½d. No Drawing.]

### A.D. 1852, October 8.—N° 308.

LEWTHWAITE, JOHN.—" Improvements in cards and tickets, " and in machinery for cutting, printing, numbering, and " marking cards, tickets, and paper."

This invention consists of improvements on Nᵒ 11,812, A.D. 1847.

1. The cards and tickets are made of scaleboard, either covered on both sides with paper, or on one side with paper, and on the other a loose woven fabric, or else prepared by saturation in glutinous, oily, or other suitable matter, and baked and dried under pressure.

2. For cutting railway tickets and similar articles, the apparatus consists of a series of cutters on a lower frame, and a corresponding series in an upper frame, which is hinged to it, and brought down by hand. The edges of the cutting blades are kept in contact during the whole length of the cut. A yielding gauge is used, which ensures a clean cut to a narrow slip. The tickets when cut fall into the spaces between the lower frame cutters, and are lowered one step towards the spaces in which they accumulate by means of blocks connected with rack and pinion.

3. In printing, numbering, and marking cards and tickets, the improvements consist in arrangements for feeding in the cards or tickets, distributing the ink by means of a reversing or reciprocating roller, and, in the case of printing in colors, for inking the type and numbering wheels in one or various colors, and changing the colors in order to produce check lines across the face of the ticket or card; also in means for indicating the printing of every card or ticket, and causing the machine to stop working after having done a certain amount of work, or in case of any parts of it getting out of order.

[Printed, 2s. 4½d. Drawings.]


A.D. 1852, October 9.—Nᵒ 325.

JOHNSON, JOHN HENRY.—(Communicated.)—" Improvements " in composing and distributing type."

The mechanism for distribution is carried by a frame, turning easily about a vertical rod working on steel points. A segmental frame, fitted round its circumference with a number of vertical holes, corresponding to the various characters, is fitted to the fixed part of the machine. Immediately above the segment, and carried by the oscillating portion of the machine, is a vertical spindle, which is brought down into any of the vertical holes by a handle, which serves also to turn the machine on its centre. The upper end of the vertical spindle, in its descent, acts upon a small bell-crank lever, and releases the letter from the galley, which is placed horizontally on the top of the moveable frame. On the attendant depressing the handle, the point of the spindle is brought into any desired hole, and the letter released and pushed into its proper compartment.

The composing machine is similar in principle to the distributor, the galley being in this case situated below the compartments, in order that the depression of the handle may cause the letter to drop from its compartment into it. By another arrangement the levers for releasing the letters may be actuated by means of keys, arranged similarly to a pianoforte keyboard, each key being lettered to correspond to the letters in the compartment which it acts upon. On the depression of any key a corresponding letter is released from its compartment, which is inclined so as to allow the letters to slide down, and be always ready to be pushed into the conducting channel, down which the letters to be employed slide to the composing table.

[Printed, 2s. 4½d. Drawings.]

## A.D. 1852, October 13.—N° 364.

SMITH, MATTHEW.—(Provisional Protection only.)—" Improve-
" ments in machinery for weaving and printing."

These consist in forming the loops of terry fabrics by means of a rod supported by slides on the breast beam, and carrying as many short bent wire hooks as there are yarns in the pile warp, instead of the long wires usually employed for that purpose ; and further, in the use of double clips for unwinding a positive and uniform quantity of the pile warp from the warp beams. Instead of cutting the pattern for printing warps in solid blocks, the blocks are made with grooves, and adjustable pieces fitted into them. The pattern is formed by sliding the adjustable pieces to and fro in the grooves, and by this means their position can be easily changed.

[Printed, 2½d. No Drawing.]

## A.D. 1852, October 15.—N° 406.

BLAIR, ANDREW.—" Improvements in printing or ornamenting
" fabrics."

The invention consists in so arranging a machine that both sides of the fabric passing through it may be printed at one and the same time. Two exact counterpart surface-printing rollers are geared together, each being supplied with the necessary color by means of a " sieve " cloth passing round a series of adjustable guide rollers on the main frame. This duplex arrangement being multiplied for printing several colors, "just as the single roller " arrangement has hitherto been multiplied."

[Printed, 5½d. Drawings.]

## A.D. 1852, October 21.—N° 477.

GOVER, HENRY CHARLES.—" Improvements in the apparatus " used in printing with colors."

The invention consists of printing several colors in succession on the same paper or fabric. There is a separate platen carrying a block or printing surface for each color, the platens being all at equal distances from a common centre. An inking apparatus supplies color to each of the printing surfaces after the impression. The several pieces of paper or fabric are placed in succession on to suitable surfaces formed or affixed to a rotating table, there being as many such surfaces as there are platens, so that at each rotation of the table all the colors and impressions of the several blocks will be printed, the table being caused to move each time a distance equal to that between two neighbouring printing surfaces.

The drawings attached to the Complete Specification represent an annular machine, divided into six equal compartments, one of which is left blank for changing the sheet, and the others furnished with platens working in vertical guides, and a fixed printing surface below them. The platens are worked by knee levers in connexion with rods, which receive their motion from friction pullies working in a cam wheel. Between each of the printing surfaces is a distributing table. The inking apparatus for each printing surface is double, and consists of an ordinary ductor and three inking rollers (conical) which passes to and fro with alternating motion over the printing surfaces when the platens are raised. The tympans are pressed down by the platens, and guided in their motion by groove pieces. A method is given of adjusting the several blocks to register, without taking them off, by means of a frame with adjusting screws, the points of which press against an inner frame containing the block or plate.

[Printed, 6½d. Drawings.]

A.D. 1852, October 22.—N° 491.

WILSON, James.—(Partly communicated.) — " Improvements
" in printing fabrics of silk or partly of silk."

The invention consists in combining the process of printing
with the class of piled fabrics called "tissue." The fabric is
woven without pile, and the pile subsequently raised by cards
and teazles. It is then shorn so as to be ready for the printer.
The fabric after being soaked in an aqueous solution of muriate
or oxymuriate of tin is dried, passed through calendering rollers,
and gummed with a weak solution of gum dragon. The printing
is performed with blocks by hand or machine. The colors may
be thickened with gum or starch. After the impression the
material is hung up, and exposed to a steam bath, aired, and exposed to a steam bath again. It is then well rinsed, passed
between pressing rollers, and laid in a bath of water slightly
acidulated with sulphuric acid, brushed, and dried. It is afterwards
dressed by hand with hot irons, " or in the usual manner by
" cylinder."

[Printed, 2½d. No Drawing.]

A.D. 1852, October 23.—N° 503.

HISCOCK, Albert.—(Provisional Protection only.)—" The
" application of ornamental printing to certain fabrics which have
" hitherto not been printed upon."

The invention consists in the adaptation of ornamental printing
to " cotton nets," and in the application of such fabrics, when
printed, to any of the various purposes for which they are usually
employed. " The ordinary blocks or rollers are employed, with
" such modifications only as are necessary, for most effectually
" ensuring the transfer of impressions from the blocks or rollers
" to the open net fabrics. In other respects but little alteration is
" required in the ordinary mode of printing upon woven or other
" fabrics is required."

[Printed, 2½d. No Drawing.]

A.D. 1852, October 26.—N° 530.

PAGE, Henry.—(Provisional Protection only.)—" Improvements
" in paper staining."

The invention consists in apparatus for applying colors to the
sieve preparatory to their being taken up by the block. This

apparatus is divided into compartments, and being filled with the colours required is pressed on to the sieve, where it deposits sufficient color in patches to be taken up by the block.

[Printed, 2½d. No Drawing.]

## A.D. 1852, October 30.—N° 574.

GEDGE, JOHN.—(Communicated.)—"Improvements in printing " presses or machines."

The object sought to be obtained by the invention is an increased rate of production without increasing the speed of working the press or machine. Two " pairs " of cylinders and two forms are used, each form being divided into two parts, arranged upon a horizontal table. The sheets are passed in by tapes, &c., to the first pair of cylinders and printed white. They are then carried by guides to the other pair, and perfected, after which they are discharged on to one of two receiving boards alternately. " The " inking of the forms and distribution of the ink are similar to " the methods employed in other printing machines. Each of " the impression cylinders may be fitted with grippers to avoid " the necessity of long return tapes."

[Printed, 1s. 5½d. Drawings.]

## A.D. 1852, November 1.—N° 597.

WALKER, HENRY.—(Provisional Protection only.)—" Improve-" ments in machinery and apparatus used in cylinder printing."

The invention consists, first, in casting type or making blocks or forms with the curve of the cylinder to be used, and fastening the same on to the outer periphery of the cylinder, so that they will not fly off when the cylinder is subjected to a rapid rotary motion. Secondly, in alterations and additions by which the machine may be used with cylinder motion " instead of the reci-" procating motion now in general use," or that a perfect cylinder may be used for the " type form," instead of a sectional or panelled cylinder for flat-faced parallel type. Thirdly, in preventing the inking rollers heating and becoming soft by the high speed used, two or more sets being brought into action successively. The paper may be laid on in web or " in the usual manner." Fourthly, in printing one or more colours the blanket cylinder is enlarged, " as compared with existing newspaper machinery," and " operates on the paper while it is travelling round the cylinder

" by a series of type cylinders, each with its separate inking appa-
" ratus and its own color."

[Printed, 2½d. No Drawing.]

A.D. 1852, November 9.—Nº 694.

GRIFFIN, CHARLES.—" Improvements in apparatus for fixing
" type or printing surfaces in a chase."

The invention consists in using a combination of inclined planes
and screws.

[Printed, 4½d. Drawings.]

A.D. 1852, November 11.—Nº 715.

WYPER, JAMES COWAN.—(Provisional Protection only.)—" Im-
" provements in the figuring and ornamentation of bookbindings
" and covers of a similar character."

The invention consists in substituting lithographic or block
printing for the ordinary "tooling" or embossing. The design,
with any lettering or titling is transferred to a stone or cut on a
block, and is then printed on the cover. If the surface to be
ornamented be of a light tint, as paper, light leather, or cloth,
the device may be printed in black or other dark ink, or gold or
other leaf. Bronze may be applied instead of ink, in the ordinary
manner of color printing. " It is also clear that the printing
" of the devices may be accomplished by the zincographic, ana-
" static, or other modification of the common lithographic processes,
" tooled work in gold or other leaf being successfully imitated by
" any of these processes."

[Printed, 2½d. No Drawing.]

A.D. 1852, November 15.—Nº 753.

SANDIFORD, ROBERT.—" Certain improvements in apparatus
" for block printing."

The invention is applicable to printing calicoes, paper hangings, &c. by means of blocks, but more particularly to printing
patterns upon handkerchiefs or other similar articles, in two or
more colors. A light frame carrying the blocks is connected
to the printing table (suitably clothed and furnished with a
color sieve at each end) by means of four or more parallel links.
The printer, laying hold of these links, " has merely to keep lifting

" the blocks from one sieve to the other, and back again, whilst
" two mixers or ' tierers ' keep the sieves properly furnished with
" color, and a boy winds on the calico, &c., as it is printed."

A drawing is given of the invention as adapted for printing with
four blocks, each of the four sides of the table being furnished
with a sieve and a block. In this arrangement the blocks are not
connected. Each is provided with two links, the fixed centres of
which are links exactly in the centre between the table and the
sieve. Each block in this instance is worked separately, but the
parallel links act in the same manner as in the preceding case.

[Printed, 6½d. Drawings.]

## A.D. 1852, November 20.—N° 809.

GREEN, WILLIAM.— " Improvements in the manufacture of
" textile fabrics and in machinery or apparatus for effecting the
" same, parts of which improvements are also applicable to print-
" ing and embossing generally."

The invention consists, first, in imparting a glossy appearance
to the fabric by combining the silk and cotton of which it is
composed, so that at one portion of it there is more of one
material than at another. Or the surface is rendered glossy by
applying small filaments of silk, " silk waste," feathers, asbestos,
metallic powders, &c. to yarns of cotton, and weaving them in
the ordinary way, or weaving the cloth of suitable materials
and applying upon it the above filaments (if the metallic powders be used with stains or dyes). The fabric thus composed
is then stamped, embossed, or printed "by any suitable ma-
" chinery." The machine invented for this purpose operates by
flat pressure upon one, two, or more blocks, which may be arranged
for printing and embossing, or for embossing or printing only.
If for the former, the colors are applied to them from reservoirs
placed beneath, by capillary attraction or otherwise. The blocks
are arranged for printing two or more colors at once, for which
purpose they are divided into several portions, each having a
separate color apparatus. Below or above the blocks are platens,
which rise and fall to give the required pressure. The fabric is
passed automatically through the machine by tapes passing over
rollers at each side of the machine. When solid blocks are used
the coloring rollers are made of the ordinary material, or of fragments of skin pressed into a mould and treated with tanning

matter. An embossing cylinder, working against a paper or suitable bowl, is, when required, employed in connection with the above, its action tending to diffuse the color and produce peculiar effects.

[Printed, 5½d. Drawings.]

A.D. 1852, November 24.—N° 839.

HIGGIN, JAMES.—" Improvements in the manufacture of certain " mordants used in preparing woven or textile fabrics for printing, " staining, or dyeing them, and in the mode or method of using " the same or other mordants for the said purposes."

These consist, first, in manufacturing aluminous stannates of an alkali, to be applied to the ordinary purposes for which the stannates of soda are employed; secondly, in manufacturing compound acid mordants, containing a salt or salts of alumina, and a salt or salts of tin, in combination, to be used " as the chlorides " of tin are used in the arts of dyeing and calico printing;" thirdly, in fixing any compounds of alumina and oxide or oxides of tin on the fabric, by padding or immersion previously to printing or dyeing.

[Printed, 3½d. No Drawing.]

A.D. 1852, December 3.—N° 948.

STIFF, GEORGE.—(Provisional Protection only.)—"An improved " construction of printing machine."

The type table is made slightly convex, and mounted on springs on a reciprocating frame, which alternately carries it under inking rollers and a pressing roller, the sheets being fed in by tapes " or " any other suitable contrivance." The table being mounted on springs yields to " any undue pressure," but recovers its elevation on the removal of the pressure. In printing off high numbers two or more of these reciprocating frames are mounted in a line, and their motions and forms so arranged that the paper may be passed from one form to the next, and so on, by any convenient arrangement of conducting tapes or analogous contrivances, that it may pass through the whole series without delay, and be " per- " fected" or " semi-perfected " in the combined machinery.

[Printed, 2½ l. No Drawing.]

### A.D. 1852, December 3.—N° 952.

NcNEE, Duncan.—" A machine for printing with colors on cloth,
" and which is also applicable for printing ornamental designs on
" paper."

The machine is intended so supersede hand-block printing.
A series of as many printing rollers as there are to be colors is
mounted on a frame, and connected in motion by toothed wheels
or otherwise, so as to register. Each roller has a color apparatus,
consisting of sieve rollers or distributing cloth and color box.
The fabric is stretched on a flat horizontal table, on which the
machine is made to travel by hand; and the printing rollers being
in contact with the surface of the cloth, all the colors of the
pattern are printed simultaneously as the machine is moved
forward. Register is obtained by a connecting bar attached to
cranks on the axle of each of the printing rollers. There is an
arrangement of rollers to prevent the piece touching the fabric,
when it is desired to move it without doing so.

[Printed, 5¼d. Drawings.]

### A.D. 1852, December 9.—N° 1005.

KOPP, Emile, and GATTY, Frederick Albert.—" Improve-
" ments in printing or dyeing textile fabrics."

The invention consists :—1. In the application or combination
of arsenic acid together with the other materials used in the preparation of steam colors, instead of tartaric or other acid, " by
" mixing the arsenic acid with the color, and printing and pro-
" ceeding in the manner generally adopted by calico printers for
" the purpose of producing steam colors." 2. In the application
of arsenic acid to Turkey red or other dyed cloths for the purpose
of causing the discharge of its dye or color ; and 3. In the
application of phosphoric acid to Turkey red or other dyed cloth
for the purpose of causing the discharge of its dye or color.

[Printed, 2½d. No Drawing.]

### A.D. 1852, December 13.—N° 1043.

DANGERFIELD, Frederick.—(Provisional Protection only).—
" Improvements in the lithographic press."

These consist, first, in dispensing with the use of the lever for
obtaining or removing the pressure; secondly, in taking the im-

pression by the reverse action of the bed of the press or when it is being returned to its place; thirdly, in the bed of the press running throughout on its bearers, and not rising from the slides to meet the pressure; fourthly, in the cylinders working with iron cogwheels and a winch, thus obtaining the reverse motion of the bed by the forward movement of the handle of the press, and so preventing the necessity of the workman moving from his place. The scraper box works in moveable sides suspended to the sides of the press, with the bridge forming the top of the press. Self-acting pressure is gained by sliding rests working in grooves in the bed of the press, which on the return of the bed catch in the sides and force the scraper perpendicular, in which position it is retained, the rests then passing clear of the sides, and the pressure continuing until necessary to be removed. The tympan is made self-acting by means of a cord attached to it and led through pulleys over the back of the press, and passing beneath it is fastened to the outer end of the bed farthest from the cylinder, and thus works down and up as the bed moves to and fro. The tympan frame does not work on hinges, "as in the press now in use," but is fixed to a moving crosspiece which works in uprights on either side of the end of the bed nearest to the cylinder. The stone is retained in its proper position by means of a moveable stay working in the same grooves with the rests.

[Printed, 2½d. No Drawing.]

A.D. 1852, December 14.—Nº 1058.

APPEL, RUDOLPH.—"Improvements in anastatic printing and "in producing copies of drawings, writings, and printed im- "pressions."

These consist, 1, in bringing the polished surface of the zinc or other metallic surface used for transfer into a state better adapted for the process, by subjecting it to the action of hydro-chloric, nitric, sulphuric, "and even other acids," in vapour or liquid form.

2. In damping the back of prints, &c., sought to be transferred, by means of blotting paper saturated with dilute nitric acid, and transferring them when so damped by passing them with the plate through a roller-press. By this means the finest lines of the print are preserved.

3. "Appelotype," or producing on the plate after removal from the transfer press the finest as well as the darkest shades. For drawings with graduated tints, the paper should be prepared with a strong solution of gelatine and a weak solution of animal gall, and the design executed in lithographic or similar ink, the plate washed successively with a decoction of oak bark water, gum water, sweet oil containing turpentine, and gum water. It is then charged with a soft lithographic roller, and printed from as in lithographic printing.

4. Where the ink is too dry to set off,* the paper is subjected to a hot solution of strontia, or other alkaline earths, or certain salts of the alkalis which have an alkaline reaction, until it will set off slightly. It is then placed between sheets of bibulous paper in dilute nitric acid until the strontia is dissolved, when it is dried. It is then put upon the plate, and transferred in the usual way.

5. Adding to the ink of a design not made in transferable ink, so that it can be transferred to the plate, and will then, as it is technically called, "charge up." The paper is damped, and placed face downwards on waxed or greased paper, a sheet of paper is laid over it, and the whole subjected to hot pressure. "The wax " or grease will be drawn up to and combine with the ink, but " will not adhere to the paper. The design can then be trans- " ferred " in the usual way.

The above process is stated not to be applicable in the case of " a certain paper † patented by Messrs. Glynn and Appel," as from such paper " it is impossible to obtain a transfer."

[Printed, 3½d. No Drawing.]

A.D. 1852, December 15.—No 1061.

D'HOMME, PHILIPPE.—(Communicated.)—"Certain improve- " ments in the manufacture of window blinds, curtains, and " hangings."

This consists in printing in oil colors upon calico, silk, canvas, paper, &c., by means of zinc plates. The surface of the plate, having been filed and hammered flat, is washed with spirits of wine or alcohol. The design, executed in an ink of lampblack, gum, and varnish, is transferred to it in the ordinary way; after

---

* In "The Jewel House of Art and Nature," A.D. 1595, § 40, is described a method "How to renue old letters that be almost worn out of date" by rubbing them over carefully with gall water, "for that will strike a fresh hew again unto the old and worn out coppress."

† No. 13,717. A.D. 1851.

which, the plate is powdered with blacklead or red chalk to absorb any greasy matter which remains, and the disappearance of the design facilitated by passing over it a sponge moistened with water. This transfer serves as a guide for all the colors. The design, having been fixed with an acidulated preparation of nut galls, gum tragacanth, nitric acid, alum acid, and hydrochloric acid, the plate is inked (with an oily ink), and an impression taken in the ordinary manner. Before taking a second impression, the plate is washed over with a mixture of tragacanth gum water and the acidulated preparation. Several plates are employed for the several colors, and made to register by a pointed apparatus attached to the press.

The cloth is rendered stiff and transparent before printing, by means of a solution of gum tragacanth, and is covered, after the impression, with a thin coat of caoutchouc, in turpentine on the opposite side to that which has received the impression.

The press consists of a sliding table drawn forward by means of a band or chain connected with a hand-wheel, and returned by a weighted cord. The plate is fixed upon a dry, hard piece of wood upon the table. A sheet of skin or leather is stretched upon a frame, as in the ordinary lithographic press, and an elastic cushion formed of sheets of paper. The rubber is hinged to one side of the frame, and depressed by a lever acted on by a pedal, and recovering itself by a weight.

[Printed, 5½d. Drawings.]

A.D. 1852, December 20.—N° 1109.

DURANDEAU, Jean.—(Provisional Protection only.)—" Cer-
" tain means of obtaining marks and designs in paper."

" This system consists of employing the zinc or other plates
" used for staining paper for transfer of marks and designs in
" paper; (that is to say,) on the zinc plates the marks or designs
" are written, engraved, lithographed, etc.; and the paper, being
" placed between the zinc or other plates, is made to pass in a
" laminating machine, and thus the designs or marks on the
" plates are transferred on to the paper, or rather indented in it."

[Printed, 2½d. No Drawing.]

A.D. 1852, December 29.—N° 1191.

NEWTON, William Edward.—(Communicated.)—" Improve-
" ments in the manufacture of carpets."

The invention relates, first, to the manufacture of three-ply and two-ply carpets, in graining or weaving together uncoloured warps and wefts in "plys," and subsequently printing the figures in colors by means of blocks or cylinders on one or both surfaces.

The "discovery" on which the above manufacture is based is that the plying process prevents the colors printed on one ply from penetrating to the other ply, so as practically to injure its other surface to an extent which renders it unfit for the reception of colors and use as a carpet. The invention relates, secondly, to the manufacture of single ply printed carpets of a peculiar make, which admit of being printed with a perfect figure upon each side. Strong stout cotton or other twine for the warp is stretched tightly in the loom, so as just to yield sufficiently to allow the necessary motion of the harness; over this is then thrown uncolored woollen filling, when the carpet is to be printed on one or both sides, or the filling may be of some light color over which the figure is printed in heavier color, or the fabric may be woven of uncolored filling and printed upon one side, where an uniform white color is desired upon the other. The filling is beat up very hard over the stretched warps, and the latter are thus entirely concealed from view, while they serve to prevent the passage of the coloring matter from one side of the carpet to the other, and greatly increase the strength of the carpet. The fabric thus produced is then printed on one or both sides.

[Printed, 4½d. No Drawing.]

---

## 1853.

A.D. 1853, January 5.—N° 22.

GERARD, GUSTAVE EUGÈNE MICHEL.—" Improvements in " manufacturing and treating caoutchouc."

The material, combined with from 25 to 40 per cent. of red or yellow ochre, chalk, oxide of zinc in powder, and 10 per cent. of essential oil, or waste caoutchouc melted by fire, is made into sheets by placing it, after it has been " suitably worked up " with dissolving and colouring matter, in a kneading machine, " at the " top of two rollers of about one foot in diameter, heated from " 220° to 240° Fahrenheit," revolving at a speed of about three feet per minute. The sheet is received on an endless cloth.

Caoutchouc tubes are made from the same mixture by a hollow cylinder, " similar to those used for manufacturing vermicelli or " macaroni," heated from 212° to 240° Fahrenheit, and closed at the lower part by a perforated disk, similar to a plate for drawing wire. The disk is furnished inside by a suitable mandril, and heated by steam.

To produce hollow or relief designs on such sheets, a tissue containing the design, and made of cotton hemp, metallic wire, &c., is soaked in soapy water and pressed together with the sheet under a heat of 220° to 240° Fahrenheit. Imitation oil cloth and leather are similarly produced, by fixing the composition on a light cotton by the ordinary process, and producing the ornamentation as above described.

[Printed, 3½d. No Drawing.]

### A.D. 1853, January 5.—N⁶ 26.

EDWARDS, FRANCIS.—" Improvements in the method of let- " tering, figuring, and ornamenting the surface of enamel used " for dials and other purposes."

Impressions printed with any suitable oil on a glutinous mate- rial are transferred to the enamel, finely ground enamel or metallic oxides being dusted over it when ready to undergo the process of firing in a suitable furnace or kiln. Or the surface of the enamel being charged with spirits of turpentine, printed impressions on paper made with a peculiar ink, composed of a suitable oil and powdered enamel or metallic oxides, may be " transferred at once, " and fired as before named."

[Printed, 3½d. No Drawing.]

### A.D. 1853, January 17.—N⁰ 115.

BELLFORD, AUGUSTE EDOUARD LORADOUX.—" Improve- " ments in the manufacture of blocks for printing music."

The stave lines are entirely omitted in the composition of notes, " which thus becomes as simple and as easy as that of all other " typographical compositions." From this form a plaster moul is obtained. Staves composed of five lines are placed exactly at the same distance from each other in an apparatus, and made just to touch the plaster mould where they indent the stave lines. The material employed to form the block is then poured into the mould. The lines passing beyond the column are cleared away with a chisel.

[Printed, 6½d. Drawings.]

## A.D. 1853, January 18.—N° 128.

NEALE, ROBERT.—" Improvements in copper and other plate
" printing, and inking, and wiping, and polishing by machinery
" the engraved plates and cylinders whilst used in the process."

The invention is calculated to enable plate and cylinder printers
to take impressions from engraved metal surfaces, " with a rapi-
" dity unattainable by any known means at present adopted."
The plates are placed upon a series of beds upon endless chains,
the beds being provided with heaters. The impression is given
on the upper side of the chains by the plate passing between
two cylinders, the upper one of them having an endless blanket
passed round it, and a roller immediately above it. The inking
apparatus consists of two sets of rollers on the under side of the
chains, each set consisting of a trough roller and two rollers
arranged vertically above it. The upper of these rollers ink the
plate as it passes along the under side of the chains. The rollers
are made of soft cloth placed on an iron shaft, and afterwards
turned true in a lathe. By an arrangement of stencil plates in
connexion with these upper inking rollers a variety of colors may
be printed from the same plate at the same time. On leaving the
inking rollers the plates come in contact with a revolving belt of
leather, or other suitable material, passing over a soft roller and a
drum below it. The belt wipes off the chief portion of the ink,
which is taken from it by a scraper and saved for future use. The
plate next passes over rollers in rapid action, which polish it fit for
the impression.

[Printed, 1s. 1½d. Drawings.]

## A.D. 1853, January 22.—N° 167.

MEDWORTH, JOHN.—" Improvements in lithographic presses."

The invention consists in mounting the scraper in a moving
frame, so that in moving in one direction it is upright and
performs its scraping action, whilst on moving back it goes out
of action by assuming an inclined position. The frame is
caused to move to and fro by means of a rack and pinion; and
the tympan is caused by a weight to rise from the stone
after the scraper has passed back, and it assumes a proper
position over the stone when an impression is to be taken by the
movement of the scraper or presser frame. In order that the
tympan may be in the most convenient position for the passage of
the scraper a second bar, somewhat higher than the ordinary one,

is placed under it, which keeps the tympan raised to the proper level of the stone, the bar to which the leather is fixed being below that level. In order to regulate the point where the pressure of the scraper shall take place a support is fixed to the bed or framing of the press, which upholds the scraper till it arrives at the part where the pressing is to commence; and in order to keep it up to the regulating screw it is upheld by a spring at each end.

[Printed, 5½d. Drawings.]

A.D. 1853, January 25.—N° 189.

NEWTON, ALFRED VINCENT.—(Communicated.)—" Improve-" ments in the manufacture of printing surfaces."

The invention consists in the employment of particular materials for the formation of moulds and stereotype plates taken from types, woodcuts, &c.

For the matrix two mixtures (A) and (B) are used; (A) consists of fine plastic clay (2), fine silica (1), paper pulp ($\frac{1}{12}$), and molasses ($\frac{1}{2}$ gill to a quart of the mixture), (B) consists of fine clay (9), paper pulp (1), and fine dehydrated plaster of Paris (3). (a)

For the stereotype a mixture (C) is used, consisting of fine silicious sand (2½ parts), gum shellac (1 lb.), and tar (3 oz.), kneaded while hot.

To receive writing or drawing with a style or pen a composition (D) is used, consisting of a peculiar clay not liable to crack in drying, or clay and plaster of Paris made into a paste, and spread on a plate with which it can be heated, so as to soften the mixture (C). When so heated it is treated with beeswax and afterwards saturated with oil. On cooling a thin coating of fine clay is brushed over it to absorb the oil, and the design inscribed on it with any suitable instrument. A mixture (E), silica (7) and clay (1), made into a paste with alcohol and water (equal parts), is used for the " occasional filling up of the backs of stereotype " plates." For filling up parts of the matrix a composition (F) is used, composed of silica (6), clay (1), and molasses (2 teaspoonsful to a gill of the mixture).

The form being made ready in a chase a thin film of gutta percha, gum elastic, oiled silk, &c. is laid over it. (A) is then

(a) The plaster, it is stated, is to be added "only at the time the mixture is to be used, otherwise the tendency of the plaster to set would render the mixture too unyielding for its purposes." See, as to a means of retarding the setting of plaster for any required time. Casentini and Barnard's patent, " Hydroboron," N° 2401 of 1858.

spread in a thin coating on a plate rather larger than the form, and (B) on a piece of cotton cloth. The latter is laid upon the form and covered by the coated plate. The whole is then subjected to pressure, by which a general conformity of the composition is effected, and the coatings of (A) and (B) firmly united. A second and third impression are subsequently taken, the film being removed for the latter, so as to bring the composition into contact with the types, which, to prevent adhesion, are previously oiled. The matrix thus formed is dried, and may be kept for any length of time.

For the stereotype casting the mould is heated, and upon it is laid fire, a thin coating of (C), then a piece of loose texture grass cloth, and upon that a second layer of (C). The whole is then heated until the material becomes plastic, when a heated plate with an oiled surface is laid over it, and the whole subjected to pressure until it cools to 100° Fahrenheit. The plate is then detached by immersion in water, oiled, and trimmed for use.

The following is given as the "lithographic process :"—" Spread
" on the usual coating of clay, and when dry and warm, put on a
" very slight coating of wax; let the plate be hot enough to melt
" the wax; the object of the wax is to harden the coat. The out-
" line of the object is lightly drawn with the pencil; the cutting
" is done with suitable tools. The operation is principally one of
" scraping out the material. The deeper the shade desired the
" deeper must be the depression formed by scraping, regard being
" also had to the direction of the light falling upon the object.
" The blanks are now to be filled up with mixture (F), and the
" plate cast as usual."

[Printed, 4½d. No Drawing.]

A.D. 1853, February 1.—N° 276.

NEWTON, ALFRED VINCENT.—(Communicated.)—" Improve-
" ments in block printing."

In order that the printing surface may be kept longer in contact with the material to be printed than is the case where a platen is brought down by a crank or a printing cylinder is used, the platen which carries the blocks or pattern to be printed is mounted intermediately between two apparatus for distributing color, and when the platen is in a raised position, the transmitting rollers (which are alternately brought into contact with the endless sieves of their respective color boxes) are caused to traverse over the blocks or pattern surfaces and color them. The platen is carried by guide rods, which slide up and down in fixed guides, by reason of a pair of rotating cams, upon which pins projecting from the guide rods rest. The pressure of the block upon the material is also affected by the rotating cams. It is fed on to the table of the machine by rollers, and clips or holders are employed for holding down the material to prevent its being carried up by the ascending platen. Intermittent motion is given to the feed-roller by means of a click and ratchet wheel (which receive their motion from a segment rack), for the purpose of ensuring a perfect register of the pattern.

[Printed, 7½d. Drawings.]

## A.D. 1853, February 16.—N° 410.

NEWTON, ALFRED VINCENT.—(Provisional Protection only.) —" Improvements in the manufacture of printing surfaces."

The invention relates to the manufacture of gutta-percha and india-rubber, and of the two gums combined with metals or the oxides of metals reduced to a granulated state; and 2nd, to the mode of manufacturing such compounds into moulds or matrixes and into stereotype.

The gum is softened in hot water and passed repeatedly through " the usual grinders or pressing cylinders," the metallic substance used being dusted on the surface and worked in. The metals or oxides are peroxide of iron, peroxide of antimony, or the two combined, also copper oxides, and the oxides of lead and zinc. When these substances are used, this composition may be worked up again and again. " When this is not required, plumbago or the flowers of the earths (as clays, ochres, and the crude metallic " ores of zinc, tin, lead, copper, iron, antimony, &c.) may be " mixed in with the plastic gum and the flowers of the metals " proper, and of earthen and glass ware may in like manner be " employed to produce a composition fit for the manufacture of " printing surfaces." The composition thus made is rolled into sheets, and formed into the required matrix by passing it with an original through a press somewhat similar to a copperplate printing press. The mould thus produced, when hard, is capable of imparting a counterpart of the device, figures, or letters which it contains to a sheet of the composition above mentioned.

For the purpose of making etching plates the sheet composition is pressed on to plate glass by heat. The plates are drawn upon in the usual manner, the tools passing through the entire thickness of the composition, leaving the finished line at the lower surface. Into the moulds thus formed, plastic material is impressed (as in the case of the stereotype plate herein-before referred to), to form a printing surface. " In like manner dupli-" cates of copper, steel, or zinc plates, or wood or metal blocks " may be produced."

[Printed, 2½d. No Drawings.]

### A.D. 1853, February 25.—N° 483.

GOODELL, FREDERICK.—(Provisional Protection only.)—" An " improved apparatus for the distillation of rosin oil, and for an " improved method of bleaching and deodorizing the same during " the process of manufacture."

The distillation of the rosin oil is effected in an egg-shaped still, the thickness of which tapers upwards, and from which it flows through a worm or pipe coiled in a tub and kept cool by a continuous flow of cold water. At the outlet of the worm is a wooden trough lined with sheet-lead or zinc, and filled with chloride of lime or other cheap chloride, by slowly passing over which the oil issuing from the worm becomes bleached and deodorized. The oil is succeeded by bright varnish as the product of the receiver. " The residuary carbonaceous substance left in " the retort is cleaned out after every charge and may be sold as " a base for black paint and printers' ink."

[Printed, 2½d. No Drawing.]

### A.D. 1853, March 1.—N° 514.

McADAMS, JOHN.—" Improvements in machinery or apparatus " for printing on leaves of books their designations, numbers, or " devices, or those of their pages, which machinery or apparatus " may also be used to advantage for printing, designating numbers " or devices, or various other articles."

The invention consists :—1. In so combining with the hinged links of a chain a set of types, that one or more of the types composing the designating number or device of a single page of a book shall be placed on each link of the chain, and also that the designating numbers or devices shall be arranged on the several links in succession, in the order in which they are to be printed on the pages of a book. 2. In combining with two chains of type a separate plate or rest placed between them, and a contrivance for compressing it between and by them, so that when a sheet of paper is laid on the upper surface of the separate plate, and another sheet placed against its lower surface, and the compression takes place, a printed impression may be produced on the upper side of one sheet and on the lower side of the other. 3. In combining with each of the flat links of a chain, the types designating the number or devices of the two opposite sides of a page or sheet of paper or other material. 4. In combining with a chain made as last mentioned, and two platens or stamps, a flat bed or plate having an intermittent revolving motion, and constructed so as to present during such semi-revolution some link of the chain, first with the face of its type upwards, and next with the said face downwards, and so that an imprint from one of the designating devices on said link may be produced when said device is upwards, and another produced when the next or other designating device is downwards.

[Printed, 1s. 2½d. Drawings.]

## A.D. 1853, March 3.—N° 541.

WRIGHT, JOHN.—" Improvements in machinery for manu-
" facturing bags or envelopes of paper, calico, or textile fabrics."

The object of this invention is to manufacture the above articles with economy and expedition, and when required, to print a name, title, or other device upon them during the progress of the manufacture. One end of the roll of paper is passed between two rollers, which, as they revolve, take the paper off the roller on which it is wound, and paste or gum the two edges; a cutter is then made to cut off a portion of the paper the requisite length of a bag, and forceps or jaws take the piece of paper so cut, and deposit it at the top of two other rollers, between which it is forced by a strong current of air. The rollers as they revolve draw in the paper, fold it, and press its edges together, at the same time that the device is imparted to it, by one or more rollers furnished with type. The bag ultimately falls out of the press in a perfect state.

[Printed, 7½d. Drawings.]

## A.D. 1853, March 7.—N° 566.

CALLES, ANDRÉ.—(Provisional Protection only.)—" Certain
" improvements in typographic characters."

" The invention consists in manufacturing typographic types
" by means of machinery which by giving the necessary action to
" the moulds and punches replaces for the cast the several opera-
" tions performed by workmen."

Finished drawings, showing the general arrangement and details
of the machinery, were filed with the Provisional Specification, but
no explanation of them is given.

[Printed, 10½d. Drawings.]

## A.D. 1853, March 10.—Nº 607.

WALMSLEY, JAMES.—" Improved machinery and arrangements
" for block printing."

The invention consists of certain apparatus for printing druggets
and other fabrics by blocks arranged on each side of a table or
tables of a suitable width and length.   Each pair of blocks is connected with apparatus enabling it to traverse across the whole
width of the table, and print at any part of it.   These blocks
move from opposite sides of the table alternately, one advancing as
the other is receding, the color being supplied to the under side
of the block during its motion over a color roller at the side of the
table; thus two or more impressions are printed on the fabric before
moving it forward lengthways of the table to receive fresh impressions from the same pair of blocks.   The blocks are pressed down
upon the fabric by means of tappets or cams affixed to shafts running lengthways of the table.   To prevent the shrinking of fabrics,
such as drugget and felt carpeting, the fabric on either side is
firmly secured between nippers formed of two pieces of wood or
metal attached to a chain whereby the fabric is kept of the proper
width and distension during the process of printing in its progress
through the machine.

[Printed, 11¼d. Drawings.]

## A.D. 1853, March 11.—Nº 618.

ALEXANDRE, EDOUARD.—(Provisional Protection refused.)—
" A new mode of advertising."

" My invention consists in printing or impressing advertisements
" on envelopes, or on the margins of letter paper."

[Printed, 2½d. No Drawings.]

A.D. 1853, March 21.—N° 693.

TAYLOR, ISAAC.—" Improvements in machinery for printing
" woven and other fabrics."

The improvements relate to the employment of thin shells for
cylinder printing, which, instead of being conical interiorly so as to
be driven up tight upon the mandril, are cylindrical within and
without.   They are without nib or key, and are of no greater thickness than is required for the purpose of engraving.   The shell is
passed over a mandril so as to fit truly but easily upon it.   This
mandril forms one of three cylinders which are lodged in a line as
to their several axes between two jambs inclined towards each other
at an angle more or less acute, as may be required by the nature of
the work to be done by the machine.   The exterior of these rollers
being the engraved roller, the middle cylinder acts as the boll, and
the exterior cylinder, on the other hand, is a support roller bearing
upon the boll.   The mandril, with the engraved shell upon it, works
by its spindles in a carriage, which carriage moves at ease, yet with
a correct fit, in grooves upon the inclined jamb.   This jamb or the
sliding carriage is brought within such a distance of the axis of the
boll as to impinge upon it some little way more or less above the
line of the horizontal diameter of the boll, and, therefore, giving it
a tendency always to bring the two cylinders in a tight pressure the
one upon the other.   The three cylinders being thus disposed, the
motive power is applied not to the spindle of the engraved roller,
to do which requires an absolute fixture of the shell upon the
mandril, but to the axis of the middle cylinder or boll.

Machines for printing in several colors may, it is stated, be constructed on the same principle.

[Printed, 1s. 2½d.   Drawings.]

A.D. 1853, March 21.—N° 696.

STATHER, JOHN.—" Improvements in printing."

The invention consists :—First, of a mode of producing blocks,
moulds, or forms, in which the letters, &c. to be represented are left
plain, the surrounding portions being those which are printed by
taking impressions in a material capable of being moulded in the
requisite manner from reversed letters, &c. in relief.   Secondly, of
a mode of printing letters, &c. upon the surfaces of papers, cloths,
or other articles by means of a flat plate, on to or upon the surface

of which the intended letters, &c. are first printed reversed, and in one or several colors, in such a manner that the said flat plate shall, by pressure against the surface of the paper or other material intended to be printed, transfer to or print upon the material the impression it has received. Thirdly, of a mode of printing letters, &c. upon the surfaces of papers or other articles by means of a roller or cylinder, on to or upon the surface of which the said letters, &c. are first printed reversed, and in one or several colors, by means of a small roller or several small rollers (according to the number of colors to be used) working in conjunction with the larger roller which receives upon upon its surface from the smaller rollers impressions producing or representing the intended letters, &c., and transfers such impressions to or upon the surface of the paper or other material to be printed, by causing the same to be pressed against the surface of such larger roller by the action of another roller working in conjunction with it.

[Printed, 11½d. Drawings.]

A.D. 1853, March 26.—N° 732.

WARRALL, JAMES.—" Certain improvements in the method of " preparing, treating, and furnishing cut, piled, or raised fustians, " and other similar goods or fabrics, and in the machinery or " apparatus connected therewith."

The improvements relate to the preparation, treatment, or finishing of fustians having a piled or napped surface when finished, and consist principally in certain processes for " dyeing up " or printing the pieces previously to the pile being raised, thereby dispensing with the process of stiffening, scouring, and cleansing the cloth. The cloth as taken from the loom may be " animalized " by padding on " or otherwise impregnating it with oil, grease, soap, or other fatty matters, and afterwards dried over steam cylinders or on a stone. The face of the cloth is then hardened, and " cartooned " by passing over a red-hot singeing plate. The pieces are then arranged by suspension in a cylinder so as not to touch one another. The cylinder is then filled with high-pressure steam, and so kept until the cloth and whole apparatus is well heated, when the steam is shut off, and the cylinder filled with a solution of soap, potash, soda ash, soda, or other alkaline ley. When the cloth has been thus sufficiently boiled, it is removed and "washed off" in pure water, and all superfluous water removed by means of a mangle or "hydro-extractor." A strong solution of chloride of lime is next "padded" on to the surface of the cloth, which must be then passed through a very weak solution of the same, and the bleaching finished in the usual manner, according to the color required. The piece being dried is padded on or passed through a mordant composed of gelatine, with a solution of iron, copper, tin, or other mineral, and dyed up if necessary, or printed with the pattern required, the "padding" or printing answering for the mordant to fix the color required, and also for the stiffening for the cutter as well as for the "feel" or "handle" required when finished. The cloth is then stretched in order to bring the warp and weft threads as nearly as possible into their original rectangular position, and the pile cut or the napped surface raised in the usual manner, the back of the cloth having been previously "perched" if a nap is then required. Should the cloth require an extra "feel" or "handle" it may be again stiffened at this stage of the process. The pile or nap upon the face and back of the cloth is then dressed or raised by means of the ordinary dressing or raising machinery, and the face shorn off by the usual shearing machinery, according to the finish required.

[Printed, 5½d. Drawings.]

A.D. 1853, March 28.—N° 737.

PERRY, THOMAS JAMES.—"Improvements in printing."

The invention consists in making one or more angular or other depressions on one side of each of the types and a corresponding elevation on its opposite side, so that when set up they shall interlock. The types are set up for cylinder printing in "trays," one side of which has an elevation and the other a depression similar to those in the types. The ends of the trays, each containing a column of type, are fastened by a ring on to the cylinder. The machine shown consists of two pairs of rollers side by side, in one of which (the left) the pressing cylinder is uppermost, while in the other (the right) it is placed beneath the type cylinder. Each printing cylinder has an inking apparatus of the ordinary construction. The inking rollers are kept to the surface by springs or weights. The paper (damped) is printed in roll. It is guided by tapes between the two pairs of rollers by which it is "perfected," after which it is cut into proper lengths by passing between a roller and a knife.

[Printed, 7½d. Drawings.]

## A.D. 1853, March 29.—N° 744.

SMITH, LUKE.—"Improvements in machinery for weaving and " printing."

The invention consists :—First, in winding the binding warp and the warp for the back cloth of fustians and other fabrics of the like nature on separate beams, instead of on the same beam "as here- " tofore," whereby the warps are more easily maintained at a uni- form tension, and are more accessible for repairs. Secondly, in an improved mode of applying the swell to the shuttles, whereby the swell may be made to act on one or more shuttles in the same shuttle box. Thirdly, in an improved combination of parts form- ing a weft stopper, applicable to looms for weaving, with one, two, or more shuttles. Fourthly, in the application of a spring or springs to the under side of the lay bottom, or in other convenient place, to act on the picking stick, and prevent the rebounding of the shuttle. Fifthly, in an improved combination of machinery for weaving terry or looped fabrics, without the aid of wires, by which improved combination of machinery a portion of the terry warp is caught hold of by the crossing of the binding warp and the weft, and formed into a loop or terry by the beating up of the reed. Sixthly, in another improved combination of machinery for weaving terry or looped fabrics, in which the depth of the loops or terries is determined by a series of flat wires passing between the dents of the reed. Seventhly, in the application of three shuttles traversing the sheds at the same time for weaving certain fabrics. And, lastly, in an improved mode of constructing the blocks used in printing warps and other articles, whereby the pattern on the block can be changed with great facility.

The invention as applied to printing is specially adapted to N° 13,633 of 1851 (Luke, Mark, and Matthew Smith), its object being to facilitate the change of pattern without cancelling the entire block. For this purpose the entire block surface is fitted with grooves into which are slidden dovetailed pieces which receive the color to be impressed on the material. The bottom block or table is also fitted with adjustable pieces corresponding with the pieces in the top block, so that the material when printed is not sullied by the bottom block or table.

[Printed, 11½d. Drawings.

## A.D. 1853, April 4.—N° 796.

NEWTON, William Edward.—(Communicated.)—" Improve-
" ments in producing plates or surfaces which may be used as
" printing or embossing surfaces, or as door plates, dial or number
" plates, or other plates or surfaces bearing inscriptions or devices
" of various kinds."

The invention consists, first, in producing intaglio-graphic printing and other plates from forms of intaglio types by taking a casting in plaster of Paris, or other suitable material, the surface of the letters meanwhile being held in close contact with a glass plate, or its equivalent, so that when set the surface of such material will be in the same plane with the surface of the types. The form of types thus surrounded may be stereotyped. These plates produce the " intaglio-graphic effect heretofore and now " generally known by the expensive processes of xylography and " chromo-lithography." Secondly, in producing embossing plates, or reverse duplicate in relief, by taking a cast in plaster, &c., from an intaglio-graphic plate, a second plaster cast from the first, and stereotyping both such plaster casts. Thirdly, in producing what are called illuminated printing plates for printing shaded intaglio-graphic letters, characters, or figures, by producing a plate, as set forth in the first part of the invention, from a form of shaded intaglio-graphic types, and then removing the plaster from a form of types, so that after printing with the intaglio-graphic plate, the shadows can be printed either with the form of types after the plaster has been removed, or with a stereotype taken therefrom. And, finally, in producing polychromatic printing plates from an intaglio-graphic plate by taking a cast therefrom in relief, and from such relief obtaining a " stencil plate or plates," from which the plate or plates is or are obtained, to have the letters, characters, or figures in whole or in part in duplicate of the intaglio-graphic letters or devices, and in relief so as to register therewith.

[Printed, 7½d. Drawings.]

### A.D. 1853, April 5.—N° 810.

MAVITY, William.—"A new or improved method of manufac-
" turing letters and figures to be used as printing type, lettering
" for sign and window boards, and other such like purposes."

The invention consists in making letters, figures, &c. in several
parts, and afterwards combining the same, thus effecting "great
" economy in the manufacture of plain and ornamental letters,
" letters, and figures made in moulds and dies, as well as facilities
" in the production of large letters and figures in stamps and
" presses."

The drawings represent the letters E, L, F, P, T, formed of
"parts" on the principle of this invention.

[Printed, 6½d. Drawings.]

### A.D. 1853, April 5.—N° 812.

PURCELL, George.—"A new method of adjustment in the art
" of printing by means of certain combinations of various sized
" spaces and quadrats."

Except in some cases of nonpareil and pica, it is stated that
" spaces or quadrats of such different bodies or sizes have to be
" fitted without any one such space or quadrat bearing a correct
" proportion to any standard." To obviate the difficulty and
delay which have arisen in compositors' work, and more especially
in rule work, from this cause, uniform graduated spaces and
quadrats are used. The spaces and quadrats of the different
bodies of type are graduated to pica; as, for example, an em
quadrat of pica of any body being taken as a standard, a number
of multiples and submultiples of this breadth are constructed of
thicknesses suitable to the following printing types of any body,
namely, double pica, great primer, english, small pica, long primer,
bourgeois, brevier, minion, emerald, ruby, pearl, and likewise
multiples and submultiples suitable to the half-bodies of such
respective types. "The multiples of the breadth of an em pica
" quadrat which I propose to use are once, twice, three times, four
" times, five times, and six times, and the submultiples I propose to
" use are $\frac{1}{8}, \frac{2}{8}, \frac{3}{8}, \frac{4}{8}, \frac{5}{8}, \frac{6}{8}, \frac{7}{8}, \frac{1}{6}$, and $\frac{2}{6}$, to the body and half-body of
" the before-mentioned types; and I also propose to add to pica of
" every body spaces bearing one-eighth and one-sixth proportion
" to such pica."

[Printed, 2½d. No Drawing.]

A.D. 1853, April 6.—No. 823.

GATTY, FREDERICK ALFRED.—(Provisional Protection only.)—
" Improvements in printing or producing colours on textile
" fabrics."

The improvements consist in the composition of a mordant of
chlorate and hydrochlorate of alumina, prepared by decomposing
alum or sulphate of alumina by the mixed salts of chlorate of lime
and chloride of calcium. " By the use of this mordant I dispense
" with the chlorate of potash, generally employed for fixing and
" oxidizing steam colours, thereby producing the same results
" more effectually and economically."

[Printed, 2½d. No Drawing.]

A.D. 1853, April 6.—No. 829.

JOHNSON, WILLIAM.—(Provisional Protection only).—" Im-
" provements in the manufacture of safety paper."

"The invention consists in the employment of the rough and
" irregular surface, produced by the fracture of a piece of cast iron
" or other brittle material for giving the requisite watermark to
" paper employed in the manufacture of bank notes, cheques,
" coupons, &c. A bar of such material being broken transversely,
" a piece of soft metal gutta percha, or other suitable material, is
" inserted between the broken surfaces and receives a correct im-
" pression of their irregularities. From this matrix is obtained
" the regular design which is required, and which is transferred to
" the wirecloth on which the paper is made."

[Printed, 2½d. No drawing.]

A.D. 1853, April 9.—No 857.

TAYLOR, HERBERT.—(Communicated.)—" Improvements in
" ornamenting surfaces or fabrics applicable to various useful pur-
" poses, such as for covers of furniture, imitation tapestry, carpets,
" or hangings."

The invention consists of a method of painting or ornamenting
cloths of all kinds which have been previously prepared with a
mordant that will combine chemically with the colors as they are
laid on, and blended one with the other. The invention further
includes a method of developing and permanently fixing the colors
thereon by steam, and restoring the cloth to its natural pliable

and soft condition, by washing out the excess of colouring matter, and leaving the picture indelibly fixed on the cloth. " The " printing upon cloth," the patentee observes, " by blocks " or rollers is well known, the cloth having been previously " prepared with a mordant for fixing chemically the colors. " But with blocks or rollers only one color can be laid on the " cloth, and no blending can be done, for two reasons, viz., that " the second colour destroys the first in a great measure, and the " mordants used exhaust their chemical effect upon the first color, " and would not act upon the succeeding ones. Another method " of ornamenting or painting, as upon canvass in oil colors, or " upon velvets and satins in water colors, is equally well known ; " but in neither of these latter cases are mordants or chemical " colors used, nor are the colors permanently fixed in the material " so painted upon. Besides, such pictures are merely ornamental, " and cannot be applied to useful purposes, as the pliability of the " cloth is lost, and the picture or ornament being upon the surface " and not in the body of the cloth, it will be easily understood " that to apply a fabric so ornamental to any useful purpose would " entirely destroy it."

[Printed, 4½d. No Drawings.]

## A.D. 1853, April 11.—N° 864.

URQUHART, WILLIAM.—" Improvements in the manufacture " of printers' type, and other articles used in letterpress printing."

The invention consists, first, in cutting punches to be used in the manufacture of type " with whole words or parts of words or " terminations," and forming from such punches a copper matrix, in which the type is cast, " in the manner usually practised by type " founders." Secondly, in a " new mode of constructing and " arranging its case to be employed for containing such said type." Instead of an " upper " and " lower " case, the types formed as above are arranged and disposed in alphabetical order in the several compartments of a single case; the words corresponding with a particular letter in compartments at the top, and terminations having the same initial letter in a vertical line beneath such compartment. The lowest row of compartments contains Italic and single Roman characters corresponding to the above alphabetical arrangement.

[Printed, 5½d. Diagrams of the case.]

## A.D. 1853, April 18.—N° 933.

McNAUGHTON, WILLIAM.—" Improvements in printing yarns
" or worsteds for weaving carpets, also in printing carpets, woollen,
" silk, cotton, and other textile fabrics or fibrous substances."

The invention consists of a machine for printing various patterns
or devices or plain surfaces of color upon both sides of the substances or materials at one and the same time. A series of cylinders,
upon which are fixed certain patterns or devices (or the surfaces
may be plain), are arranged one above the other, and connected by
wheels and pinions, so as to ensure as nearly as may be perfect
uniformity of motion of each pair of cylinders as they rotate, and
thereby to register; color is supplied by means of rollers working in
troughs containing the necessary coloring matters. The machine
is placed in a vertical position for printing small patterns, and in a
horizontal one when printing large patterns.

[Printed, 1s. 3½d. Drawings.]

## A.D. 1853, April 25.—N° 992.

TILLIE, WILLIAM, and HENDERSON, JOHN.—" Improve-
" ments in printing shirting fabrics."

The invention relates to " so arranging the designs and fabrics
" from which printed shirts are to be made up, that the body of
" the shirt and the various trimmings, as the fronts, collars, waist-
" bands, and ornamental finishing pieces or 'tabs' may be simul-
" taneously printed, with a more effective result in the after process
" of manufacture than hitherto." The roller carrying the whole
of the required designs is arranged to print the piece as it were in
the length of the shirt. On one end of the roller are the patterns
for the several minor trimmings, which are thus printed along one
edge of the piece, whilst the main body of the rollers carries the
body and front designs. In printing a lot of shirts in this way a
set of pieces are first printed with the trimmings thereon, and thus
a set of narrower pieces to produce body fabric for the arms, the
pieces being just the width of the body pattern only on the roller.

[Printed, 6½d. Drawings.]

## A.D. 1853, April 28.—N° 1031.

BERRY, JAMES, and BOOTH, THOMAS.—" Improvements in
" machinery, or apparatus for printing or staining woven fabrics
" and paper."

The invention consists in using sieve rollers made of some flexible material, as gutta-percha, india-rubber, or "composition," working in contact with printing rollers. In the drawings a machine is shown, consisting of a drum, round which the fabric is conveyed in the usual manner, and printed by a series of printing rollers, each with an elastic "sieve" or trough roller in contact with it.

[Printed, 6½d. Drawings.]

## A.D. 1853, May 2.—Nº 1056.

GREENWOOD, James.—" An improvement in fixing mordants " on fabrics."

This consists in the application of chloride of lime (known in commerce as " bleaching powder ") or chlorine, in combination with other bases than lime.

[Printed, 2½d. No Drawing.]

## A.D. 1853, May 2.—Nº 1064.

MONTFRANT, François.—(Communicated.)—" Improvements " in lubricating materials."

The invention consists in manufacturing these materials " by " the employment of all fatty oils (with the exception of coleseed " oil) disacidified by means of milk, and caused to blend and " intermix with fat or a fatty body by means of a resin or a " resinous composition."

A " compound for paint, oil, &c." is mentioned as one of the " lubricating materials." It is composed of—

" Resin, 1 per cent. of the oil employed,
" Lard, 2 per cent.,

" With the addition of the drying material usually employed, say " litharge, 1 per cent."

[Printed, 3½d. No Drawing.]

## A.D. 1853, May 13.—Nº 1182.

STIFF, George.—" An improved construction of printing ma- " chine."

The type table is made slightly convex and mounted on a reciprocating frame, so as alternately to carry the type under inking rollers and a pressing roller, paper being fed in the latter by tapes or other contrivance. The table is mounted on springs so as to yield when subjected to pressure, but otherwise to retain its elevation.

For printing high numbers two or more of these reciprocating frames are mounted in a line, and their motions so arranged relatively to the forms they carry (with a view to perfecting), that the paper may be passed from one " form " to the next, and so on by any convenient arrangement of tapes or analogous contrivances.

[Printed, 5½d. Drawings.]

### A.D. 1853, May 14.—N° 1193.

HIGGIN, James.—" Improvements in printing or dying woven " or textile fabrics, and in the manufacture of certain substances " to be used in the arts or processes of dyeing and printing."

The invention consists in substituting silicates of the alkaline earths diffused in water for cowdung in the operation termed " dunging."

[Printed, 3½d. No Drawing.]

### A.D. 1853, May 17.—N° 1217.

VIZETELLY, James Thomas George, and VIZETELLY, Henry Richard.—(Communicated.)—" Improvements in print- " ing machines."

The invention relates to an arrangement of mechanism for preventing the " setting off" on the blanket of the perfecting cylinder, and consists in the employment of an extra sheet of oiled paper or cloth, which is interposed between the printed side of the sheet and the second cylinder, and is caused to meet the printed sheet as it comes upon the second cylinder, so that both are carried round that cylinder simultaneously.

[Printed, 5½d. Drawings.]

### A.D. 1853, May 25.—N° 1287.

MITCHEL, William Haslett.—" Improvements in means for " distributing and composing types."

The invention consists of machines for distributing and composing. In the former the type is received (after being forced out by " lips or pushers" from a " distributing stick ") on one of a series of endless belts parallel to each other (or an apron), and deposited on an inclined plane; cross-pieces are secured to the

frame of the machine at a sufficient distance above the belts to
allow types to pass under them, and a second set of cross-bars
carry guide-bars which form two spaces on each belt for the reception of type. The inclined plane has in part of its face a series of
straight grooves to conduct the types from the passages formed
by the guide-bars to the receiving grooves. A second part has
branching grooves which "discriminate" between thick and thin
types. If a thin type is dropped on any one of the belts it
will run end first down the incline plane beneath the bridge; but
if a thick type is dropped on it the bridge deflects it down a
side groove into a separate receiving groove. The types then pass
into the teeth of a " pushing wheel," by which each type is raised
so as to be vertical when it is deposited in its appropriate groove,
the type and the whole row along the groove being moved to the
thickness of the type deposited.

In the composing machine the upper portion is triangular in
plan, and consists of a series of parallel belts increasing in length
as they approach the delivering end of the machine. Above these
are compartments filled with types removed by any suitable "grab"
from the distributing machine, and caused to fall on to the series
of belts by the striking of one of a set of keys. With these is
combined a diagonal belt driven so that types deposited on it from
any one of the series reach a composing wheel, through the intervention of a " conductor," in the same order in which they have
been taken from their several compartments. By this wheel,
similar in construction to that used for distributing, the types are
set up into a line.

[Printed, 11½*d*. Drawings.]

## A.D. 1853, May 28.—Nº 1317.

FRANCILLON, FRANCOIS.—" Improvements in dyeing and
" printing silk, wool, and other animal fibres."

The invention consists in a method of fixing upon silk, wool,
and other animal fibres, such as hair, feathers, skins, &c. the
green oxide of chrome, called by French chemists sesqui-oxide of
chrome, or the chromic oxide of Berzelius. This oxide is either
applied or fixed alone or (in order to produce various tints) in
combination (either at the time of applying it to the material, or
afterwards) " with certain acids such as phosphoric, phosphorous,
" arsenic, or arsenious acid, or with certain oxides such as those

" of iron, lead, copper, or other metal, or with coloring matters
" which require the assistance of an oxide, in order to combine
" with the fibre, and which find in the chromic oxide a mordant;
" and, lastly, with that no less numerous class of astringent
" matters by means of which so many fast colours are produced."

[Printed, 3¼d. No Drawing.]

A.D. 1853, May 30.—Nº 1330.

GREEN, WILLIAM.—" Improvements in treating or preparing
" yarns or threads."

The invention consists :—1. In coating such threads with dry
powdered colors in addition to the dye color usually employed,
and thus producing a greater intensity of color than is attainable
by dyeing only. The dyed thread is singed, passed through a size
trough, and then through a trough containing the dry color.
2. In producing glossy effects upon yarns or threads by coating
them with metallic powder, as in (1). 3. Coating yarns or threads
with metallic solutions, pigments, or compositions, these being substituted for the dry color in (1). 4. Burnishing or brightening
yarns or threads coated as above with metallic powder, by exposing
them in their passage through the press to the friction of polished
surfaces of steel and agate; and 5. Producing figured or ornamental fabrics by printing yarns, after they are arranged for the loom,
with any design or pattern in gold size or other suitable adhesive
matter, and applying thereto dry powdered colors or bronze or
other metallic powders, so as to produce a figure or pattern thereon,
the color of such yarns or threads being different from the color
applied thereto.

[Printed, 7½d. Drawings.]

A.D. 1853, June 2.—Nº 1351.

JOHNSON, JOHN ROBERT.—" Improvements in the manufac-
" ture of type and other articles used in letterpress printing."

The mould is composed of four parts besides the matrix. Two
of the parts (the sides) are fixed in a plate or table parallel to each
other. Another part (the body piece) slides up between the two
fixed ones, first forming one side of the mould and afterwards delivering the casting from the mould. This part also carries a register
to guage the position of the matrix. The fourth part (or top) slides
over the opening between the two fixed sides, and by its sliding

moves the casting on to an inclined shelf which has a movement
to and from the opening between the fixed sides. The fourth side
also carries a register for the matrix so that by placing a different
size of matrix between the two registers the mould will be adjusted
for the change of thickness. The matrix is moved away from the
casting at right angles to the face of the type or other article, and
is forced up to its stool or step by a lever and spring. The movements of the parts of the mould are effected by cams. The metal
is pumped into the mould " in a like manner to what has hereto-
" fore been done."

[Printed, 1s. 4½d. Drawings.]

A.D. 1853, June 3.—N° 1361.

WAHLER, WILLIAM.—(Provisional Protection only.)—" Litho-
" graphic printing being a self-acting lithographic printing ma-
" chine to be propelled by hand, steam, or other motive power."

The peculiarities of the invention consists in the method of
damping the stone, the arrangement of the cylinder for giving
the pressure, and the arrangement or disposition of the excentrics
and levers for producing the various actions. The only manual
labour required is for laying on and taking off. The stone runs
alternately below an inking roller fixed in a pendant lever, and a
damping apparatus of a peculiar construction. The impression is
given by a segment cylinder and scraper.

[Printed, 8½d. Drawings.]

A.D. 1853, June 18.—N° 1485.

HANNINGTON, GUY.—(Provisional Protection only.)—" Im-
" provements in producing railway and other tickets and cards."

The invention consists of a machine whereby the several processes of punching, printing, cutting, and binding " cardboard for
" railway tickets and cards are performed in passing through the
" machine. The apparatus for performing each of the processes
" is not new, but it is the combining of the several processes so
" that the tickets are received on to a wire or binder in regular
" succession, and so that no complete ticket can be obtained by
" the machinery, except by destroying the part thereof which is
" bound, that constitutes the peculiarity of my invention."

[Printed, 2½d. No Drawing.]

VALLS, LEON. — (Provisional Protection only.) — (Communicated.)—" Improvements in the production of printing surfaces."

A matrix or mould having been obtained from a suitable engraved plate of wood or metal, an impression in relief is produced in gutta-percha, or materials in which gutta-percha is a principal ingredient, either by melting or preparing it in the form of a thin sheet, softening it by heat and forcing it into all the interstices of the mould or matrix in which it must be allowed to remain until quite cold, when it may be removed.

[Printed, 2½d. No Drawings.]

BROOMAN, RICHARD ARCHIBALD.—(Communicated.)—" Im-
" provements in printing or in producing designs and patterns
" on stuffs and fabrics."

These consist, in first stamping or otherwise impressing the design on such fabrics with a compound of gutta-percha, bitumen, and Assam gum or other substance rendered adhesive by heat or partial dissolution. The fabric thus prepared is submitted to heat or to a solvent, so as to render the resinous matter adhesive, and has then applied thereon metal powder, metal leaf, flock powdered colors, or other dry powder. The superfluous powder being removed, the design will be found printed in gold flock or other powder employed.

[Printed, 5½d. Drawings.]

SIEVIER, ROBERT MOORE.—" Improvements in the manu-
" facture of piled fabrics and in machinery for effecting the same."

The invention consists in printing on the warp threads a pattern of double the length usually required, by means of a printing or coloring roller of double the width necessary for a single cloth, so that when such printed warp is woven between two backs (the backs being made by the aid of separate warps placed in the loom by well-known means), the printed warp being woven first into one of these back warps and then into the other, the fabric so woven, may, when cut into two pieces by a knife passing to and fro by a crank, produce two distinct pieces of cut pile fabric having a proper length, and similar pattern or design thereon, which would not be the case if printed for a single cloth. When required, the pattern is made twice the width of the woven fabric, and so that it will repeat in a geometrical form, and lay side by side when cut open so as to save an expensive drawing in the first instance. The fabrics are woven by a double box shuttle loom and two shuttles, when the cloths are required to have each two selvages, but one only when the cloth is woven together only on one side.

[Printed, 7½d. Drawings.]

A.D. 1853, July 5.—Nº 1603.

NEWTON, ALFRED VINCENT.—(Communicated.)—" Improved " machinery for printing."

The main object of this invention is to carry on "job printing " " with greater expedition than heretofore," and without the neces- sity of employing skilled labour.

In the Provisional Specification (which has no drawing) it is stated that the bed of the press is set vertically, and is supported by a vibrating frame, that the platen is mounted on a horizontal rocking shaft, and the paper being laid thereon and secured by a frisket, the platen is moved round on its axis until it is brought in front of the form, which is then (it having been previously inked) pressed forward for the impression against the platen by the straightening of a toggle joint " connected therewith and to " the framing of the machine." Mounted on the top of the framing is the ink-distributing roller, and over it small inking rollers, which convey the ink to the form, are made to run. These rollers are carried in vibrating arms, which as they are depressed cause the rollers to run over the face of the type, the platen being at that time clear of the type, and in a position to receive a fresh sheet of paper.

In the Specification filed in pursuance of the Letters Patent, it is stated, that " since the application for Letters Patent was made, " some changes have been effected in the construction of the " press by the inventor, with the view of rendering it more simple " and efficient, and to this end instead of mounting the platens " on a rocking axle, as explained in the Provisional Specification, " the inventor is now enabled to dispense with the movement of " the platen, and as a substitute for the toggle joint for pressing for-

" ward the type against the platen, a mechanical equivalent is used
" therefor." "The general principle of construction," it is further
stated, " is in no respect departed from by the introduction of
" these modifications."

[Printed, 6½d. Drawings.]

A.D. 1853, July 6.—No. 1609.

FONTAINE MOREAU, PETER ARMAND LE COMTE DE.—
(Communicated.) — " Improvements in typographical printing
" presses."

The invention consists in mechanical arrangements for obtaining
several different colored impressions on the same side of a sheet
of paper, by means of a cylinder holding the sheet in contact with
its surface until all such impressions are obtained, and as many
forms (flat) as there are colors to be printed. Each form is inked
by a separate set of inking rollers, in connexion with trough and
distributing rollers. There is a contrivance of "lifts" by which
each form, in running to and fro, passes clear of the other forms'
inking rollers. Two or more cylinders may be used, each corresponding to a form, and each form being inked by a separate set
of rollers. The sheet passes from one cylinder to another, two or
more sheets being impressed simultaneously. By this combination, both sides of the sheet are printed in several colors or hues
by a single passage through the machine. The sheets are forwarded on endless bands or blades.

By another part of the invention a travelling motion is given
to the inking rollers in addition to the revolving one. The ink
holders are heated to increase the fluidity of the ink. Oscillating
motion is avoided in the pressure roller by fixing on its driving
cog-wheel a sliding bolt which enters successively into the driving
rack or frame and keeps it either steady or motionless.

[Printed, 1s. 11½d. Drawings.]

A.D. 1853, July 9.—N° 1639.

BOULÉ, JEAN THEODORE, and CAILLAUD, FRANÇOIS.—(Provisional Protection only.)—" Improvements in composing and
" distributing type."

A series of finger keys (one for each of the letters or characters
in the case) act in such a manner on a series of forceps as to
cause the type corresponding to the finger key acted upon to be

withdrawn from the case and fall down a grooved channel or hopper to the galley which is caused to move each time that a letter is deposited to the extent of the thickness of the type. In distributing type according to this invention the letters or characters are taken one by one by a pair of forceps, and dropped into the end of a series of grooved channels (the direction which they take being governed by finger keys), and letters and characters are thus replaced in their proper divisions in the case.

[Printed, 2½d. No Drawing.]

A.D. 1853, July 13.—Nº 1667.

MORTON, ARNOLD.—" Improvements in the manufacture of " paints, pigments, and materials for house painting, paper " staining, and decorative purposes generally."

The invention consists in substituting various compounds for the linseed and other oils for spirits of turpentine or other spirits and " dryers" used in painting, and for " sizes" and " gums" used in paper staining and coloring, and in treating the various " stainers" and body colors to fit them to be used therewith. The paints, &c. thus produced are " inodorous," or nearly so, and innoxious. Various " vehicles" are prepared for this purpose, according to the natural affinities of the colours treated. Vehicle Nº 1 consists of soap and milk thoroughly mixed, and mixed with alum, and ground in a color mill. Vehicle Nº 2 consists of milk, soap, and pure or rough sulphate of zinc pulverized, prepared in a similar manner. Vehicle Nº 3 is prepared and treated in the same way, but the mixture is " subdued" by sugar of lead or acetic acid. Vehicle Nº 4 (termed a " semi-vehicle") consists of milk and soap only, mixed as before, but not ground. " This being added in sufficient quantity, will subdue the ex- " cess of any acid or sulphate in any stainer or color containing " same."

Body colors are prepared from China clay or Cornish white, by mixing it with any vehicle except Nº 4. The whole is mixed dry, saturated with boiling water, worked in a pug mill, and ground fine,—from sulphate of lead and ordinary dry white lead, by half saturation in water working in a pug mill, adding Nº 4 to subdue acid and sulphates, and Nº 2 to fasten it and render it durable, and from lime, by mixing with a solution of lime in water an amount of alum sufficient to decompose the lime. The mixture is continually agitated, and water added. The mixture is then drawn off and strained, after which it is pressed to the consistency of " satin white." The white must be neutral, and mixes freely with any vehicle except 4. " To prepare a white " from sulphate of barytes, grind the same in water. This will " also freely work and mix in vehicles 1, 2, and 3. To prepare " a white from dry zinc white, grind the same in water, to which " I would add vehicle N° 2."

To work raw and burnt umber stone ochre (raw and burnt), Indian red, Venetian red, brown and spruce ochre, burnt and raw sienna, so that they may be worked as stainers in their genuine state, apart from body colours, add genuine alum pulverized sufficient to impregnate the same when finely ground in water, and add N° 1, 2, or 3.

For ultramarine blue, indigo blue, Prussian blue, chrome yellows, deep and lemon, lamp black, and drop black, it is simply requisite to grind them in vehicles N° 1, 2, or 3. This applies also to blue verditer and green verditer, scarlet, crimson, and purple drop lakes; also vermillion, except that N° 2 must be used.

Emerald greens are to be subdued with the semi-vehicle N° 4, and finely ground in vehicles N° 1 or 3.

[Printed, 4½d. No Drawing.]

## A.D. 1853, July 15.—N° 1692.

TAYLOR, ISAAC.—" Improvements in machinery for printing."

The invention, like N° 693 of 1853, is intended to facilitate the use of thin shell rollers, which do not require adjustments for fixing immoveably upon the mandril while printing, but may be passed on to a cylindrical mandril at an easy fit, and also of the thick shell rollers " at present generally employed " in calico printing and other analogous processes, and also to obviate the inconveniences resulting " from the springing of the roller while " revolving, and the faulty printing resulting from the several " rollers requiring different degrees of pressure bearing upon the " same boll, and being made to compress the same thickness of " elastic material." It consists in employing three cylinders, or any combination of sets of three cylinders, the axes of which are always parallel, one of the three being freely deposited between the other two, from one or both of which it receives rotatory motion by contact and pressure, the nip which it undergoes being greater in proportion as its position between them is lower in relation to the horizontal diameter of the sustaining cylinders. The three cylinders are driven by power applied to the axis of one or both of the sustaining cylinders. Either the upper or lower cylinders may be engraved, the middle one in the latter case acting as the boll.

[Printed, 7½d. Drawings.]

A.D. 1853, July 19.—No 1714.

BREESE, CHARLES.—" A method of forming designs and " patterns upon papier maché, japanned iron, glass, metal, and " other surfaces."

The invention consists in printing upon paper in an adhesive matter, and transferring the impression to the surface to be ornamented. The paper is removed and the pattern has applied to it a powder of some substance which resists the action of acids, after which the surface is exposed to the action of fluoric acid. Or the impression on the paper may be treated with the powder, and then transferred, the paper removed, and the process continued as above described. Vitrifiable colors or metals used for this purpose are applied according to the process known as " burning in."

In some cases the coloring medium may be mixed with adhesive composition. Patterns in lead, gold, silver, metal, leaf, or bronze, after being printed with the adhesive mixture have leaf powder applied, and the superfluous parts of such leaf or powder wiped off. When required it may be " stoved, varnished, polished, &c." For burnished gold or silver the leaf is laid on with ordinary gilding water, the pattern printed with an adhesive composition, sprinkled with resinous powder, the leaf removed from the other parts by an acid or rubbing, and the composition removed with turpentine or other solvent. The same treatment is adopted with reference to metallic surfaces, covered with silver and gold by the " amalgama- " tion process," marble, wood, &c. are ornamented by transfer of impressions obtained as above, preferring those in watery compo- sition. Dyes, pigments, or varnishes of any required colour are then applied to the surface, after which the transferred impression is removed, leaving the pattern of the original color surrounded by a ground of the color produced by the dye, pigment, or varnish.

[Printed, 3½d. No Drawing.]

### A.D. 1853, July 23.—N° 1740.

NAPIER, James Murdoch.—" Improvements in letter-press
" and other raised surface printing machines."

The invention consists in a peculiar combination of the form and
inking apparatus in platen presses, by which the form is inked
four times for each impression. After the impression the form
passes under the rollers which ink it for the first time. While
the form is at rest, for change of the sheet, these rollers pass to
and fro over the form, and thus ink it a second and third
time. The rollers then become stationary, and the form in
passing under them as it is run in is inked for the fourth time.
The inking table is rigidly connected with the type table. The
distributing rollers are carried by the frame, which carries the
inking rollers, so that the distribution of the ink is effected by the
combined movements of the inking table and the distributing
rollers. The inking table at one time passes under the rollers, and
when at rest the rollers pass over the inking table. During the
printing of a sheet the frame which carries the inking and distributing roller travels out and in, but, instead of inking the form
during this operation, the distributing and inking rollers run upon
the inking table; the ink is then further distributed, and the inking rollers covered with ink. The distributing rollers may be
placed diagonally " in the usual way, and the common method of
" supplying ink from the ink duct by a messenger roller direct to
" the inking table may be employed; or, if preferred, the ink may
" be distributed first upon a cylinder by a travelling mouse roller
" (as used in what are called the American machines), and after-
" wards delivered to the table for further distribution."

[Printed, 7½d. Drawings.]

### A.D. 1853, July 26.—N° 1754.

COLE, Frederick.—(Provisional Protection only.)—" An im-
" provement in the lythographic press."

The impression is taken by a cylinder " in place of the scraper
" now in general use," the cylinder being connected with a frame
which moves horizontally over the stone, and is worked by webs
attached to a rounce wheel capable of alternate action. The frame
has a rising and falling motion due to its weight, and the resistance
of the stone, thus adapting itself to different thicknesses of the stone.
The frame is also raised or depressed at pleasure by means of a

guide with graduated perforations. A weight is placed in a frame directly over the rollers. A table at either end of the press adjusted to the thickness of the stone receives the cylinder when it has passed by a forward movement over the stone, after which "on " another sheet being laid on, it is printed by the reverse action." The tympan is self-acting, by means of the alternate motion of the cylinder and counter-weights attached.

[Printed, 2½d. No Drawing.]

A.D. 1853, July 26.—N° 1755.

COLE, FREDERICK.—(Provisional Protection only.)—" Facili- " tating and improving the process of inking in printing."

1. The common inking table "now in general use" is placed on the off side of the press, the surface of it being nearly on a level with the surface of the types; and, 2, is brought into play by a pedal, the "ink cylinder" working in one direction only, and the composition cylinder passing to and fro over the inking table and types. The latter movement is effected by a piston or rod, and the former by a sash rising and falling alternately in grooves in the sides of the framework of the table. Two levers, a wheel and axle, and cords communicate the motion of the treadle to the various parts of the press, the return motion being caused by a weight.

[Printed, 2½d. No Drawing.]

A.D. 1853, July 29.—N° 1774.

JARRETT, GRIFFITH.—" Improvements in machinery or appa- " ratus for stamping or printing colored surfaces."

1. Self-feeding, coloring, and stamping hand press, adapted for the desk, counter, or writing table. A piece of carbonic or other colored paper is interposed between the die and the material to be printed, the former being secured in an open frame which traverses under the dye, by means of a screw worked from the handle of the press, and thus shifts the position of the colored paper for each impression. A revolving ink roller is sometimes substituted for the colored paper.

[Printed, 6½d. Drawings.]

A.D. 1853, August 3.—N° 1819.

CUMMING, JOHN.—(Provisional Protection only.)—" Improve- " ments in printing shawls, handkerchiefs, piece goods, paper

" hangings, and similar materials, and in the apparatus connected
" therewith."

The invention relates to a machine which obviates the necessity
of engraving or otherwise producing numerous repeats of the
pattern upon the printing rollers, the entire piece being printed
from small rollers or segments of rollers containing but one or two
repeats of the pattern. The fabric is stretched upon a flat horizontal table. The printing apparatus is in a carriage, and slides
in V grooves upon a framing, which framing itself is capable of
traversing in a direction at right angles to that of the carriage's
traverse. The lower part of the carriage is made to turn round
upon the upper, so that it and the printing rollers may be
set round horizontally to any desired position. The printing
rollers are fed from color troughs, which travel with them by
means of blankets or ordinary rollers. Register is ensured by
pinions attached to the printing rollers working in racks fixed
to the carriage. The printing rollers are built up of rings, so that
a great variety of patterns can be produced from a few simple
elements. The carriage is by means of a crank run over the fabric
so as to print the extent of the pattern. The carriage then, during
a pause in the crank's motion, moves sideways to the extent of a
repeat, when the crank is again set in motion and the roller runs
backwards, so as to produce a second repeat of the pattern upon the
fabric. The carriage moves sideways again, and the same movements are repeated until the whole of one side of the border is
printed. The lower part of the carriage with the rollers is then
turned round horizontally, and the border, at right angles to the
first, is printed in the same manner. Or if it is simply a ground
pattern which is being printed, a series of impressions having been
made across the piece, the carriage is moved forward a space and
then traversed back in a parallel direction. Or again, if piece goods
are being printed, the piece is made to move forward after each
traverse across it, if the carriage and the latter simply traverses
and re-traverses the same ground.

[Printed, 2½d. No Drawing.]

A.D. 1853, August 4.—N° 1825.

MOSS, THOMAS. — " Improvements in printing bank notes,
" checques, bills of exchange, and other documents requiring like
" security against being copied."

The invention provides against documents being copied by anastatic or other processes, and consists in printing the document in the ordinary manner, and after or before such impression, printing the same surface with a device, more or less extensive, with transparent ink, either colored or not, by which any attempt to obtain copies therefrom would fail by reason of the two impressions, which are distinct on the original, appearing in the copies as one impression produced by one and the same ink.

" By this means it will be evident that, although the impression " of transparent ink or varnish will not interfere with the printed " and written matter composing the document from which it is de- " sired no copy should be taken, such impression of transparent ink " or varnish will, in the event of any attempt to take a copy by " anastatic or other means produce a combined impression com- " posed of the two impressions on the original document, and the " compound impression will be all similarly inked, and offer a " confused impression which could not be in any way useable as " a document."

[Printed, 2½d. No Drawing.]

## A.D. 1853, August 6.—No 1845.

GREEN, JOHN.—(Provisional Protection only.)—" Improvements " in printing machinery."

One or more forms are fixed to a cylinder, the other part of which is used as a distributing table. Around the cylinder are several pressing rollers and inking rollers, which ink the form after passing under the pressing rollers. The paper is supplied by tapes in long uncut webs, folded to and fro into the size of sheets, into which the webs are to be cut when printed. The first time of passing through the machine it is caused to fold again to and fro, but in the second time of passing through the machine, and when it has been printed on both sides, it is cut into sheets by passing between two rollers, one of which carries a serrated blade, and passes between a slit or opening in the other roller, the edges of which slit project and are elastic, and thus, by receiving more pressure than the other parts of the roller, hold the paper very securely when the blade is passing through the paper. The paper is printed opposite each pressing roller, and in order to prevent two impressions coming on the same part of the surface, the paper on receiving an impression by one pressing roller is conducted away from the cylinder by a carrying roller before it comes to the next pressing roller. The sheets as they are cut are piled alternately to the right and left on inclined tables or receiving boards.

[Printed, 2½*d*. No Drawing.]

A.D. 1853, August 10.—N° 1861 (*a*).

PRINCE, ALEXANDER.— (Provisional Protection only.)—(Communicated.)— " A press applicable to the several purposes of " lithography, autography, typography, chromo-lithography, or " printing in colors, copper-plate printing, cylinder printing, em- " bossing, and copying letters."

This press is described as " quite as efficient and considerably " cheaper than either of the above-mentioned distinct and separate " presses." The elements of this press consist of a wooden " rake " with a " rake holder " in a box on cylindrical springs. Beneath this rake is a carriage with a leather to bear the friction given for the impression attached to one end of it. This carriage receives the stone, type, or original to be copied. It is supported by uprights and driven by a cylinder beneath it, which is worked by a star-wheel. It is guided by " rules " and " rails," the latter sliding against the interior face of the former, which are kept parallel by cross bars. The sheet is laid on by hand. The rake descends upon the leather for the impression by the action of an excentric lever. On removing the pressure, the cylindrical springs return the rake and disengage the carriage, which is then moved so as to remove the stone or register.

For chromo-lithography, a peculiar piece of mechanism is introduced for the purpose of holding the paper in its proper position on the stone.

For embossing, a " T piece," the lower part of which contains the die in a tube, is introduced into the rake holder. The carriage is removed and a table or block, covered with cloth, placed upon the cylinder.

For typography the cylinder is removed. The form is placed in the carriage and a tympan and frisket substituted for the leather. The impression is given by the descent of a plate (connected with the rakeholder) by means of a lever.

---

(*a*) An addition to this Provisional Specification was subsequently filed.

For copper-plate printing two cylinders are used. "The print-
" ing is effected after the usual method. It will be observed that,
" in the above state, this press may be used as a cylinder for
" pressing paper and ᵢcards. While the press is mounted for
" lithography, copper-plate printing, and typography, it may be
" also used for letter copying. In the first case, put a leather over
" the register and roll it under the cylinder. In the second case,
" pass the letter between the cylinders. And, in the third case,
" the copy is obtained by the flat pressure of the plate," above
described.

[Printed, 7½d. Drawings.]

A.D. 1853, August 13.—N° 1900.

GWYNNE, JOHN.—" Improvements in the preparation of a black
" powder from coal, and in the application thereof to the manu-
" facture of paints, blacking, and various other purposes."

The other purposes mentioned "are sugar refining, purifying
" syrup, refining oils, filtering chemical preparations and water
" for domestic use, deodorizing feculent matters, and arresting
" decay in all cases in which 'charcoals of any description' had
" been used, and in the manufacture of printers' ink, Frankfort
" black, and gunpowder." There are two modes, the one dry the
other wet, of producing the impalpable powder. The first consists
in placing the carbonaceous matter, "ground to a fine powder by
" any of the usual modes," inside a churn or other suitable apparatus, by the revolution of which the powder is shaken out
" through a textile screen in sufficient volume and continuous
" quantity to float about and fill the apartment in order to separate
" by gravity the fine from coarse particles." The former are
deposited on upper shelves fixed in the apartment, while the latter
fall into drawers placed lower down. The second, or wet process,
consists in immersing the material with from six to eight parts of
its own quantity (by measurement) of water in a closed vessel.
The material, and the water containing it, is then thoroughly
agitated, until the grosser and larger particles subside at a certain
rate of rapidity by their gravity, whilst the finer, lighter, and
smaller particles descend or subside at a lesser rapidity, and are
intercepted in their descent or subsidence in the containing vessel
at the point which is found to be fittest for the state of division.

[Printed, 3½d. No Drawing.]

A.D. 1853, August 16.—No 1920.

NEWTON, ALFRED VINCENT.—(Communicated.)—" Improve-
" ments in the purification and distillation of rosin oil."

These consist in the use of a novel construction of kettle or still
capable of resisting to a great extent the injurious effects of unequal
contraction and expansion; and, secondly, in a process for dis-
tilling the oil and separating it from the more volatile products at
distinct parts of the still, and simultaneously with the conduct of
these operations effecting the bleaching and deodorizing of the oil,
by means of serpentine pipes leading from the still-head.

The residual product of the still in these processes is stated to
be applicable " with advantage as a base for black paint or for
" printers' ink."

[Printed, 5½d. Drawings.]


A.D. 1853, August 18.—No 1936.

CURTAIN, WILLIAM.—" Improved machinery for printing tex-
" tile fabrics, oilcloths, leather, paper-hangings, and other similar
" fabrics or materials."

The object of this invention is to print complicated patterns of
many colors with increased facility and despatch. The blocks
are mounted on springs in a travelling frame running on rails at
each side of the machine, and are thus brought one by one in their
proper order under the platten. The coloring apparatus consists
of as many troughs as there are colors to be printed, each trough
being provided with a color roller over which passes an endless
sheet or blanket, which receives the color from the color roller
and carries it across the machine and under the blocks which are
mounted on pins at their four corners. The blocks are forced
down on the color troughs by pistons, and recover themselves by
means of the springs. The frame containing the blocks must
then be moved forward until a second block is brought under the
platten, which being made to descend a second time will press the
printing block on to the surface of the fabric, and produce a second
impression thereon, and so on until all the blocks have been
printed, when the pattern on the fabric will be complete. The
fabric is then moved forward the length of the pattern in order
to bring a fresh part of the surface under the press, and the
operations are renewed until the printing of the whole length of
the fabric is completed.

[Printed, 1s. 5½d. Drawings.]

### A.D. 1853, August 29.—N° 1998.

FOSS, John.—" Improvements in printing apparatus."

The invention is a hand printing instrument, consisting of a frame (with a handle), in which is placed a roller having thereon the printing surface, and two inking rollers which are drawn towards the printing roller by bands of vulcanized india-rubber or other convenient means, such inking rollers being caused to come in contact only with the printing "form" or surface. The apparatus may also be further combined with an inking trough and roller to supply ink to the inking rollers.

[Printed, 6½d. Drawings.]

### A.D. 1853, September 6.—N° 2049.

CALLES, André.—(Provisional Protection only.)—" Improve-" ments in manufacturing typographic characters,"

Ordinary moulds are used in this invention, the peculiarity consisting in the use of "mould-carriers" or frames, which give the necessary movements to the various parts of the mould for casting and discharging the type as well as regulating the size of the letter. The mould-carriers are fixed to an upper plate which by means of an excentric has a to-and-fro motion, with an interval of rest for the injection, and by the action of a moveable piece upon the excentric, opens and closes the cock which supplies the metal from the melting pot.

[Printed, 2½d. No Drawing.]

### A.D. 1853, September 9.—N° 2073. P.

GRANT, Philip, and DOHERTY, John.—(Provisional Protection only.)—" Improvements in the mode or method of cutting " and finishing brass rule and wood reglet used in the art or " process of letter-press printing and other similar purposes, and " in the machinery or apparatus employed therein."

Instead of the "usual method" of cutting brass rule and wood reglet by the hand-saw and plane, the sheet brass is passed from a cylinder through or between studs or slides on to a second cylinder, during which time it comes in contact with knives which act upon the edges of the brass, so as to make one edge perfectly flat and smooth, and the other edge of a **V** form, thus delivering the rule perfectly true and clean as it is wound on the receiving cylinder,

from which it may be taken and cut into the necessary lengths.
Or other cutters are fixed to the frame of the machine by a regulating screw or similar contrivance. Wood reglet is made by a
mechanical plane and circular saw, the former to plane the true
height and the latter to cut it to the required width, the several
sizes being again subjected to the same process for planing or
adjusting them to the exact size or thickness of nonpariel, pica, &c.

[Printed, 2½d. No Drawing.]

## A.D. 1853, September 12.—Nº 2110.

NEWTON, ALFRED VINCENT.—(Communicated.)—" An im-
" proved manufacture of printing blocks and cylinders."

The invention consists in forming moulds for casting printing
surfaces by means of prisms of two different lengths. These
prisms are set up so that the short ones form the sunken part of
of the mould and the long ones the raised portions. Separate
moulds can be thus set up for each colour to be used in a pattern. The prisms may be of type metal, iron, copper, or other
suitable material; and the printing blocks may be made of any
material that by fusion or by mixture with water or oil may
be rendered sufficiently liquid or plastic to be poured or forced
into the moulds, such as type metal, plaster of Paris, and clay, a
mixture of shellac and fine sand, papier mâché, highly vulcanized
india-rubber, or gutta-percha, the latter being preferred from its
impervious and elastic qualities. In like manner cylindrical or
segmental printing surfaces may be formed, the types being
suitably shaped for such purposes.

[Printed, 5½d. Drawings.]

## A.D. 1853, September 13.—Nº 2115.

ADAMS, CHARLES FREDERICK, GEE, WILLIAM, and DAVIS,
GEORGE.—(Provisional Protection only.)—" The application of
" the processes of lithographic and zincographic printing to the
" printing of words, patterns, designs, and marks on metal, glass,
" wood, or other hard substances in sheets, slabs, or flat pieces
" with or without the intervention of transfer or other paper or
" any other flexible material."

The subject is transferred in greasy ink or crayons to stone or
zinc, which when treated with a solution of acid and water is ready
for use. Before printing from it, it is wetted, and while wet has a

roller charged with greasy ink passed over it, depositing the ink on the lines of the subject only. The substance to be printed on is then laid " on the stone or zinc or under the stone or zinc, and " pressure being applied the printing is accomplished."

[Printed, 2½d. No Drawing.]

### A.D. 1853, September 13.—Nº 2117.

SINGTON, ADOLPHUS.—(Communicated.)—" Certain improve-" ments in machinery or apparatus for grinding or setting " 'doctors' used in calico and other similar printing machinery."

The invention consists of a frame grooved or fluted upon the top, and carrying a travelling carriage furnished with a setting tool, which is actuated by means of a chain and pulley, or otherwise, to which rotary motion is communicated from a winch handle (or driving pulley) by means of spun gearing; the " doctor" secured by clamps or fastenings at each end of the frame is raised or lowered as occasion may require to meet the tool. After being thus planed, straightened, or set, the " doctors" merely require one or two touches of a stone or "hone" to remove the " burr" left by the former process; they are then ready for use. There is also an arrangement for giving to the " doctor" a concave or convex edge as necessity may require.

[Printed, 7½d. Drawings.]

### A.D. 1853, September 14.—Nº 2126.

WILSON, JOHN.—" Improvements in and applicable to machines " for printing fabrics."

The invention consists, first, in substituting an endless web of cotton fabric for the woollen blanket usually employed as an elastic surface on the pressing cylinder; secondly, in the application of one at most " stretchers," which prevent the creasing of the endless web previously to its entering the machine; and, lastly, in driving the drying cylinders, over which the endless web passes by means of the motive power, instead of allowing them to be driven by the endless web, "as is now customary when " a woollen blanket is employed."

[Printed, 6½d. Drawings.]

### A.D. 1853, September 14.—Nº 2134.

KAY, RICHARD DUGDALE.—" Improvements in block printing."

The invention consists of a new mode of shading, mixing, or blending colors used in block printing.

By the method termed "tobying" them, in use for printing several colors by one application of the block, the colors are stated to have been "invariably plain, not shaded, and the object " has been to keep one colour separate and distinct from " another."

The invention consists in uniting or mixing the colors in regular or definite proportions by modifying the ordinary "toby" apparatus, and thus obtaining all the effect produced by the usual methods of "rainbowing" and "many more, with considerable " economy of time, labour, and general expense."

An impression is taken from the pattern block upon a block of wood planed to a true surface, in a color that will clearly show the pattern on the wood. One or more holes of the shape indicated by the block are then cut in the second block, and divided into as many compartments "as may be necessary, " each hole containing the same or totally different colours." The top of the division of each hole is made level with the surface, and a channel formed from each division of the hole terminating at one end of the wood in two separate orifices. A layer of flannel is fixed with adhesive matter on the wood, and the hole on the upper surface of the flannel surrounded with a "line of resin or " other suitable matter to retain the color within certain limits." Different colors are introduced into the divisions of each hole, such colors uniting only when they have "both risen to the " exterior surface of the flannel covering the hole." When the union of the two colors has thus taken place, the pattern block is applied to the hole and transferred to the cloth to be printed, which is thus printed in blended shades.

[Printed, 3½d. No Drawing.]

A.D. 1853, September 15.—N° 2140.

WHITE, CHARLES.—" Improvements in blocks for block " printing."

The invention relates, first, to certain descriptions of paper-hangings used for borderings and other like decorations, and secondly, to printing with blocks generally.

After stating that by the then obtaining mode " to print a " complete pattern with, say, four colours, it customarily requires " one block of " 21 inches by 10½ inches for each colour, the Specification proceeds thus :—

" Now supposing a pattern to require four blocks 21 inches " square to print a perfect pattern in four colours, on the prin- " ciple now commonly adopted, by my invention I could perform " the same work with one block 21 inches square, thereby saving " the labour and expense attending the carving of the three " extra blocks. I effect this improvement by composing my said " single block of 21 inches square, out of four blocks, each 5¼ " inches broad and 21 inches long, which being laid side by " side, and being screwed or otherwise fastened to a back board " form one firm block. Each narrow block may be supposed to " be of the full width of any intended bordering or other requisite " pattern; thus No. 1 may contain all the parts of the pattern " requiring to be printed blue, No. 2 all the red, No. 3 all the " brown, and No. 4 all the yellow, and so on in like manner for " any other colours. The workman proceeds in the use of this " compound block the same as if he were using the common " single block, with the exception that he prepares the compound " block with four colours at once. When he has printed as many " pieces as desired with the block as first arranged, he next alters " the block by taking out the top narrow block and placing it " below the other three, and arranging his colours in the same " order. The result will now be that the impressions of the " narrow block No. 2, will fall on the previous impressions made " by No. 1, and so on throughout. Therefore the narrow blocks " No. 1, 2, 3, and 4 will ultimately effect all that would have " been effected had four separately engraved or carved large blocks " been used, the saving here obtained being not in the labour of " printing, but in the first cost of the blocks by making four " narrow blocks do the duty of four large blocks, and the order " of their changes will rank as follows :—

| First printing operation. | Second do. | Third do. | Fourth do. |
|---|---|---|---|
| Block No. 1. | No. 2. | No. 3. | No. 4. |
| 2. | 3. | 4. | 1. |
| 3. | 4. | 1. | 2. |
| 4. | 1. | 2. | 3." |

[Printed, 2½d. No Drawing.]

A.D. 1853, September 15.—Nº 2148.

POOLE, Moses, — " Improvements in distributing printers'
" type (a)."

The types are made with notches or grooves, corresponding
with projections in passages in a receiving apparatus through
which they are made to pass. They are placed in " holders "
from which they are pressed by means of springs at the time
that " suitable apparatus for receiving the type from the holders
" come opposite thereto." The several receiving apparatus are
applied to a disc which is excentric to the plate " which carries
" the holders, and the disc receives motion by a crank on a shaft
" which is concentric with the opening in the plate, by which
" arrangement the receivers carried by the disc are in succession
" brought opposite each of the holders," or the holders to the
receivers.

Each distributing channel is thus made to do " exactly what a
" man would do, if having notched types and corresponding open-
" ings he was taking successively each type between his thumb and
" forefinger and trying to push it in at each successive opening."
The types are divided into six portions and " if there are 60 kinds
" of type mixed with the machine, may be made to send 10 kinds
" into each receiving channel which will have to be brought to
" another machine to be separated completely."

[Printed, 10½d. Drawings.]

A.D. 1853, October 6.—Nº 2286.

HARGROVE, Alfred Ely, and RICHARDSON, Ralph.—
" Improvements in machinery or apparatus for printing."

(a) The machines "about to be constructed according to this invention "
are stated to " have 30 receiving channels. These distribute the 25 characters
most in use (which form 75 per cent. of the total quantity). The remaining 25
per cent. will have to pass through the machines a second time in order to be
separated. " This will be effected by means of additional notches cut in the
back of such characters."

In the course of the Specification a brief description is given of Goubert's
clay and Rosenborg's and Sorenson's (Great Exhibition, 1851) machines for a
similar purpose. Between the first-mentioned invention and the present, the
difference is stated to be this, " in the former the types arrive to the openings
sideways by sliding on the surface into which the openings are cut, whilst in
this machine they come to the openings or the openings come to them endways,
following a curve whose last element is perpendicular to the face of the
opening."

The following is stated in the Specification as the result of experiment with
a " trial machine." It was " found capable of distributing 200,000 per hour, one
apprentice being sufficient to feed it," the machine thus distributing the
composition of 80 good workmen, composing at the rate of 2,500 per hour, or
performing the work of 20 good workmen distributing at the rate of 10,000
per hour.

The invention consists, first, in a simple mode of communicating a reciprocating motion to the type table of a press; and, secondly, in the use of an impression cylinder, provided with two or more impression surfaces, and also in the means of actuating the same. The former is effected by means of an excentric, or cam wheel or drum, on the periphery of which is a groove or feather, in or against which works a pin or pins attached to the under side of the table. The groove or feather on the periphery of this cam wheel is made in an oblique direction on the periphery. Or a cam wheel might be mounted obliquely on a horizontal shaft immediately below the table, the inclination of the cam groove or feather being such that, measuring from one extremity of the cam or excentric to the other, the horizontal distance will be exactly that which the table will be required to traverse to and fro to take in the paper, print the same, and deliver the printed sheet. A large toothed wheel on the axle of the main cylinder gears into a smaller wheel below, on the axle of which is a mitre or bevil wheel which drives a similar wheel on the axle of the cam drum or excentric, and by the excentric groove or feather acting on the pin or pins under the table, the rotary motion of the cam or excentric will communicate a reciprocating motion to the table on which the form is placed, or the power may be applied to the cam drum.

[Printed, 6½d. Drawings.]

A.D. 1853, October 12.—No 2343.

MAUMENÉ, EDWIN JULES.—" Improvements in the treatment " lignite or wood coal, and in obtaining various useful products " therefrom."

The claims in the Specification to this Patent are for the manufacture from lignite or wood coal of the following substances :—

1. A black pigment employed for making blacking or printers' ink. The lignite, when carbonized, is washed in dilute muriatic acid, afterwards in water, dried, and ground to a fine powder.

2. A substance suitable for decolourizing solutions of sugar, &c.

3. Artificial fuel.

4. A volatile oil.

5. Naphthaline, paraffine, and similar products which are without the peculiar disagreeable odour which is possessed by similar products obtained from coal tar.

[Printed, 3½d. No Drawings.]

A.D. 1853, October 12.—N° 2345.

MAPPLE, HENRY, and MAPPLE, DANIEL MOORE.—(Provisional Protection only.)—" An improved printing and signal
" electric telegraph, with electric alarum attached."

" The printing portion consists of a type wheel, to revolve by
" means of one or more permanent or electro-magnates, being
" made to vibrate in front of an electro-magnate, and thereby
" bringing the required letter to the point required.  Or the type
" wheel or letters can be brought to the required point by placing
" one or more magnets on the axis which carries the type or
" letters.  The type wheel is placed in a shifting frame, and when
" the letter is brought to the required point the said shifting
" frame will be allowed to move, by the electric current being
" applied at the distant station ; and by the shifting of the frame
" the letter or symbol will be impressed on the material prepared
" to receive it ; the inking of the type is done by causing the type
" to revolve in contact with a roller prepared with printing ink."

An improved key frame or pedal is attached to the instrument
for making and breaking the current, the speed of working being
regulated by a break.

The alarum consists of weights or balls which, being released by
the action of a current on a lever, fall on any sounding material,
or raise a hammer.  In order that the permanent magnets may
retain their power, the points or ends of such as move are tipt with
iron ; " these iron points are carried into the electric coils, so that
" the electric current will act upon the iron points or ends.  These
" iron points or ends can be bent at right angles, or otherwise, as
" may best suit for keeping the electric current from the permanent
" magnet."

Instead of centers or pivots, as now generally used, a piece of
silk or other yielding substance is passed through or over the
permanent magnet, and this silken or other substance is stretched
and kept tight by a spring or weight at one or either end, and thus
the silken or other like substance forms an axis on which the
magnetised body is allowed to move.  By twisting the thread on
one side to the other the pointer is put in exact position.

[Printed, 2½d.  No Drawings.]

A.D. 1853, October 15.—N° 2387.

APPLEGATH, AUGUSTUS.—" Improvements in printing and
" embossing paper, with a view to prevent forgery."

The object of this invention is to prevent forgery by the process of photography. It consists in causing several colors to be applied by an engraved surface simultaneously in pattern and in register on the whole or part of the surface of the paper used for such documents; "and I prefer to combine the printing of the parts, if any " be required, of the document with the printing of the many " colored device in one machine, and when the documents are to " be stamped I prefer that the requisite stamping or embossing " machinery should be in combination with the printing machi- " nery." By these means, although copies may be taken by photography in one color of the whole of the printing on a document, the obtaining of a similarly colored document will be prevented.

[Printed, 10½d. Drawings.]

## A.D. 1853, October 17.—N° 2396.

APPLEGATH, Augustus.—"Improvements in letter-press " printing machinery."

The invention relates to "perfecting" machines. Three forms are used, two for printing white and one for the reiteration. They may either be fixed on a reciprocating table or on cylinders. If the former, the similar forms are at the ends, and the reiteration form in the middle, of the table. Each of the end forms passes to and fro under a pressing cylinder, having suitable tapes and conducting apparatus for the paper, and the third form is by the motion of the table caused to pass under two pressing cylinders. The forms are inked "in the ordinary " manner." In the latter case the forms are fixed on three cylinders, two performing the white printing, and the third the reiteration. They are inked "in the ordinary manner," and the paper supplied to them "by tapes and cylinders placed between the " cylinders on which the forms are fixed."

The Drawings represent, 1, a rotary machine, which prints two sheets at each revolution of the type cylinder. Two type cylinders, each of 100 inches in circumference, are used, the type being fixed upon them in "typeholders, similar to those used at the 'Times'(a)

---

(a) The following remark is made in the Specification as to the performance of this machine. " Admitting the rate of motion in this machine to be the same as that which produces good work," at the "Times" the type cylinder will make 3,000 revolutions per hour, and 6,000 sheets or 12,000 impressions. The perfection of this machine would be when working taper type or letter having its sides slightly inclined, and with wood engravings made to the proper curve.

" vertical machines, either in single columns or in pages." The distributing surfaces are fixed opposite to the forms, and are supplied " in the usual manner" by a vibrating roller from a color box. The inking rollers are in a carriage, and are drawn into contact with the type and distributing surfaces by india-rubber springs, being also partly confined by bands of iron or gun metal " as usual in fast machines." Four pressing cylinders are used of half the diameter of the type cylinders with which they are made to gear. The sheet is conducted from one type cylinder to the other by conveying drums; in gear with one of which is a wheel which gives motion to the upper feed rollers. Dropping rollers are worked in the ordinary way by cams. The sheets being printed at too great a rate for one taker off, are alternately delivered at different points.

2. Rotary machine, by which four impressions are obtained at each revolution of the central type cylinders, which has upon it the type of the "outer" form, or that which contains the wood engravings when required. The "inner" form and a duplicate are carried by cylinders at the ends of the machine. The latter are furnished with two pressing cylinders and inking apparatus, the former with four. The conveyance of the sheets is by conveying drums, as in (1) (a).

3. A " double-action, flat or plano-cylindric machine," by the side of which is represented the "usual book machine," as patented about 1823 by the patentee. The outer form is in the middle of the press, and prints both at its forward and backward movement at one or other of two pressing cylinders. Two inner forms are at the ends of the press. The forms are inked as usual (b).

[Printed, 10½d. Drawings.]

A.D. 1853, October 19.—Nº 2410.

RAY, WILLIAM (Senior).—" Improvements in printing textile " fabrics and other surfaces."

The invention relates to printing from relief cylinders, " as a " substitute for the usual hand-block work." A transverse

(a) " At the 'Times' rate," it is observed, " this machine will perfect 12,000 sheets or 24,000 impressions."

(b) In the old press, with which the improved invention is compared, the " whole lineal motion" was about 47 inches, in this it is rather more, or 57 inches, " in order that the whole form may pass under two inking rollers for each impression."

guide frame is placed above and across a flat printing table; and in this frame, as a horizontal guide, a travelling printing carriage is fitted to work over the table at pleasure. The lower side of the main guide rail carries a toothed rack into which a spur wheel in the first motion shaft is arranged to gear. This shaft together with the whole of the other gearing is carried into the travelling carriage, so that on causing the first motion shaft to revolve, the carriage with all the printing apparatus is caused to traverse its guide. On the first motion shaft is also placed a roller or drum over which the endless sieve or feed cloth is passed, a similar drum being fitted up alongside for working in concert with the first in supporting the sieve. This second drum presses on the upper side of a supplying roller partially immersed in the color box, carried along with the gearing and carriage. A continuation of the gearing also actuates a lower horizontal shaft, on which is placed the surface printing roller arranged to traverse in contact with the fabric stretched across the table beneath. The lower length for the time being of the endless sieve traverses in contact with the upper side of the printing roller, so that as the machine is worked to traverse the roller, the latter thus receives an uniform supply of color. In printing shawls in the piece way, the fabric is passed over the table, and the printing carriage is then run over it to print the "repeat." The piece is then shifted at a right angle to the traverse of the printing carriage to the required distance, and the carriage is retraversed to produce the second repeat, and so on. The table is capable of swivelling round upon a vertical spindle, so that the operator may present fresh borders or surfaces of the piece to the printing operation after one impression has been completed. In printing more colors than one the parts are reduplicated to the required extent, so that one color follows the other throughout the series. And instead of using a fixed table with traversing rollers, the apparatus may be modified by using a traversing table to pass beneath the rollers, producing a like result.

[Printed, 6½d. Drawings.]

A.D. 1853, October 19.—N° 2413.

LITTLE, WILLIAM.—(Provisional Protection only.)—" Improve-" ments in typographic printing."

This invention relates to printing where type is set round the surface of the cylinder, and the improvements consist in forming the type wedge-form, that is, each type and space is formed with two inclined sides and two parallel sides in such manner that the columns of type, when set up and placed on the cylinder, are round the cylinder, and not longitudinally or in a line with the axis of the printing cylinder. The "leads" are also made wedge shape, and have at their ends projections on which the column rules, which are segments of circles, come, and thus facilitate the fastening of the whole to the cylinder.

[Printed, 2½d. No Drawing.]

A.D. 1853, October 21.—N° 2430.

JOHNSON, JOHN HENRY. — (Provisional Protection only.) (Communicated by Jaques Lefevre of Paris.)—" Improvements in " the treatment or manufacture of gutta percha, and in the appli- " cations thereof."

The invention consists in purifying gutta percha, and forming two distinct substances, one dry and tough, the other greasy and resinous. For the former, the gutta percha is passed through a mill worked by a revolving cone in an indented chamber, after which it falls on to toothed rollers beneath, between which it is drawn and squeezed so as to be freed from foreign matter. The stringy or tough parts are fumigated and rendered white, so that it. may receive any color required. It is liquified by the use of carburet of hydrogen. Thus liquified it may, with equal parts of glue and treacle, be used in the construction of inking rollers. Mixed with gluten, gum, lac, and copal, it makes a varnish which prevents oxidation, and action of acids on glass and metals. For applying the same to wood, a certain amount of pitch is added. "The gutta percha may be solidified by being treated " whilst in a soft state, having added to it a solution of the gutta " percha obtained by the carburet of hydrogen, . . . when the " mass is passed through rollers to render it perfectly homogeneous." Gutta percha thus prepared may be applied to all kinds of objects of art or manufacture, such as tubes, moulded or drawn articles, vases, statuettes, &c. Presses may also be constructed of it for the impressing of paper-hangings, &c., the whole of the colors being impressed at once. The pattern is engraved on gutta percha cylinders in the following manner :—A thin coat of wax is laid upon a cast-iron plate, and in this wax is traced the desired pattern, which is transferred to the gutta percha cylinder in relief. Around this cylinder are arranged as many inking rollers as there are colors.

The carburet above mentioned, with five to seven per cent. of alcohol and sulphuric acid added, will dissolve all the fatty, gummy, and resinous bodies, and will serve to clean various articles, as stuffs, kid gloves, and silks of the most delicate tints. It may also be employed for dissolving the gummy portion of silk cocoons, and for many similar purposes.

[Printed, 2½d. No Drawing.]

A.D. 1853, October 21.—N° 2440.

GATTY, FREDERICK ALFRED.—" Improvements in printing or " producing colors on textile fabrics."

The invention consists in preparing a mordant "composed of " chlorate and hydrochlorate of alumina, by which the colors are " fixed and oxidized without the use of chlorate of potash."

[Printed, 2½d. No Drawing.]

A.D. 1853, October 24.—N° 2451.

BREWSTER, CHARLES.—" Improvements in printing ma- " chinery."

The pressing cylinder and inking rollers are in a carriage driven by a pinion on a shaft in the middle of the press. The inking rollers take up their supply from a large roller at one end of the press, the latter being supplied by a vibrator from a trough roller immediately below it. At the other end of the press is a feeding table from which the sheet, on the return of the cylinder, is caught by "fingers or clips" upon the cylinder which carries it round to the impression, and discharges it on to "creeping tapes" in a frame connected with the carriage of the pressing cylinder, which lift it off the type as the cylinder moves outwards. Pressure is produced by a peculiar arrangement of levers acting on the axis of the cylinder. At the end of its printing course it comes against the ends of sliding bars, which elevate it to a level at which it is carried on the return free of the form.

[Printed, 9½d. Drawings.]

A.D. 1853, October 25.—N° 2463.

NEWTON, ALFRED VINCENT. — (Communicated.)—" An im-
" proved construction of printing press."

This invention relates to an arrangement of machinery intended
chiefly for printing "job work" with great expedition. The type
is mounted on a reciprocating table or carriage, which slides in
guides and enters a stationary ink distributing cylinder (through
the periphery thereof) when the type is to be inked, in order that
the inking rollers (which are carried by rotating arms mounted
on the axle of the cylinder) may pass over the face of the type
in making the circuit of the exterior periphery of the ink-distributing cylinder. When the type is inked it is driven forward
by the throw of a crank, and pressed into contact with the paper
or other material intended to receive the impression. It is preferred to use paper or cardboard in continuous lengths, and to
give the same an intermittent motion that a fresh surface may
be brought opposite the type while being inked. The paper or
other material is drawn forward between suitable guides and
held quiescent while the impression is being made. After each
imprint a pair of shears is made to close upon the paper or other
material, and shear off the portion that last came from under the
pressure of the type. When this has been effected the paper or
other material receives a forward traverse motion, and the printing operation is then repeated. By the action of its extended
axle against a stationary cam on the framing, one inking roller in
each set "has a vibrating motion while" upon the cylinder. but
only an onward motion while passing over the form.

[Printed, 6½d. Drawings.]

A.D. 1853, October 25.—N° 2464.

BOGUE, DAVID.—(Communicated.)—" An improved mode of
" producing printing surfaces."

The design to be reproduced is transferred by pressure to a polished
plate of metal or alloy. The parts of the surface "which correspond
" to and lie under the lines, letters, or marks of the transfer" are
then protected by first washing the whole plate with gum water
slightly acidulated with nitric acid, allowing it to remain there
five minutes, and then cleaning it off with water. While still wet
a roller furnished with lithographic ink is passed over it. Resin

ground to an impalpable powder is then distributed over the
surface of the plate with cotton, wool, or a camel's hair brush,
and the plate exposed to the heat of a spirit lamp, so as to make
the rosin combine thoroughly with the ink. The plate is then
submitted to the action of dilute nitric or other suitable acid,
either by immersing it therein (the back of the plate having been
previously varnished to enable it to resist the action of the acid)
or by building a wall round the edge of the plate and covering the
with the acid. The corroding action of the acid is allowed to proceed until the level of the exposed surface is sufficiently reduced
to admit of the plate (when the transfer is cleared off) being
printed from like a wood engraving. Before mounting it upon
the block, the " broad whites " are cut away so as to prevent them
from taking the ink from the printing roller and spoiling the
impression. " By this means I am enabled to reproduce engrav-
" ings of all kinds, and to prepare plates from which books, when
" out of print, may be reproduced without the necessity of
" resetting the matter."

[Printed, 3½d. No Drawing.]

## A.D. 1853, October 26.—N° 2470.

WOODWARD, George Gower.—" Improvements in the manu-
" facture of carpets."

The invention consists, first, in a novel combination of thread,
worsted, or woollen yarns to form the warp of pile fabrics known
as Brussels, tapestry, Wilton, and other carpets, or any piled,
terry, or looped fabrics, figured or woven of various colors in the
manner of carpeting. The "self" or single-colored yarns are
combined with parti-colored yarns, thus having one or more
warps of the parti-colored combined with one or more warps of
the self or single colored yarns. Any pattern can thus be produced in an unlimited number of colors, either with or without the
use of the jacquard machine. The yarns of the different colors
required for the design are wound upon bobbins on warp rollers
in the order in which they are to be used in producing the design.
Secondly, in a novel combination of yarns made of the aforesaid
mixture, either printed, colored, or dyed of various colors in
different shades with other yarns of a self or single color.
Thirdly, in the use of the material called the patent flax cotton,
and of any of the mixtures of wool, linen, cotton, or silk yarns

for the manufacture of Brussels, tapestry, or other carpets or piled fabric manufactured in the manner of carpeting. Fourthly, in a mode of printing, dyeing, or coloring yarns, and arranging them previous to weaving. The parti-colored warps, as well as the self-colored ones, are dyed or printed by direct immersion, so as to give them all the brilliancy and durability of ingrained colors, by allowing certain portions of the yarn to fall into pans or small coppers containing the dye at stated intervals, the combination and arrangement of which will produce the intended design or pattern. The arrangement of the warps above described does not interfere with the number of those warps of cotton or linen termed "ground" and "stuffing" warps which form the body and back of the carpet.

[Printed, 5½d. Drawings.]

## A.D. 1853, October 26.—Nº 2481.

VIZETELLY, James Thomas George.—"Improvements in "producing plates for printing purposes, by which the manipula- "tory process of engraving is superseded."

The invention is applicable, first, to the reproduction from a printed impression of any engraving upon any of the metals usually employed for engraving without reference to the time at which such printed impression may have been taken; secondly, to a like reproduction of any illustrated work or periodical publi- cation in which a combination of engraving and letterpress exists, or of works consisting of letterpress only; and thirdly, to the creation for the purposes of printing of original plates or en- gravings in relief from prepared pencil, crayon, or ink drawings, such plates being produced on any metal usually employed for the purpose. When access can be had to the engraving, an impres- sion is taken from it in transfer ink, and transferred, while fresh, to the surface of a plate of zinc, copper, pewter, steel, or other metal usually employed. When the transfer is set, the surface of the plate is floated with a mixture of nitric acid, distilled water, and alcohol or spirits of wine by means of which the surface of the plate becomes etched, with the exception of such parts as are covered by the transfer, which consequently remains in relief. When access cannot be had to an engraving for the purpose of obtaining a transfer, an "ordinary impression" is taken on paper over the ink lines of which a slight coating of gum-water is passed, "after the manner practised by lithographers to set or fix " drawings on stone," by means of which the printed lines of the subject to be reproduced can be re-inked with transfer ink. The impression thus re-inked serves as the medium for obtaining a transfer on the metal plate, which is afterwards etched as above described.

For the creation of original plates, it is only necessary that the subject to be produced should be drawn on paper with transfer ink or crayon, transferred to the metal plate, and etched in by the means employed in the foregoing processes. The "whites" are bitten away to various degrees of depth in proportion to their more or less isolated position, the depth of the most considerable being increased with scrapers or gouges.

[Printed, 3½d. No Drawing.]

### A.D. 1853, October 27.—N° 2490.

M'NAUGHTON, WILLIAM.—(Provisional Protection only.)— " Improvements in printing yarns or worsteds for weaving carpets, " also in printing carpets, woollen, silk, cotton, and other textile " fabrics, and felted fabrics or fibrous substances."

The invention relates to improvements upon N° 933 of 1853, consisting in the " use and application of hollow metal cylinders, " either separately or in combination with wood, instead of being " wholly of wood, for printing patterns, or devices, or plain sur- " faces of color upon yarns or worsteds for weaving carpets; also " in printing carpets, woollen, silk, cotton, and other textile or " felted fabrics, or fibrous substances, or materials, which im- " provements are based upon the principle of construction pre- " viously described, set forth, and represented in the Specification" (N° 933 of 1853) before referred to.

[Printed, 2½d. No Drawing.]

### A.D. 1853, October 29.—N° 2505.

MACLURE, ANDREW.—" Improvements in lithographic printing " presses."

The invention relates to the damping and inking apparatus, and is applicable to presses where the stone is stationary during the damping and inking. The damping apparatus, consisting of a roller or sponge and water trough and inking rollers connected with an ink trough, are both in a frame which passes to and fro over the stone. On the main driving shaft is a bevilled pinion which revolves freely or becomes fixed upon it according as a clutch is slidden to and fro by a lever, the former taking place when the inking and damping apparatus is to remain at rest. On the frame are adjustable inclines which, by their action upon bell-crank levers, causes a vibrating roller at intervals to move from a trough roller to a distributing roller, from which the inking rollers are supplied. The several rollers are worked by intermediate mechanism from the driving shaft. The damping roller is linked to the frame and surmounted by cups containing a supply of water. The inking rollers pass twice over the form, the damping roller once only, it being raised clear of the stone on its return by the links by which it is suspended coming against inclines on the stationary frame work of the press.

[Printed, 1s. 1½d. Drawings.]

A.D. 1853, October 31.—Nº 2515.

COUBROUGH, ANTHONY PARK.—" Improvements in printing " textile fabrics and other surfaces."

The invention relates to block printing machines. In printing eight colours by this apparatus a set of four horizontal printing tables are fitted up in a line, at uniform distances, at a suitable height above a platform for the hand-block printers to work at. Each table is fitted with an endless blanket passing over guide rollers at the opposite edges of the table, and thence descending beneath the table platform to a horizontal roller, set beneath the vertical centre line of the table. The printed fabric is held on a beam set at one end of this line of tables, and as the printing goes on the piece is passed along with a piece of grey cloth interposed, as in cylinder printing, between the blanket and the fabric to be printed over the first table. A printer stands on each side of the table, each printer, if necessary, having a different colour on his hand block. These two operators then give their united impressions in succession to the length of cloth exposed on the table top. The traversing apparatus then carries the fabric forward for the next repeat. The driving gear is placed at one end of the machine, and a horizontal shaft passes alongside the machine with bevel or other gear to drive all the bottom rollers at a regular uniform rate, and then prevent stretching the fabric. The fabric is thus passed from one table to the other, round suitable adjustable guides, so that time is allowed for drying between the impressions. This operation is carried on continuously. By carrying the endless blankets to a considerable depth below the printing tables, time is allowed for the drying of the blanket before the same surface is again brought into operation. Cylindrical or curved surfaces in intaglio or relief may be used instead of the flat blocks above referred to. The continuous system of gearing affords " special facilities for 'blotching,' the blotching cylinder being set " at the end of the apparatus and driven round at a regular rate " to give uniformity of effect."

The apparatus represented in the Drawings is arranged to print six colors.

[Printed, 11½d. Drawings.]

## A.D. 1853, November 1.—N° 2531.

HEYWOOD, JAMES.—(Provisional Protection only.)—" Certain " improvements in machinery or apparatus for printing yarns."

The invention relates to printing such yarns as are required to be partially printed in the "hank," leaving intermediate spaces blank, and to be subsequently employed in manufacturing clouded or speckled goods or fabrics. Any convenient number of hanks of yarn are distended endwise by passing them over two side rods or rails contained in a suitable framework, such hanks presenting a flat horizontal surface capable of being printed upon when placed side by side. The parts of the yarns to be left blank are pressed between flat ribs or bars so secured or held together (the yarn being nipped between them) as entirely to prevent any of the printing color being introduced upon such spaces. The printing part of the apparatus is composed of small revolving printing rollers or bowls which furnish themselves with color placed in small troughs underneath them, the whole apparatus being completed by a printing table or board situated above all and over the yarn, this table being covered with a printing blanket or bed. The operation of printing is performed by passing the rollers along longitudinal supporting rails under the yarns (which are distended in hanks crosswise) from one end of the frame of yarn to the other, thus printing any width or color of stripe or pattern required simply by a suitable arrangement of the width of the retaining bars or stripes, and a corresponding interposition of the printing rollers operating between them.

[Printed 2½d. No Drawing.]

A.D. 1853, November 1.—N° 2532.

BALE, THOMAS SANDERS, and LUCAS, DANIEL.--" Improve-
" ments in ornamenting the materials of an article manufactured
" in pottery, as bricks, tiles, slabs, &c., and also in glass, slate,
" stone, and other plastic substances."

These consist of the improvements in pottery manufacture known
as " ground laying," and in imitating marble and partly colored
work and printing ornamental patterns on stone, slate, &c.

The outline of the pattern is drawn on and pricked through
fine tissue paper through which fine charcoal is pounced upon
the ware. The parts intended to be different from the ground
are then pencilled in with a " water stencil" of rose pink, sugar,
and water. The piece is then oiled and bossed with a dabber
to lay the oil on evenly, and upon this the required color ground
very fine is dusted; after being dried, the piece is well washed
in clear water. The stencil being soluble comes off, and the
color is left on, forming the pattern, it is then cleaned, dried,
and fired in the kiln. Or the outline may be printed and
transferred " in the usual way," and then fired, after which the
stencilling, oiling, grounding, &c. is repeated as before. For
" printing stencil ground laying" the pattern is first engraved
and the article to be ornamented sized with a mixture of Canada
balsam and turpentine. An impression is taken on tissue
paper, the stencil consisting of rose pink (3), whiting (2), fine
ground flint (2), lampblack (1), sugar of lead (½), and resin (2),
well mixed with printers' oil, and transferred to the sized surface,
and after a short time washed away with soft soap and potash.
It is then oiled with Canada balsam and linseed oil, but without
the usual bossing, after which the ground colour is brushed,
dusted, or laid on " in any convenient manner." It is then
fired with the " stencil on," and on coming out of the kiln the
stencil is easily rubbed off with fine sand and water "leaving
" the color and pattern on the article beautifully sharp and defined
" and clean at the edges."

For delicate work the article is oiled and dusted over with the
ground colour, an impression in stencil or tissue paper is trans-

ferred to the moist surface, then carefully peeled off, when it brings away with it the color from all the parts of the article which the printed stencil has come in contact with, the other portions not touched by the print forming the pattern.

For gilding, gold dust is used instead of color. The article is then fired with the stencil on. The stencil is rubbed off on its leaving the kiln.

For substances which will only bear a slight temperature, as stone, slate, wood, &c., an impression is taken in opaque colours and transferred to the back of the piece. The paper is then washed off, after which it is oiled to receive the ground colour which is brushed or dusted through perforated paper, &c. The piece is then sized with a solution of isinglass and water, and whilst wet gold leaf is applied, and is seen through on the front side where there is no color. It is finished by painting it over with any desired color. It may be protected from damp by a coating of gutta percha, &c.

" Opaque bodies not necessary to be fired " are sized with isinglass and water and the gold dried, a little varnished, and afterwards hardened to set the varnish. The print is then transferred and washed off, after which it is oiled and the color applied as before, and the whole afterwards varnished.

Chimney pieces, pillars, &c. of stone, slate, wood, &c. are simply ornamented by painting over them with the desired colour, an impression is then taken of the pattern in any ordinary way, and transferred to the surface of the article. " The paper is after- " wards washed off, leaving the pattern, as marble, &c., behind." It may afterwards be varnished.

" Bricks, blocks, pillars, and similar articles too heavy and " costly to be made entirely of glass may be beautifully deco- " rated by ornamenting the glass in manner described, and then " using it as a veneer."

[Printed, 3½d. No Drawing.]

A.D. 1853, November 15.—N° 2647.

DELCAMBRE, ADRIEN.—(Provisional Protection only.)—" Im- " provements in machinery for distributing type."

" I place a page or column of type in a galley similar to that " used in printing offices at present, but furnished with an " arrangement which enables me to collect several lines into one

" long line for more convenient distribution. This long line of
" types is collected into what I call a reservoir which is placed at
" right angles to an inclined plane, more particularly described
" hereafter. This reservoir is made to slide by the hand of the
" workman from right to left, and left to right, and is provided
" with a piece of mechanism which enables him to set a type free
" or separate from the line when he finds that it is opposite the
" place of distribution, into which he wishes to guide the par-
" ticular type. The inclined plane is provided with numerous
" grooves corresponding to the number of receptacles for the
" distributed type. In order, however, to give more room to
" the working of the mechanism, worked by the hand of the
" workman, there are two inclined planes placed one over the
" other terminating in one common exit, so that although there
" is only one horizontal row of receptacles there are two inclined
" planes one above the other, leading to the same horizontal
" receptacle. I further provide a bar which by its vibration (put
" in motion by a pedal or any other motive-power) causes the type
" in the receptacles to be pushed forward to make room for suc-
" ceeding types."

[Printed, 2½d. No Drawings.]

A.D. 1853, November 16.—No 2654.

RONALD, JOHN.—" Improvements in fixing colors on yarns
" and cloths."

These improvements consist in the application of heat externally
to the vessel or chamber in which yarn or cloth is introduced for
the purpose of having the colors fixed in place of introducing
" free steam into the box or chamber without external heat as has
" been heretofore the practice."

[Printed, 5½d. Drawings.]

A.D. 1853, November 18.—No 2680.

MELVILLE, JAMES.—" Improvements in printing textile fabrics
" and other surfaces."

The invention relates to improvements on No 14,047 of 1852.
A large cylinder or drum is used on the impressing surface, it is
carried upon a horizontal spindle or suitable end standard framing,
each end standard projecting on the printing side to form supports
for a longitudinal slide, rest, plate, or bed, planed and filled like a

slide lathe to carry the surface printing roller. The latter is built up solid on a short spindle, the ends of which are centred to admit of its being turned true. The same end centres answer to carry the roller during printing, one of the sliding head-stocks having a short adjustable centre like the following headstock of a lathe, while the other one supports in a bearing one end of a correspondingly centred spindle, which projects beyond the head-stock and carries a toothed pinion in gear with a large wheel fast on the main drum shaft. The roller spindle is connected with the driving shaft by a "dog" or adjustable catch plate, as in a lathe, so that the setting of the roller is facilitated on starting. The end portion of a device is printed by setting the slide rest and roller to one end of the carrying plate or bed. At the next repeat the slide rest with its printing roller is traversed along the supporting plate, and this operation is repeated throughout the entire length of the main drum. A serrated plate with stops corresponding to the particular repeats is screwed to the front of the slide rest, which by means of a catch facilitates the setting of the roller at each shift. The gearing spindle of the printing roller is of considerable length, to admit of this shaft for the repeats, the connexion with the driving pinion being by a groove and feather "in the usual way." [A modification of this arrangement of the spindle and pinion is described.] The bottom blanket is cemented to the face of the drum and covered with a glazed cloth, the latter being coated with gum or other adhesive matter, to prevent slipping (or pins may be introduced for the purpose). In printing long lengths of goods, as in carpeting, the different colors are laid on by corresponding sets of surface rollers set one in advance of the other as regards the revolution of the drum. Thus each color roller prints in succession, and the apparatus being kept constantly working in the same direction, the forward revolution of the drum carries round the piece just so many times as is necessary for the due repetition of the impressions to saturate the piece.

[Printed, 11½d. Drawings.]

## A.D. 1853, November 19.—N° 2694.

POTTER, JOHN GERALD and MILLS, ROBERT. — "Certain " improvements in the manufacture of carpets."

The invention relates to "a mode of economizing the worsted " used in the manufacture of terry carpets from printed warps,

" and at the same time rendering the pattern with increased fide-
" lity." "We calculate the exact amount of warp which the terry
" fabric is required to take up in the formation of one loop, and
" multiplying this measurement by the number of divisions com-
" posing the length of the pattern, we ascertain the amount of
" warp surface required to be exposed to the printing operation to
" complete one pattern. We then prepare a warp cylinder with a
" circumference corresponding to the warp surface to be printed,
" and graduate the cylinder agreeably to the divisions on the
" paper pattern, and number it in like manner. The operator is
" then enabled to produce the pattern on the warps in such a
" manner that when woven into a terry fabric the pattern will be
" faithfully rendered without the undue expenditure of wool
" which is at present required to produce a similar result."

[Printed, 3½d. No Drawing.]

A.D. 1853, November 25.—No 2748.

JOHNSON, JOHN HENRY.—(Communicated by Auguste Feld-
trappe, of Paris.)—"Improvements in the production of printing
" surfaces."

The invention "relates to an improved system or mode of
" engraving the printing cylinders and plates employed in calico
" and other printing, and to the production of the rollers for
" compressing or cutting such cylinders." The outline of the
pattern is traced out upon cylinders either by an impressing roller
by hand or other means, either in small dots or in diagonal lines
ruled close together. The cylinder is then varnished and its
whole length and circumference traversed by a steel or diamond
point, which cuts it in parallel diagonal lines in an opposite
direction to the former diagonal lines, the cutter raising the
varnish and slightly entering the metal. In this state the pattern
parts of the roller are again coated with varnish, the ground of the
pattern being bitten with the acid. The ground of the pattern is
likewise formed by a cutting roller diagonally grooved or otherwise cut, and placed in two bearings in the position usually
occupied by the diamond holder. This roller is rolled slowly over
the varnished surface of the cylinder, exposing the metal by
penetrating the varnish in diagonal lines at a certain angle,
according to the inclination given to the cutting roller, and
leaving between each cut made by it an unengraved portion suffi-

ciently large to carry the "doctor" as "in grounds made by ma-
"chinery." The parts which have been outlined are again covered
with varnish, and the roller placed in aqua fortis. In patterns or
designs which may be commenced without the aid of the cutting
roller, the cylinder, plate, or cutting roller to be engraved is coated
with an even layer of varnish, and traversed, as before described,
by diagonal or other parallel lines. The pattern is conveyed to
the surface by an exact transfer on tracing paper of all the details
and tints of the pattern. The parts to be left white are coated
over when the surface is submitted to the action of acid. In
this way the different light tints are produced to the required
depth. For the darker tints " a system which gives more life "
is adopted. The first light tints being " bitten," the roller is
freed from varnish and again coated, and the unwrought parts are
then traced by parallel lines but in a different direction, the
number of such lines being diminished or augmented, and the
depth of the same regulated according to the tint required. After
being cut or grooved in the ordinary manner, the light tints are
recoated, and the darker tints left to the action of the acid. To
improve the appearance of the pattern and prevent the light tint
from clouding, the cylinder is entirely varnished and lined with
closer lines and by a tool of a peculiar form, in an opposite
direction to the engraved lines. The white parts are again covered,
and the whole is again submitted to the action of the acid for a
short time. For patterns of many tints or shades the white portions are first traced out and cleared, and the impressing roller
tempered and applied to the cylinder. The cylinder is then
re-coated with varnish and the biting process proceeded with to
the required depth for the second shade, and so on for the rest.
If this pattern contain large dark surfaces the engraved roller is
cleaned and re-varnished entirely, so as to fill the hollows with
varnish. It is afterwards ruled diagonally in either direction,
according to the requirement of the design, and the operation
carried on as above described.

[Printed, 3½d. No Drawing.]

A.D. 1853, December 6.—N° 2836.

JOHNSON, JOHN HENRY. — (Communicated by Benjamin
Underwood, of Brooklyn, U.S.)—" Improvements in printing oil-
" cloths and other fabrics."

. The invention consists " in providing a series of suitable move-
" able sections of wood, metal, or other material, and so arranging
" them together in forms or cases that they shall collectively con-
" stitute blocks, patterns, or devices, from which various orna-
" mental figures and designs in one or more colors may be printed
" upon oilcloths, carpets, and other fabrics, and from sections
" facsimile electrotype plates or casts may also be taken in metal
" or other suitable material, the said facsimile plates being also
" employed to print the said ornamental figures, thus avoiding the
" ordinary mode of producing said blocks, patterns, or devices,
" which is a slow and costly process."

[" The usual mode of producing the ordinary blocks, patterns,
" or devices " for the above purpose is described.]

The workman having the patterns before him, sets up the design
in a case, " in much the same manner that the printer sets up the
" ordinary printing types." For the purpose of holding the sections more securely the lower parts of them have " angular pro-
" jections on their under edges," which fit into correspondingly
shaped grooves in the case. If plain ended sections are used, they
require to be screwed up. The block thus formed is ready for
electrotyping, casting, or moulding. When required for cylindrical
printing, the plates cast from the composed blocks are bent round
a suitable cylinder, and thus may " be employed to print any kind
" of suitable fabrics, in much the same way that calico printing is
" performed." If sections without any projections are used, they
set up in the case " from the copy, just as the printer sets up the
" ordinary printing sections, and when the case is full, it is locked
" up in the manner before described. In this way a different
" ' block ' is made up for each color designated in the copy."

[Printed, 5½d. Drawings.]

A.D. 1853, December 7.—Nº 2842.

KNOX, ANDREW LAWSON.—(Provisional Protection refused.)
—" Improvements in ornamenting a certain description of textile
" fabric."

" My improvements relate to such fabrics as are ' raised ' by
" carding or other similar treatment upon one surface, and consist
" in producing patterns upon the other side thereof by printing,
" staining, embossing, or other such process."

[Printed, 2½d. No Drawing.]

### A.D. 1853, December 9.—N° 2870.

MORLEY, GIDEON.—(Provisional Protection only.)—" Orna-
" menting or producing pictures on japanned goods, pannels,
" covers, or other material whereby a vast amount of artistic skill
" and labour is superseded."

" The invention consists in first printing a sky or background
" suitable for the subject intended to be produced. And, next,
" printing in outline (on paper) from a copper or other plate, the
" intended subject in a suitable colour, the same to be transferred
" on or below the sky or background before mentioned. I next
" paint the shadows and other parts of such outline pictures with
" transparent or suitable colours, when I again have recourse to
" the process of printing and transferring, using the same colour
" as employed in the first printing, but the detail of the subject in
" this case must be fully defined. I then use the body colours
" and high lights in suitable places for giving effect, thus pro-
" ducing apparently a well finished painting."

[Printed, 2½d. No Drawing.]

### A.D. 1853, December 14.—N° 2895.

GRANT, PHILIP.—" Improvements in printing presses." These
improvements are calculated to economize time and labour.
The table of the press moves backwards and forwards in the
grooves, by rack and pinion, and chain, strap, and pulley, or similar
contrivance. The descent of the platen is caused by levers under the
framework of the press, acted upon by cams or excentrics fixed on
the main shaft and working against friction bowls on the lever
ends. The inking apparatus is partially self-acting by means of
rollers revolving in suitable bearings fixed on the side frames.
These rollers receive their supply from a doctor, and are either
made of the usual composition or covered with caoutchouc or
similar elastic material. Different colored inks are used at the
same time by fixing springs or blocks between the ink rollers on
the table upon which they revolve, the exact size or length of the
distance between the lines of letters or type which are of different
coloured ink, or by rollers suspended from suitable fixings and
elastic springs, so that when the type arrives under any inking
roller which is not required, the said roller will be raised up by
means of the springs or blocks, and fall down to its former position

when it has passed the said lines of letters on which it is not required to act. The feeding apparatus is also partially self-acting
by means of endless guides as conductors made of tape, cord, cloth,
parchment, or other suitable material worked on rollers. A light
frame is attached to the platen, from which frame cords, wires,
tapes, or similar materials are stretched across in the marginal
spaces between the type, and so connected with the platen that
when it rises they lift the paper from the type after the impression
is taken.

[Printed, 6½d. Drawings.]

A.D. 1853, December 14.—N° 2896.

GATTY, FREDERICK ALFRED, and KOPP, EMILE.—" Improve-
" ments in printing and dyeing cotton, wool, silk, and other fibrous
" substances."

The invention consists " in the use of lactic acid, and its neutral
" and acid salts, as substitutes for tartaric, citric, and other acids,
" and acid salts, when such acids and salts are used. 1. As a
" resist, printed on cloths, to be afterwards padded or printed over
" with mordants. 2. As a discharge, to be printed on cloths pre-
" viously impregnated with mordants. 3. To precipitate the red
" colouring matter of safflower from its alkaline solutions. 4. In
" dyeing silk and wool those colours to which vegetable acids or
" salts are required. 5. For the preparation of steam colors,
" especially those containing alkaline prussiates; and 6. As white
" and colored discharges upon Turkey red and other colors."

[Printed, 2½d. No Drawing.]

A.D. 1853, December 15.—N° 2913.

BRANSTON, FREDERICK WILLIAM.—" Improvements in
" certain tablets, labels, and signs, or their surfaces, exhibiting
" letters and designs."

These consist in manufacturing tablets, labels, and signs, more
especially such as are liable to exposure in the open air, exhibiting
letters, designs, or ornaments, " by the application of letterpress
" or other surface printing upon glass, in gold, silver, or other
" lustrous material, in combination with coatings of paint and
" encasements or backings of cement, as herein-after firstly
" described, and also by the application and use of ornamental

" letters and designs constructed as herein-after secondly described,
" in combination also with paint and backings of cement."

1. Having set the necessary letters to describe any particular
article, the types are " inked " with common gold size, and the
impression transferred on to glass, and while such transfer is wet,
gold or silver leaf, or other lustrous material, is placed thereon
according to taste. When dry the printed surface of the glass is
covered with paint of any desired colour, and after the paint is dry
it is covered all over with a suitable cement, such as will not injure
the paint. The tablet or label is then ready to be fixed in its
standard or frame for use.

2. Having printed the design on paper those portions of
the lettering which are intended to be formed into ornamental
letters are cut out, leaving portions of the printing to form the
shadowing to these ornamental letters. The paper with the
letters so cut out is then fixed with size to the under side of
the glass. Crushed metallic leaf or copper foil, or gold, silver,
bronze, or other metallic ornamental paper, or coloured papers,
satins, silks, or other textile materials are then fixed, according to
choice, behind the cut out spaces of the letters, and thereby, for
that which has been cut out, substitute glittering, or brilliant, or
ornamental, or coloured letters, with bold printed shadows which
are then seen through the glass, after which the whole is covered
with cement, as before, which has the effect of solidifying the glass
and preserving the ornamental letters from perishing and fading.

[Printed, 3½d. No Drawings.]


A.D. 1853, December 19.—N° 2948.

TREBELHORN, John, and BOLLEY, Pompeius, Dr.—" Im-
" provements in the process of bleaching vegetable fibrous sub-
" stances."

" In the bleaching of vegetable fibrous substances as hitherto
" practised, those substances have been subjected to boiling
" in the caustic alkaline solutions. Now, by the use of certain
" metallic solutions, such as the oxide of tin mixed with caustic
" alkaline in the bleaching of vegetable fibrous substances, whether
" it be bleaching of yarns or fabrics for the market, or the bleach-
" ing as a preparation for dyeing and printing, such boiling may
" be dispensed with."

[Printed, 2½d. No Drawings.]

A.D. 1853, December 16.—N° 2934.

KNOX, ANDREW LAWSON.—" Improvements in ornamenting
" certain descriptions of textile fabrics."

The invention relates to fabrics which are raised upon one
surface by carding or other similar treatment, and also to fabrics
which are woven with loops or other such raised loose threads on
one side, as terries for instance, and consists in producing patterns
upon the other sides of such fabrics by printing, staining, embossing, or other like process. The weaving and finishing of the
fabrics constitute no part of my invention. They may be produced
by any of the ordinary methods, and if intended for the first
mentioned class of goods carded on one side by the machinery
usually employed for that purpose, whereby a fabric is produced
known by the name of " swandown." Upon the other side, I
print the required design, as commonly practised for textile
fabrics.

[Printed, 2½d. No Drawing.]

A.D. 1853, December 22.—N° 2974.

BESNARD, LOUIS ADOLPHE FERDINAND.—(Provisional Protection only.)—" A new system of printing by means of litho-
" graphy without leaving a particle of paper upon the canvass."

" I take a prepared canvass thoroughly dry and smooth, I then
" lay the canvass in the press and place the sheet of paper with
" the drawing upon it on the canvass and press it, by which
" means the drawing is transferred to the canvass. I then take
" off the paper, I next wash the canvass over with a solution
" composed of half water and half gelatine, and dry it. The time
" occupied in drying varies with the temperature. This fixes the
" drawing. The proportions of the solution may be varied
" according to circumstances."

[Printed, 2½d. No Drawing.]

A.D. 1853, December 28.—N° 3012.

McNEE, DUNCAN, and BROADFOOT, ALEXANDER.—" Im-
" provements in printing with colors on cloth, which are also
" applicable to printing ornamental designs on paper or other
" surfaces."

The invention relates principally to the printing of handkerchiefs, shawls, plaids, and other similar articles by means of
a machine of the same kind as that figured and described in
No 952 of 1852, certain improvements being introduced into
the construction of that machine for the better distribution of
the colors to the printing rollers, namely, in the position of the
color box, which is placed at a lower level, and also in the construction of the same, whereby it can be more easily filled or
supplied with the printing color. " We also apply a contrivance
" for guiding the sieve of the machine parallelly on the stretching
" rollers, namely, by fixing one or more cords or rows of studs
" on its inner surface, which fall into corresponding grooves on
" the stretching rollers, and thereby prevent the sieve from
" shifting end-long on the rollers. We likewise attach guide
" wheels on the machine to insure its parallel movement on the
" printing table in the process of printing.

[Printed, 5½d. Drawings.]

## A.D. 1853, December 29.—No 3020.

ROUX, CLAUDE ALPHONSE.—"Improvements in printing warps
" or cut pile and similar fabrics."

The object of these improvements is to print warps for cut pile
and similar fabrics, firstly, so as to prevent the colour running
beyond the patterns at the edges; secondly, to prevent the
threads from shifting in their relative position after being
printed; thirdly, in more effectual and cheaper ways of printing
than have been employed in printing. These objects are attained
by, firstly, printing warp for cut pile and similar fabrics, by
means of hollow parallelopipeds or tubes closed at the bottom
with felt or other suitable material, these tubes being filled with
the colors required, and put together or composed so as to
form the design, an impression of which is produced by pistons
acting simultaneously on the colors in the tubes as described
above; secondly, applying the jacquard machine to printing warp
for cut pile and similar fabrics; thirdly, printing warp for cut
pile and similar fabrics by means of color troughs and perforated parallelopipeds or pistons as described.

[Printed, 7½d. Drawings.]

A.D. 1853, December 30.—N° 3024.

LORD, James.—(Provisional Protection refused.)—" Improve-
" ments in manufacturing, ornamenting, and applying fabrics for
" articles of clothing, and in the application of certain fabrics to
" such purposes, and in producing shapes for articles of clothing."

The invention " refers, firstly, to the production of ornamental
" designs or other effects, by weaving, printing, or other process
" upon fabrics intended to be used for articles of clothing, with
" the said designs or effects around the body, and consists in
" producing the same during the operation of weaving or sub-
" sequently thereto in the direction of the selvages of the goods."

The other heads of the invention are, making up articles of
clothing with the warp threads around the body " so that fewer
" seams will be required," application of a fustian with strips or
patches to petticoats, producing shapes for chemises or under-
shirts, petticoats, and shirts. The last-mentioned articles are
produced by the application of three distinct warp rollers, the
threads from the centre one being for the body, and those on
either side for the sleeves.

[Printed, 2½d. No Drawing.]

# 1854.

A.D. 1854, January 5.—N° 22.

SCHISCHKAR, Edward, and CALVERT, Frederick Crace.
—" Improvements in dyeing and printing textile fabrics and
" yarns."

The invention consists in imparting to them a bright metallic
lustre or glossy appearance, by impregnating them with sulphates
or metallic oxides of copper, lead, or bismuth, and decomposing
such sulphates or oxides, by means of sulphuretted hydrogen, in
an apparatus as much as possible confined or hermetically closed.

[Printed, 4d. No Drawing.]

### A.D. 1854, January 6.—No 31.

TAIT, ROBERT. — (Provisional Protection only.) — " Improve-
" ments in the manufacture or production of ornamental fabrics."

The invention relates to fabrics of the " zebra " class, wherein
the ornamental patterns or devices are produced by a combination
of figure weaving and colour printing. " Such fabrics are woven
" by means of any suitable figure-working machinery, with one
" side flushed or back-lashed, whilst the other or pattern side has
" a pattern or device thrown up upon it by the weaving action.
" This latter or figured surface is afterwards printed with the
" desired colour, pattern, or ornament in two differrent and
" totally distinct designs."

[Printed, 3d. No Drawing.]

### A.D. 1854, January 7.—No 42.

CARALLI, NICHOLAS MICHEL.—(Provisional Protection only.)
—" Improvements in the manufacture or production of orna-
" mental fabrics."

The invention relates to " zebra " fabrics. " A plain, twilled,
" or other fabric is used as the material for producing this duplex
" pattern, no flushing or back-lashing being used. Such fabric
" is then printed by any of the known means, with a distinct
" pattern or device in the zebra or similar style, on each side, so
" that the piece answers the end of showing two dissimilar styles
" of ornamentation."

[Printed, 3d. No Drawings.]

### A.D. 1854, January 7.—No 44.

EDWARDS, HENRY SUTHERLAND.—(Provisional Protection
only.)—(Communicated.)—" Improvements in preparing textile
" fabrics, or materials for the purpose of their better retaining
" colours applied to them."

The invention consists in passing them through a bath of
water holding in solution alum, sulphate of zinc, protochloride of
tin, caustic potash, and nitric acid, or other similar chemicals.
These ingredients are separately dissolved, and then mixed, the
nitric acid being added after the mixing.

[Printed, 3d. No Drawing.]

WILKINSON, John.—(Provisional Protection only.)—" Im-
" provements in the manufacture of dies for producing printing
" surfaces for calico printers; applicable also for embossing."

" The surface upon which the design is to be produced, is
" coated with the ordinary etching wax, and part of the pattern
" etched thereon by passing the tracer of the pantograph over
" the design; the outline thus produced is bitten in in the usual
" manner, and a print or tracing obtained therefrom, which is
" now transferred to the tracing point of the pantograph, and
" the etched plate, with another etching ground, returned to its
" former place. By now passing the tracing point over a ground
" work, or other second portion of the design taken on a trans-
" parent surface, and placed upon the impression first obtained,
" that second portion of the design will also be etched upon the
" metal surface first operated upon, the print or other impression
" obtained therefrom acting as a scale to register the several
" portions of the design. Secondly, my invention consists in a
" method of making the roller, dies, or tools for impressing
" printing surfaces. Having obtained the proper length of
" design to correspond to the periphery of the roller to be
" impressed, I plane away or otherwise remove the metal surface
" at each end of the said length of design, so as to leave it
" raised above the general surface, by which means the plain part
" is prevented from pressing out the pattern imparted to the
" roller, tool, or die."

[Printed, 3d. No Drawing.]

GRANT, Philip.—(Provisional Protection only.)—" An im-
" proved roller used in the processes of letter-press, copper-plate,
" and lithographic printing."

The roller is covered with caoutchouc or other elastic material,
instead of composition, in order to make it " more durable, and
" consequently economise the expense of it."

[Printed, 3d. No Drawing.]

BROWN, William. — (Provisional Protection only.)—" Improvements in printing machinery."

The invention relates to machinery, by which letter-press and other printing can be executed in two or more colors, " without " the sheet of paper being detached from the printing cylinder."

" I do not alter the framework or arrangements for inking " common to ordinary printing machines, but I use a smaller " cylinder, making a number of revolutions, one for each color: " and the tables (of which there is likewise one to each color) are " placed equidistant from the same point on the cylinder. The " mode of holding the sheet of paper is by the common gripper " motion, and to this I apply a cam worked by a rod connected " to a crank, whereby the cam is thrown up to engage the sheet " of paper on the cylinder at the proper time, and after the " proper number of revolutions of the cylinder, the cam is thrown " down to disengage it, and during the time the sheet of paper " is in its progress the cam lies betweeu the engaging and dis- " engaging points."

[Printed, 3d. No Drawing.]

A.D. 1854, January 25.—No 190.

REID, ARCHIBALD LOCKHART.—" Improvements in printing " textile and other surfaces."

The invention relates particularly to printing on muslins and other piece goods, devices which are to be subsequently embroidered, and consists in the use of a continuously revolving roller of zinc or composition metal, on which the pattern has been produced " in the usual manner," and which by its action against a counter-pressure roller, an inking and a damping apparatus are in contact with the printing roller, the former consisting of a trough roller engraved " in such a manner as to " take up a definite quantity of color, which it transmits by two " intermediate wooden clothed rollers to the printing surface. " Instead of using a metallic surface for printing in the manner " herein-before described, a roller coated with isinglass or other " similar matter or composition may be used, the pattern being " indented or engraved upon the isinglass surface so as to take " up the necessary ink or colour." The counter-pressure roller may be dispensed with, the fabric being in that case stretched on a table or flat surface. The printing apparatus is then supported on a carriage, and made to traverse over the fabric beneath it;

" or the printing apparatus may be fixed, whilst the table upon
" which the fabric is stretched is traversed below it in receiving
" the impression."

[Printed, 10d. Drawings.]


A.D. 1854, January 27.—N° 202.

SIMENCOURT, Alphonse Cajetan de.—"Improvements in
" composing and distributing type."

In the composing machine the types are ranged upright in
inclined open cases, and made to slide down by a weight. At the
bottom of these cases are a series of " nippers" of peculiar construction, which embrace the lowest type. By depressing a finger
stop on the upper arm of the nipper a type is withdrawn from its
compartment. As soon as the finger is removed from the stop the
type drops through a hopper, the nipper opening by the introduction of a cone, and is received in its upright position on a " jus-
" tifier" in the composing stick. Similar mechanism is employed
for distributing the type. The dead matter being placed on an
inclined plate, a line of it is caused to drop (by the rising of a
hinged blade which cuts it off) into a narrow box, carried by a
sliding piece, which runs along a rail above the several compartments of the type store. Nippers (similar to those used in the
composing machine) on the sliding piece seize the foremost type,
which, when the finger rests upon a stop, falls into the lower part
of the sliding piece, and thence into the several boxes of the case.

[Printed, 1s. 9d. Drawings.]


A.D. 1854, January 31.—N° 241.

MEEUS, Pierre Joseph.—"Improvements in producing me-
" tallic surfaces."

1. Articles composed of gum, gutta percha, caoutchouc, and
similar substances are gilt, &c. by applying gold or other metallic
leaf to them under heat and pressure. Other articles required
to be gilt or coated with metal are covered with gum, gutta
percha, caoutchouc, or similar substance, to which a coating of
gold or other metal has been transferred. The same heat and
pressure that on one side attach the metallic leaf attach on the
other side the stuff which is to be ornamented with the em-

broidery, &c. By painting on the metallized surfaces with coloured and transparent varnishes, an effect resembling mother of pearl is produced in the case of silver and white metals, and warmer tones in the case of gold and darker ones. The four operations are performed by an apparatus composed of four cylinders, *a*, *b*, *c*, *d*. The cylinder *a* receives a strip of sheet gutta percha, and is so heated as to render the gutta percha adhesive. The cylinder *b* receives a strip of gold or silver (either plain or figured) at the corresponding point. The pressure of the cylinders *a* and *b* forms gilt streaks or stripes, which are deposited on the fabric which is brought by the compressing cylinder *c* on to the gutta percha, while still in a soft state. Thence the fabric passes down between the colouring cylinder *d*, which imparts to the metallic stripes or streaks the pearly appearance desired. Ribbons, gold and silver lace, and trimmings of every description, are similarly produced.

2. Several methods are described of imitating embroidery and embossed or figured goods of all descriptions on yielding fabrics and bodies, and the production of ribbons, trimmings, braid, gold or silver lace, fringes, and articles of the like description, in gold, silver, platinum, or other metals, either plain or coloured, tinted or shaded, so as to resemble mother of pearl, &c.

[Printed, 4*d*. No Drawing.]


A.D. 1854, February 2.—N° 265.

GLASSFORD, JOHN HAMILTON.—"Improvements in litho-" graphic and zincographic printing."

A flat stone, having the design upon it, is placed on a carriage with reciprocating motion. It is periodically furnished by rollers supplied from a stationary inking slab at one end of the press. Near the centre of the framing is a frame holding a damping surface, and jointed at its two ends to two crank pins on the tops of a pair of vertical shafts. As the stone is passed beneath this damper the revolution of the shafts produces upon it a most efficient damping traverse in curvilinear lines. Adjoining this is an adjustable scraper, set in side standards. The scraping edge is hinged with a back stop, so that as the stone passes beneath it the stop acts, and causes the edge to stand fast, whilst, on returning, the hinge yields, and allows the stone to pass freely to be damped and inked, the front edge of which is slightly bevilled.

The tympan is also self-acting, being set on a hinged centre, on a piece having a short traverse action, so that as the printing stone comes forward it folds down the tympan over the stone. To aid this movement the framing carries curved guides, over which pulleys, on the edges of the tympan, are contrived to work. This enables the tympan to be turned backward and forward, so as to come on to and lift off the stone at each traverse of the latter, without shocks. Fabrics, when printed in lengths, are wound upon a roller at the printing end of the framing, and drawn forward through a slot in the tympan, and wound up when printed, by means of self-acting rollers. Or they may be passed in the opposite direction; that is to say, being unwound from a roller between the scraper and the inking details, and passing over the stone to a taking-up roller on the other side of the scraper; or again, the delivery roller may be carried by the tympan frame. The whole of the movements are actuated by a single continuously revolving shaft overhead, and suitable cams or clutches are provided for effecting the several intermittent motions. The inking and damping apparatus, disposed as above, may be made to supply two stones. "The same general process is pursued when the "zincographic system is adopted."

[Printed, 1s. 5d. Drawings.]

A.D. 1854, February 6.—No. 287.

MEERE, Auguste Louis Nicolas Comte Van Der.—"The "manufacture of artificial whalebone, or a substance capable of "being employed as a substitute for whalebone and tortoise shell."

The invention consists in softening horn, and rendering it flexible like ordinary whalebone, by means of glycerine, or other similar chemical agent. The horn is shaped or moulded to the required forms, and immersed in a mixture of white wine or other suitable alcholic liquid, and nitric or other acid, and afterwards immersed in water for several days.

The substance thus produced is stated to be well adapted (among other things) for the binding of books. "Sheets of the "prepared horn," called from its flexibility "artificial whalebone," may be "engraved and employed for printing upon paper, calico, "or other substances."

[Printed, 4d. No Drawing.]

### A.D. 1854, February 6.—Nº 289.

**GRAHAM, James Balie.**—" Improvements in the production
" of printing surfaces."

The invention " relates especially to the blocks or rollers used
" for printing textile and other goods.  The matrix of the printing
" surface is formed out of a series of metal pins of any suitable
" section, firmly and regularly bound up into one mass, the ends
" of the whole series being coincident or in plane.  The operator
" then, having his pattern before him, depresses such of the pins
" as are intended to print.  He thus produces the intended figure
" in intaglio, the pins left standing at their primary level corre-
" sponding to the ground or surface not intended to print ; a cast
" taken from this matrix in gutta percha, type metal, or other
" material, forms the printing surface.  As all the pins are of the
" same length, it is obvious that the pins pushed down or depressed
" at one end appear prominent at the reverse face, hence the
" operator has the power of making reverse or counterpart printing
" surfaces simultaneously, the two being in exact correspondence
" with each other.  If desired, the actual pin surfaces themselves
" might be used as the printing medium.  And in casting or
" moulding from such matrices, either the first mould being a
" a reverse of the matrix may be (*a*) [used, or a second mould may
" be] taken from the first to present a printing surface exactly
" like the matrix itself.  Printing surfaces so produced may be
" employed either as blocks or as surface rollers, and they may
" be used as *intaglio* printing surfaces, by arranging them to
" print from the sunk parts, just as in cylinder printing.  When
" the matrix pins have been used for one design they may be
" dressed up to a plane surface for future operations."

[Printed, 7*d*.  Drawings.]

### A.D. 1854, February 13.—Nº 342.

**BROWN, William.**—(Provisional Protection only.)—" Improve-
" ments in printing machinery."

Two horizontal platens are placed one above the other, both
working on column guides, and actuated by crank rods.  At each
end of the machine is a drum, raised and lowered in the same

---

(*a*) The part within brackets is omitted in the Complete Specification.

times as the platens, and over them passes an endless band carrying the paper frames fitted with grippers and tapes, the guides of the platens carry two conical pins, which enter cones in the bands so as to ensure accurate register. The paper cylinder is driven by a connecting rod in one direction only, the backward movement of the rod taking place during the impression. Upon the main columns are suitable guides carrying friskets (one to each platen), which rise sufficiently to allow of the inking rollers acting. The inking rollers remain stationary during the change of the sheets.

" The frames which carry the inking rollers work in suitable bear-
" ings on each side of the machine, and carry an inner frame with
" the rollers, which, after having inked the form, fall upon a
" cylinder below, in order to gain their next supply of ink and to
" be below the endless bands during the impression. The frames
" are actuated by toothed wheels, working in a rack fixed on each
" side of the said frames, the backward and forward motion being
" given through teeth wheels from a crank placed between the
" frames of the machine. The inking apparatus may be any of
" the ordinary construction. In order to carry the sheet perfectly
" flat during its progress, I use tapes or bands of vulcanised india-
" rubber."

[Printed, 3d. No Drawing.]

A.D. 1854, February 9.—N° 310.

DALTON, JOHN.—" Improvements in the construction of bowls
" or cylinders employed in printing and other processes, and
" which improvements may also be adapted to other mechanical
" appliances."

The invention consists in constructing the above of segments of wood having the fibres or grain placed vertically to the centre.

[Printed, 7d. Drawings.]

A.D. 1854, February 9.—N° 316.

BOILEAU, EUGENE.—" Improvements in producing raised
" printing surfaces."

The object of the invention is to produce plain and coloured ornamental designs, chiefly checks and plaids, upon paper and other materials, by the use of types. Its chief advantages (independently of the facility of varying the pattern) are, first, that a pattern in one color, with cross lines, such as a plaid, can be printed from a raised surface at one operation instead of two, the lines being ordinarily produced by "rules" which at one printing will only give lines running in one direction; secondly, that in color printing "a more brilliant effect than heretofore" may be obtained, inasmuch as the colors may be applied without crossing each other, and thus each color will throughout its surface retain its primitive appearance. "In order to produce a raised surface from which "to print a plaid pattern in one colour from a type (in the "way ordinarily practised by type founders) containing the outer "lines of two sides of a square, and all the inner lines included in "the pattern, and by means of repeats of this type I am enabled "to produce a raised printing surface, the pattern of which may "be modified, according to the taste of the printer, by varying "the mode of arranging the types. To print the same pattern of "plaid in colours, I form types with a given portion of the pattern "on their surface, and other types with another given portion, "and so on, according to the elaborateness of the pattern and the "number of colours designed to be reproduced, making the set of "types represent the complete pattern; and having set up these "several kinds of type in different chases, but, according to one "given arrangement, I work off so much of the pattern as each "contains in different colours on the same material, whereby I re- "produce the complete pattern in various colours, as desired."

[Printed, 1s. 2d. Drawings, containing specimens in color and gold.]

A.D. 1854, February 13.—N° 348.

BROWN, SAMUEL RUSSELL.—(Provisional Protection only.)— "Improvements in printing textile fabrics and other surfaces."

The invention relates to a system of relief or surface printing, more especially applicable to "sewed muslins." The pattern or device is primarily produced in intaglio by "Wright's mould- "making machine," or other suitable contrivance. From this a cast is taken in type metal, gutta percha, or other material, which cast is in the form of a flat plate, with the pattern in relief. The cast is then bent round a roller, and the muslins or other goods printed by it "according to any of the existing systems "of roller or cylinder printing."

[Printed, 3d. No Drawing.]

WRIGHT, WILLIAM. — (Provisional Protection only.)— " Im-
" provements in ornamenting walls and other similar surfaces."

These consist in producing designs on the above by means of
moulds charged with " any suitable plastic but non-resilient ma-
" terial." Having painted the surface with a ground color or
flat tint, a metal mould, the section of which is of the form of the
design, is charged with putty. The bottom of the mould is then
covered with paint of any required color, and being applied to the
wall, &c., and instantly removed, leaves the design printed.

[Printed, 3d. No Drawing.]

A.D. 1854, February 18.—N° 392.

WELLS, BENJAMIN WESTON.— " Improvements in printing
" floor and other cloths."

The invention consists in obtaining " solid work " by imparting
pressure to the printed pattern while the colors are in a moist
state, by means of a block or blocks containing a counterpart in
colors of each pattern. By this means the necessity of a double
set of pattern blocks, and consequently double printing from
pattern blocks, is avoided.

[Printed, 3d. No Drawing.]

A.D. 1854, February 20.—N° 406.

MELVILLE, WILLIAM.—(Provisional Protection only.)—" Im-
" provements in printing textile fabrics and other surfaces."

The invention consists :—First, in dispensing with the usual
" angle or meter " cuts for producing the blanks at the corners of
shawls and other fabrics, by removing or bevilling off from the
table the parts at which the fabric is not to be printed, so that as
the roller traverses over the piece the impression misses at those
parts. " In this system of printing the printing roller is dispensed
" with, its impression surface in the same plane or coincident with
" the particular slopes or inclines of the borders of the table, so
" that as each border is printed, the surface is accurately covered,
" whilst at the termination of that slope and the commencement
" of the one adjoining it, the latter being out of the roller's plane
" is missed by the roller." The printing tables may be either

fixed or traversing. The same system is applicable to a drum or large cylinder surface, by which a great number of pieces can be printed at once in a very small space by arranging the drum with " circumferential recesses, in addition to the angular recesses " before referred to. The pieces can thus be each contracted by " being drawn into the circumferential recesses, so that two of the " borders only (in printing borders) are left exposed to the print-" ing surface."

Fabrics may be printed on both sides by placing them in two wire gauze frames which hold them at an uniform tension.

In the case of the drum, the necessary "stopping-out" cuts may be accomplished by the use of a piece of thin copper disposed above the fabric and the drum, and having a self-acting movement for withdrawing it as the other roller passes over it. The copper is cleaned by a "doctor."

Fabrics are ornamented by printing a device in adhesive matter, and then printing gold or other metallic pigment over it by another block or roller which fixes such pigment.

[Printed, 3d. No Drawing.]

A.D. 1854, February 24.—No 451.

FISHER, CYRIL JEDDERE.—(Provisional Protection only.)—" Improved means of detecting forged and counterfeit bank notes, " bills of exchange, cheques, or other documents, labels. or trade " marks."

" My invention consists simply in printing on the notes, bills, " or other documents, labels, or trade marks, impressions taken on " metal plates from feathers, insects, the leaves of plants or other " natural objects or artificial or manufactured articles. The means " whereby impressions of natural objects are obtained on metal " plates are well known, but any plan whereby such impressions " may be obtained may be employed for the purpose.

"The object of the invention and of the application to the above " purposes of such impressions obtained in any convenient and " suitable manner, is to obtain a design which cannot by any " known means be copied with sufficient accuracy to defy detec-" tion, and which cannot be reproduced even by adopting similar " or analogous means to those originally employed for the " purpose."

[Printed, 3d. No Drawing.]

A.D. 1854, February 25.—N° 462.

KEENAN, JAMES.—(Communicated.)—" Improvements in form-
" ing blocks or surfaces for printing."

The invention consists in obtaining a printing surface by
cementing sheets of wood, felt, or other suitable substance cemented to a block after the pattern has been cut through them
by means of a saw "such as is used for cutting scrolls and other
" forms." When felt is used, it is first saturated with a solution
of shellac and pressed, and afterwards coated with rosin and pitch
by the aid of heat and subjected to pressure.

[Printed, 6d. Drawings.]

A.D. 1854, March 4.—N° 529.

ABATE, FELIX.—" Improvements in printing on and ornamenting
" surfaces."

The invention consists in various processes for making imitations
or representations of natural and artificial objects by printing them
with the objects themselves. The surface of the object is wetted with
diluted acid, or acid salt, or exposed to the vapours of an acid. An
impression is then taken on wood, calico, paper, or other vegetable
substance, and exposed for a few moments to a strong heat. Or
it is wetted with a "non-crystallizable" mordant, and the article
printed with it afterwards dyed. Or the article is first dyed and
printed on with a discharging fluid. A fabric may be imitated by
the above processes by embossing a sheet of tinfoil upon the fabric
through pressure between two sheets of vulcanized india-rubber,
and then passing the sheet of tinfoil through a bath made of dyeing stuff, thickened with any adhesive and transparent mixture,
such as glue, gum, sugar, lichen, &c. When the surface to be
printed on is hard or curved the impression is previously taken on
a sheet of vulcanized india-rubber stretched on a frame, and the
sheet laid upon such surface. A cushion of vulcanized india-rubber
or gutta percha filled with water is then laid upon the sheet, and
on this cushion is laid a block of the exact shape of the surface.
Lastly, the whole is subjected to the action of the press. "Or,
" also, I paint on a thin sheet of glue and sugar or lichen,
" or any other soluble and adhesive composition, and I stick this
" on the article."

[Printed, 4d. No Drawing.]

A.D. 1854, March 6.—No 593.

RONALD, John.—(Provisional Protection only.) — " Improve-
" ments in printing yarns and threads."

Instead of causing a carriage with a color box and roller to pass
across from end to end of the drum on which the yarn or thread is
wound, giving the impression to the yarn or thread as it passes
under the drum, the color is " impressed upon the yarn or thread
" by means of a series of parallel rollers brought into contact with
" the yarn wound upon a drum. These rollers extend from end
" to end of the drum, each roller being partially immersed in
" colour contained in a colour trough, the rollers corresponding
" in number with the number of colours required for a pattern."

[Printed, 3d. No Drawing.]

A.D. 1854, March 8.—No 556.

DEVINCENZI, Guiseppe.—(Provisional Protection only.)—
" An improvement in producing ornamented and figured surfaces
" and surfaces for printing from."

The invention relates to " nature printing." The object to be
reproduced is placed upon a hard surface, and a copper plate,
previously softened, by annealing or otherwise, laid over it. The
whole is then submitted to strong pressure, when the impression
of the object will be produced upon the plate, which during the
process becomes hard, and fit for printing from, or for a matrix
from which to produce impressions or embossing in softened
copper and in other metals and substances. The plate so reproduced from the first copper plate may also be employed to reproduce a facsimile of the original plate by a repetition of the first
process, without, however, the intervention of any substance between the metals. Again, the softened plate, with the design or
object produced thereon, may itself be employed as an ornamented
metal surface.

[Printed, 3d. No Drawings.]

A.D. 1854, March 10.—No 581.

NEWTON, Alfred Vincent.—(Provisional Protection only.)—
(Communication.)—" Improvements in the manufacture of raised
" printing surfaces."

The figures required are cut out in whole or in sections from thin sheets of felt, of wood, or other suitable substance of the thickness of the required relief, and are then secured by glue, cement, or other suitable means to the face of the printing block or cylinder. The felt is saturated with a solution of gum shellac in alcohol, and then compressed; and, finally, the printing surface is coated with rosin or pitch and turpentine, over which a hot iron is passed to smooth the surface, and cause the overlying substances to penetrate the material.

[Printed, 3d. No Drawing.]

A.D. 1854, March 16.—N° 628.

POISSON, Cyprien, and MARTIN, Louis Jacques.—(Provisional Protection only.)—(Partly communicated by Henri Louis Talle of Paris.)—" Improvements in printing fabrics."

"The object of our invention is to fix colors on fabrics.

### Description of the Process.

" 1st. Preparation of the fabrics. 1°. In a pint and three-" quarters (un litre) of water, mixed with a pint and three-quarters " (un litre) of liquid ammonia or volatile alkali, we steep the fabrics " for ten minutes, and dry them, after which we imprint with " colours, as follows :—

" 2d. Preparation of the said colour. 2°. We take five parts " of baked linseed oil, and one part of liquid ammonia; we grind " the colour, and then imprint the fabrics either in the manner " used by lithographers, or with the ordinary machines of cotton " printers.

" 3rd. When the fabrics have been prepared and printed as above " directed, two days after the printing we make two separate baths, " one composed of four ounces and a half (125 grammes) of rock " alum dissolved in a pint and three-quarters (1 litre) of water, " and the other composed of a pint and three-quarters (1 litre) " of liquid ammonia mixed in a pint and three-quarters (1 litre) " of water.

" 4th. The fabrics, when printed, are passed through the alum " bath, and immediately afterwards through the alkali bath, in " order to obtain a precipitate of alumina upon the fabrics, which " perfectly fixes the colour.

" We preserve the right of using all the alkalies, either in crystal
" or liquid, either in the preparation of colours, or for saponifying
" or for steeping the fabrics."

[Printed, 3d. No Drawings.]

A.D. 1854, March 20.—N° 661.

PERKINS, JOSEPH.—" Improvements in metallurgy, especially
" applicable to the production of type and ornamental forms."

The mould of an original, taken in gutta percha or other plastic
substance, is rendered conducting, and placed in connexion with
a battery to receive an electro deposit. When the surface has
been so covered, instead of increasing the deposit till the metal is
of sufficient strength to allow the cast to be relieved from the
mould, the raw surface of the back of the electrotype is wetted
with a saturated solution of zinc in hydrochloric acid or other
equivalent solution, and a sufficient quantity of some metallic
alloy run in " in the ordinary manner," when the cast is completed,.
and may be detached from the mould. Where such casting has to
be made in parts, the alloy may, by being heated, be made to act as
solder.

[Printed, 3d. No Drawing.]

A.D. 1854, March 20.—N° 662.

PERKINS, JOSEPH.—(Provisional Protection only.)—" Improve-
" ments in working metals, especially adapted for producing
" surfaces to blocks for printing calicoes, silks, paper, and other
" fabrics."

The pattern is made on a plate of tinned metal. The outline is
formed of strips of brass, and the other parts of pieces of brass,
and between those are placed pieces of zinc. Heat is then applied
so as to cause the tinned surface to take hold of and solder the
under edges to the whole of the patterns : and when this is fully
soldered and firmly fixed, the upper surface is " cleaned off," 'so as
to produce the desired level. The whole work is then immersed in
dilute sulphuric or muriatic acid, or other solvent that will dissolve the zinc without injuring the other portions of the work.
" For plates for Bandanna presses and discharge printing, it will
" be necessary to prepare a plate and cut away right through the
" same at the parts where the pattern is to appear. In preparing

" other articles, such as open work, I dispense with the solid plate
" aforesaid, merely connecting the pieces of brass and zinc together
" with solder."

[Printed, 3d. No Drawing.]

## A.D. 1854, March 25.—No 698.

LOCHHEAD, James, and PASSENGER, Robert.—" Improve-
" ments in the manufacture of glass or other vitrified substances."

This is described as " in some measure a perfecting " of a
former patent (No 396 of 1852), and consists:—1. In the manufacture of glass or other vitrified substances by the use of two
or more cylinders placed in or under cover of a furnace or kiln,
the lower cylinder being plain, and the upper cylinder furnished
with teeth which lay hold of the semi-fluid glass.  2. In a means
of re-heating glass or other vitrified substance, in order to perforate, print, or impress the same, the latter operation being
effected by passing them through double cylinders, one or both
of which are engraved with the pattern to be produced.  3. The
glass in its molten or semi-molten state is prevented from
adhering to the cylinders or tables' by means of knives.  4. The
metal is, while in the furnace, transferred from the large or " jour-
" ney " pot commonly used, by which the metal can be brought
in the quantities required for use, besides which the metal is purified
by the transfer.

[Printed, 9d. Drawings.]

## A.D. 1854, April 1.—No 752.

JOHNSON, John Henry. — (Communicated.) — " Improve-
" ments in printing fabrics, and in the machinery or apparatus
" employed therein."

The invention " relates to the application of caoutchouc, either
" more or less hard, in combination or not with other matters, or
" gutta percha, when hardened in a similar way, to the manufac-
" ture of printing rollers or cylinders."  A cylinder of wood or
metal is covered with a coat of prepared caoutchouc in a soft
state, and then submitted to a high degree of heat, " as described
" by Charles Goodyear in his several patents for the manufacture
" of a hard material from caoutchouc."  The cylinders thus
hardened are " engraved in intaglio or relief," in the same manner

as ordinary copper printing cylinders or rollers, and as such coating contains a large amount of acid, may be used in printing with acid as a direct printing medium, and a white figure may thus be printed direct upon a blue or other colored ground.

[Printed, 3d. No Drawing.]

A.D. 1854, April 3.—No 763.

DEVINCENZI, Giuseppe.—" Improvement in producing orna-" mented and figured surfaces for printing from, also the harden-" ing or preparing of certain objects to be employed in the " process."

1. Plates or surfaces of metals and alloys are softened so as to receive by pressure sunk impressions of natural or manufactured objects, and then hardened so as to render them fit for printing from, either by an independent process, or by the compression to which they are subjected in receiving the said impressions.

2. The design is drawn upon a softened metallic plate with varnish or other adhesive matter, with which are incorporated some hard granular or molecular substances,* and impressed upon such plate by pressure, or upon hard steel, paper, or other substance, and impressed into a softened plate. In some cases impressions are taken of drawings upon soft metals, either to obtain an ornamentation thereon or to obtain a mould for reproducing by the galvano-plastic process or stereotyping, or even for printing from direct.

3. Soft substances, such as wood, flesh, &c. are hardened for the above mode of treatment by saturating them with bichloride of mercury and chloride of ammonium, or submitting them to dry heat.

[Printed, 4d. No Drawing.]

A.D. 1854, April 4.—No 777.

GLASSFORD, John Hamilton. — " Improvements in litho-" graphic and zincographic printing."

The essential feature of this invention is the use of an automatic cam beneath the table, which, at the proper period of the table's

---

* Dr. Franklin's method, see ante, p. 93 (n.)

traverse, brings up the stone or plate upon it so as to be acted upon by a fixed scraper. The front entering edge of the stone is bevilled to allow of easy admission beneath the scraper. "The " common press may also be modified to produce a somewhat " similar effect, by using a moveable scraper, as at present, but " connected to the traverse movement of the press in such " manner as to be brought into action at the moment of com- " mencing to print."

[Printed, 7d. Drawings.]

## A.D. 1854, April 5.—Nº 780.

ROSS, GEORGE.—(Communicated.) — "An improved mode of " preventing the alteration of bank bills from one denomination " to another."

The invention consists in impressing paper, while in a pulpy state, with the denomination of the bill or note by means of water-lining or printing thereon in the ordinary way by wire secured to the vellum, or by types slightly raised on the surface of the cylinder. The characters may be printed in colors and in such a manner as will ensure the color sinking deep into and entirely penetrating the body of the paper by means of a cylinder, with points upon its surface points set close to each other in lines forming the desired figures. The holes made by the points are instantly closed by pressure rollers.

[Printed, 3d. No Drawing.]

## A.D. 1854, April 5.—Nº 781.

NEWTON, WILLIAM EDWARD. — (Communicated.) — "Im- " proved apparatus for printing piece goods or fabrics."

This invention consists in the combination of a series of blocks fixed to a table or stationary platen, with an endless chain register, by which any number of colors may be simultaneously applied, and a section of the figure completed each time the blocks are depressed; the blocks are moved out on each side of the machine on horizontal bars by means of cog-wheels and racks. The fabric is fed forward by hooks upon the endless chain over the sur- face of the table between each impression a distance equal to the width or length of the blocks. The blocks are connected with their carriages by means of pins and springs, which recover them after the impression, ready to be withdrawn for receiving color.

A slow motion is given to the blocks as they move in, and a rapid one as they move out, by means of a sector or its equivalent. The color is applied to them at one end of their course, and the impression taken when they are at the other.

[Printed, 10*d*. Drawings.]

## A.D. 1854, April 7.—N° 817.

JOHNSON, JOHN ROBERT.—" Improvements in the manufacture of type and other raised surfaces for printing."

The object of the invention is to obtain " harder, tougher, and " more enduring type and raised surfaces for printing," by employing tin in large proportions with antimony, and so greatly reducing or wholly omitting the use of lead with such metals. Type thus produced "is so hard, tough, and enduring, as to " allow of its being used as a punch on the ordinary type-metal " now used." The best proportions are tin (75) and antimony (25). " When lead is used, it must not exceed fifty parts in a hundred " of the combined metals employed."

[Printed, 3*d*. No Drawing.]

## A.D. 1854, April 13.—N° 868.

DEVINCENZI, GIUSEPPE.— " A method or methods of pro- " ducing engraved, figured, and typographic surfaces for printing " and embossing from, and for ornaments, also certain machinery " employed therein."

The invention consists, first, in producing, on metallic or non-metallic surfaces, printing surfaces or moulds for the same from prints, engravings, drawings, MSS., &c. The surface should be steel, copper, zinc, or a hard alloy, polished and free from grease. On this the design is (*a*) drawn with lithographic pencil or ink, (*b*) written on paper with the same, and transferred to it, or (*c*) drawn on lithographic stone or zinc, and the necessary number of copies for transfer obtained. (*d*) The print or engraving to be transferred is damped with acidulated water or gum water, and in that state has greasy matter (tallow or stearine dissolved in oil of lavender, or wax, pitch, colophony, or asphalte diluted with oil of lavender,) applied to it with a sponge or brush. The paper is then washed and dried, after which it is again damped with thin gum water, and transferred. (*e*) " I use " for such transferring purposes printed work, which I obtain by

" means of my printing machines before mentioned, ($f$) and,
" finally, I obtain these impressions in a greasy matter by a
" photographic process, by producing by the action of light,
" either direct on such surfaces, or on a lithographic stone, to
" transfer from afterwards an impression of any bituminous or
" resinous substances." The greasy designs thus made are
inked with varnish (asphalte, turpentine, and wax), or common
printing ink, " by a process precisely similar for that used for
" inking in zincography and lithography. Or the impression
" may be inked with any varnish, and dusted over with rosin
" powder, or any vitrifiable or fusible matter, which is afterwards
" melted by heat." Surfaces thus prepared are used as electro-
positive metals, or as positive electrodes, in connexion with a
galvanic battery, by which they become engraved in all portions
not covered by the non-conducting impressions. Or the metallic
surface may be covered by electro deposit with another metal, on
which impressions are produced by the above means. The first
surface is employed as a positive electrode, and the layer thus
removed wherever there is no impression.

By means of these various processes, perforated sheets of metal
are produced suitable for inlaid work. The sunken parts being
filled up by electro deposit, or with shellac, &c., the plates may
be used as name plates, &c. The same effects can be produced
by acids as by the electro-chemicals, the substances most suitable
to act upon being stone. " And by the same processes I obtain
" on glass or crystal either engraved ornamental work, or
" engraving for printing purposes." The above means are also
used to produce reproductions by electroplating, stereotyping, or
pressing the impression covered with emery in contact with a
softened metal plate.

Secondly, " in producing, by means of machinery which I call
" printing machines, prints resembling the ordinary typographic
" printing, or impressions of typographic characters on some
" surface."

The " printing machines" are intended to produce print work
with a very limited number of stamps or types, " which do not
" generally exceed the number of printers' characters or signs."
They are of very varied construction. One described in the
Specification consists of a wheel, over which the paper to be
printed passes in roll, and above which is a type cylinder, the
types being fixed on springs. A key shaft driven by foot, and

arrested by finger stops, arrests the type wheel with any desired character (previously inked by an endless band in connexion with an ink trough) above the paper. The type is struck down upon the paper by a hammer worked by an electric current made and broken by the action of the machine. There are arrangements for making up such print into words, lines, and pages. Paper or other fabric, covered with a layer of printing ink, may be used as a substitute for the endless band. This machine may also be used for printing for the blind.

[Printed, 1s. 6d. Drawings.]

A.D. 1854, April 17.—No 886.

TANNAHILL, DAVID.—" Improvements in lithographic and " zincographic printing."

The pressing cylinder, in a frame, traverses to and fro over the printing surface by means of screw shafts disposed longitudinally under the table, and passing through nuts in the pressure frame. It prints in one direction only, the printing surface being lowered on the return of the cylinder by the action of a series of cams on transverse spindles actuated by the movement of the traversing frame. An endless cloth or belt, which acts as a tympan, is passed under the pressure roller, round two guide rollers on each side of it, and over a tension roller some distance above the pressure roller, these rollers being carried in suitable bearings in the traversing frame. The web to be printed is taken off a roller at one end of the machine, passed under the pressure roller, then upwards with the endless cloth, and between the upper tension roller of laths and a " bearing " roller, on which it is wound. The damping and inking may be performed by hand, or by " self-acting " mechanism, arranged in various ways," carried by the traversing frame.

Another mode consists in arranging two impression rollers, with their details, in a single traversing frame, so that two pieces or fabric may be printed at once.

[Printed, 11d. Drawings.]

A.D. 1854, April 24.—No 937.

NEWTON, WILLIAM EDWARD.— (Communicated.) —" Im- " proved machinery for casting type."

The invention consists of various improvements on N° 13,058, A.D. 1850. The adjustable part of the mould is mounted in a groove, or between guides or registers, to adapt it to the varying thicknesses of type, It is attached to the head or joint by means of a set screw, which admits of its being moved slightly in a lateral direction. The head is also affixed to the fixed part of the mould block by means of a rib screw, so as to admit of being turned in either direction. The mould and mould block are placed in a vertical instead of an inclined position, " as is usual." The type is discharged by means of a simple rod connected at one end to a fixed point of some part of the framing, and at the opposite end to the moveable part of the mould block, and actuated by the movement of the mould block and its appendages which brings the opening of the mould to the nipple of the melting pot. The mould block is moved to and fro by means of a crank pin working in a curved slot, formed in an arm connected with the standard of the mould block. By this means the use of cams, springs, and levers is dispensed with, and the motion is rendered " more smooth and certain than " heretofore."

The next improvement relates to a novel contrivance, whereby the metal is prevented from being forced back into the well instead of through the nipple, when pressure is applied to it by the descent of the piston. A moveable plug is placed on the spindle of the stopper in a chamber immediately behind the nipple, and when the stopper closes the nipple, and the piston of the pump rises, the molten metal runs into the nipple chamber past the plug. Upon the piston descending, pressure is applied to the metal in the nipple chamber, and forces the plug against the hole or opening at the back and through which the metal entered, and thereby prevents its return, so that immediately the stopper is drawn back the metal rushes out into the mould.

[Printed, 10d. Drawings.]

A.D. 1854, April 28.—N° 965.

HEYWOOD, JAMES.—" Certain improvements in machinery or " apparatus for printing yarns."

The invention relates to such yarns as are to be partially printed in the " hank," leaving intermediate spaces blank, to be subsequently employed in manufacturing clouded or speckled goods or fabrics. Any convenient number of hanks are distended endwise by passing them over two side rails contained in a suitable framework, such hanks presenting a flat horizontal surface capable of being printed upon when placed side by side. The parts of the yarns not to be printed are preserved between flat ribs or bars, so as entirely to prevent any of the printing color being introduced to them. The spaces of the yarn exposed between such ribs or bars are open to receive the printing colors. The printing part of the apparatus is composed of small revolving printing rollers or bowls, which furnish themselves with the colour placed in small colour troughs underneath them, and a printing table or board situated over all, the table being covered with a blanket or bed. The operation of printing is performed by passing the rollers along longitudinal supporting rails under the yarns, from one end of the frame of yarn to the other, thus printing any width or colour of stripe or pattern required, simply by a suitable arrangement of the width of the retaining bars or strips, and a corresponding interposition of the printing rollers operating between them.

[Printed, 8d. Drawings.]

## A.D. 1854, May 4.—N° 998.

MEE, CORNELIA.—(Provisional Protection only.)—"An improved " foundation for working out ornamental designs or patterns."

" I propose to print on paper or other suitable material a series " of squares of any size, but so arranged that every square printed " thereon shall break joint (horizontally or vertically), equidistant " with the other squares" (shown in accompanying drawings). " On this foundation ornamental designs of any description may " be drawn or shaded, and covered with various coloured bead " work or any other suitable material."

[Printed, 5d. Drawing.]

## A.D. 1854, May 5.—N° 1006.

HASELER, EDWIN.—" An improvement or improvements in " ornamenting metals, papier maché, horn, and shells."

The mode adopted is that of printing and transferring to the said surfaces "negative designs" (designs representing those portions which in the completed ornament consist of the uncovered surface of the material), and afterwards gilding, silvering, bronzing, coloring, or treating by acids or other chemical agents to the surface to which such negative design has been applied, and finally removing the negative design by a solvent, so as to leave those portions of the surface unaffected which were covered with the negative design.

[Printed, 4d. No Drawing.]

### A.D. 1854, May 10.—N° 1040.

SPARRE, PETER AMBJORN.—" An improved mode of prevent-
" ing the alteration or falsification of written documents."

The invention consists in covering the surface of the paper with a design printed in two colors, " by Congreve's process, or any " other suitable means," one of these colors being indelible, the other easily washed out. Upon the portion of the paper so printed is to be written the document, or that portion of it, as the signature, &c., which it is desired especially to protect. In case of any attempt to tamper with the document, by washing out the colour, the delible one only is removed, and the fraud rendered evident.

[Printed, 3d. No Drawing.]

### A.D. 1854, May 12.—N° 1064.

POOLE, MOSES.—(Communicated.)—" Improvements in engrav-
" ing and printing on glass, and of figuring and ornamenting the
" same."

Peculiar arrangement of machinery, whereby an " embossing " cylinder," upon which the pattern or device to be engraved upon the glass is etched or otherwise countersunk, is caused to roll with a rocking motion in contact with the glass, emery or other suitable cutting material being interposed between the bearing surfaces of the two.

[Printed, 9d. Drawings.]

### A.D. 1854, May 18.—N° 1110.

JOHNSON, JOHN HENRY.—(Communicated by Meinrad Theiler.)—" Improvements in printing telegraphs."

The invention consists in causing wheels situated at the corresponding stations to revolve at the same speed. The uniformity of this motion is required, at the most, for half a second. A revolving shaft, having a series of tappets or arms spirally arranged upon it, is fitted beneath a series of keys representing the various characters in use. Each tappet is acted upon by a distinct key, the under side of the keys being fitted with projecting catches which hold the tappets on the depression of the keys. At the end of the shaft is another tappet which serves to hold the shaft stationary by means of a spring lever which hooks on to it. This lever is, however, released, and the shaft allowed to revolve whenever any one of the keys is depressed. The shaft continues to revolve until the particular tappet corresponding to the key comes in contact with its catch, when the shaft is stopped and the electric current established by means of an escapement wheel, driven by clockwork, upon the end of the shaft. This wheel is insulated at the part where it turns upon the shaft, and is fitted with a blade spring attached to the side of it by an insulated junction, the other end being connected to an arm on the end of the shaft. The latter is brought into contact with a stud fitted to one side of the escapement wheel, first when the key is pressed upon, and, secondly, when the shaft is stopped by the catch. The spring has thus the effect of breaking the communication between the wheel and the tappet shaft during the rotation of the latter so long as the keys are left untouched. The current passes through the two shafts on to the next station, and returns by another wire attached to a piece of copper at the other end of the key-board, where the negative pole of the battery is situated. A square piece of metal presses upon a piece of ivory let into the copper, and is so arranged that when the key-board is at rest the metal rests upon the ivory and the current is broken, but the moment a key is depressed the metal slides off the ivory on to the copper, and establishes a communication. The printing mechanism is actuated by clockwork, and an escapement wheel similar to the former driven at the same speed. The type wheel is carried on the same arbor as the escapement wheel. It is kept in contact with a roller covered with perforated gutta percha, which carries the colour inside. The characters on the wheel correspond in order to the characters on the keys, and when a key is depressed the wheel stops with that character downwards, and the paper, which is cut into a long tape or strip, is pressed against it by a lever and magnet each time a letter is to be printed. A blank key is fitted in the key-board to produce the spaces between the words.

In many cases it is necessary to employ two printing wheels, either being actuated at pleasure by reversing the current. For this purpose certain modifications are requisite. The key-board is composed of two ranges of keys similar to a pianoforte. Each set acts upon a separate rod, and each rod is fitted with the same mechanism for establishing and breaking the current as above described.

[Printed, 1s. 6d. Drawings.]

A.D. 1854, May 18.—N° 1111.

MACLEAN, John, and FINLAYSON, Thomas.—" Improve-
" ments in the manufacture or production of ornamental fabrics."

The invention relates to yarns or warps which are to be woven into piece goods. The warp, prepared as for the loom, is delivered from a roller at one end of the machine, and passes between a pair of relief printing rollers, exact counterparts of each other, furnished from troughs with a discharging agent composed of sulphuric acid and nitric acid, diluted with water and thickened with fine pipe-clay. It then passes by means of rollers through several compartments of a washing tank, the divisions of which are of regularly increasing height, so that the water flows from one into the other in a direction opposite to that of the warp's traverse. The water enters at the last compartment, and a row of jets is made to play upon the warp as it issues from it. The warp next passes between squeezing rollers and over steam cylinders, by which it is thoroughly dried. It is then wound upon a beam, ready to be transferred to the loom. The washing tank travels on rails, so that its distance from the printing rollers can be adjusted. Where the above discharging agent is used the printing surfaces may be of gutta percha. Warps intended for scarfs or similar goods are treated in such a manner as to leave the fringe portion untouched by the discharging agent. This is effected by a cam movement, so geared with the driving mechanism as to lift the upper printing roller for a short time as each length of scarf is printed. An apparatus for starching the yarns may be interposed between the washing trough and the drying cylinders.

[Printed, 1s. 5d. Drawings.]

## A.D. 1854, May 24.—N° 1160.

BALL, Thomas.—" An improvement in manufacturing orna-
" mented looped fabrics."

" Heretofore in manufacturing loop-made fabrics, whether pro-
" duced by warp threads looped into each other or by knitting
" machinery, the same have in some cases been made with or have
" had pile raised thereon, but hitherto the pile yarn has only been
" used of self colors, and has only produced the pile of one
" color, or of a mixture of colors, or in stripes of different colors,
" by which ornament can be produced only to a comparatively
" limited extent. Now my invention consists of printing with one
" or more colors the pile surfaces of such loop-made fabrics, after
" they have been produced in warp or knitting machines, by which
" very beautiful and novel effects can be obtained to these elastic
" and piled fabrics."

[Printed, 3d. No Drawing.]

## A.D. 1854, May 26.—N° 1177.

LORD, James.—" Improvements in the manufacture of articles
" of ladies' under-clothing."

These consist in—1. "As applied to articles of ladies' under-
" clothing, the production of "Vandyke," scolloped, or other such
" edges, by causing a portion of the warp threads to fail in being
" interwoven with the weft. 2. As applied to fabrics for petti-
" coats, the production of open parts or pipings, by weaving
" double cloth at intervals. 3. As applied to fabrics for petticoats,
" the weaving of stripes or other patches, so as to produce at
" those parts a fustian or other such fabric, whether the same be
" subsequently cut or remain as woven. 4. As applied to chemises
" or under shirts, the application to a fabric of ornamental parts
" which indicate the shape, or a portion thereof to be cut out,
" whether such ornamental parts be obtained by weaving or
" printing."

[Printed, 6d. Drawings.]

## A.D. 1854, May 30.—N° 1194.

BELLFORD, Auguste Edouard Loradoux.—(Communicated.)—" Improvements in machinery for making bags of paper
" or other suitable material."

E E 2

The material is as wide as the depth of the bag; a portion the length of the bag is drawn off by rollers, and laid upon an inclined plane, where such length is cut off by a blade, while other blades cut away part of one edge, so that the remaining part of the same edge can, when the piece is doubled, be lapped over it to form the bottom of the bag. A "folding creaser" creases and folds the sheet by driving it through a slot. The folded piece is seized and drawn through the slot by a pair of rollers, assisted by other rollers which carry it into a swinging frame or "conveyer." This frame has a small rising and falling movement. It receives the folded paper when at its highest, and delivers it when at its lowest, on to an apron with intermittent motion. The apron conveys the bag to a pasting or lapping apparatus, where the bottom of the bag is closed, and then to a second similar apparatus, where the side of it is closed. A second endless apron assists in carrying the paper and holding it still during the pasting and lapping. The paste feeder is a cylinder revolving in a paste trough. The aprons subsequently throw the bag finished out of the machine. The bag is printed while passing from the bottom pasting to the side pasting apparatus by means of a type cylinder, revolving with the same velocity as the bag, and inked by rollers; pressure is given by a pressure cylinder above the type cylinder, the impression being given to the under side of the bag. The bag is carried by an apron or series of cords into a chamber at the end of the machine, where it is dried by a current of air.

[Printed, 1s. 6d. Drawings].

## A.D. 1854, May 30.—N° 1198.

MIDDLETON, LEWIS STIRLING. — (Provisional Protection only.)—" Improvements in the manufacture or production of " ornamental fabrics."

The invention relates to ornamental fabrics of the " poncho stuff " class, and consists in having the body or ground fabric woven from yarns or threads of the color of the intended ground of the piece. At the same time, certain stripes or lines of grey or bleached yarns are also woven in. The fabric is finally ornamented by printing a pattern or device on both sides or faces of the stripes, " thus extending the application of varieties of color."

[Printed, 3d. No Drawings.]

A.D. 1854, June 2.—N° 1228.

TAYLOR, Isaac.—" An improvement in producing thin metal
" shells adapted to printing."

A sheet of copper or other suitable metal is bent round a mandril or stock, and its edges turned over inwards in the direction
of the radius, and secured by rivets or otherwise. The outer
surfaces of the two bends thus brought together and presenting
a double protrusion, are then subjected to pressure, so as to reduce
these protrusions to the level of the general surface of the cylinder,
and at the same time so as to produce such a continuity of the
metallic substance as that a planishing tool in passing over the
joint may cause the line of contact to disappear. The shell as
thus jointed receives a general planishing and polishing, and is
then in a state to receive the engraving.

[Printed, 7d. Drawings.]

A.D. 1854, June 2.—N° 1230.

WILKINSON, William. — (Provisional Protection only.) —
" Improvements in stamping, raising, or printing patterns upon
" leather, textile, thread, cut pile, or similar fabrics, and also for
" dressing textile, cut pile, and other similar fabrics previous to
" the stamping and printing."

The material is put while in pieces into slide stretching frames
between two straps pressed upon by two rollers. Each selvage of
the web and the same straps must be provided with straps or rollers
to prevent the web from running in, so that it may be properly
stretched. " In printing gloves I use a dressing board covered
" with wool fabric or sponge, or soft leather, or other suitable
" material of the shape of the glove to be dressed, so that while
" the glove is in the process of being dressed, the pattern desired
" for the back of the fabric may be printed at the same time
" while the process of dressing is going on."

Shirts of single-loop elastic manufacture, children's socks and
stockings, and gloves of cut pile are similarly figured.

" I also stamp or print kid or leather gloves with patterns while
" on suitable dressing boards as also kid or leather fabrics to be
" cut up into gloves. For giving the patterns I use rollers with
" engraved patterns or engraved blocks, or other ordinary means
" now in use."

[Printed, 3d. No Drawings.]

A.D. 1854, June 2.—N° 1225.

WHITEHOUSE, EDWARD ORANGE WILDMAN.—" Improve-
" ments in effecting telegraphic communications."

The invention relates principally to carrying out the details of
N° 2885 of 1853. Its principal object is to obtain as nearly as possible the same speed in the transmission and recording of messages
by the use of a single wire. It consists, first, of an arrangement
and construction of the alphabet and symbols described in the
former Specification, adapted to the use of a single-wire recording
telegraph, by means of an automatic division of the receiving paper
into letter blanks or letter lengths, on which the marks representing the letters or symbols are deposited, the letters being printed
by a single touch, though several consecutive marks may be necessary for its formation. Secondly, in the arrangement and use of a
" magneto-electric decomposition printer," whereby the letters and
symbols in use under the former Patent are made available for
transmission by a single wire, a single touch only of the keys or
studs being required, although several successive marks be necessary for the formation of the letter. Also in the use of a "traveller"
and " circuit pieces," by means of which " short circuits " are
automatically made and broken. Thirdly, in a mode of applying
" short circuits " to telegraphic purposes, wherein a succession of
rapid alternating currents derived from any generator of magneto-
electricity, or the currents derived from a battery by the aid of
a " commutator," are made available by automatically short
circuiting at the proper moment those currents not intended to
travel, by mechanically calling into play a local battery at the
distant station. Also a mode of applying the same principle for
the removal of the inconvenience arising from the effects of
" induction " or " earth " currents, or " recoil " current in
underground and submarine wires, by automatically short circuiting those currents, the induction or recoil from which might
interfere with the integrity of the indication and due working of
the apparatus. Fourthly, in the construction and arrangement
and mode of using the receiving magnets or " relays," especially
fitted to actuate the recording and printing apparatus by mechanically calling into play local batteries. Fifthly, in a mode of
receiving despatches from several stations simultaneously, upon
the same slip of paper, without risk of interference with each
other. Sixthly, in the construction and arrangement and mode of

use of an automatic "commutator" which is to give the command
of a battery current thrown into the alternating form by the
revolution of a magnetic needle. Likewise the use of this arrangement in combination with the essential parts of the electric
decomposition printer. Seventhly, in the use of a dial indicator
and type printer actuated by one or more local batteries mechanically called into play, primarily by the action of the travelling
current upon the " relay " or receiving magnet, and secondarily,
by other movements resulting therefrom.

[Printed, 4s. 6d. Drawings.]

A.D. 1854, June 6.—No 1256.

ATKINSON, DAVID.—" Improvements in printing, and in the
" machinery or apparatus to be employed therein or connected
" therewith."

The fabric to be printed is passed from one roller below the
level of the press to another between two rollers, the upper one
containing the design, and the lower one clothed with an elastic
material and acting as a pressing cylinder. If the fabric be
printed in rolls it is divided (by means of a cutter) after the
(impression) into any required lengths, and finally passes into a
receiving box. The printing roller, which may be either of zinc
or stone, is surmounted on one side with a wetting and on the
other with an inking roller.

[Printed, 10d. Drawings.]

A.D. 1854, June 10.—No 1283.

BARCLAY, ANDREW, and BARCLAY, JOHN.—(Provisional
Protection only.)—" Improvements in printing textile fabrics and
" other surfaces."

The invention relates principally to improvements on No 14,047,
A.D. 1852, and No 2686 of 1853. On one end of the large drum or
cylinder employed in those patents for the impression or printing
surface is fixed a spur wheel of the same diameter as the drum
which drives the printing roller at the side. The ring frames or
wheels upon which such drum is built are each cast in a single
piece, for strength and accuracy. The teeth of the large spur
wheel, as well as those of the pinion driven by it, are formed on
the stepped or sectionally divided system, to secure smoothness in

working, without the necessity of adopting a very fine pitch in each set of teeth. The drum is driven by a pinion in gear with the large spur wheel, instead of a pinion in gear with a separate spur wheel keyed on the shaft of the drum. The spur wheel which drives the printing roller pinion has as many teeth as there are required to be repeats of the pattern round the circumference of the drum. For patterns which will not divide into the circumference at that part of the circumference where a piece is taken out of the drum, a number of wheel teeth are also omitted, and a segment fitted on, having a number of teeth, the line of which bulges outwards from the line of the regular teeth. This segment is in a different plane from the regular teeth of the wheel, and gears with an elliptical wheel on a shaft connected with the printing roller. These parts are so arranged that the segment turns the printing roller so much more round than the regular teeth would do, as brings the roller to the same position for starting as it had before the revolution of the drum. The printing roller is carried in bearings in the frame which carries the color trough and sieve tension rollers, and this frame can be lifted clear of the traversing carriage. The carriage is kept against the large drum by levers jointed to the carriage. "Certain classes of fabrics or yarns" are wound spirally on the large drum, and so printed. The printing roller is set at right angles to the line of fabric, and is made to traverse longitudinally as it and the drum revolve, so as to make its continuous line of impression coincide with the spiral line of the fabric. The roller may be made in three or more pieces, the central portions being fixed loosely on the spindle, so as to yield a little to the curvature of the drum. The large impression drum is encompassed with a piping of steam, which dries the fabric when printed.

[Printed, 3d. No Drawing.]

A.D. 1854, June 17.—No 1322.

NEWTON, ALFRED VINCENT.—(Communicated.)—"Improve-"ments in machinery for block printing."

The invention relates to a mode of arranging on a prism, which rises and falls for the impression, continuous portions of so much of a complete figure or design as is to be printed in one color, and combining together a sufficient number of such prisms to admit of the design being perfected in the required number of colors or shades of colors at one operation. The prisms are mounted so as to rotate axially, so as to bring round and print the several sections of the design in succession. The fabric to be printed is traversed under the printing surface by means of an endless apron with intermittent motion. The blocks receive color while elevated from sliding trays, which are withdrawn clear of them as they descend on the fabric. The trays are supplied with color from a stationary hopper under which they slide. The fabric is kept from following the prism after the impression by holding-down bars worked by toggle-jointed levers.

[Printed, 10d. Drawings.]

A.D. 1854, June 27.—N° 1415.

ANTROBUS, RICHARD LEICESTER.—"A new or improved " method of printing oil-cloth for floor and table covers, paper- " hangings, and other surfaces."

As many pairs of rolls as there are colors to be printed are placed so that a piece of cloth or paper may pass successively between the whole series. The bottom roller of each pair is plain, the top one engraved with the pattern (in relief) of a particular color. The first pair prints a ground, the second the color next in extent of the ground, and so on for the several colors, the fabric emerging with the design complete. Color is supplied to the printing rollers by rollers placed over them, and furnished by a brush at the bottom of a trough with a slit in the bottom of it.

[Printed, 6d. Drawings.]

A.D. 1854, June 28.—N° 1422.

EDWARDS, HENRY SUTHERLAND.—(Communicated.)—"Im- " provements in preparing textile fabrics or materials for the " purpose of their better retaining colours applied to them."

The invention consists in passing such, when intended to be printed by the ordinary printing rollers, through a bath, consisting of water holding in solution alum, sulphate of zinc, proto-chloride of tin, caustic potash, and nitric acid, or other chemicals of analo-gous properties. The alum, sulphate of zinc, proto-chloride of tin, and caustic potash, are separately dissolved in water, and then thrown into one bath, the nitric acid being added last. When the materials are intended to be printed by the lithographic press, they are passed through two separate fluid baths; the first of alum, sulphate of zinc, proto-chloride of tin, and American potass; the second of alum, sulphate of zinc, and nitric acid.

[Printed, 3d. No Drawings.]

A.D. 1854, July 5.—N° 1478.

VENABLES, JOHN, and MANN, ARTHUR.—(Provisional Protection only.)—" Printing self and other colours in bas-relief or " raised work, on china, earthenware, glass, Parian stoneware, " bricks, block tiles, quarries, hardware, Japan, and papier maché " ware."

" We take plates of wood, stone, metal, or other hard material, " and carve or engrave them much deeper and broader than has " hitherto been in use, by which means we get a much greater " body of the matter used, and so produce the bas-relief or raised " work upon the articles to which the same is applied. We after- " wards rub into the said plates the self or other colours to be " printed and transferred on the above-named wares, until the " carved or engraved parts are filled with the same. We then lay " a soft fabric of paper or cloth upon the plates, and subject the " same to a degree of pressure, by which means the self or other " colours are deposited on such fabric. The fabric, with the " pattern or device thereon, is then laid upon the ware and gently " rubbed, whereupon the pattern or device is transferred and fixed " upon the ware in bas-relief or raised work."

[Printed, 3d. No Drawing.]

A.D. 1854, July 6.—N° 1490.

CARALLI, NICHOLAS MICHAEL.—" Improvements in the " manufacture or production of ornamental fabrics."

The invention relates to the manufacture of the several classes of woven fabrics known as " zebras," used for various articles of ornamental dress. The groundwork of this duplex pattern is either a plain fabric, " having no flushing or backlashing on either of its " surfaces," or a double fabric woven " according to any of the " existing systems," in which intermediate flushed threads are worked into both sections of it. A distinct zebra pattern is then printed " by any of the existing means or agencies " on each side of the fabric. In this way a single piece of zebra fabric " answers

" the end of showing two dissimilar patterns or ornamental
" devices ; and hence by reversing the exposed pattern surface,
" the wearer of a dress made from material of this kind may pro-
" duce totally distinct ornamental effects at pleasure."

[Printed, 3d. No Drawing.]


## A.D. 1854, July 7.—N° 1493.

LACEY, WILLIAM.—"A new or improved method of making
" copper rollers, cylinders, and tubes."

The invention consists, first, in making one new roller from two
old ones. The pattern and "nib" are removed from one of the
rollers, which is afterwards expanded by passing a draw burr
through it, or otherwise. It is next heated, and the unexpanded
roller introduced into it. On cooling, the outer roller becomes
firmly united to the inner one. The compound roller thus formed
is reduced to any required size by drawing, rolling, or otherwise.
Secondly, in casting hollow copper cylinders in cast-iron moulds,
so constructed that the metal enters the moulds at the bottom,
and thus produces a sound casting, free from the air bubbles
carried down by the stream of metal. The mould is composed of
two nearly semi-cylindrical portions, and contains a central core
or mandril, solid or hollow, or formed of a tube slit from end to
end, and the edges made to overlap, so that the diameter of the
core may be compressed by means of rings and screws, and the
cores removed from the cylinder cast upon it. The "nib," when
requisite, is produced by making a groove in the core or mandril,
" as is well understood."

[Printed, 5d. Drawings.]


## A.D. 1854, July 12.—N° 1522.

GATTY, FREDERICK ALBERT.—(Provisional Protection only.)—
" An improvement in the manufacture of printed receipt stamps."

The invention consists in using for such stamps colors which
change or disappear when treated with acids or other chemical
agents. The colors recommended are " lead orange, ultramarine
" blue, or some other colours of the same kind, mixed with glue
" or gummy substances, without any varnish or oily substance."

[Printed, 3d. No Drawing.]

### A.D. 1854, July 13.—N° 1535.

FLITCROFT, William, and EVANS, Thomas.—(Provisional Protection only.)—(Communicated.)—" Improvements in printing " and finishing floor-cloths, or any other fabrics or materials " printed in oil colors."

Instead of using for each color a color block and a blotch block " as now adopted," one color block only is used for each color in the pattern, and one finishing or flushing block, which flushes all the colors at once. The latter, which exactly fits the pattern, is used dry, being pressed upon the material having the same color on it, and therefore does not require wiping or cleaning at every application.

[Printed, 3d. No Drawing.]

### A.D, 1854, July 13.—N° 1539.

LAWSON, Lionel.—(Provisional Protection only.)—" Improve- " ments in printing."

The invention consists in heating and thereby reducing the consistency of the inks used in letter-press printing, without detriment to the quality of the work. The inks for this purpose are composed of varnishes, with a large proportion of lamp-black. Drying substances and gums, which are not applicable to cold inks, may also be introduced. Sometimes the form and inking tables are heated, to prevent the rapid cooling of the ink. The ink is heated by " steam, hot air, or otherwise," and either " in " the ink trough itself or separately from the machine."

[Printed, 3d. No Drawing.]

### A.D. 1854, July 14.—N° 1548.

WIBERG, Martin.—(Provisional Protection only.)—" Improve- " ments in the construction, setting up, and distribution of types " for printing."

In the composing machine, these consist in arranging the type holders in pairs of alphabets of the same kind, with the first letter of one alphabet opposite the last letter of the other, and in em- ploying finger keys, acting by means of levers, to draw either of two opposite letters, &c. from the type holders, the selection being controlled by pedals, in order that the letters desired may be brought into one line, and then collected by a " type collector."

The "type collector" has an indicator which marks the progress of the composing. The holders of capital letters are arranged also in two lines.

For the process of distributing, the types are formed with a nick on each side, that on one side being in the same position and of the same size in all, and that of the other in the same position and of the same size only in types of the same indication. These types being placed in a frame, with elastic pressure acting upon that side of them where the recesses are alike, a rib or projection from a plate presses upon the opposite side of the type, and by catching into all those which are alike, pulls them out, after which they pass into their appropriate type holders or reservoirs for resetting. The apparatus according to this invention should be so arranged that setting and distribution be simultaneously effected. The thickness of each type is a multiple or sub-multiple of the thickness of the rest.

[Printed, 3d. No Drawing.]

### A.D. 1854, July 15.—No 1554.

BRINDLEY, ELIJAH HENRY.— " Certain improvements in " printing or ornamenting china, earthenware, and glass."

The invention consists in the use of spherical or other flexible and elastic blocks by means of which the pattern or portion of a pattern may be readily adapted to the form of the article to be ornamented in colours, gold, or lustre. The elasticity of the spherical or other than flat blocks also admits of their being expanded by the operator, so as to produce variations in the size, shape, and character of the figures printed from them, as may be required to adapt the same figures or pattern or portions of a pattern to pieces of ware of different sizes and shapes.

[Printed, 7d. Drawings.]

### A.D. 1854, July 18.—No 1575.

ARCHER, CHARLES MAYBURY.—(Provisional Protection only.) —" Treating all kinds of paper whereon any printing, engraving, " engrossing, letter-writing, or lithographing has been printed or " impressed, so that the said printing, engraving, engrossing, " letter-writing, or lithographing may be completely removed, " discharged, or obliterated from the said paper, and so that the

" said paper may be readily re-used in sheets or be re-converted
" and worked up again into its primitive pulp by the ordinary
" method and be again manufactured into and be used as paper."
The printed paper is immersed in a bath of pure sulphuric or
other acid, which decomposes the oil, lamp-black, &c. of the
printing ink and discharges it from the paper "by a gradual
" evolution and efflorescence." To precipitate the event and prevent the "destructive or deflagrating influence of the acids," the
paper is then plunged for a few minutes into water, either hot or
cold. The paper may then be brushed with a soft brush, and
after being bleached by immersion in spirits of ammonia or other
alkali, presents an almost normally clean surface (after the stamp
of the types has been pressed out) for further use, either for
printing purposes or re-conversion into pulp. The residual products, other than the pulp and paper, are collected and re-converted
into printing ink, or used as a pigment, a lubricating compound,
or for electric telegraphic battery purposes.

[Printed, 3d. No Drawing.]

A.D. 1854, July 18.—No 1582.

FONTAINE MOREAU, Peter Armand Le Comte de.—(Provisional Protection only.)—(Communicated.)—"Improvements in
" zincography."

The invention consists in producing by electro-galvanic agency
designs in relief on plates of zinc, which may be used as printing
surfaces or as moulds for a gutta-percha matrix for the formation
of "cliché" plates by the galvano-plastic process. The zinc
plate is levelled and roughened, after which the design is drawn
on it with lithographic ink or pencil. Powdered resin, Burgundy
pitch, and asphaltum are then sifted over the design. The plate
is next slightly heated and afterwards placed in a weak solution
of sulphate of zinc in face of another plate of the same material
and size, and the two are put in communication with the poles of
a galvanic battery, so that the zinc plate with the drawing may
serve as anode to the other, and consequently have those (the
intended sunken) parts decomposed. To increase the depth of
the sunken parts, those sufficiently bitten in are insulated, and the
others again submitted to the action of the battery. When the
drawing is sufficiently bitten in, the plate is removed and cleansed.
" Pen or crayon drawings on stone, zinc, or autographic paper

" may be transferred, as is well understood, to a zinc plate and
" reproduced thereon in relief by the process above described."

[Printed, 3d. No Drawing.]

## A.D. 1854, July 21.—No 1604.

KNIGHT, John, and STUBBS, James.—" An improvement or
" improvements in the manufacture of bricks, tiles, pipes, and such
" other articles as are or may be made of clay, which improvement
" or improvements may also be applied in the manufacture of
" artificial fuel and to other mixing and tempering processes."

The invention consists, first, in the introduction of steam and
water into the cylinders or piston-boxes of machines for fashioning
clay or other plastic substances prior to the application of the
moulding surface, which very much facilitates the motion of the
pistons and the moulding of the clay. Secondly, in the use of a
second die or mouthpiece in machines in which the clay is cut
into bricks, tiles, or other articles after emerging from the said
machines, the second die or mouthpiece being placed between the
die or mouthpiece in which the brick or other article is roughly
formed and the rack or platform on which it passes prior to being
cut. Thirdly, in impressing devices or inscriptions upon the said
articles by means of rollers placed on the rack or platform, rollers
being placed so as to impress any required side or sides of such
articles. Fourthly, in fixing cores or bars in the dies of brick-
making machines, so that the perforations made by the cores or
bars are closed before the stream of clay passes from the machine.
Fifthly, in moulding artificial fuel into masses having perforations
therein, and using nitre or nitrate of soda in the composition of
artificial fuel. Sixthly, in using a friction sheeve in brick making,
and communicating motion to the pistons of brick machines by
means of a rocking shaft.

[Printed, 6d. Drawings.]

## A.D. 1854, July 22.—No 1618.

JOHNSON, William.—(Provisional Protection only.)—(Communicated.)—"Improvements in the treatment, cleansing, and
" dyeing of fibrous and textile materials."

For cleansing and discharging colors such materials are
treated alternately with solutions of different temperatures of

hydrate or other soluble salt of lime and alkaline carbonates. For mordants, hypochloride, and muriate of alumina, salts of magnesia, picric, and formic acid, and their salts, are used. For sizing fibrous materials, paper, yarn, and cloth, salts of magnesia, searate, or marzorate, and oleate of alumina are employed. In dyeing or printing madder or Turkey red, the following ingredients are used : —Nitric, picric, carbolic, and mimotannic acids, and their salts ; also glue, gelatine, chondine, albumen, hypochloride and formiate of alumina, salts of magnesia, ammoniacal and butter soaps ; also combinations of madder with acetic acid, or with alkaline hydrates or carbonates, or turpentine, naphtha, and alcohol. In dyeing with indigo, sulphate of indigo is decomposed with salts of lead, lime, barytes, or strontia, by which means are obtained acetates and other solutions of indigo. " For fixing colors, vegetable casem or " lactarine, such as is found in peas or beans, is used ; also soluble " silicates ; also a combination of tannin with animal gelatine."

[Printed, 3d. No Drawing.]

## A.D. 1854, July 22.—Nº 1619.

DILKS, James.—(Provisional Protection only.)—"The applica-" tions of printed or painted linen, cotton, or other textile fabric, " either plain or ornamental, for binding more effectually than " heretofore packets or parcels of lace, hosiery, or other articles."

Bands for the above purposes, it is stated, have "heretofore" been " composed of paper only or of a combination of paper with " linen, cotton, and other fabrics." It is proposed by this invention to use " oil or water colours, or other glutinous substances, " applied either by hand labour or machinery, to linen, cotton, or " other textile fabrics for the ornamentation thereof for the pur-" pose above described."

[Printed, 3d. No Drawing.]

## A.D. 1854, July 26.—Nº 1648.

DELAYE, Pierre Victor.—(Provisional Protection only.)— " Improvements in printing blocks."

This invention consists in forming those used for " calico, paper, " and similar surfaces " of movable pieces or "parallelopipeds." These are placed in a frame or open box of any shape, square or rectangular being preferred, some of them being longer than and protruding above others, so as to form one or more colors of the pattern or design, "the latter having to be represented on a card " similar to embroidery pattern paper for the purpose of reading " it therefrom, which is done in a manner similar to that of " setting type." An impression may be taken from the block composed as above "in the usual way."

[Printed, 3d. No Drawing.]

A.D. 1854, August 5.—Nº 1720.

CUNNINGHAM, JOHN.—" Improvements in the preparation or " production of printing surfaces."

The invention relates to a mode of reading off patterns upon rollers or blocks. According to one modification of it, applicable to the production of pattern matrices, as described in Nº 289 of 1854 (J. B. Graham), the pins or types which form the pattern matrix are depressed by pickers, acted on by a treadle; and arranged in a frame similarly to the punches in a "piano" machine for jacquard cards. Or the perforation may be performed by means of a cast-iron frame, on the top of which, at both sides, are fixed two parallel iron bars or slides, along which slides a rectangular frame by means of a screw spindle. The sliding frame has also another upon it sliding at right angles to the line of its own motion. It has also an escapement, worked by a treadle beneath, and similar to those used in the piano machine for perforating jacquard cards, except being made duplex or with details for working in opposite directions. The escapement acts upon a rack on the (back) side of the third or upper movable frame, the rack being capable of being shifted so as to be acted upon by either escapement. The upper frame is connected with mechanism by which the direction of its action may be reversed. The pattern matrix frame is fixed on this third frame, and the apparatus for depressing the prickers is arranged so as to act upon it in this position. The operator depressing the keys indicated by the pattern, causes the pricker frame to descend, and the prickers thereby to depress the corresponding pins in the pattern matrix. The pattern matrix is then moved laterally by the escapement and rack so as to bring a fresh portion of it under the pricker frame, when a similar operation is performed for that portion.

[Printed, 4d. No Drawing.]

A.D. 1854, August 5.—N° 1721.

GATHERCOLE, JAMES.—(Provisional Protection only.)—" Im-
" provements in bordering or producing devices upon the edges of
" envelopes, letter paper, or other articles of stationery."

The then mode of effecting this is stated to consist " in placing
" the edges to be bordered or colored in a diagonal direction, one
" above the other, the margin of each to be colored to be left so
" as to receive the coloring matter, the coloring matter being
" then carefully brushed over such exposed margins." . . . " In
" bordering envelopes, where the edges of both the back and front
" sides are colored, four operations are necessary, and the color
" must be carefully dried between each, whilst from the edges of
" the envelope or paper being slightly rough the effect of the
" color is uncertain and jagged."

The invention consists in substituting for this the " the ordi-
" nary printing process." The degrees of mourning are represented by the number of marginal lines used, a border of three
indicating the deepest. The lines may be also printed with an
ornamental device, either in mourning or other colours, and the
device on the seal and any printed letter-press desired to be
outside the envelope may be put on " at the same printing
" operation." The lines may also be printed so as to leave a
blank space at the extreme edge of the paper or envelope, by
which the effect of the colouring is considerably heightened. It
is proposed also to use lavender and other colours to express
lesser degrees of mourning.

[Printed, 3d. No Drawing.]

A.D. 1854, August 8.—N° 1737.

WHITE, CHARLES.—(Provisional Protection only.)—" Improve-
" ments in printing blocks for printing ornamental or decorative
" paper."

After stating that blocks " as hitherto used " are, to prevent
warping, composed of three layers, generally 21 inches square or
21 inches by 10 inches, the patentee says, " I propose in making
" my block to use one piece of wood only in thickness, and in-
" stead of the block being one square piece or surface, by having
" several narrow or border slips (according to the size of the
" pattern to be printed) attached together in any simple manner,

" so that the several slips or any one of them can be removed or
" transposed, and re-arranged to form different patterns. Thus,
" instead of by one large block printing one pattern over the
" whole surface of paper, I have by my arrangement each slit
" forming a pattern, and a much smaller surface of wood is
" required to be cut in one pattern, thus effecting a considerable
" saving in the expence of printing blocks, both in the wood and
" the cost of the patterns."

[Printed, 3d. No Drawing.]

A.D. 1854, August 18.—N⁰ 1805.

WALTON, Joseph Fowell.—" Improvements in obtaining
" impressions from lithographic stones or plates."

The invention consists in producing on paper, from plates or
stones, imitations of drawings made with a camel's-hair pencil or
stump. The stone, &c. is grained "as for a drawing to be made
" with lithographic chalk," and the design drawn on it with a
hair brush or stump in lithographic ink dissolved in distilled
water. " The drawing is then prepared in the manner usually
" practised of preparing chalk drawings on stones or plates."
When the drawing is prepared the preparation is washed off, and
the stone left to dry; the latter is then rubbed gently over with
powdered pomice and placed in a slanting position, when a solution of resin made with a volatile solvent, " such as is commonly
" used for aquatinting," is poured over the whole of the drawing.
When this ground is perfectly dry, the stone or plate is gently
warmed, and a strong mixture of nitric, muriatic, or other powerful
acid (1) and gum water (5) thrown over it. After about a minute
the ground and drawing are washed off with spirits of turpentine,
and the stone or plate is ready for printing.

[Printed, 4d. No Drawing.]

A.D. 1854, August 30.—N⁰ 1899.

LEHUGEUR, Louis Pierre, and UTTINGER, Michel —
(Provisional Protection only.) — " Improvements applicaole to
" machinery for printing fabrics."

The invention consists, first, in obtaining increased uniformity in
the supply of color; and secondly, in dispensing with the number
of children " usually employed." The color table is made elastic

by means of springs, and is covered with a cloth so that at each stroke of the printing block fresh color will be supplied, the apparatus being so arranged that the cloth and the color, which is contained in a reservoir or basin, shall be kept together; and " when the printing operation is finished, and the colour is required " to be changed, the colour cloth can be scraped and the cover of " the colour reservoir moved forward by a single stroke, and the " colour reservoir closed, so that the colour cannot dry by evapora- " tion or exposure to the air as in the ordinary method of working, " in which the colour is found to dry in the brushes on the printing " frame, and in the vessels. A considerable economy will be effected " by so arranging the parts as, according to the old plan, a consi- " derable quantity of colour is lost, dropped, or wasted by the boy " who supplies the colour. It will be understood that the serious " loss of colour which arises from these various causes is obviated " by the improved system. We have also done away with the false " colour vessel, which is dirty, expensive, and requires much care " and attention, as the oil-cloths must be frequently renewed and " supplied with false colour."

" In carrying out the object of our invention we employ an " elastic bed for supporting the printing cloth. This elastic bed " does not require any attention, and possesses the advantage of " being always clean. The printing cloths are prepared in such a " manner that the colour cannot pass through them, by which a " further economy of colour is effected, and cleanliness is ensured. " Our printing apparatus is so arranged that the printer can dis- " pense with the assistance of boys without fatiguing himself or " losing time, that is to say, that in an establishment where fifty " printers are at work, four or five boys would be sufficient to " attend on the working men, whereas one boy to each man is " usually required; and for changing the colour, as when a printer " has finished printing with one colour and desires to take another, " a few moments will suffice for the attendants to draw the one " that has been finished and placed another ready for working."

[Printed, 3d. No Drawing.]

A.D. 1854, September 2.—N° 1923.

KAY, RICHARD DUGDALE. — " Improvements in machine " printing."

" The improvements relate to that part of the material used for " machine printing called the lapping, and consists of using a series

" of thin cotton fabrics, or fabrics of linen warp and cotton weft,
" coated on one side with india-rubber cement. These cemented
" fabrics are folded face to face with the uncemented surface
" outside. One of such folded fabrics is then wound on to the
" cylinder to the thickness required. The pressure in the act of
" winding will cause the cement to permeate through every fold
" of the fabric and the whole will become one solid mass."

[Printed, 3d. No Drawing.]


A.D. 1854, September 4.—N° 1932.

MITCHEL, WILLIAM HASLETT.—(Provisional Protection only.)
—" Improvements in means for distributing type."

A "follower" is propelled backwards and forwards on slides.
On this follower is a hook connected or disconnected from a
shuttle, so as to leave the shuttle stationary when required, while
the follower completes its motion in its slides. The types as they
are in line are placed in a groove at right angles to the motion
of the shuttle and follower, and the first type in the line lies close
to the surface of the shuttle, but does not touch it, being blocked
by an arm or stop passing through the shuttle in a groove sufficiently long to allow the shuttle to move. To this stop a wire
is connected, which the follower takes at its extreme motion,
pulling it away and letting one type into a vertical groove in the
shuttle. The face of the shuttle is provided with as many grooves
of the depth of the type as there are type to be distributed. The
follower and shuttle are disconnected at the point where the groove
designed for the first type in the line comes opposite to the said
type, whereby the shuttle is left stationary to receive the same.
The removal of the hook that connects the follower and shuttle is
effected by grooves or notches cut in the vertical top edge of the
type, which take a series or combination of levers in the shuttle,
raising some above while others are depressed below the surface of the shuttle. These levers raise a series of catches as the
shuttle is drawn along until they come opposite the catch that
has notches filed in it corresponding with the combination or per-
mutation of the levers. This catch not being raised, disconnects
the follower from the shuttle, and the type is deposited in the
corresponding groove, and carried away by the shuttle in its backward motion, and when the shuttle has arrived at the extreme
point of motion a plate on which the bottom of the type had been

resting is withdrawn, and the type falls into the corresponding groove of a series of horizontal grooves, in which each separate letter is set up in line as it drops down from the shuttle.

[Printed, 3d. No Drawings.]

## A.D. 1854, September 11.—N° 1979.

WORRALL, James, junior. — (Provisional Protection only.)— " Improvements in the method of treating and printing such fus- " tian goods or fabrics as are called 'cords and thick sets' or " velveteens."

" My invention consists simply in printing such goods and " fabrics as are above-named after the process of " cutting " them, " in contradistinction to any other method of treatment as hitherto " employed or practised."

[Printed, 3d. No Drawings.]

## A.D. 1854, September 19.—N° 2021.

CUNNINGHAM, John.—" Improvements in the preparation or " production of printing surfaces."

The invention relates to N° 289 of 1854 (B. Graham), and N° 1720 of 1854 (Cunningham). The improvements on the former consist, first, in leaving the pins or types of the built-up mass higher at the borders or edges than the general level of the rest, so as to act as register points for casts of the same or different patterns.

Secondly, in making the pattern type of two or more kinds of metal, or so as to present different appearances, and arranging them in compartments each filled with types of the same kind. This facilitates reading in the pattern the variety of types corre- sponding to the variety of colours in the ruled pattern.

Thirdly, in casting from the above. Two plates of peculiar con- struction are fitted upon that side of the frame upon which the metal is to be cast. These plates, when drawn apart, leave a winding zig-zag or other shaped groove along their meeting or junction edges immediately over the mass of pattern types. The metal is introduced at the back of these plates, when it finds its way through the zig-zag groove, which leaves a "feather" on the back of the casting.

Fourthly, in producing indented metallic or other surfaces resembling engraved surfaces. The types having the required engraved faces are set up in a mass as before, and rendered solid by pouring in metal at the back. The matrix thus formed is used as a die for producing the required surfaces.

The improvement on N° 1720 of 1854 consists in substituting wire for the prickers in use in the apparatus for marking or setting out patterns on rollers or other surfaces, the wires being similarly actuated as in the "well-known piano jacquard cutting machine," and cut so as to leave short lengths in the wood, which form the printing surface.

[Printed, 1s. 4d. Drawings.]

A.D. 1854, September 26.—N° 2066.

CORNIDES, Louis.—" A new mode of manufacturing a trans-
" parent medium, plain, printed, and colored, of gelatine in
" combination with other substances."

A plate of glass, coated with gelatine, sugar, and water, has transferred to it an impression taken on fine paper washed with gum arabic, or on a composition of glue, treacle, and whiting. The transferred drawing is colored by giving it a coat of gelatine and then proceeding as described in N° 2762 of 1853. Or the gelatine may be colored by hand, a waterproof medium such as wax and drying oil being placed upon it, and the color laid on in the parts not covered by such medium. The medium is removed by washing with spirits of turpentine. The gelatine when finished is coated with varnish. Gelatine, collodion, or other varnishes are combined to form a transparent coating for glass.

To manufacture a transparent medium as a separate substance, a clean surface of glass or other polished surface is first coated with collodion, and when this coating is dry it is then coated over with gelatine, and subjected to the above processes, on the comple-tion of which the entire coating is drawn off.

[Printed, 4d. No Drawing.]

A.D. 1854, September 26.—N° 2070.

CLAYTON, Thomas, and HARROP, Robert.—"Improvements
" in ornamenting wood, and in the machinery or apparatus con-
" nected therewith."

1. Imitations of the grains of choice woods are produced on common wood by means of rollers or flat dies containing the grain

in relief, and heated so as to slightly char the surface they are applied to. 2. Scroll-work borders or other devices are made by flat dies "(or rollers if preferred)" sustained at one end of a bar of iron, the other end of which is enveloped on a furnace so as to maintain the die at a heat nearly uniform. By depressing the hot die the design is transferred to the wood which may be at once removed, and the operation continuously repeated.

[Printed, 9d. Drawings.]

A.D. 1854, September 26.—N° 2071.

SINCLAIR, JAMES.—" Improvements in treating, cleaning, and " ornamenting paper and other surfaces."

The invention consists in producing ornamental devices in colors upon paper, &c. " by the frictional attachment thereto of pigment " matters of colored powders." The paper, &c. is first printed in adhesive matter " in the usual way," and passed through an apparatus consisting of a " duplex roller arrangement," the lower roller of which is clothed with soft leather, and revolves (at a high rate) in a color box, while immediately above and resting upon it is a plain roller, revolving slowly and running loosely in its bearings. The printed sheet is passed between the rollers at the rate at which the upper roller is revolving. The superfluous color is removed from it in a second machine; or the whole operation may be performed in one machine, the color being dropped on the fabric by a vibrating hopper, and the superfluous color removed by a brush made to act as a " doctor." The fabric then passes under a series of polishing or finishing rollers composed of strips of caoutchouc.

The second machine consists of a slowly-traversing table or apron fitted with self-acting clips for holding the material, and a series of rollers with longitudinally disposed strips of caoutchouc, arranged to rotate at a very high speed.

Leather for book-covers, cases, &c., and woven goods, as ladies' dresses, may be similarly treated, either as the sole means of ornamentation or in conjunction with printing or dyeing. Flock material may also be similarly applied to paper and cloth surfaces.

[Printed, 1s. 4d. Drawings.]

HARE, CHARLES BOWLES.—(Provisional Protection only.)—
" An improved mode of manufacturing printing blocks."

The invention consists in grooving printing blocks (chiefly for
the printing of floorcloths), by setting a series of circular saws, on
one shaft, at a certain distance apart, and thereby grooving the
surface of the blocks in one direction. The block is then turned,
and the saws again brought into action, when the block surface
is grooved across the grooves first made, and the required alterations left on the face of the block, which is then finished " in
" the usual manner."

[Printed, 3d. No Drawing.]

CROSSLEY, THOMAS.—" An improved mode of manufacturing
" printing blocks."

The block (of any suitable wood) is divided by fine saw cuts at
right angles to each other, and has the surface removed, except at
those parts which correspond to the figure required to be printed.
The block thus prepared is then pressed upon the softened sheet
of gutta-percha or india-rubber, and the plastic material thereby
forced into the minute interstices of the prisms which compose
the figure. The prisms are thus bound solidly and firmly together, and the surfaces produced having all the absorbent qualities
of the vegetable gum and all the strength of the wood itself. The
wood is stated to be far less liable to warp than where felt is
employed.

[Printed, 6d. Drawings.]

SCHEUTZ, GEORGE, and SCHEUTZ, EDWARD.—" Improve-
" ments in machinery or apparatus for calculating, and printing
" the results of calculations."

The invention consists principally in an arrangement of wheels
which can be moved backwards and forwards independently of
each other. Two sets of such wheels are arranged so that all those
representing "terms" of the same order are in the same plane.
When the machine is working the wheels representing even dif-

ferences turn in one direction, and those representing odd differences in the other, those representing the odd and even differences respectively in the two cases remaining stationary. Whilst the calculating wheels which represent the tabular numbers, or "the "zero difference," are at rest, the figures thereon which express a given tabular term are reproduced by type wheels actuated by rack and toothed cams. The type wheels are adjusted to print straight by means of a suitable ruler working on a fixed centre. The impression is taken on lead or other material suitable for a matrix, by the rising of the table on which such material is placed.

The means by which the printing, thrusting in the rule, and removing the printed lines are effected "contain nothing new or "unknown." Each wheel for tabular numbers is combined with a toothed volute, cam, or snail, on which bears a spiral toothed cam or the portion of a toothed cylinder, the latter transmitting the movements of such wheels to the type wheels. Each calculating wheel carries the whole of the numbers contained in the system it represents upon its circumference. Each calculating wheel, excepting those which represent tabular numbers, has, moreover, a catch working on a trap, which turns together with a vertical axle on which it is fixed. When the trap is working it catches one of the teeth of the calculating wheel in the row immediately above, and represents any of the figures corresponding to the same vertical column as in ordinary numerical expressions. Thus, any wheel that represents units and can set a trap to work can, by means of that trap, turn another wheel which represents units, and so on, for the wheels representing tens, hundreds, and so on, to the extent to which the machine is arranged to calculate. The vertical axles are turned by means of pinions simultaneously acted on by a rack, which is put in motion by the pinion, which is driven by a toothed segment, which is moved in alternate directions by means of a mangle wheel driven by any convenient means. When any of the calculating wheels turn to or beyond the tooth which corresponds to its zero, it works on a lever between that wheel and the next wheel in the same row in such a manner that the latter is carried forward a single step. In the operation of carrying, the calculating wheels are brought into action by arms or levers affixed to each of two traversing upright arms, which are driven by a chain and chain pulley.

[Printed, 1s. 4d. Drawings.]

A.D. 1854, October 21.—N° 2251.

GREEN, WILLIAM, and PICKETT, JOSEPH.—" Improvements
" in treating or ornamenting textile materials or fabrics, and
" paper, and in machinery or apparatus effecting the same."

Effects similar to "watered" and "shot" silks, are produced on
paper by printing on such paper in some adhesive matter a variety
of fine lines, to which color is subsequently applied, the paper
being afterwards embossed to break up the continuity of the lines.
Secondly, effects similar to those produced by the jacquard apparatus are produced on textile fabrics and paper by printing or
printing and embossing combined. The pattern by which the
material is to be printed is cut up into a series of fine lines and
dots corresponding in size, &c. to those portions of the warp or weft
which are thrown up by the weaving operation on the surface of
the material imitated. The pattern is printed in adhesive matter,
and bright metallic color applied to it. Or the fabric is merely
printed on in a series of fine lines, the continuity of which is
afterwards broken up by embossing. Thirdly, producing patterns
or designs with metal or dry powders, by forming a suitable
" ground" (impression in fine lines and dots taken in mucilaginous adhesive matter), and then rendering certain portions
adhesive by heat or moisture, and pressure. Metallic or tinted
surfaces are imparted to the fabrics after being "blocked," by
embossing them, and moistening or rendering sticky the most
prominent parts, and applying color to the same. A further
object of the invention is "to produce ornamental and figured
" effects " with " flock" or dry colors upon textile fabrics,
without " size-printing " the same previous to printing the
required pattern with varnish. Fourthly, metallic powder is ap-
applied to the material by cold rollers or blocks "done over" with
such powder. If the pattern has been printed in adhesive matter,
the roller used is plain ; if it requires heat or moisture to make it
adhesive, the roller is engraved. Fifthly, in producing "watered"
effects upon paper, or other fabrics which are not ribbed, by
passing them under pressure between ribbed surfaces of india-
rubber, &c. Sixthly, in covering the entire surface of textile
materials or fabrics on either side with " flock " or other fibrous
dust or powder, and causing the flock on one side to be united
with and held by that on the opposite side. A thin open fabric
is selected for this purpose, and saturated with a solution of

india-rubber, gutta percha, or similar matter in bisulphuret of carbon. Lastly, in machinery for ornamenting textile fabrics and paper with "flock" metallic powder, or dry colors generally.

The roll of paper is placed on a spindle on which a slight amount of friction is caused by a weight. It passes between straining bars between rollers, where it is printed with varnish or other adhesive matter. It then passes over a small roller and up an incline, when it is powdered with flock from a box above. The flexible material forming the incline is agitated by cams, which causes the flock to rise in "a kind of a cloud" on the paper, and the superfluous flock to fall off. If the pattern so printed requires filling up with colors, the paper is next drawn between engraved rollers, the number of which, of course, varies with that of the colors to be printed. Guide pins are placed opposite the first of these rollers to insure register between the colours and the flock.

[Printed, 11d. Drawings.]

A.D. 1854, October 24.—Nº 2264.

ADAMS, ISAAC.—" New and useful improvements in machinery " for printing."

The invention relates, (1) to distributing the ink and inking; (2), to pointing the sheet on the tympan; (3), taking the sheet from the feed board, and carrying it under the platen; (4), giving the impression; and (5), removing and piling the printed sheets.

The platen is, for convenience of access to the form, placed in a carriage which runs on horizontal rails. The inking apparatus consists of a trough roller, which, by means of a vibrator, supplies a drum above it. The ink is distributed on the drum by a roller, the axis of which is inclined to that of the drum, and which is made to travel backwards and forwards along the drum. The reversal of the motion of this small roller is due to the action of a fixed piece in the framing, which throws the centre of gravity from one side to the other of a rocking shaft. The drum is hollow, so as to admit of being heated by steam, &c. The inking rollers (attached to the front of a frisket frame) rest upon this drum to receive their supply during the impression. Drawings are given of two and four inking rollers arranged on this plan. The motion of the frisket frame is due to the action of a friction roller upon an "alternator" or slotted piece of a peculiar form fixed upon a rocking shaft below the table. The feeding tympan is inclined to the platen, and furnished with register points of a peculiar kind, which are withdrawn at the moment that nippers upon the frisket frame lay hold of it. Several forms of these nippers are shown. The impression is given by the rising of the type table under the action of toggle-jointed levers worked by a second "alternator." The type table is counterbalanced. A "set-off" sheet is wound on rollers, one on each side of the platen. The printed sheet on its outward travel has its front edge raised by bellows worked by the rocker shaft or other means, so as to be drawn off the frisket by a series of rollers and tapes, which present it to a fly frame, which turns over and deposits it on a pile at the side of the pressman. There is an arrangement of a slide connected with a treadle, by which the pressman can prevent the action of the first "alternator," and consequently the rising of the type table for the impression. The platen is surmounted by a paper "horse."

[Printed, 4s. 5d. Drawings.]

A.D. 1854, October 26.—Nº 2286.

FONTAINEMOREAU, PETER ARMAND, le Comte de.—(Provisional Protection only.)—(Communicated by Leopold Muller and Antoine Widl, of Vienna.)—" Improvements in transferring " colored pictures, portraits, and engravings."

" By means of a lithographic process I obtain an exact outline of the subject to be transferred upon paper, which can then be " transferred either upon paper, stone, glass, leather, metal, wood, " or any other substance; and by submitting this to a litho- " cromic operation, I obtain the colored reproduction of the " object."

[Printed, 3d. No Drawing.]

A.D. 1854, October 31.—Nº 2313.

VORSTER, CHARLES. — (Provisional Protection only.) — " Improvements in the manufacture of ribbons."

The fabric is printed in colours in the piece, and further ornamented by pressing, stamping, or punching. It is then " cut " into ribbons of a breadth corresponding with the pattern."

[Printed, 3d. No Drawing.]

A.D. 1854, October 31.—N° 2315.

JOHNSON, JOHN HENRY. — "Improvements in lithographic " printing presses."

The invention relates to presses driven by power. The pressing cylinder is driven by racks on a reciprocating table carrying the stone, the latter being driven by a mangle wheel arrangement, in which motion is given to the actuating pinion by a driving shaft with fly-wheel and pulleys, the pinion adjusting itself to the upper or lower rack pins on the under side of the table by means of a universal joint, by which it is connected to the driving shaft. The pressing cylinder is required to revolve in one direction only, for which purpose the spur wheels at each of its extremities are void of teeth at those portions of their peripheries which correspond to the extreme end of the table; it is stationary on the return of the table. When the table has completed its backward travel, two small catches take into the blank spaces on the wheels, at which time the stone passes under damping and inking rollers. The latter are slightly inclined, so as to produce a to-and-fro motion, by which the ink is better laid on. They receive ink from an inking table on the sliding table, by which means they are brought into gear again with the racks, ready for another impression, and the inking and damping rollers are elevated by a cam and lever, so as not to be in contact with the stone. The sheets are fed on to the cylinder from a suitable table, and are thereby presented to the stone, being pressed thereon by the aid of weighted levers, which act upon the pressing cylinder. The cylinder is kept stationary by a pin inserted into an opening in the periphery of the spur wheels attached thereto, and which pins are removed when the roller is to turn again. The sheets are laid hold of and held by grippers on the pressing cylinder. An apparatus is attached for pricking the sheets for register.

[Printed, 10d. Drawings.]

A.D. 1854, November 8.—N° 2367.

McDONALD, ALLAN, and McINTOSH, ALEXANDER.—"Im- " provements in machinery for stretching and smoothing cloth or " woven fabrics preparatory to or in the course of being printed."

In order to stretch the fabric in the direction of its width (the " ordinary method " of which is stated to be by means of stretching rails), a "self-acting tenter" is used, consisting in an arrangement of pulleys placed at the ends of a drum or assemblage of drums and rotating on the same shaft with the drums, but round axes of rotation oblique to such shaft.

[Printed, 10d. Drawings.]

A.D. 1854, November 6.—N° 2345.

WALLACE, JAMES, Junior.—"Improvements in zincographic "and lithographic printing."

The invention consists of a press in which the material is printed in web. A printing cylinder of stone or zinc, mounted on solid metal core, has below it a counter-pressure roller, and above it two inking rollers, one above the other, both resting by their own weight on the roller below them. The upper one is supplied with ink by hand or otherwise. The spindles of the counter-pressure roller revolve in bearings, which work in short vertical slots in the side standards. These bearings have bracket arms fixed to them, extending in front of the machine, to carry the roller from which the material to be printed is unwound. The brackets also extend behind the machine to carry the take-up roller, and are, with the bearings of the counter-pressure roller, raised and lowered simultaneously by means of an excentric movement acting on the bearings, or the delivery roller may be carried in bearings in the fixed framing, the take-up roller only being carried in the moveable brackets. The fabric, previously to its being printed, passes over one or two "breadtheners" of the common fixed grooved description. The machine is driven from the printing or counter-pressure roller. The other rollers are driven by frictional contact, except the take-up roller, which is driven by a pulley and cord from the pulley on the same spindle as that carrying the spur wheel. The spur wheel is in gear with a pinion on a separate shaft, upon which a winch handle is fixed, or which is driven by any suitable motive power. The printing roller is moistened by means of a saturated roller and pad, the latter removing the superfluous moisture. This damping apparatus is put in and out of action by excentric or other suitable movement. A granulated surface is produced on the zinc roller by a self-acting apparatus, in which, whilst a slow rotatory motion is given to the roller, a rubber supplied with emery powder is made to work upon its surface.

[Printed, 1s. Drawings.]

## A.D. 1854, November 9.—N° 2373.

PRETSCH, PAUL.—"Improvements in producing copper and "other plates for printing."

The invention consists in obtaining printing surfaces or moulds for printing surfaces from photographic images on glass or other suitable materials. The coated glass or other plates, when taken from the camera or copying frame, are treated with solutions containing alcohol, water, borax, and other like suitable chemical ingredients, by which means certain parts of the photographic copy appear raised, and others sunk, and are then made firm, if necessary, by applying astringents and dry varnish. The surfaces thus produced, or moulds taken from them, are then made conducting, and an electrotype, stereotype, or other copy taken of such surface or mould for the printing surface.

[Printed, 3d. No Drawing.]

## A.D. 1854, November 13.—N° 2401.

GOBERT, ANTOINE EDOUART BRISBART.—"A new kind of "stamping press."

The material to be stamped is placed on a table, upon which are two uprights serving as guides to a slider provided with a projecting foot and furnished with a socket, to which the stamp is affixed. Motion being imparted to the lever by a handle, one of its arms draws the inking roller over the inclined cover of an ink case, whilst the other causes the slider to come down. The ink in this form of the press is placed in a wedge-shaped reservoir; or an elastic block charged with color may be used.

By another arrangement the handle is dispensed with and the lever inverted, the stamp being fixed loosely in the socket, so as to adapt itself to the inclination of the table. The ink holder of this press is composed of a closed reservoir perforated on its upper side with small holes, and a cloth tightly stretched over it, without touching, by two small iron rods.

[Printed, 9d. Drawings.]

## A.D. 1854, November 24.—N° 2490.

DE LA RUE, THOMAS.—"An improvement in the manufacture "of compositions suitable for printing rollers, printing ink, and "flexible moulds."

The invention consists in the use of glycerine in such manufacture.

1. Cuttings of hides or skins known as "glue pieces," cleansed by soaking in water, are cut into slices and laid in a copper, with as much glycerine as will cover them. The copper is heated, and kept at about 175° or 190° Fahrenheit, until the cuttings are dissolved, when the liquid is run off and cooled. This composition is used for the manufacture of printing rollers, in the same way as that hitherto used of glue and treacle. Instead of using "glue " pieces," the composition may be prepared by employing glycerine to dissolve glue, isinglass, or gelatine, "the process being aided by " a moderate heat, as when dissolving glue in water." 2. For ink, the glycerine is united with precipitates of logwood or other vegetable coloring matter, and printed with "in the ordinary " manner of letter-press printing." Such ink is "fugitive, and " peculiarly applicable to the printing of bankers' cheques," &c. 3. For flexible moulds, the glycerine glue prepared as above is melted on to, and allowed to set on the surface from which it is desired to obtain a mould. When cold, the mould may be removed " in like manner to when using other preparations for flexible " moulds."

[Printed, 3d. No Drawing.]

A.D. 1854, December 6.—No 2564.

MARTIN, ALBINUS.—(Communicated.)—" Improvements in the " the production of indigo dye colours in dyeing and printing " textile fabrics and fibrous materials."

The materials to be dyed or printed are submitted to baths containing respectively a salt of manganese, orpiment, and caustic alkali, and then to a hot ash or alkaline indigo vat.

[Printed, 3d. No Drawing.]

A.D. 1854, December 21.—No 2690.

VENABLES, JOHN, and MANN, ARTHUR.—(Provisional Protection only.)—" Printing and fixing self and other colours in " China, earthenware, Parian, gypsum, stoneware, bricks, blocks, " vats, slabs, tiles, quarries, glass, metals, hardwares, gums and " gummeous substances, and papier maché ware."

The design for China, earthenware, Parian, gypsum, stoneware, bricks, blocks, vats, slabs, tiles, and quarries, is carved or engraved with instruments or acids on plates of wood, stone, metal, or other hard material. The self or other color to be fixed is then rubbed in, and paper or cloth laid upon the plates and subjected to pressure, by which means the self or other colours are deposited on such fabric, and the same is brought into contact with the said articles of ware while they are in a plastic, " slip," or other state susceptible of receiving such design. For glass, metals, and hardware, the design is produced as above upon a fabric, and brought into contact with glass, &c., while they are in a fused, soft, or heated state. The same method is adopted with reference to gums and gummeous substances, and papier mâché ware, to which the design obtained as above is applied "while they are in a " soft and plastic state."

[Printed, 3d. No Drawing.]

A.D. 1854, December 28.—N° 2736.

COCKCROFT, John.—"Improvements in machinery or appa-
" ratus for printing woven or textile fabrics and yarns."

The invention consists in a peculiar arrangement of the calico or grey piece, by which the endless woollen mackintosh or cotton blanket, "as now generally used," is dispensed with. The calico is peculiarly arranged on a roller, so as to form several folds as it passes to the machine. In this way it advances to and round the cylinder, the under fold forming a perfect substitute for the woollen blanket, and the surface fold answering the purpose of the calico " hitherto used in conjunction with the blanket or mackintosh."

[Printed, 11d. Drawings.]

A.D. 1854, December 29.—N° 2749.

WIDNELL, Henry.—"Improvements in the manufacture of
" carpets and other textile fabrics."

" In printing the threads or yarns, the process is the same as
" that known as Whytock's plan for printing maps, except that
" instead of including on the printing paper the ground colors
" in the places in which they occur in the pattern, the colouring
" on the printing paper is arranged so as to take only the several
" rows in succession of the device or pattern on the ground, as
" such device or pattern is marked on the said printing paper.
" By this means the pattern as transferred stands on a few lines,
" as compared with the original, because the whole of the ground

" is left out. The threads are then printed from this paper in the
" ordinary manner. The ground colour may be inserted after the
" completion of each row, or it may be done before the colored
" worsted or other material is put in. The loom referred to under
" the second part of my invention has a frame, on the top of
" which are placed two beams, containing warps or chains of
" cotton or other material. Inside this frame works another
" frame on a pivot or axle in the centre, resting on the outer
" frame. Across the top of this inner frame the heddles are
" placed, through which the warp threads of one beam pass, the
" threads of the other beam passing through the intermediate
" spaces; consequently, when the frame is moved to or fro, the
" warp ends which pass through the heddles are brought back-
" wards or forwards, thereby making a ' shed' through which the
" weft is passed."

[Printed, 6d. Drawings.]

# 1855.

A.D. 1855, January 3.—N° 14.

FONTAINE, HIPPOLYTE. — " Improvements in engravers'
" presses."

1. Two printing tables are placed at a suitable distance on slots
or slides at the frame side. On the under side of each is a transverse roller, with a pinion keyed on each end, and on each side a
stud-wheel partially toothed, and gearing into these pinions.
The stud-wheels turn in opposite directions, and are angularly so
placed that the toothed segments stand diametrically opposite
each other. Hence, by gearing into each roller alternately, each
table has a to-and-fro motion in an opposite direction to the
other. The same arrangement of gearing causes each roller
periodically to stand still during the revolution of half the circumference of the stud-wheel diminished by the toothed portion.
The reverse motion of the stud-wheel is obtained by driving from
one side by a train of change, carrier, and level wheels. 2. The
pressing cylinders lie across each table in movable and elastic
bearings, their pressure being regulated by means of screws and
connecting frames. 3. " Stretching rollers " are mounted in spring
or elastic bearings for the purpose of stretching the blanket

wrapping round them and the pressing cylinders. 4. The apparatus for inking the plates consists mainly of two couples of inking rollers, capable of moving to and fro in suitable slides, on a frame. In the middle of the slides is a heavy feed roller, which is lifted up in its slotted bearing when the rollers pass, and is made to dip into the inkholder, and by turning on the said couples of inking rollers, communicates to each of them the necessary quantity of ink. In the middle portion of the inking table, which is between the slide frames, there is a marble or other surface, for taking off the surplus ink that has been given to the inking rollers by the feed roller, and also for spreading the same. At the two ends of the inking table there are suitable surfaces on which to lay the plates to be inked. The said surfaces or plate-holders are hinged, so as to be turned out of the way when required; the shape of trellis-work with shark edges is given to them so as to offer the least possible surface to the inking rollers. 5. A wiping apparatus for the above, in which the main feature is an endless delivery or transmission, made of any suitable material or substance, by which the plates are made to pass under and against cushions.

[Printed, 1s. 4d. Drawings.]

A.D. 1855, January 5.—N° 32.

LIVESEY, John.—" Improvements in printing, and in the " materials and apparatus connected therewith."

The invention consists, first, of a self-inking apparatus placed in an iron frame, and travelling in the direction of the pressing cylinder by the aid of pulleys on cross rails above it. A trough roller conveys the ink by an excentric motion to a distributing roller, which works at an angle with and travels from end to end of the first of a series of inking rollers, from which it receives its travelling and rotatory motion. On arriving at the end of the inking roller, or of that portion over which it is necessary for it to travel, the trough and distributing roller is made to turn at an opposite angle by a small self-acting catch, and the angle of the distributing roller having been thus reversed, it is caused to travel in a contrary direction. Secondly, in the use in lithographic machines of large sized transfer rollers, composed of segments of stone secured to a foundation of iron. Thirdly, in the employment of printing or transfer rollers, composed of zinc plates or

segments of wood secured to a suitable metal frame, the wooden
segments having stereotype casts attached thereto. Fourthly, in
clothing damping rollers for lithographic presses with successive
layers of flannel, calico, and velvet. Fifthly, in the use of cutting
rollers for dividing continuous lengths or webs of printed fabrics
into sheets of the required size. Sixthly, in a lithographic ink,
composed of typographic ink (1lb.), strong lithographic ink (1½
oz.), and rosin 1½ oz. To give blackness and brilliancy, ½oz. of
Venice turpentine is added cold to every 2lbs. of the composition.
Seventhly, in an improved process for facilitating the transfers of
old engravings or prints, from which transfers it is desired to print.
The engraving, &c. is soaked for five or ten minutes in a preparation of distilled water (3 oz.), caustic potass (1 oz.), essence
of lavender (¼ oz.) The excessive moisture is removed by putting
the engraving, without pressure, between blotting-paper sheets,
after which the stone or zinc plate on to which the transfer is to
be made is slightly heated, and the transfer made by pressure.

[Printed, 1s. 4d. Drawings.]

## A.D. 1855, January 8.—Nº 48.

NAGLES, ALBERT.—(Provisional Protection only.)—" Improve-
" ments in machinery or apparatus for cleaning the surfaces of
" woven fabrics, and also for distending or spreading the same
" either before or after or during the processes of bleaching,
" printing, or other similar operations."

The invention consists in, 1, clearing the surface of calico, linen,
or other cloth, of knots or fibrous or other loose matters by
means of a rapidly revolving roller furnished with brass or other
metallic knives or blades, wound like the threads of quick threaded
screws around the said roller; 2, distending or spreading out
the cloth so as to complete its manufacture smoothly and evenly
" without the assistance of tentering pins or other substitute."
The apparatus consists of small revolving rollers with surfaces of
right and left-handed screws commencing in the middle. They
are divided in half their length for the purpose of being set or
adjusted slightly out of line with each other. " The goods may
" also be conveniently " untwisted" in the piece or pieces by
" placing the waggon of pieces on a turntable at the ends of
" any of those machines, and thus the turning of the waggon of
" pieces easily accomplished, either in one direction or the other,

" as occasion may require to "untwist" the pieces in their
" progress."

[Printed, 3d. No Drawing.]

A.D. 1855, January 10.—N° 68.

LEHUGEUR, Louis Pierre, and UTTINGER, Michel.—
" Improvements applicable to machinery for printing fabrics."

The object of these is, first, to obtain greater regularity and
uniformity in the supply of color; and, secondly, to obviate the
necessity of employing so many children as are usually employed
in the operation. The improvements are applicable to any
machinery for block-printing fabrics.

The color table is covered with a cloth of air-tight material, and
the required elasticity imparted to it by means of a collapsible
vessel of india-rubber, &c., and provided with a counterbalance
weight, filled with water or other liquid. The color is placed in a
trough at one end of the cloth, and the latter supplied from it by
means of a horizontal brush or other suitable contrivance, which
extends across the table, and is worked backward and forward
over the cloth by means of a lever, the apparatus being so arranged
that the cloth and the color in the reservoir shall be kept together,
and when the printing operation is finished, and the color is required
to be changed, the color cloth can be scraped, and the cover of the
reservoir moved forward by a single stroke of the lever, so as to
close it, and prevent the color from drying by evaporation, "as
" is the case in the ordinary method of working."

[Printed, 7d. Drawings.]

A.D. 1855, January 26.—N° 200.

LEESE, Joseph, Junior.—" Certain improvements in the process
" of printing calicoes and other textile fabrics."

The improvements relate to the "resist" (or paste made of salts
of copper and flour printed on the goods to protect them from the
action of the blue vat or dye), and consist in recovering the copper
from the washings of the cloth, and from the acid solution which
is used subsequently to remove it, ("which has heretofore been
" considered waste,") by evaporation or addition of zinc or iron,
or by the use of ammonia, and also in substituting ammonia,

sulphate of manganese, salts of iron, the sulphurets of the same
two metals, or mixtures of these salts, also of resins dissolved by
alkalis or other solvents, for the salts of copper.

[Printed, 3d. No Drawing.]

A.D. 1855, February 5.—N° 272.

CARRÉ, PIERRE JOSEPH. — (Provisional Protection only.) —
" Improvements in ornamenting fabrics with metal leaf."

The fabric to be ornamented is fastened on paper, cardboard,
or other suitable material, and embossed by a block at the same
time that it is printed, with a suitable mordant for attaching the
metal leaf. The leaf is spread on a sheet of paper, prepared with
an unctuous or other body, suitable for temporarily attaching
the sheet to the paper. The sheet of paper with the leaf thereon
is then placed on the engraved block, over it is placed accurately
by register points, the fabric already embossed and printed with
mordant, and the whole is covered by several folds of cloth,
then pressed and heated while under pressure, so as to cause the
leaf to adhere firmly. Finally, the fabric is removed from the
press, separated from the paper, cardboard, or other material to
which it was attached, and any superfluous leaf is removed by
brushing.

[Printed, 3d. No Drawing.]

A.D. 1855, February 6.—N° 281.

SMITH, PETER.—" Improvements in machinery or apparatus for
" printing textile fabrics and other surfaces."

The invention (shown as applied to an eight-color machine,
in which as many rollers are placed about a central pressing
cylinder) consists in the adaptation of lifting and traversing
apparatus to cylinder printing machinery for facilitating the
shipping and unshipping of the printing rollers and mandrils as
is required in working such machinery. An open rectangular
frame large enough when traversed to one side to overhang all
parts of the machine, runs on wheels on railways above the framing
standards. The frame stands at right angles to the axis of the
printing cylinders, and its two ends are fitted with a pair of freely
running rope or chain pulleys. One end of these chains has a
hook for the purpose of lifting the mandril, the other is wound

round a hoisting barrel. On one end of the hoisting barrel shaft is a worm wheel having in gear with it a worm on the upper end of a vertical shaft carried in collar bearings on the side of the main standard framing, and descending to a level to suit the convenience of the attendant, a handle being fitted at this part for fitting the shaft. A similar shaft is fitted up close to the one just described for effecting the horizontal traverse of the frame. The upper end of this shaft is connected by a pair of bevil pinions with a horizontal shaft passing across the machine above the frame. This shaft carries a spur pinion gearing with a horizontal rack passing along the centre of the frame. Or two racks may be used, one on each side of the frame.

[Printed, 9d. Drawings.]

A.D. 1855, February 8.—N° 297.

WILSON, JOHN.—(Provisional Protection only.)—" Improve-
" ments in the manufacture of rollers for printing and embossing
" calico and other fabrics."

The invention consists in the use of zinc instead of copper rollers for the above purposes, "the object being to produce rollers " at less expense than heretofore."

[Printed, 3d. No Drawing.]

A.D. 1855, February 10.—N° 319.

BESNARD, LOUIS ADOLPHE FERDINAND.—" An improved
" composition for fixing lithographs and engravings on canvas
" after being transposed or reproduced by a printing press."

A spoonful of linseed is boiled for a few minutes in a quart of soft water. To half a glass of this mixture (strained) are added 400 grains troy of white moist sugar. A second bath is made of 800 grains troy of pure white gelatine, boiled and stirred in a quart of water and strained. This is mixed with the former, and, when boiling, a camel hair brush saturated with the mixture is passed quickly and lightly over the lithograph or engraving (which has been previously transferred to the canvas by means of transfer paper which is entirely removed), up and down, across, and to and fro, thus leaving the drawing completely freed from the smallest particle of paper. This application of the above solution fixes instantaneously the drawing to the canvas, which is hen coated with varnish (cold, and not too thick) by means of a fish-tail brush. The canvas thus prepared is ready for painting on by the ordinary methods.

[Printed, 3d. No Drawings.]

A.D. 1855, February 10.—N° 320.

BELLFORD, Auguste Edouard Loradoux.—(Communicated by Professor Frederic Kuhlmann, of Lille.)—" Certain materials to " be used for cementing and printing, and also applicable to " printing and dressing or finishing fabrics."

The novelties introduced into this branch of manufacture consist in :—1. Completely substituting solutions of silicate of soda or of potash, for oil, essence, glue, &c. for any kind of painting, printing, varnishing, and gilding on any kind of surface or object, and using for these paints artificial or natural sulphate of barytes to be applied in many cases as substitutes for white lead and zinc white. 2. The use of solutions of silicate for fixing in the cold state paints, enamels, varnishes, and gilding upon porcelain and glass, and in the case of the latter, when it is desired to obtain a plain or uniform tint, by doubling or lining the white glass with a sheet or leaf of coloured glass fixed upon it by means of silicate. 3. The mode of joining pieces or panes of glass edgeways by means of a cement consisting of an alkaline silicate and certain oxydes. 4. Preparing, with silicates obtained by the dry process, lime and some siliceous matter, a mortar to be used instead of painters' and hydraulic cements, and also cements for joining iron and for mouldings and other plastic purposes. 5. The use and application of soluble silicates in letter-press printing and writing materials by forming black or differently colored printing ink, and also an indelible writing ink. 6. Manufacturing plain and velveted paper-hangings, sand and emery paper, by using the silicate. 7. Using the silicates for printing fabrics and fixing upon them printing colors such as ultramarine and lakes. 8. Using the said silicates for finishing fabrics and stiffening paper pulp, and also for fixing the latter in a pulverulent state on paper and on fabrics. 9. The method of coloring, preparing, or dyeing calcareous stones, shells, or other substances whose base is carbonate of lime, by boiling them, with or without artificial pressure, in a more or less concentrated solution of sulphates of insoluble oxyde, and by fixing the colours or colourless oxydes thus absorbed by means of an alkaline silicate. 10. The method of using hydro-fluosilicic either for hardening directly calcareous stones by covering them with a silicious cement, which also prepares them for receiving the silicious painting above described, or for fixing the potash that is contained in stones that have been hardened by the application of silicate of potash, or else for merely rendering insoluble the silicious colours after they have been applied.

[Printed, 4d. No Drawing.]

A.D. 1855, February 16.—N° 355.

WRIGHT, SAMUEL BARLOW, and GREEN, HENRY THOMAS. —" Improvements in the manufacture of encaustic tiles."

The invention consists in causing clay to be " expressed through " a suitable die in the form of a sheet (as has been heretofore " practised in the manufacture of other tiles)." It is received on a tray with vulcanized india-rubber sides moving past the expressing machine at a like speed. It is acted on in its movement by a roller, which produces the desired pattern. The hollow parts of the pattern are next filled up with fluid clay or slip from suitable vessels, and the clay cut into tiles, the excess being scraped off the surface of the tiles. The tiles when partially dried are passed under a revolving scraper or surfaces, and afterwards faced by a revolving polisher. When dry and ready for the oven they are made true, square, and slightly undercut at the edges by a revolving stone or grinding surface previous to firing.

[Printed, 1s. Drawing.]

A.D. 1855, February 20.—N° 371.

SCHOTTLANDER, HENRY.—" Improvements in ornamenting " looking-glasses."

A design is printed or painted in colors upon the back of the glass before it is silvered. When silvered the parts not covered with color become ordinary looking-glasses and form the basis or ground of the design. Or the design may be made the reflecting part by covering the whole of the back with color and scraping away the form of the design. " The chromo-printing or the " printing of pictorial or ornamental designs, as well as mere " letters in colors direct upon glass . . . distinguishes itself from

" the well-known method of chromo-printing upon paper, by the
" following peculiarities:—That the colors employed must be
" prepared in a more solid body, less liquified than those used for
" printing upon paper, on account of the latter being more porous
" and spongy. . . . That in chromo-printing upon glass, the
" printing being upon the back of the glass, the colors are laid on
" in reversed order, that is to the last in the one case are applied
" first in the other."

[Printed, 3d. No Drawing.]

A.D. 1855, February 21.—N° 383.

NORTON, FREDERICK WILLIAM.—(Provisional Protection
only.)—" Improvements in the manufacture of printed or colored
" warp fabrics."

The invention relates to that class of printed warps generally
used in the manufacture of tapestry and velvet pile carpets, and is
intended to facilitate the accurate setting of the printed threads.
In carrying it out in practice "the warp printer goes to work in
" the usual manner, and after putting the first thread upon the
" drum, and before printing that thread, he prints with a dissolved
" gum resin, or with any other suitable pigment or substance a
" small line across the thread so wound up. This operation is
" repeated before commencing to print each of the threads
" intended to form the printed or figured warp always printing
" the gum line upon the same division of the drum throughout
" the pattern."

[Printed, 3d. No Drawing.]

A.D. 1855, February 25.—N° 408.

LEBEL, VICTOR JOSEPH, FOURNIOL, JEAN, and REMYON,
JEAN BAPTISTE.—" Improvements on typographic presses."

The improved presses are applicable to all sorts of printing in
colours, either from blocks, type, stereotype, or stone, and are
well adapted for printing colored posting bills, show cards, playing cards, patterns for embroidery, and similar articles. To prevent
each of the inking rollers from touching any but the required parts
of the form during its passage beneath them, they are furnished
with a narrow wheel or roller at each end, which enters a corresponding groove at the side of the form. These grooves and the
rollers are each placed in a different line, so that each inking roller

only descends upon that block or stone, or portion of the form
which is required to receive the color with which such inking
roller is charged. The inking rollers may be of ordinary composition when ordinary printing ink is used. Rollers covered with
leather may be substituted when stone or zinc plates employed for
printing in the manner of lithography, and these rollers may be
loaded or pressed down upon the stone, if necessary.

[Printed, 10d. Drawings.]

A.D. 1855, February 26.—N⁰ 414.

BROWN, WILLIAM.—" Certain improvements in machinery for
" printing."

The invention consists, first, in the use of a carriage and
parallel motion rods in connexion with the type table, which
brings it down upon the platen; secondly, in a carriage and combination of levers for giving a traversing motion to the inking
rollers, by which the type is inked as the table rises; thirdly, in a
peculiar arrangement of a pinion "ratchet" and spur wheel in
connexion with an endless band for feeding in the paper or other
material.

[Printed, 5d. Drawing.]

A.D. 1855, March 1.—N⁰ 452.

VIGOUREUX, STANISLAS.—" Certain improvements in print-
" ing, ornamenting, and dressing woven and textile fabrics."

The fabric is placed on a hollow table or box, the upper surface
of which is perforated with small holes. A plate engraved, perforated, embossed, or corrugated with any required pattern, is laid
upon the fabric and covered by another plate, on which are laid
several thicknesses of cloth, so as to form a sort or cushion, and a
strong plate is placed upon the whole and forced down by screws,
hydraulic, or other suitable pressure; steam, hot water, or hot air
is then admitted into the hollow table, to moisten and heat the
fabric, and force it into the cavities or perforations in the pattern
plate. The pressure is continued after the steam has been
shut off. The fabric may be dyed before or after the above operations, and it may be printed at the same time, by charging the
surface or the cavities of the plate with color. Or the plates may
be heated and the pressure given to a roller or rollers, so that in all

cases the pattern be produced on the fabric by the combined action
of heat and pressure. The fabric may be rendered more lustrous
by afterwards passing it round heated cylinders. The pattern
plates and table may be of the length of the fabric to be operated
upon, or the pattern may be repeated at several successive operations. Two or more pattern plates and piles of fabric may be
placed one above another in the press, and operated upon at the
same time.

❙⊏ [Printed, 6d. Drawings.]

A.D. 1855, March 2.—Nº 467.

NEWTON, ALFRED VINCENT.—"Improvements in the con-
" struction of printing presses."

The invention consists, first, in hanging the type table (which
rises and falls for each impression) upon springs, so that the
weight of the bed (several hundred pounds), and the elasticity of
the springs, will be sufficient to overcome about three-fourths of
the motion in falling and rising, the remaining part being overcome by cam attachments, which come into operation just before,
and after the weight of the bed and springs cease to operate. By
these means the press is worked " with proper ease and without
" the least perceptible jar." Secondly, in arranging the inking
rollers and frisket on separate carriages on the same ways, and
moving at such relative velocities that the frisket may remove the
sheet from the form quickly whilst the inking rollers travel more
slowly, and so that the inking rollers return to the ink trough
after inking the form, without awaiting the return of the frisket.
Thirdly, in "pointing" the sheet by an automatic movement,
so that the operator can with both hands hold and control the
sheet for the nippers without letting it go, as " heretofore done."
Fourthly, in the use of a blast of air to fix the sheet on the
register points for reiteration. Fifthly, in " taking off " by means
of inverted cups, from which the air is exhausted, and which come
down upon it and cause it to adhere to them. The cups may be
arranged on hollow arms on a hollow shaft, so that the paper may
be drawn off, turned over, and laid upon the table in proper
position for being again passed through the press.

[Printed, 1s. Drawings.]

A.D. 1855, March 5.—N° 492.

WOOD, JAMES.—" Improvements in ornamenting woven fabrics
" for bookbinders and others."

The invention consists in applying Dutch metal leaf to woven
fabrics, by printing on to the fabric with adhesive composition,
and then applying the leaf by block or surface printing. The
designs are prepared "in the ordinary manner." The printing
fluid (which prevents the leaf from tarnishing) is made with
varnish mixed and boiled with beeswax, to which mixture, while
hot, oil of lavender is added " before or after the embossing of such
" fabrics, in the usual manner," to imitate leather and otherwise.

[Printed, 3d. No Drawing.]

A.D. 1855, March 6.—N° 501.

TARDIF, EUGÈNE.—"An improved construction of numbering
" apparatus."

The invention consists in applying to a hand-stamp a contrivance
for turning the numbering discs during the transit of the apparatus from the article stamped to the inking pad, so as to print
in "as quick succession as impressions can be given off from a
" simple stamp." The click which acts upon the units' disc
wheel is attached to a sliding bar, which works in guides in the
frame of the numbering apparatus, and the sliding rod connected to a rod which passes through the handle of the apparatus,
and carries a button or knob at its upper end to receive the pressure
of the thumb of the operator. A coiled spring in the handle
returns the rod after each depression, and thereby draws the click
into the proper position for acting upon the next succeeding tooth
of the units' disc wheel. A rest is applied to the lower part of the
apparatus, which enables the operator to bring down the printing
surface with great precision on to the article to be printed.

[Printed, 7d. Drawings.]

A.D. 1855, March 9.—N° 531.

MURDOCH, JAMES.—(Communicated.)—"An improved method
" of enlarging or reducing designs, maps, and other similar
" articles; also apparatus or machinery to be employed in the
" same."

The invention consists, first, in enlarging the above by transferring the designs to a sheet of caoutchouc or other suitable elastic material, and then stretching the material equally in all directions, and in reducing such designs by transferring them to a sheet of caoutchouc or other suitable elastic material, which has been previously equally stretched in all directions, and then allowing the same to contract. Secondly, in transferring designs to or from the elastic material by the following means:—A circular tray of somewhat larger diameter than a table beneath which it is placed is moveable vertically by means of a screw working in the boss of the tray, and is guided by four columns which pass through holes in the tray. The screw is turned by a train of wheel work. The sheet of caoutchouc is spread over the table, and secured to the table by means of a ring bolted down upon the former. By drawing down the tray by means of the screw, the required stretching of the caoutchouc is effected. To give pressure for transferring the tracings, there is a platen fixed to a lever working above the table, hinged at one end to a standard bolted to the bed of the machine, and connected at the other by a rod to another lever below worked by a screw.

[Printed, 7d. Drawings.]

## A.D. 1855, March 14.—No 568.

NEALE, ROBERT.—" Improvements in copper and other plate " printing."

The invention consists in wiping and polishing the engraved plate "without the assistance of the human hand." The plate is attached to a reciprocating bed, above which is the inking, wiping, and polishing apparatus. The inking-roller carriages are constructed in such a manner that the line to which the ink is applied can be confined to the engraved portion, which " saves " ink, facilitates wiping, and secures clean margins to the " paper." The " wipers " (of which there are three sets) are of fine smooth leather stuffed with elastic material, and attached to spokes of a wheel working on a vertical axis. This wheel is made so nicely adjustable that the wipers touch the plate with the least degree of pressure required to clean it. The wipers are themselves cleaned by passing over revolving endless belts of cloth supplied with suitable chemical or other materials, or belts of brushes. The chemical materials are, for the first set of wipers,

spirits of turpentine; for the second, a solution of caustic potass
and lime mixed with turpentine. The third belt, which completes
the polishing, is dry, and is supplied with powdered whiting. The
blankets are kept tight by passing them over a roller attached to
one end of a weighted bent lever. The paper is fed in by means
of an endless belt, "in a well known mode." The pressure of the
pressing rollers is confined to the engraved portion of the plate by
means of a piece of leather or other material placed on either side
of the tympan, and made of the exact size of the engraved portion
of the plate, and so placed as to come over that portion only. This
prevents the indentation of the paper, and keeps its edges clean.

[Printed, 9d. Drawings.]

### A:D. 1855, March 25.—Nº 675.

GEDGE, John.—(Communicated.)—"Improvements in the mode
" or modes of transferring designs on to woven, textile, or other
" fabrics, or on paper; and in the machinery used for such
" purposes."

The ink is furnished by a trough roller below a horizontal ink
table to a roller working in a lever above it, by which it is spread
upon the table as it runs to and fro. The table furnishes ink as
it runs under a series of vertical rollers to the lowest roller of the
group, by which the ink is forwarded to the one above it, which
deposits it on the printing roller, to which the design has been
transferred. The upper roller in the series is a pressing cylinder,
which, when not pressed down for printing (by a lever attached to
it), is raised by the action of a spring. The printing roller is also
furnished with a damper supplied with water from a pipe "perfo-
" rated in a similar manner to those used on the common road
" watering carts." Both the dampers and inking rollers are kept
to the stone or zinc by weighted levers. The printing roller
moves continuously in one direction, and there is a contrivance
for periodically lowering the inking rollers, which have reciprocating motion, owing to the motion of the inking table. The
fabric is printed in web.

[Printed, 6d. Drawings.]

### A.D. 1855, March 30.—Nº 710.

BABCOCK, George H., and BABCOCK, Asher M.—"Im-
" provements in presses for printing in colours, called ' Polychro-
" ' matic Printing Presses.' "

The type is fixed upon beds which move perpendicularly to the face of a prism having one side more than there are colors to be printed (in the drawings three). The additional side is for the purpose of feeding and flying the sheets. At each corner is hung a frisket frame, which is pressed down upon the platens by cams acting upon rollers attached to each side of the frisket. On the shaft of this frisket, and near the centre of it, is fitted a helical spring, which, as the face of the prism comes up, and the cams release the frisket, raises it to deliver the printed sheet and receive a new one. At the next turn this frisket is closed, and the succeeding one rises. The sheet is held fast when once taken on until all the colors are printed. The inking rollers are carried at the ends of a set of oscillating or vibratory arms attached to the rocking shaft which works the beds. There are two rollers in each arm, and as many arms as there are printing beds. The rollers are fitted in slots in the arms, and are pressed out towards the ends of the arms by doubled-leaved springs pressing against the sides of cam-shaped projections. The ink fountains and distributors are of the ordinary construction. When the arms are stationary the inking rollers are kept in contact with fixed revolving cylinders, from which they receive their supply. The prism or polygonal tympan is rotated at the required movement by the aid of a connecting rod and lever acting upon a disc fast on the tympan shaft. This disc is fitted with as many pins as there are sides of the polygon, and the pins are acted upon by springs so as to enter a slot in the actuating lever arm, and cause the disc to be moved the proper distance at the correct time. The disc is held steadily after each movement, by the pin last acted on dropping into a hole in a fixed plate attached to the side of the machine. "When more " than three beds are used, it is proposed to place the polygonal " tympan and beds in a vertical position, and feed in the sheets from " above. . . In this case the additional side of the platen or tympan " will not be required." The beds may also be made stationary, and the platens made to move outwards against them by a series of levers and connecting rods, as above described with reference to the beds.

[Printed, 10d. Drawings.]

A.D. 1855, April 7.—N° 770.

ROLLASON, ALEXANDER.—" Certain improvements in photo-
" graphy."

The invention consists in transferring the film on which the image is formed on glass or silver, to paper, cloth, or other suitable medium. The picture having been formed on a base of collodion, albumen, gutta percha, or other gum, the back is varnished " as usual," and the picture subjected to a slight washing of dilute nitric or equivalent acid or alkali, which has the effect of detaching it from the glass or silver. The paper or other medium is then gummed on the back, the gum being mixed with honey to render it more tenacious. When the gum is nearly hard the medium is stripped off, and the picture brought away with it from the glass. Should the gum get quite hard, one edge of the picture is moistened with distilled water which liberates it.

[Printed, 4d. No Drawing.]

A.D. 1855, April 7.—No 774.

ARESTI, JOSEPH.—" A method of obtaining improved effects " upon drawings washed and painted on stone."

The invention consists in producing " the light granulated effect " hitherto peculiar to aquatinta etchings upon copper or steel " plates," by the application of a series of light graduated stipples or dots to the design (drawn or transferred on the stone) by means of a hair pencil or pen dipped in a mixture of gum water, nitric acid, and indian ink. The work is then brushed over with a mixture of spirits of turpentine and olive oil (equal parts), and charged with printing ink by a roller. The marks or dots formed by the mucilage rejecting the printing ink will appear light, and the intervals surrounding such dots by retaining the black ink produces a stippled tint the reverse of the effect of chalk or crayon drawings, but harmonizing with the painted or washed drawings with which it is intended to combine and protect. Dots or lines to suit every degree of strength and texture of the printing are thus formed, and may be made severally to occupy small spaces, and afterwards united and arranged by the usual retransferring process to the full size required. An impression is then taken from this arranged tint upon transfer paper with the usual strong inks, and dusted over then with finely-powdered asphaltum and resin (equal parts). It is laid upon the surface of the painted drawing and transferred to the stone prepared by the usual acidulation " by the ordinary " methods." The work is next etched with a mixture of water

(100 parts) to 10 of nitric acid (10), and candied sugar (10), and the whole washed off with spirits of turpentine and oil (equal parts). It is then charged with ink, and printed " by the " ordinary methods of lithography."

[Printed, 4d. No Drawing.]

## A.D. 1855, April 11.—N° 799.

DOPTER, JEAN VINCENT MARIE.—" Certain improvements " in printing fabrics."

The invention consists, first, in reducing to powder cloth printing colours (either steam or application colours), mordants, or madder, cochineal, and other dyeing substances, mordants corroding on dyed or printed fabrics, and such substances as form " resists " or " spares." Secondly, applying these powders to printing or tracing off on every kind of fabric by lithography, chromo-lithography, zincography, copper-plate engraving, typography, and also by all the modes of printing that are carried on in different colors with fatty or glutinous substances that can be powdered upon. Thirdly, in powdering over the stone, wood, or metal on which the drawing or engraving has been made, coated with either a fatty or glutinous substance that is made to receive the powdered color, and by the application of a considerable pressure, is then fixed on the fabric previously damped for that purpose. Fourthly, in covering the fabric with a gelatine coating, which resists the color, except where such coating is printed upon. Fifthly, in applying on the fabric previously damped a thin sheet of gelatine printed and powdered upon, which being dissolved by steam leaves the color on the fabric, Sixthly, in printing on any solid and smooth body that can be powdered upon, and transmit the print thus powdered to paper, wood, metal, varnished leather, or other fabric, coated or uncoated, with gum, varnish, &c. Seventhly, in printing on paper or other solid body, glutinous soluble substances that by pressure and previous damping take off on the fabric any fatty substance duly powdered with the proper color. Eighthly, in fixing the paper or other fabric intended to be printed or traced off upon some solid body by means of an agglutinative substance in order to bring the patterns of different colors into their proper places.

[Printed, 4d. No Drawing.]

A.D. 1855, April 18.—N° 853.

KAY, JOHN.—" Improvements in preparing and printing textile " fabrics and other surfaces."

The invention relates more particularly to the cleansing, stretching, and smoothing calico and other woven goods previous to or at the time of their being printed. The apparatus employed for this purpose may be applied to printing machines of various kinds, but as adapted for the ordinary cylinder printing machines it is preferred to fit it up in the following manner :—At the back or on the entering side of the printing machine is a small framework carrying a pair of helical scroll-blade rollers parallel to each other, geared together with equal-sized wheels rotating in concert but in reverse directions, and geared so as to work continuously with the machine itself. The contiguous ends of the right and left scroll blade coming together at an angle, the effect of the rollers is to stretch the fabric across its width, and at the same time to clear off any loosely adhering fibres and foreign matters. For this purpose the acting edges of the blades are sharpened or made thin, so as to aid the clearing action. The direction of the rotation of the rollers is contrary to that of the fabric's traverse. There is an arrangement worked by a handle, by which the relative position of the scroll-blade rollers can be adjusted by the printer, so as to regulate the stretching and cleansing effect.

This invention, or a modification thereof, is also applicable for preparing textile fabrics prior to drying and beaming them.

[Printed, 7d. Drawings.]

A.D. 1855, April 19.—N° 866.

HINDLE, JAMES.—(Provisional Protection only.)—" Improve-" ments in machinery or apparatus used in the process of printing " woven fabrics."

The invention consists in dispensing with the grey cloth usually interposed between the blanket and the fabric, and cleansing the blanket whilst the machine is in motion, " by passing it between " rollers revolving in water, or any suitable liquid, and then " drying it by means of heated cylinders and steam-chests, and " then conveying it to the printing process perfectly cleansed " thus having constantly a clean blanket without stopping the " progress of the work, or using calico or other material for the " purpose."

[Printed, 6d. Drawings.]

## A.D. 1855, April 19.—Nº 867.

BISHOP, WILLIAM. — (Provisional Protection only.) — " An " improved mode of ornamenting writing papers."

The invention relates to a mode of ornamenting the surface of writing papers, "without detracting from their utility as " writing papers," by printing patterns upon them in pale flat tints, which "harmonize with the color of the paper, and so " contrast with the color of the writing ink as not to interfere " with the legibility of any writing that may be put upon it," indicating at the same time the presence of ornamentation " somewhat like that produced in damask weaving." Such papers may be cut up into letter and note sizes, and sold in quires, or used in the manufacture of envelopes.

[Printed, 3d. No Drawing.]

## A.D. 1855, April 19.—Nº 870.

JONES, WILLIAM.—" Improvements in printing calico and " other fabrics."

The invention consists in regulating the tension of the grey or back cloth used as a substitute for the blanket in machines for printing calico, muslin de laine, or other fibrous substances. This is effected by means of weighted rollers, whose centres work in sliding blocks, which are at liberty to move up or down in grooves in the framing, or the roller centres may be fixed in levers or otherwise, so that they shall be free to move and act upon the grey or back cloth.

[Printed, 9d. Drawings.]

## A.D. 1855, April 19.—Nº 875.

JOHNSON, JOHN HENRY.—(Communicated.)—"Improvements " in the manufacture or articles of hard india-rubber or gutta " percha or compounds thereof, and in coating or covering " articles with the like materials."

This invention consists in the manufacture of book-covers, letters for signs, inkstands, penholders, and pens, type, and stereotype, and buckets for water, acids, and other corrosive liquids, from india-rubber, gutta percha, or compounds thereof, " by first moulding them, while in a soft state, and then sub- " mitting them to a high degree of heat in steam-heaters or to

" the action of a sulphur bath. The moulds may sometimes be
" composed of plaster, but it is preferred to make them of porce-
" lain, glass, metal, or gutta percha." During the process the
article may be imbedded in magnesia, which causes it to come out
of the mould quite black.

[Printed, 4d. No Drawing.]

A.D. 1855, April 20.—Nº 880.

MACÉ, HYPOLITE.—"Improvements in transferring colors or
" metals in design on and from paper and stone on to surfaces."

The object of the invention is not only to transfer designs but
to keep such designs any length of time in store, and transfer
them at pleasure. The design having been transferred to the
stone is printed on unsized paper in any color, gold preferred.
It is left a day or two to dry, when a layer of Burgundy or
white and Venetian turpentine dissolved in spirits of turpentine
is spread over the design, but not over the white of the paper.
" When the transfer is to be made on to porcelain or other sur-
" faces, such surface is to be covered or brushed over with the
" mixture, allowed partially (say, for a few minutes) to dry; the
" prepared design is to be then laid thereon and fixed with a
" moist sponge. When the paper is retired, the design will have
" left it, being transferred on to the porcelain or surface operated
" upon. In one part of the process I shall have to throw off the
" superabundant gold; to avoid the loss of any portion of which
" I propose to use a receiver or box, having a sliding bottom or
" shelf of glass, of which article the back, sides, &c. are also to be
" made or lined."

[Printed, 4d. No Drawing.]

A.D. 1855, April 27.—Nº 953.

MASSIQUOT, JEAN CHARLES GUILLAUME. — (Provisional
Protection only.)—" Certain improvements in lithographic presses
" and inking apparatus connected therewith."

The scraper is in a carriage driven over the stone by a crank.
A loose frame, carrying a plate and sheet to lie on the paper placed
on the plate, is raised or tilted by a catch upon the carriage
entering a swan-neck or hook on the frame (a). Pressure is ob-

(a) See ante, Nº 10,018, p. 247.

tained by a weight travelling with the scraper and acting upon it by an adjustable lever of "the second kind." The crank shaft is stopped for the change, and the tilting frame kept raised by disengaging a clutch on the driving shaft. The inking rollers are in a carriage, in front of which is a "tympan or moistener," and are then driven with a reciprocating motion after each backward and forward stroke of the scraper carriage transversely over the plate or stone so as to ink the same. "The tympan is raised out of " contact during the back stroke by means of an inclined plane, " suitably fixed on the press, raising the swivel bearings of the " moistener, raising the swivel bearings of the moistener, and " a horizontal spring slipping under them so as to prevent the " moistener from descending again ; another inclined plane " throws the tympan into contact again for the succeeding inking " stroke by pushing the spring aside."

[Printed, 3d. No Drawing.]

## A.D. 1855, April 30.—N° 970.

DÉPIERRE, Pierre. — (Communicated.) — " Improvements in " dyeing, part of which improvements is applicable to the manu- " facture of ink."

1. As a substitute for cream of tartar in dyeing wool, a decoction of the female flowers of the alder well powdered.

2. The same fruits will also serve to dye cotton, silk, and mixed fabrics black after such fabric has been subjected to mordanting. For this purpose a bath is prepared of water and sulphate of pyrolignite or other salt of iron, or with nitric acid, hydrochloric acid, and copperas. After the fabrics have been acted on by the mordant, they are ready for immersion in the dye liquor. They are afterwards subjected to a developing bath made of pyrolignite or acetate of iron.

3. To restore to all kinds of silk the whole or a portion of the loss which they have undergone in weight by the cleaning process, and to cause them to take any colour required in dyeing, they are passed through a decoction of alder flowers or fruit, clarified by sulphurous acid, &c., or bleached with gelatine.

4. The alder flowers will also serve to make good ink by the usual processes, and to furnish all the salts which can be obtained from the finest gall-nuts, the process being the same.

[Printed, 6d. No Drawing.]

A.D. 1855, May 8.—N° 1027.

LINGARD, THOMAS TAYLOR. — "Certain improvements in
" presses, which improvements are also applicable to raising
" heavy bodies."

The invention consists in raising a table, &c. by means of
wedges or rollers actuated in various ways :—1. The movement
of the wedges or rollers is due to nuts working on a right and left
handed screw, the revolution of which causes the wedges to advance towards or retire from each other on inclined planes on the
table. 2. The screw has a thread in one direction only, and is so
connected with one set of the wedges or rollers as to be free to
revolve, but has its lateral motion so fixed as to move the set of
wedges or rollers along with it. The other set of wedges or rollers
are connected by means of a nut with the screw, as in the former
case, and by turning the screw the wedges or rollers are advanced
towards or moved from each other and along the incline upon
the table, as in the former case. 3. The wedges or rollers are
connected by means of rods with eccentrics, cranks, or levers so
placed upon a shaft that, by turning it, the wedges or rollers are
advanced towards or moved from each other as before. The
invention is applicable to lateral as well as vertical pressure, "and
" also to the lifting tables or rollers of printing machines."

[Printed, 7d. Drawings.]

A.D. 1855, May 21.—N° 1139.

SILBERMANN, IGNACE JOSEPH.—" Improvements in printing
" on any kind of surfaces."

The invention consists in producing the required pressure by
injecting gas, steam, and any fluid or liquid into a flexible bag or
other vessel of caoutchouc, gutta percha, or other impervious substance. It is used to print on a globe of gutta percha, caoutchouc,
gold-beaters' skin, &c., from the interior engraved surface of a
sphere for the manufacture of celestial and terrestrial globes, maps,
lithographs, &c. ; also for printing on plane surfaces basso-relievo
and ornamental labels for bottles and pots of all descriptions.
The moulds in which such vessels are blown being previously
engraved and inked with indelible substances, such as are commonly used in printing or tracing out, or painting on china,
glass, &c. The process " also allows the perfect inking of all

" engraved surfaces, and of all forms, curved or plane, and prin-
" cipally by the rollers used for inking the engraved cylinders for
" printing fabrics." The inking surface is " caoutchouc, plane,
" curved, spherical, or cylindrical, as required for the surface
" engraved."

[Printed, 3d. No Drawings.]

## A.D. 1855, May 24.—No 1168.

SEEGERS, Auguste Frédéric Godfrid.—(Provisional Protection only.)—" Improvements in the manufacture of hangings
" of paper and of textile fabrics."

These consist in printing flock hangings with gold, silver,
copper, or colours, by means of copper blocks engraved *en creux*,
or in relief, and impressed hot upon the paper or fabric by means
of a fly press or other suitable means. The adhesion of the metal
or colour is effected by applying to the parts where the engraved
block will strike, a mordant in powder, as gum lac or other fusible
material, and placing upon it a thin sheet of metal or stratum of
colour. The surplus material is removed by a brush. " By
" omitting to use metallic leaf or colour in powder and employing
" the blocks cold, imitations of Utrecht or Amiens velvet may be
" obtained."

[Printed, 3d. No Drawing.]

## A.D. 1855, May 24.—No 1179.

ADDENBROOKE, Joseph. — " Improvements in machinery
" for folding envelopes."

The invention consists in additional machinery which stamp in
" cameo," or a device on colored or white ground, and in printing
by letter-press or any of the known processes of printing during
the operation of folding. In the apparatus shown in the Drawings
the coloring of the cameo or type takes place prior to the paper
being laid under the stampers or pressers. There are three color
rollers for the cameo and one for the type, the whole being in a
frame guided by a piece working on rods, and being furnished from
a circular plate revolving on a vertical axis, the color being supplied
to such plate by a trough roller.

[Printed, 6d. Drawings.]

A.D. 1855, May 26.—N° 1205.

NEUFFER, GOTTLIEB.—(Provisional Protection only.)—" An
" improved mode of producing patterns upon floor-cloths and
" other ornamental coverings for floors, walls, tables, and other
" surfaces."

The invention relates to the production of imitations of inlaid
woodwork, marbles, chintzes, &c. The material having been
coated with oil color and dried, the pattern of an inlaid wood
is printed on it in delible colors, and fixed in lacker or varnish
in those parts in which the pattern is to remain. When the
lacker or varnish is dry those portions of the pattern which are
not wanted are washed away. The second portion is then produced in a similar way, the processes being repeated until the
entire design has been produced and fixed upon the prepared
material. The whole is finished with several coatings of lacker or
varnish. " It will sometimes be found convenient to produce one
" portion of the design in an oil colour," and the rest as above
described.

[Printed, 3d. No Drawings.]

A.D. 1855, June 1.—N° 1256.

WHYTOCK, RICHARD.—" Improvements in colouring yarns or,
" threads intended to form elements of various loom fabrics, and
" for crochet work and knitting."

Instead of coloring yarns upon cylinders or tables " as usually
" practised," a mode is adopted of coloring them by means of
two pulleys revolving in contact, the one under the other, over a
layer of threads, the lower one being charged with color; also by
means of one or more pulleys pressing upwards upon a plate of
glass or other hard substance placed over the layer of threads.

[Printed, 10d. Drawings.]

A.D. 1855, June 2.—N° 1258.

BOYD, JOHN. — " Improvements in letter-press printing
" machines."

The invention relates to printing posting bills, &c., in various
coloured inks by one continuous operation, and by which impressions can be taken from two or more forms at the same time,
the same being equally applicable to taking impressions from a

single form. It consists, first, in stopping the pressing cylinders during the back action of the reciprocating table; secondly, in the use of conically shaped impressing cylinders and horizontal circular rotating or partially revolving tables as applied to letter-press printing machines; and lastly, in the application of a quadrant (or sector) motion to the under side of the tables of the machine, to give it a reciprocating motion.

[Printed, 4d. No Drawing.]

A.D. 1855, June 9.—N° 1318.

VARLEY, CROMWELL FLEETWOOD.—" Improvements in elec-
" tric telegraphs."

The invention consists, first, in increasing the power of electro-magnets by getting double action from the same quantity of wire. The wire coil is surrounded with iron, nickel, or other magnetic metal, which gives magnetism of an opposite kind to that of the core. Secondly, in applying the above to telegraphic relays, which will complete one or two circuits, by using an armature magnetized, either permanently or by induction, from a larger magnet so as to avoid demagnetization. In the drawing given, " Baine's " machine is represented as being worked by the relay. Thirdly, in increasing the power and permanence of permanent magnets by forcing a stream of water past the red-hot steel whilst under the influence of the electric helix, the steel taking the place of the core. For hardening the steel, solutions of prussiate of potash are ordinarily used, but for extreme hardness, freezing mixture of mercury, or dilute sulphuric acid is employed. Fourthly, in three several modes of translating the system of the Patentee, N° 2555 of 1854, viz. (a) for translating it into Morse's system and *vice versâ;* (b) sending alternate currents, as used for working the Patent in conjunction with Morse's; (c) translating from one submarine or subterranean circuit into another. Fifthly, in re-establishing by the use of wheelwork or pendulous bodies the length of short signals lost during translation, thus enabling long lines containing many translators (a) to be worked with but little loss of speed and with greater accuracy. Sixthly, in a double

(a) " By translator," the Patentee states, " I mean the apparatus used for bringing fresh batteries into play to enable correspondence to be maintained direct between stations whose distance apart is too great to admit of connecting the wires into one continuous electrical circuit."

marking apparatus with a triple key-board, in which a band of paper is moved by wheelwork at a uniform rate, while a positive and negative current passing round the magnets causes the impressions to be received from two levers actuated by the magnets. When one armature is attracted, a mark is produced on the right-hand side of the paper slip, and when the other armature is attracted a mark is produced on the left side. Seventhly, in the use of a marker heated by electricity to perforate the paper, the perforated strips being again used for retransmitting the despatch to one or more stations automatically. Eighthly, in measuring into submarine or subterranean wires definite quantities of electricity, so that the charge of such wire shall be as nearly as possible the same with short or long contacts. Ninthly, in reducing the residual magnetism of the electro-magnets used in printing or translating apparatus by means of a stop which when struck down by the printing lever carrying the armature, cuts off the current, and the moment the armature leaves the magnet, the current reflows round the coil, and the armature is re-attracted, continually vibrating through a very limited space, almost appearing to be still. Or the stop is made to cut off a portion of the current round the magnet.

[Printed, 2s. 4d. Drawings.]

A.D. 1855, June 18.—N° 1383.

LITTLE, WILLIAM.—" Improvements in printing machinery."

The invention consists in the application of bent electrotype and compound electrotype and stereotype plates to horizontal cylinders revolving continuously. The plates are bent by means of three rollers, a drawing of which is given. One or more portions or sections of the surface of the cylinder are made moveable, yet readily fixed to the cylinder in order to have printing surfaces affixed to them.

The form of machine preferred consists of one cylinder carrying the printing surface or surfaces, with three pressing cylinders, each arranged with double feeding apparatus, so that two feeders may be constantly employed to each. The part of the surface of the cylinder not occupied by the printing surface or surfaces is made into an inking table, and when three impression cylinders are used, three sets of distributing rollers are employed. " By

" these means a comparatively small diameter of cylinder with
" printing surfaces thereon may be used, and a very large number
" of impressions obtained in a given time."

[Printed, 9d. Drawings.]


A.D. 1855, June 18.—N° 1388.

BESSEMER, Henry.—" Improvements in the manufacture of
" rolls or cylinders used in the lamination,' shaping, and cutting
" of metals, in crushing ores and other substances, and in calen-
" dering, glazing, embossing, printing, and pressing."

These consist in casting or founding the rolls or cylinders for
the above purposes in molten steel, or with a mixture of molten
steel and pig or refined iron. The rolls required to be solid are
cast with their axes entire; those which require to be hollow
are cored out.

[Printed, 4d. No Drawing.]


A.D. 1855, June 21.—N° 1420.

RIOUX, Pierre Francois, and DE PARIENTE, Leon.
—(Provisional Protection only.)—(Communicated.)—" Improve-
" ments in the fixing of metallic ornaments upon paper, flock,
" leather, cotton, silk, or any other fabrics to which such orna-
" ments may be applicable."

The above materials are placed upon an elastic bed of vulcanized caoutchouc or other material which will bear heat. A slight
impression of the design is made by a heated block, cylinder, or
die. The metallic surface is caused to adhere to the design thus
produced by sprinkling the design with powdered dry albumen,
gum lac, and rosin, copal varnish, or other suitable body, upon
which the metal leaf is "dabbed" down with cotton wool, &c.
The block, cylinder, or die is then again pressed over the surface
in the same place it was in the first instance, and the design is
fixed upon the fabric. For leather or other such substance, the
albumen and attaching bodies must be in a liquid state.

[Printed, 3d. No Drawing.]


A.D. 1855, June 23.—N° 1445.

SILBERMANN, Ignace Joseph.—" A new system of manu-
" facturing globes, and other printed plane or curve surfaces."

The invention consists, first, in printing by means of curve or plane moulds made of such substances as can be etched, graved, or embossed. Secondly, in inking the engraved surface with common ink for obtaining a plain print, or with indelible inks proof against heat when the printed surfaces are to be baked or moulded in the heated state. Thirdly, in moulding or casting the matters to be printed on the engraved inked surfaces.

" When these three operations, engraving, inking, and mould-
" ing, have taken place, the matter thus moulded and solidified
" by cooling or any suitable means is painted upon. Each of
" the three above-mentioned operations when considered sepa-
" rately are well known, and merely consists in the combination
" of ordinary printing with ordinary moulding, which constitutes
" the novelty of my principle."

[Printed, 3d. No Drawing.]

A.D. 1855, June 26.—Nº 1456.

LEISS, FREDERICK, and SCHNEIDER, CHARLES.—" Manu-
" facturing mica letters, numerals, shop-signs, figures, arms,
" devices, and ornaments."

The above articles are produced in gold, silver, and various colors, transparent or opaque. The mica (glimmer) is slit into sheets of the required thickness, cut into forms or printed on and colored " according to the ornament or object required to be
" produced, or by putting the forms under gelatine or mineral
" substances, which causes a brilliant transparency and show of
" colours, and gives the appearance of projection. The invention
" is also applicable to slides of magic lanterns and similar objects
" for the use of science and art, also transparent arms, devices,
" emblems, chromatrop figures, and the like, for the purposes of
" illumination, where perfect transparency is required." Also for book covers, screens, fans, with mirrors, " lamp glasses with
" reflectors, passe partouts for portraits, and drawings in sketch
" books, albums, &c., of which the sheets of mica form in the
" meantime, frame and covering, &c.

[Printed, 4d. No Drawing.]

A.D. 1855, June 28.—Nº 1478.

BESLEY, ROBERT.—(Communicated.)—" An improved manu-
" facture of metallic alloy, applicable to the casting of type and
" other articles."

The object of the invention is to produce a harder alloy than that commonly used, which shall be capable of being run with facility into moulds or dies. The ingredients are lead, regulus of antimony, nickel, copper, zinc, and tin. The zinc is subjected to a white heat to drive off any sulphur it may contain, and while in a fluid state the nickel and copper are introduced. By continued stirring the mixture of these metals is effected, and a small quantity of lead added thereto. Another portion of lead is melted down with the regulus of antimony in a separate vessel, and the mixture is then added to the fluid alloy. The whole is subjected to a high degree of heat before any attempt is made at clearing off.

[Printed, 3d. No Drawing.]

### A.D. 1855, July 13.—N° 1569.

HIGGIN, JAMES.—(Provisional Protection only.)—" Improve-
" ments in clearing and brightening dyed and printed fabrics."

"The invention consists in a modification of the ordinary clear-
" ing process applied to dyed or printed fabrics when certain dye
" stuffs are used. It is usual to pass goods dyed guarancine,
" guaranceaux, or other preparations of madder, either alone or
" mixed with other dye stuffs, through a solution of chloride of
" lime in water, then dry or expose them to steam, rinse them in
" water and dry them. I propose to add to the chloride of lime
" solution a liquid containing silicic acid in solution, and use this
" mixture instead of the chloride of lime as above, finding thereby
" a great improvement is effected in the whites and colors of
" printed goods, and consequently in the color of self-color dyed
" goods."

[Printed, 3d. No Drawing.]

### A.D. 1855, July 18.—N° 1611.

ALMGILL, THOMAS.—(Provisional Protection only.)—" An
" improved mode of printing on calico and other fabrics and
" matters, and in machinery and apparatus to be employed
" therein."

The improvement in printing relates to machinery for " surface
" printing," and consists in having the pattern or device cut or
etched through thin copper, tin, wood, or other substance, and

put on a wire fabric, which fabric and pattern are fastened on
a hollow perforated cast-iron cylinder; the perforated cylinder
with pattern revolving round a fixed mandril, hollow at one end,
to which is fastened a color feeding box, working color-tight
inside the perforated cylinder. The wire is used with a view to
distribute the color equally, and not as the sole means of transferring the pattern to the cloth, though in some patterns it is
proposed to use only wire in the way mentioned.

[Printed, 3d. No Drawing.]

A.D. 1855, July 21.—N° 1654.

GOODYEAR, Charles. — (Provisional Protection only.) —
(Partly a communication.)—" Improvements in the surfaces used
" for printing."

A compound of india-rubber and sulphur, with or without
other matters, " preferring to use at the rate of about one part by
" weight of sulphur to two parts by weight of india-rubber," is
introduced into suitable moulds and pressed therein. It is then
subjected to high temperature in order to obtain the change into
hard material. Or blocks being first formed may be cut to
produce the printing surfaces thereon. For intaglio printing,
blocks or plates of the material first prepared with smooth surfaces
may be engraved in like manner to copper and other metal plates;
and when for similar printing to lithography, a compound of
india-rubber, sulphur, and powder of lithographic stones or oxide
of zinc subjected to high temperature is used.

[Printed, 3d. No Drawing.]

A.D. 1855, July 24.—N° 1676.

WOOD, Benjamin.—"An inproved preparation of colouring
" matter for the manufacture of ink, artists' colours, and for other
" purposes for which such colouring matter may be applicable."

1. Ink which will not corrode metals. Common carbonate of
soda (9 oz.) is dissolved in water (27 quarts), to which is added
about 8 ounces of citric acid, and when this solution has been
brought to the boiling point, 1½lb. of cochineal is put in and the
boiling continued for about one hour and a half, after which the
liquor is strained and allowed to settle and cool. The clear liquor
is boiled up again, and about 9 ounces of common alum added

thereto, and the mixture kept boiling for five minutes, after which the liquor is drawn off into coolers and allowed to precipitate, which it will do as the liquid gradually cools. When the precipitation has finished, the supernatant liquid is drawn off, the precipitate filtered so as to drain off as much of the liquid as possible, and washed in distilled water to remove any acid contained in it, drained and dried. If required in a liquid state, it is subjected to a solution of caustic ammonia, which dissolves it.

In order to produce a red ink with the above, distilled water is added to the solution of coloring matter above described. To prevent the ink from decomposing or becoming mouldy, a few drops of essential oil of cloves or oil of creosote is added.

The dried precipitate above mentioned may be also employed in the manufacture of artists' colors, for which purpose the subsequent operation of dissolving in caustic ammonia will not be required, as well as for staining, dying, " or for any of the various " purposes to which colouring matters are now applied."

[Printed, 3d. No Drawing.]

## A.D. 1855, August 11.—Nº 1824.

PRETSCH, PAUL.—" Improvements in the application of certai " designs obtained on metallic surfaces by photographic and oth " agency."

The invention relates to improvements on Nº 2373 of 1854.

" I now employ copper or other suitable plates engraved by my " said process for the formation of cylinders to be employed in " calico and similar printing, embossing, and other purposes ; or " cylinders may be formed directly by the electrotype process by " means of suitable tubular or other arrangements of my engraved " plates to serve as moulds, and the cylinders produced therefrom " may be strengthened by the insertion of metal rollers, cast metal, " and similar methods.

" When it is desired to ornament manufactured articles with " engraving according to my said improved process, the same can " be variously applied to flat, curved, and other surfaces, and, " when required, the engraved surfaces may be covered with gold, " silver, or other metals, materials, or may be inlaid with metals " or other materials."

[Printed, 3d. No Drawing.]

A.D. 1855, August 21.—Nº 1892.

MEINIG, CARL LUDWIG AUGUSTUS, and KUKLA, FRANZ XAVER.—(Provisional Protection only.)—" Improvements in orna-
" menting surfaces."

These consist in transferring oil-coloured pictures (painted, printed, or drawn on paper, &c.), on to surfaces of metal, wood, leather, oil-cloth, glass, stone, &c., so as to preserve the mineral colours. The picture is immersed in a bath prepared as follows:—Phosphorous acid, or arsenious acid, or other suitable substance having an affinity for oxygen, is combined with a suitable alkaline base, such as potash, soda, lime, &c. The object of immersing the picture is, by the reduction or deoxydation of the hardened oil, to restore its adhesive or sticky property without decomposing the mineral color or spoiling the picture. The picture is then washed in several water baths, the last but one being, if necessary, acidulated with sulphuric, nitric, or muriatic acid. It is pressed between sheets of bibulous paper, and dried. The surface to be ornamented, if not adhesive, is then covered with a thin coat of copal or other suitable varnish, and the picture placed face downwards upon it and pressed against such surface, and so left for one or two days. The paper, &c. of the picture is then soaked with water, when it can be easily removed, leaving the colored picture on the surface of the substance to be ornamented; any fibres of the paper, &c. remaining being rubbed off with a sponge and water. The transferred picture is then varnished or " otherwise treated as
" usual."

[Printed, 3d. No Drawing.]

A.D. 1855, August 23.—Nº 1905.

JONES, WRIGHT.—"Improvements in machinery or apparatus
" for printing woven fabrics and paper-hangings."

The invention consists, first, in making the inking rollers in relief cylinder-printing machines of air-tight flexible materials and filling them with compressed air, gas, water, or other liquid, thus obtaining elasticity and dispensing with the endless cloth or "sieve." And, secondly, in forming the edge of the " doctor " with projecting parts constructed upon bars or blades, or upon rollers.

[Printed, 6d. Drawings.]

**DE LA RUE, THOMAS.**—"An improvement in printing inks."

Dry borate of manganese finely powdered (1 part) is added to 100 parts of printing ink materials, and the whole thoroughly combined by grinding. The mixture should be left standing for a month to let the manganese salt operate upon the oily vehicle of the ink. In place of combining or mixing the borate of manganese with the printing inks, it is sometimes mixed by stirring it with the varnish or vehicle when heated to a temperature of about 600° Fahrenheit, in the proportion of about one part by weight to fifty or sixty parts by weight of the oily varnish or vehicle, stirring well during three or four hours. The borate of manganese is obtained by precipitation from a cold solution of a soluable salt of manganese with a cold solution of borax "as is well under-" stood," the precipitate being well washed, dried, and powdered before being used.

[Printed, 3d. No Drawing.]

**ROSE, GEORGE FREDERICK.**—" Certain improvements in litho-" graphic and copper-plate printing presses."

The invention consists, first, in giving reciprocating motion to the bed of the press by the use of one or more cog wheels, the teeth of which take into a rack or racks underneath the bed, which is supported upon friction rollers at the sides. Circular bearings, the curved surface of which is equal to the range or extent of the backward and forward motion of the bed, are sometimes used for the purpose of diminishing the friction. Another improvement consists in fitting the scraper so that it may work up and down in vertical grooves, being actuated by a screw working through the bridge, or for greater steadiness, through the bridge and middle bar. The screw is turned by a wheel at the top of it.

[Printed, 1s. 11d. Drawings.]

**JOB, ALFRED MORTIMER, and TOMLINSON, EDWIN.**—(Pro-visional Protection only.)—" A new article, to be called india-" rubber leather cloth, applicable to covering roofs, floors, trunks, " and for other similar purposes."

The invention consists, first, in combining particles of ground leather or metal dust or filings with caoutchouc, gutta percha, or both, by mastication or pressure. The softening of the caoutchouc or gutta percha is effected by any of the well-known solvents. Secondly, in printing and coloring the same, according to the taste of the manufacturer, by blocks or cylinders. Thirdly, in the application, when manufactured, to the covering of knifeboards, for setting in pins or wire teeth for making of cards, for covering drums of carding machines, for covering floors, stairs, trunks, roofs, buttons, "and all other purposes for which it may " be found useful."

[Printed, 3d. No Drawing.]

A.D. 1855, September 3.—N° 1984.

LARMUTH, THOMAS JOSEPH, and SMITH, JOHN.—" Im- " provements in machinery or apparatus for printing."

The invention consists of a hand machine for printing small surfaces, such as hand-bills, labels, &c. The paper or other material to be printed upon is placed upon a table, upon which is also a substance supplied with the coloring matter. The printing surface is carried by a radial lever, and made to alternate from the color surface to the material to be printed, such lever having the capacity of lateral as well as vertical motion. The inking apparatus may be flat, or the type may travel over an inking roller.

[Printed, 6d. Drawings.]

A.D. 1855, September 5.—N° 2011.

GLASSFORD, JOHN HAMILTON.—" Improvements in printing " textile fabrics and other surfaces."

The invention consists in producing a printing surface on zinc or stone, by transferring to such substance a series of single repeats of a pattern as a substitute for the " common system of ' milling ' " adopted by the calico printer in cylinder work." The design so produced is protected with powdered rosin, and the rest of the plate acted on with nitric acid. The acid is afterwards washed off, and the surface rubbed with soapy or greasy matter. In this state it is rubbed over with water of Ayr or other polishing material, which removes the ink and grease from the relief portions. The stone is then washed with a gum solution, and when inked in with lithographic ink, gives a " negative " impression on a dark ground with a white device upon it.

[Printed, 5d. No Drawing.]

### A.D. 1855, September 14.—Nº 2072.

HARTMANN, Jules Albert.—" Certain improvements in the
" preparation and combination of colours for printing stuffs and
" textile fabrics."

The invention consists in the production of various steam
colors from precipitated deoxidized indigo, extracts of madder,
and the prussiates of potash, &c. They are,—1. a steam indigo
blue for printing, without the use of magnesia, formed by the
combination of precipitated deoxidized indigo with silicate of soda
or other alkaline salt and gum water or other ordinary thickening
material; 2. a steam indigo blue for printing, without the use of
alkalies or alkaline earths or their salts, by the combination of
precipitated deoxidized indigo with gum water or other ordinary
thickening material; 3. a steam green color for similar printing,
by the combination of precipitated deoxidized indigo with extract
of Persian berries or quercitron or other yellow coloring material
and gum water or other thickener, with or without the addition of
silicate of soda or other alkaline salt; 4. steam violets and puce
colors for similar printing, by the combination of precipitated
deoxidized indigo with the coloring matter of cochineal, or
Campeachy or other red woods and gum water or other thickener
with or without the addition of silicate of soda or other alkaline
salt; 5. steam puce and brown colors for printing the same, by
the combination of precipitated deoxized indigo with the coloring
matter of madder and ammonia and gum water and other thickener; 6. steam puce and brown colors for printing the same,
the combination of the coloring matter of madder with the ferro-
cyanides and ferridcyanides, such as the yellow and red prussiates
of potash, and gum water or other thickener; 7. greys and black,
and various shades, for printing the same by the combination of
the aforesaid blue, green, violet, puce, and brown colors, or some
of them.

[Printed, 4d. No Drawing.]

### A.D. 1855, September 15.—Nº 2084.

SCULLY, Vincent, and HEYWOOD, Bennett Johns.—
(Provisional Protection only.)—" An improvement in the manu-
" facture of certain articles which are subject to the corroding
" action of the air and moisture."

By reason of its non-oxydizable qualities aluminium is used in place of brass, copper, and silver, for wind and stringed instruments, and also as a material for pens, penholders, and inkstands. " The metal for forming the pens and penholders we propose to roll " or beat out into thin sheets, in order to give toughness and rigidity " thereto ; we then, by the ordinary means, convert this thin metal " into the articles desired. The comparative hardness of this metal, " considering its ready fusibility, coupled with its non-oxydizable " property, will render it an efficient substitute for type metal in " the manufacture of type," medals, coins, plated goods, and articles of "virtu," whether stamped, cast, chased, "or manufac- " tured after the manner of *repoussé* work, or coated by the electro- " deposition process."

[Printed, 3*d*. No Drawing.]

## A.D. 1855, September 18.—No 2104.

DELLAGANA, JAMES.—(Provisional Protection only.)—" Ste- reotyping type high; that is to say, as high as printing type, or seven-eights of an inch high."

The invention consists in casting the stereotype plates solid, so as to answer to stereotyping and mounting at the same time.

Whereas the mounting with wood is never precise, and the plates " have to be backed up with paper to bring them to the proper height." The principal novelty in the invention consists in the differently constructed casting machines, and also in the use of type-high gauges for the same. The second part of the invention consists in casting the plates hollow inside, but still type high, which will make them lighter and more manageable.

[Printed, 3*d*. No Drawing.]

## A.D. 1855, September 19.—No 2112.

CORNIDES, LOUIS.— " Certain improvements in obtaining " impressions of prints or drawings, and in transferring, printing, " and colouring or ornamenting the same on glass and other " surfaces."

The invention relates to certain improvements on No 2066 of 1854 (Cornides), in cases where, as in that Patent, the surfaces are coated with gelatine or animal glue in combination with other substances. The coated surface is immersed below the surface of clear water, from which it is raised so as to bring up with it the impression, which has been placed face downwards upon it, and which is left in that position to dry. The whole is then laid in a solution of the known salts of alumina. The saturated paper is then removed, and the print is found to be thoroughly incorporated with the gelatine. The impression is colored by printing lithographic or other "negative" impressions on transfer paper, transferring them to the glass, and coloring them as in N° 2066 of 1854. By this process a colored picture, positive by transmitted light, is produced. The tranfer will be then washed off by spirit of turpentine, or other suitable means. When it is desired to employ two or more colors to produce a colored picture, the same may be effected by repeating the process for each separate color, or by coloring the picture in the manner explained in N° 2066 of 1854. Or the coloring may be effected by the application of finely pulverized colored glass to the coated surface of the glass by means of stencil plates and moistening the gelatine at such parts. Impressions from photographic negative pictures may be obtained on glass coated as above, by "the known photographic processes" for printing from negatives on paper or glass, the impression being subjected to a steeping bath, and coloured and coated as above. In order to render any parts of an impression transferred to the gelatine surface opaque, or in order to produce a strong effect of light and shade, an impression made on ordinary lithographic transfer paper is coated, whilst the ink is still moist, with fine metallic powder, or finely powdered glass of any desired color, and transferred to the surface of the gelatine "by any "process in use for that purpose."

To protect the impressions from atmospheric influence, the same (a) are coated with " a solution of explosive cotton in pyr-" oxylic spirit, combined with gums or resins, as set forth in a " Provisional Specification of a former Patent " (N° 745 of 1855).

[Printed, 4d. No Drawing.]

A.D. 1855, October 1.—N° 2179.

ILLINGWORTH, WILLIAM.—"Certain improvements in print-" ing earthenware, china, or other ceramic manufactures."

" Hitherto," it is stated, " the pigment or color employed in " such process has always been made or mixed with oil, for " obvious reasons well known to potters." The invention con-

(a) This is omitted from the Complete Specification, but is contained in the Provisional Specification.

sists in substituting a preparation of saccharine matter, such as sugar, honey, &c., as producing thereby greater brilliancy of color, a considerable economy in the burning, and " the ability " to employ more colors than one in the production of the " required design."

[Printed, 3d. No Drawing.]

### A.D. 1855, October 1.—N° 2190.

HOPE, GEORGE CURLING.—" An improved method of pro- " ducing figures, patterns, or designs upon textile fabrics for the " purposes of needlework."

The invention consists in producing effects resembling " ap- " plique " work by " block-printing," or by means of printing and embossing, " instead of by the employment of two separate " fabrics, as hitherto done." The pattern, figure, or device may be of a different shade or color from that of the ground on which it is printed. In carrying out the invention the pattern may be produced, or the ground may be made to form the ground by printing it either with block, stone, copper, or otherwise. The first of these is stated to be preferable, " as then the design " enters well into the cloth, and is not liable to wear off."

[Printed, 3d. No Drawing.]

### A.D. 1855, October 2.—N° 2200.

BENVENUTI, FRANÇOIS FORTUNÉ.—" Certain improvements " in typography."

The invention consists in using " two letters cast together so " as to form one type." If the word consists of an uneven number of letters, the single letter at the end is taken from one of the " uneven " or single letter cases. The even and uneven cases are ranged on circular trestles. To obviate the loss of time caused by the use of the composing stick, the compositor makes use of the galley fastened about his waist with a large belt. The galley is composed of a smooth plate rather larger than the sheet to be laid upon it, and provided with adjustable blades, between which the type is placed. The visorium is placed at the end of the galley on the upper edge, and is provided with a pencil " to " mark the place the workman stops at when he is obliged to " throw his eyes off to compose."

[Printed, 6d. Drawings.]

A.D. 1855, October 4.—N° 2211.

CROSSE, ROBERT AUGUSTUS.—(Provisional Protection only.)—
" Certain improvements in founding printers' type."

The invention consists in casting a series of letters or words or single letters upon each end of the type. " Upon the printer's " matter being composed there will be a double or duplicate sur- " face of printing matter, one being printed from the top and " another from the bottom. The only alteration in the printing " machine that will be required will be the different arrangements " of the cylinders and guide tapes."

[Prinied, 5d. Drawings.]

A.D. 1855, October 16.—N° 2307.

NORMANDY, LEWIS.—(Provisional Protection only.)—(Com-municated.)—" Improvements in the mode of writing and printing " music to facilitate the study thereof."

Three different colors are used for the lines or musical scale. A drawing is annexed, containing a specimen of the transposing scales, on which two natural gamuts are written, the one in the major and the other in the minor key. The *do* medium or funda-mental note of the key is written on a lower accidental dotted line of a green color. The *mi* is also on a green line. *Si* and *fa* are on red lines, the first of which is dotted. *Sol, re,* and *la* are on black lines, the latter being an accidental and dotted one. The other accidental lines required follow in the same order, viz., the second upper accidental line for the *do*, dotted green, the third for *mi*, green, and so on. Below the scale, the second accidental line dotted black for *la*, the third one red for *fa*, and so on.

For printing by one operation the three colors of the scale and the notes of music, three relief plates are used, one for each color. They are placed one above the other. The upper one bears the characters and black lines, the two others having lines only which are engaged in narrow clefts of the upper plate, which lines can be raised over the characters, or be withdrawn, in order to be inked, each one of a different color. " Then, by a suitable contrivance, " the characters or lines of the three plates are brought to their " respective and level position, to be printed in the usual " manner."

[Printed, 5d. Drawing.]

A.D. 1855, October 22.—N° 2360.

M'GLASHAN, Alexander, and FIELD, Edward. — " Im-
" provements in printing presses."

A perfecting single-cylinder machine, in which the "grippers"
are so arranged as to hold the sheet firmly during the whole operation, affording perfect register, increased speed, simplicity of construction, and compactness of form. The type table has a reciprocating motion imparted by rackwork gearing with wheels at each
end of the cylinder. The "bank" or feeding board is placed
parallel to the cylinder, in the ordinary position. In this board is
cut a transverse slit, in which is fitted a roller, its surface being
level with that of the feeding board. The roller is put in motion
at intervals by means of a cam, so that when the paper is pushed
towards the cylinder it remains inactive until the roller is in motion,
when the paper is carried forward between the edges of a slot in the
cylinder or drum. The paper is held in this position by grippers or
holders, actuated by a cam on the main or driving shaft, and
during the rotation of the cylinder it is carried over the surface of
one of the forms of the type, which, at the proper moment, is
brought beneath the cylinder. The impression upon one side
being taken, the cylinder rotates in the opposite direction, and the
paper is turned by means of endless bands, which travel over a
pair of rollers fitted parallel with the cylinder. The bands lift
the lower edge of the paper and turn it over, causing the printed
side to lie next the cylinder, in order that the plain side may
receive the impression of the second form. When this is effected,
a rise or incline made upon the cam fitted on the cylinder shaft
causes the grippers to release their hold, and allow the printed
sheet to pass off to the delivery board.

[Printed, 2s. 1d. Drawings.]

A.D. 1855, October 24.—N° 2380.

JOHNSON, John Henry. — (Provisional Protection only.) —
(Communicated by M. Beslay.)—" Improvements in the produc-
" tion of dies and matrices, partly applicable to the production of
" printing surfaces."

A thin plate, having the desired device formed upon it, either
by the electrotype process or by stamping, is placed at the bottom
of a mould, and an alloy of metal poured over it, "so as to form

" one solid die or matrix." The nature of the alloy depends on
the metal forming the plate. For copper the alloy is brass, for
wrought iron cast iron may be used instead of an alloy. For
copper-plate printing, the design is obtained from an engraved
plate, and strengthened by pouring the alloy upon the back of it.

According to another process the plate may be obtained at once
by the electrotype process from a glass or other transparent surface which has been coated with an etching ground, through which
the design is traced with a fine point. "Inlaid work may also be
" produced by depositing the copper over pearls, mother of pearl,
" stones, or other similar substances; a plate so formed serving
" either for the electrotype reproduction of similar plates, or as
" an ornamental article."

[Printed, 3d. No Drawing.]

A.D. 1855, October 24.—N° 2385.

RASCOL, Eugène Hippolyte. — (Communicated.) — " Im-
" provements in apparatus used in the manufacture of type and
" other articles for letter-press printing."

The mould is composed of four primary and independent parts
of hardened steel. The first is fixed on a plate on the table of the
machine, and the second immediately above it. These two parts
regulate the size of the body of the type. The third and fourth
parts, by moving to or from the former, form the thickness of the
type. The matrix is brought up to its proper place by means of
a carriage sliding in a tube, and guided horizontally by springs,
adjusted for the thickness of the type. It is brought down vertically, and guided to its proper place by meeting with a small steel
point as the carriage takes it in. The matrix being in position,
the metal is pumped into the mould "in the manner ordinarily
" practised." The parts forming the thickness withdraw simultaneously, and thus give a passage to the type, which is then
pushed by an "expulsor" between two pieces of sharp steel, which
cut off any part of the metal projecting on the thickness of the
type. Subsequently, two knives acting on the type cut off the
jet and any parts that project on the body, when the cast article
is then finished and ready for use. The movements of the whole
of the pieces are effected by means of cams and levers.

[Printed, 2s. 6d. Drawings.]

A.D. 1855, November 14.—N° 2571.

NEWTON, ALFRED VINCENT.—(Communicated.)—"An m-
" proved manufacture of electrotype printing surfaces."

The chief object of this invention is to facilitate the backing of
electrotype shells or casts for forming copper-faced fancy type.
The mould or article to be duplicated by the electrotype process is
placed in a common printer's chase, and surrounded by rules, in
order that the counterpart of their upper edges may form a flat
margin on the electrotype shell. When thus locked up, a coating
of copper is thrown upon it "in the usual way" by a galvanic
battery, and the shell thus formed removed from the copper solution and washed and turned on the back. It is then placed, face
downwards, upon a bed plate, and a mould frame set over it, so
as to bear upon the margin of the shell; a cap plate is then fitted
on, and by means of clamps the whole are tightly secured together.
The mould is then heated, and type metal poured therein. On
cooling, an adhesion between the copper shell and the type metal
will be found to have taken place.

[Printed, 6d. Drawings.]

A.D. 1855, November 19.—N° 2605.

McNICOL, JOHN.— (Provisional Protection only.)—"Improve-
" ments in machine or cylinder printing."

" I propose to make the doctor of a much stronger description
" than has hitherto been adopted, and fix very strong brass
" bushes at each end, so that when it comes in contact with the
" copper rollers and colours, I shall be enabled to print blotch
" grounds as well as white grounds, the former having been gene-
" rally done by hand, or what is termed block printing. I make
" the doctor the whole width of the copper roller, by which I am
" enabled to print a solid six, eight, or ten inches on the whole
" width of the piece, if desired; whereas, on the present system,
" a solid cannot be produced of more than about one inch and a
" half in breadth. By this method I shall also be able to pro-
" duce a more brilliant solid than can be done by the block."

[Printed, 3d. No Drawing.]

A.D. 1855, December 8.—N° 2778.

MACLURE, ANDREW.—" Improvements in lithographic printing
" presses."

This invention has for its object the application of steam or other power to such presses. The table of the press is lengthened so as to be always above the roller by which its driven. The roller has continuous motion, and the reciprocating motion which is required for the table is obtained by raising the roller or bed (by lever or otherwise), so as to gear with each other, the table being acted on by a weight or other means for its return.

[Printed, 8d. Drawings.]

A.D. 1855, December 11.—No 2804.

RUDING, ROGERS.—" An improvement in printing silks and " other woven fabrics with gold and other metal leaf and powder."

Powdered shellac, produced by precipitation, is dusted evenly over the above fabrics. The leaf or powder is then laid over the shellac, and a heated printing surface applied, which, by melting the shellac, causes the leaf or powder to adhere to the fabric in the form of the pattern, leaving the rest of the leaf or powder to be brushed off.

[Printed, 3d. No Drawing.]

A.D. 1855, December 13.—No 2815.

POITEVIN, ALPHONSE LOUIS.—" Improved photographic " printing."

One or more films of a concentrated solution of albumen, fibrine, gum arabic, gelatine, or similar organic substance, and a concentrated solution of a chromate or bichromate of potash, or any base which does not precipitate the organic matter of the first solution, are applied to the paper, stone, metal, glass, wood, &c. which is to receive the design. If the impression is to be taken by contact the film is then dried, if in the camera it may be used moist. After a sufficient exposure, if the surface has become dry, or has been used in a dry state, it is moistened with water by means of a sponge, and, while moist, the greasy ink or matter is applied to the surface, to which it will be found to adhere in those parts only which have been affected by the light. The print may be retained on the surface on which it is first produced, or transferred or printed upon paper or other suitable material, and the operation repeated. A design is thus obtained upon lithographic stone or other suitable material, from which impressions may be multiplied by the method of lithographic printing the moistened surface with a greasy ink.

Various liquid and solid colors are applied upon paper, cloth, glass, and other surfaces, by mixing such colors with the aforesaid mixture of a chromate or bichromate with organic matter, and applying this new mixture or combination to the paper or other fabric or surface. The photographic impression is produced upon this prepared surface by the action of light passing through a negative photographic picture, or an engraving or other suitable object or screen, or in the camera obscura, and it is then washed with a sponge and a large quantity of water. The albumen or other organic matter is rendered insoluble at the parts where it has been acted upon by light, and the design is thus produced in the color which has been employed. Mixtures containing different colors may be applied to different parts of the surface, corresponding to different parts of the negative or screen employed to produce the photographic impression.

[Printed, 3d. No Drawing.]

A.D. 1855, December 13.—N° 2816.

POITEVIN, ALPHONSE LOUIS. — " Improved photographic " engraving."

The invention consists, first, in engraving a plate of glass or other suitable substance coated with a solution of gelatine, which is allowed to set, and is then (either before or after being dried) exposed to the action of a solution of bichromate of potash or other chromate whose base does not produce an insoluble compound with gelatine. Secondly, in the application, in the process of photographic engraving, of a plate or surface coated with a mixture of gelatine and bichromate of potash or other suitable chromate, in either case without the addition of nitrate of silver. Thirdly, in the application of a solution of protosulphate of iron to the surface of the photographic gelatine engraving before pouring plaster upon it in the process of taking a plaster cast from the gelatine. And, fourthly, in a mode of covering the surface of the gelatine with a film of silver before submitting it to the electrotype process, by impregnating it with a solution of iodide of potassium, and then plunging it into a solution of nitrate of silver. The whole is then exposed to the light, when the iodide or other compound of silver is modified by the light, and afterwards reduced by protosulphate of iron.

[Printed, 4d. No Drawing.]

A.D. 1855, December 18.—N° 2860.

HUMASTON, JOHN PIERRPOINT.—" Improvements in instru-
" ments for composing and transmitting telegraph messages."

The invention relates to recording electric telegraphs, and consists, firstly, in a machine termed a " telegraphic compositor ;"
and, secondly, in the method of transmitting the composition
over the wires. It consists in preparing beforehand, upon slips of
paper or other suitable material, the matter it is desired to transmit. This paper is passed through the telegraphic machine at
one station, and therein effects the breaking and closing of the
circuits in accordance with the characters it contains, by which
means the quantity of matter transmitted is thus increased, it being
only limited by the velocity of the electric current and the capability
of the machine by which the circuits are closed and broken.

Corresponding holes are punched in a slip of paper in the order
and shape necessary to form the required characters on the recording machine at the opposite end of the line of wires. The machine
consists of a set of punches so arranged that by indicating the
letter or character to be made upon a finger key, a hole or set
of holes and spaces of the proper shape for that purpose will at
once be punched through the fillet of paper placed in a direction
to receive it.

[Printed, 2s. 5d. Drawings.]

A.D. 1855, December 22.—N° 2904.

DRESSER, CHRISTOPHER.—" Improvements in the mode of
" effecting what is called ' Nature printing.' "

The invention consists in printing from natural objects upon
stone or metal, with a view to multiply the impressions when the
stone or metal has been treated with. agents which render them
capable of being used to print from by the usual processes.

1. A leaf, for instance, prepared by giving it a thin coat of
lithographic ink, is placed (coated side downwards) on a lithographic stone, previously warmed so as not to " set" the ink
upon the leaf. Over the leaf is laid a sheet of paper, which is
rubbed with the finger or a soft pad, so as to press the leaf in
contact with the stone. Upon removing the paper and the leaf
carefully, a delicate and perfect impression of the latter appears
upon the stone ; even the hairs of a leaf, where they exist, being

truly represented. The stone is then subjected to the usual lithographic process, the impression being treated as if it were a drawing on stone, and impressions multiplied to an indefinite extent by the ordinary lithographic printing process. 2. The leaf is treated in the same manner with a composition of etching ground, common tallow, or "balsam of Judæa," and sweet oil, (or any like substances,) and laid upon a warmed metallic plate, when, by a similar treatment to that above described, a perfect impression is deposited. This impression is etched in in the ordinary way, or made into a printing surface by the agency of galvanism. "The latter I prefer. One variety of which, adapted " to my purpose, is fully described in the Athenæum, of March " the 8th last (1856)." From the plate thus obtained, the object is printed off " as if it were type or a wood engraving." 3. A metallic plate is thinly coated with an etching. The leaf is prepared with artists' oil paint, and laid upon the etching ground, when the latter is dissolved in those parts in which the oil comes. The plate is then washed with soap and water, and then subjected to the usual etching processes. In this case the image is concave, and is printed off by " the usual copper-plate " printing process." The process is similar for rollers and cylinders instead of plates.

[Printed, 3d. No Drawing.]

# 1856.

A.D. 1856, January 8.—Nº 59.

PIETRONI, CARLO.—(Provisional Protection only.)—(Communicated by Giuseppe Kossi, of Vienna.)—" Improvements in " printing on cloth and other fabrics."

The invention consists of machinery for printing such fabrics " on the under or lower face or side by an upward pressure of " the printing surface or surfaces, instead of a downward pressure " of a printing surface, as with ordinary printing blocks." It also comprises the " use of machinery adapted for printing cloths " or other fabrics in the manner above described, with two or " more colors, either by a single operation or by a repetition or " repetitions of the same as required."

[Printed, 3d. No Drawing.]

### A.D. 1856, January 18.—N° 145.

MARZOLO, Joseph.—(Provisional Protection only.)—" A re-
" productive organ, printing, with known notes, any musical
" fancies, and equally applicable to pianofortes, melodiums, har-
" moniums, accordeons, and generally to all keyed musical
" instruments."

" The music is printed on the paper by the simple touch or
" action of the keys with types, producing characters like those
" used in ordinary printing or copying, with the identical repe-
" tition or reprint (as often as may be desired) of the airs, effected
" by mechanical re-action on the key-board of the instrument.
" The composer may possess the exact impression of a new
" musical idea reproduced as often as required."

The drawing represents an organ or " melodium" having a
space between the common key-board and a chest containing the
organ pipes large enough to contain a metallic cylinder, round
which is a spiral grove containing a series of small uniform steel
blades. Above the cylinder, and acting upon it, is a horizontal
metallic key-board, each key of which forms a lever with two
points, one the marking point beyond the fulcrum, the other on
the opposite side re-acting from the action of the marking point.
The front ends of these levers are connected by braces or otherwise to the common key-board.

For the printing apparatus the paper is wound on a cylinder,
from which it is drawn off by rollers, and brought under types of
the notes supplied by a set of small rollers.

[Printed, 5d. Drawing.]

### A.D. 1856, January 23.—N° 180.

MEYER, Johannis Joachim Mathias.—(Provisional Protection only.) — " An improved mode of manufacturing bank
" notes, cheques, and other like documents."

It is proposed, in order to obviate the copying by transfer of
such documents, to manufacture them by a " process of double
" printing, one printing to produce a plain tint or an ornamental
" device of so elaborate a nature as to present the appearance of
" a tint upon the whole surface, or on a part only of the face of
" the paper, and the second printing to give the paper its peculiar
" designation, whether of a cheque, bank note, or otherwise.'

These two impressions are obtained (according to the chemical properties of the colors used) from copper or steel plates, or by surface or lithographic printing, care being taken " that the ink " employed in each case shall possess such qualities in common, " that when the printed paper is subjected to suitable treatment " for effecting a transfer, the whole imprint, (that is to say,) the " printed tint and the printed designation, shall come down " together on to the stone or plate on which the transfer is " made, and thereby from the nature of the work prevent the " possibility of a clear or legible impression being obtained from " such transfer."

[Printed, 3d. No Drawing.]

A.D. 1856, January 28.—N° 233.

KING, HENRY SAMUEL.—(Communicated.)—" Improved appa-
" ratus for printing and embossing."

The stamp is attached to a vertical sliding-rod, which is carried by a swinging arm, supported on a pillar rising up from a bed-plate. Fitted to the bed-plate, and on the same level, are removable inking and pressing pads. The sliding rod is borne up above the level of the pads by a coiled spring, or its equivalent, and is capable of being readily depressed by hand to bring the blocks first into contact with the inking pad, subsequently to impress the paper which for that purpose is laid on the pressing pad. Instead of a single swinging arm with its sliding rod and stamp, there may be two or more arms carried by the same centre pin, and also ink or color pads, provided with different tints to produce imprints of designs in two or more colors. In such case the blocks will each carry only a given portion of the design. When imprints are to be made in more than one color, it will be requisite to provide stops or guides to ensure a perfect register. In order to emboss and print at the same time, a counter die is substituted for the pressing pad.

[Printed, 9d. Drawings.]

A.D. 1856, February 4.—N° 299.

ROBINSON, ELISHA SMITH.—" Improvements in machinery
" for lithographic and zincographic printing."

The invention relates to an arrangement of machinery for damp-ing, inking, printing, and taking and delivering the fabric whilst the stone or zinc is in motion. The stone or zinc is in a carriage driven to and fro by rack and pinion. The damping apparatus (supported in a frame) consists of a water trough, furnished with pipes and regulating taps, connected with a perforated tube, which is placed immediately over an absorbing roller. Attached to the carriage is an "absorbing slab," which is moistened by the absorbing roller and supplies moisture to other absorbing rollers, which in turn moisten the stone or zinc. There is a contrivance of weights and levers on the trough by which the water is let fall at the proper time, and also by which the apparatus is lifted clear of the stone or zinc to allow the printed sheet to pass freely. The inking apparatus consists of an ink trough from which the supply is regulated by set screws. Under this trough is a roller set in motion by line and speed pulleys, and beneath it a second roller caused to rise and fall by the action of a lever to which it transmits the ink, which is by the second roller laid on a slab or table, where it is distributed as the table moves by diagonally disposed rollers. The table in its turn gives off the ink to the rollers, by which the stone or zinc is inked as it passes under them. The material to be printed is laid upon a board which receives a sliding motion by means of an excentric, and travels along this board until it is taken hold of by springs which draw it round a revolving cylinder so as to receive the impression when the stone or zinc passes under it. The carriage upon which the stone, &c. is fixed receives besides the inking and damping slabs four inclines working in slides, which raise the inking rollers over the edge of the stone or zinc and prevents the ink adhering to it.

[Printed, 1s. 2d. Drawings.]

A.D. 1856, February 7.—N° 331.

BERGNER, THEODORE.—(Provisional Protection only.)—(Communicated by Samuel W. Lowe, of Philadelphia.)—" A new mode " of preparing or facing the surfaces of engraved or etched plates " of metal or other substance, so that they may be readily printed " from by a press without wiping."

The engraved portion of a steel plate is filled up with gum, resin, wax, &c., so as to leave the unengraved surface bare. The latter is then, by galvanic process, coated with copper sufficiently thick to receive and amalgamate with mercury by rubbing it on the surface of the same, so as to fix a thin mercurialized surface upon the plate. The gum, wax, &c. is then removed, and the plate is ready for the press. Copper plates are prepared in the same way, with the omission of the galvanic process. On plates so coated, the ink, when applied by a "sharp" inking roller, will not adhere to or soil the mercurialized portion, while it fills and remains in the engraved lines. Common tin plate can thus be used in place of steel and copper plates. The plate being covered with an etching ground, the design is engraved through and eaten in with nitro-muriatic or other acid. The acid is then washed off and the etching ground removed. The plate is then rubbed with mercury which forms a thin mercurialized surface upon the plain portion of the plate, the mercury having no affinity for the iron, down to which the design has been eaten in. It can, therefore, as well as the steel and copper plates, be printed from continuously by "a letter press or other suitable form of press," either alone or in the same form with type. Any other material besides tin which is "capable of receiving or being made to receive a thin " mercurial coating or amalgam surface" may be used in the same way as a substitute for copper and steel plates.

[Printed, 3*d*. No Drawing.]

A.D. 1856, February 9.—N° 342.

SWAN, CHARLES, and SWAN, GEORGE FREDERICK.—(Communicated.)—"An improved colouring matter for writing, stain- " ing, or dyeing, which is also applicable to the production of a " .copying fluid."

The coloring matter, which, among other advantages, has that of not corroding metals, is composed of a mixture of bichromate of potash, subcarbonate of potash, chlorate of potash, perchloride of mercury, or corrosive sublimate, and spirits of ammonia, applied to extract of logwood. The coloring matter may be obtained in a solid form "by any suitable processes for combining the above- " mentioned ingredients, and the same subsequently liquified as " required." The coloring matter obtained from the above ingredients, either in a fluid or solid form, may be converted into a copying fluid "by the addition of any thickening ingredients " which have heretofore been employed, or which may be found " applicable for such a purpose."

[Printed, 3*d*. No Drawing.]

A.D. 1856, February 12.—N° 360.

JABLONOWSKI, J. FELIX PRUSS.—(Provisional Protection only.)—" A new process of chromo-lithographic painting on glass, " porcelain, clays, lava, and other materials susceptible of vitri- " faction, and on all metals and metallic compounds capable of " receiving an enamelled surface."

Stones and plates of steel, &c., are prepared as follows:—The design is executed in black upon four stones or plates, as follows: First, that reserved for strokes made with a pen and lithographic ink; second, that destined for the shadows or tints drawn with lithographic crayons; third, that used for shadows put on with a brush and lithographic ink; fourth, that reserved exclusively for the " lights." Each of these is at once plastered with a stratum of the following composition, namely, gum copal (5 parts), gallipot or white resin (5 parts), fatty oils (2 parts), turpentine (2 parts). " I afterwards execute the light strokes by means of a fine dry " point (as a graver), those parts of the drawing which represent " the hair, the beard, the lights, and the chiaro-obscuro." An impression is then taken on negative paper (prepared as presently mentioned), the negative drawing changed to a positive one by wetting the verso of it with water, and spreading it upon a surface previously wetted with water. When thus sufficiently wetted the impression is laid upon the surface to be ornamented, which has previously been coated with a preparation of gallipot (3) and tur- pentine (7). A roller is then passed with a slight pressure over the impression, to ensure its " more perfect spreading and adap- " tation," after which a sponge soaked in hot water is passed over it. The paper is then lifted, leaving the second preparation with the drawing thereon, and this is transferred to the object to be ornamented. This last should afterwards be well washed. The article ornamented is left to dry naturally for several days, and then dried at a stove to evaporate the oil and spirits employed. The coloring is effected with " printing oil," mixed with vitrificable colors. Oil from fresh nuts and burnt crusts of bread are heated in an iron pan until the former is inflammable, when the pan is closed. This process is continued until the oil takes fire five or six times in succession. The enamels or vitrificable colors must have their combination of silicia and lead in accordance with the matters employed in preparing the paper, carbonate of lime render- ing the enamels less fusible. Cloth, silk, and other stuffs easily impregnated with water may be substituted for the negative paper. For the first preparation of the negative paper any soluble gum, natural or artificial, or mucilaginous matter, is used; and as matters soluble in spirit and oils in the second preparation of the paper, all gums, resins, mastics, and other bodies soluble in spirit and oils.

[Printed, 3d. No Drawing.]

## A.D. 1856, February 16.—Nº 400.

GRANT, FREDERICK DANIEL.—(Provisional Protection only.)— " A method of rendering printing inks and wax odoriferous."

This is effected by mixing with such materials one or more essential oils or scents. In the printing of a bunch of flowers, for instance, separate inks are employed, the essence of the flower to be represented being incorporated with each, "so that each separate " flower may to a certain extent exhale an odour similar to that " from a living flower."

[Printed, 3d. No Drawing.]

## A.D. 1856, February 18.—Nº 406.

THOMSON, JAMES STRANG, and BARCLAY, ANDREW.— " Improvements in printing and embossing textile fabrics and " other substances, and in the production of apparatus to be " employed therein."

These consist, first, in preparing moulds for printing surfaces, by means of " a built-up mass of pins or types." The pins are of two lengths, the difference between them being the amount of the relief required in the printing surface. The composer reads off the colours of the design in the usual manner, putting into the matrix frame or holder " a short pin at each increment of surface " where the colour is to appear, and inserting a long pin at the " other parts, where blanks or other colours are to occur." As each color is read off and built up the series of pins is bound up and a cast taken of them in gutta percha or other suitable material. Embossing surfaces may be similarly produced for use " according to any of the existing plans," or applicable to the " rotary system in an arrangement of machinery modified from " the printing machinery " patented by James Melville (Nº 14,047 of 1852, and Nº 2680 of 1853). Secondly, in a mode of gearing the printing roller with the large drum, so as to allow of any size of repeats of pattern being used which will divide into the circumference of the drum, and driving the drum by means of a pinion. Thirdly, in a mode of arranging the printing roller and color feed apparatus, wherein these details are carried by a frame which can be removed in one piece from the traversing carriage. Fourthly, " certain classes of fabrics or yarns " are wound round the large drum in a spiral direction and printed on while so arranged. The printing roller is set at right angles to the line of fabric, and is made to traverse longitudinally as it and the drum revolve, so as to make its continuous line of impression coincide with the spiral line of fabric. The printing roller may be in three or more pieces, the central portions being fixed loosely on the spindle, to yield a little to the curvature of the drum. Fifthly, instead of using a large single drum, the fabric to be printed may be wound spirally, or in the ordinary manner, upon an endless web passed round two drums. Sixthly, the large impression drum is encompassed with a spiral coil of flat piping, through which a current of steam is passed to dry the fabric after it is printed.

[Printed, 1s. Drawings.]

A.D. 1856, February 28.—Nº 516.

BROOMAN, RICHARD ARCHIBALD.—(Communicated by Pierre Gédeon Barry.)—" Improvement in treating bituminous shale, " boghead mineral, and other like schistous bodies, in order to " obtain various commercial products therefrom."

The invention consists in producing from the above substances, among other products, a " black which may be used as a colouring " matter in painting, and in the manufacture of printing ink," and " a black having the same properties as animal black, and " which may be used in the decolorization of liquids, vinegar, " raw sugar, &c., and also in the manufacture of blacking." The above materials are placed in a retort, whence the distilled products pass to a receiver at some distance from it. A condenser provided with refrigerating tubes condenses the raw oils and ammoniacal waters. The oils, after being separated from the thick tar, are introduced into "purifiers," (wooden cases lined with lead, and provided with " agitators,") where they are brought into contact with about five per cent. by weight of sulphuric acid. They are then drawn off from their sediment into a second purifier, where they are united with liquid caustic soda or lime-water.

The raw oils are submitted to a primary distillation in an apparatus consisting of a cucurbit placed over a furnace, in order to separate them from the pasty or semi-liquid tar which remains in the cucurbit. From this it is drawn while still hot, and the oils submitted successively with sulphuric acid, caustic soda, and lime-water, and are then redistilled in a still of the description employed in the distillation of molasses or rum. The oils separated from the thick tar yield light essential oil, the density of the first streams of which are about 70° of Gay Lussac's areometer. Distillation is carried on until the stream attains a density of 50°. These results are collected separately. The next batch may be collected until it attains 32°. This oil may be used for lighting purposes. " The distillation may be further proceeded with, but " the heat must be progressively increased, and the product re- " sulting will be the unctuous oil, fit for greasing and lubricating " purposes. A nearly liquid tar or tarry matter will still remain " in the cucurbit, which may be converted into black grease by " mixing with it ten to fifteen per cent. of liquid caustic soda " at 36°."

[Printed, 7d. Drawings.]

A.D. 1856, March 4.—N° 550.

ROSENBERG, CHARLES THOMAS.—" Improvements in orna- " menting china, glass, and other surfaces when transferring " printed impressions."

Having obtained the design upon a series of plates by tracing over transfer paper, the high lights of each are then stopped out with Brunswick black or other varnish, and a border of banking wax drawn with it. Dilute nitric acid is then poured over it and left till the proper tint is effected. The first stopping out is then extended, and the process repeated. The banking wax is then removed, and the ground cleared off with spirits of turpentine. The parts requiring to be lightened are burnished or scraped, and the darks, if requiring strength, cut up with a graver or other tool. A thin plate of zinc is then fixed on to a block of wood, and three pins inserted in it to correspond with notches cut in the series of plates for the purpose of registering. The paper used for the impressions is prepared with a coating of starch (10 scruples), gelatine (2 scruples), and loaf sugar (5 scruples), dissolved in water (8 oz.) The whole of the series of plates having been printed in enamel colours, the porcelain, glass, &c. is prepared by a coating of rosin dissolved in turpentine, and the design transferred to it by pressing the paper, which has been moistened, against it. The paper is then wetted and gently removed, leaving the whole of the ink composing the design upon the porcelain, glass, &c.

[Printed, 4d. No Drawing.]

## A.D. 1856, March 5.—No 555.

KAY, RICHARD DUGDALE.—" Improvements in the manufacture " of fabrics from fibrous materials."

" I take what is generally known as ' Clark's felt,' which is " made of cotton, or a felt made of a mixture of cotton and wool, " either by Clark's process or the ordinary process of felting, and " by means of dissolved caoutchouc or other suitable cement, I " attach any woven fabric either to one or both sides or surfaces " of the said felt, thus forming a strong compact fabric, suitable " for and applicable to printers' blankets, roller cloths, cylinder " lappings, drawing rollers used in spinning, and as a substitute " for leather in the carding operation, or other similar purposes."

[Printed, 3d. No Drawing.]

## A.D. 1856, March 15.—No 622.

COATES, CHARLES.—" Improvements in apparatus for com- " municating motion to machinery used in bleaching, printing, " dyeing, and finishing fabrics."

The motion is communicated by means of the friction of cir- cumferences of pulleys driven from a pulley on the driving shaft. Where this frictional pressure is insufficient it is augmented by a spring or weight. The motion of the friction pulley on the driving shaft is also communicated to the friction pulley on the axle to be driven by means of an intermediate pulley mounted on a stud. In either case the machine is instantly stopped as soon as the circumferences of the pulleys are thrown out of contact, which is done when any undue power is exerted, owing to the lapping of the fabric round any of the rollers or winces of which the machine is composed. When the driving shaft passes through the cistern of the machine the casing of the shaft supports the pegs for guiding the fabric.

[Printed, 1s. 4d. Drawings.]

A.D. 1856, March 18.—N° 646.

MAW, ARTHUR.—(Provisional Protection refused.)—" Improved
" means of ornamenting the surfaces of woven, knitted, or felted
" fabrics, such as cloths, stuffs, ribbons, and other fabrics; or of
" parchment, vellum, leather, or other animal tissues, and rendering
" such fabrics or tissues applicable to various purposes."

The invention consists in the employment of " certain processes
" closely allied to the process of photography," whereby " the
" surfaces of these materials may be rendered sensitive to light, so
" that having obtained a negative picture on glass or paper, or
" some other transparent or translucent material, a positive im-
" pression or image may be transferred to the prepared surface of
" the fabric or tissue. By these means any variety of design or
" pattern may be transferred to these materials, but the particular
" nature of the design or pattern must depend, not only upon the
" taste of the operator, but also for the purpose for which the
" ornamented materials are to be employed."

[Printed, 3d. No Drawing.]

A.D. 1856, March 22.—N° 679.

JOHNSON, JOHN HENRY.—(Communicated by Charles Claude
Etienne Minié, Commandant of the School of Fire-arms at
Vincennes, in the Empire of France, and Louis François Clement
Breguet, of Paris, in the said Empire.) — " Improvements in
" electro-magnetic printing telegraphs."

A recording instrument, where a conventional alphabet is used,
has a wooden cylinder rotating by clockwork and driven by a
pinion on one end of its axis, whilst at its other end is fixed a
continuous helicoidal-grooved drum, for the purpose of imparting
a lateral movement to the strip of paper for receiving the message.
Two duplicate strips may be printed at one time by passing them
simultaneously under the recording instrument, which consists of
a lever fitted with a sharp point at its other end being drawn down
by a helical spring, so as to keep the pricker elevated until required to operate, which is done by means of an electro-magnet in
connection with one of the poles of the battery. The " manipu-
" lator" consists of a number of keys, somewhat similar to the
keys of a pianoforte, each key indicating a letter. The keys are
hinged above the cylinder by means of flat blade springs in place

of hinged joints, and the springs of the several keys are prolonged, so that their ends are over the centre of the cylinder and tangential to its surface. In this cylinder are fitted a number of metallic studs arranged in a certain order and number under each of the keys, the studs being flush, or nearly so, with the surface of the cylinder. The various letters of the alphabet are composed of a number of prick marks, arranged transversely across the strip of paper in different numbers and positions, regulated by the corresponding number and position of the studs in the cylinder for that particular letter. When a key is depressed, so as to bring its spring on to one of the metallic studs in the cylinder the curcuit is established, the pricker is immediately drawn down by the magnet to puncture the paper, which is wound off from a reel as required by a pair of feeding rollers. This descent of the pricker releases also the cylinder, which makes a revolution; and as the corresponding studs will pass in succession under the spring of the depressed key, it follows that the circuit will be made and broken as many times as there are studs, and as at each re-establishment of contact the pricker will descend, it follows that a corresponding number of prick marks will be made in the strip of paper, such pricks being placed across the paper, which has a lateral movement imparted to it by the grooved drum. At each rotation of the cylinder a catch or arm fixed to one end of it strikes a star wheel on the axis of one of the feeding rollers, and turns it a short distance, thereby drawing the strip forward longitudinally for the succeeding letter. Suitable claws or detents are brought into action when a key is depressed for the purpose of arresting the movement of the cylinder after one revolution. In the arrangement of apparatus for printing the ordinary letters of the alphabet a very slight modification is required. The cylinder, which is of metal instead of wood, is fitted with a number of projecting pins, arranged spirally round its surface, each pin corresponding to a key on the manipulator, whilst each key corresponds to a letter, number, or other character or sign. A type wheel with letters on its periphery is substituted for the continuous helicoidal-grooved drum. The pricker is also dispensed with, the end of the lever which carried it being merely required to press the paper on to the letter presented to the type wheel to print the same on the paper which passes over it. Several letters may be produced at the same time, those letters which follow one another in the same word in alphabetical order being produced with the same rapidity as a single one. Also by increasing the length of the key-board, so as to allow of several alphabets sliding on it, an entire word may be produced, whatever may be the order of the letters, by depressing the requisite keys with both hands simultaneously.

[Printed, 11d. Drawings.]

A.D. 1856, March 25.—N° 713.

ILLINGWORTH, William.—(Provisional Protection only.)— " Certain improvements in printing or coloring china, earthen- " ware, or other ceramic manufactures, and in the machinery or " apparatus connected therewith; and also improvements in the " subsequent treatment of such manufactures."

The invention consists, first, in an extension of the use of the preparation of " saccharine matter " as a substitute for oil, and in the preparation of color, as specified in N° 2179 of 1855, and consists in a further use of such matter in combination with certain animal and vegetable mucilagenous substances, as albumen, gela- tine, gluten, casine, carrageen moss, linseed, mucilage, &c. in place of oil, &c., in printing or colouring such or similar manu- factures. Secondly, in the application of " doctors " to flat plates used for printing, for the purpose of cleaning such plates, exactly in a similar manner to their operation in cylinder calico printing; and also, if preferred, in combination with the use of inking or colouring rollers for furnishing the said flat plates. Thirdly, in equalizing the power of absorption of the glaze, by dipping or immersing the printed ware into a thin mucilagenous solution, either pure or mixed with acids; and lastly, in improving the " glaze " by the introduction or admixture of mucilage.

[Printed, 3d. No Drawing.]

A.D. 1856, March 29.—N° 756.

RIPPON, John James.—" An improvement or improvements " in rollers or cylinders for printing fabrics."

The invention consisis in placing a core or cylinder of iron, of somewhat less diameter than the roller or cylinder to be manu- factured, in a suitably prepared mould, and casting thereon a hollow cylinder or casing of copper, or alloy consisting mainly of copper.

[Printed, 3d. No Drawing.]

GLASSFORD, John Hamilton.—(Provisional Protection only.)
—" Improvements in the production or preparation of printing
" surfaces."

The invention consists in producing printing surfaces from the
surface of an ordinary lithographic stone or piece of metal of a
flat form, having on it a design etched or engraved according to
the Specification, N° 2011 of 1855, or otherwise. Such flat surface
is prepared by applying to it a conducting coating, and electrotyping it " in the usual manner, or in any modified manner which
" may be found convenient for obtaining a copper or other metallic
" coating."

[Printed, 3d. No Drawing.]

GARDISSAL, Charles Durand. — (Provisional Protection
only.) — (Communicated.) — " The treatment or preparation of
" fabrics or textile materials to be dyed or printed."

The invention depends on the principle that textile materials
acquire a great affinity for colors, either with or without the use
of mordants, after being exposed to the action of nitric acid,
" or rather a mixture of nitric and sulphuric acid." The materials are for a short time placed in contact in the cold shade
with the acids. These may be imbibed in the textile fabrics
previous to the dyeings, or dissolved in suitable quantity in
the coloring matter. The power of absorption of color in the
fabrics is increased by dipping them, before the application of
mordants, in a bath of milk, of solutions of albumina, of gelatine,
of gluten, or any other azoted matters that may be coagulated by
heat, by acids, or any chemicals or agent forming insoluble compounds with these matters. Thus the albumina is fixed by gelatine, tannin, gall-nut, &c. Fine black colors are obtained by the
combination of tannin with gelatine. For the better fixing of
" certain colours," baths of fatty matters are used.

[Printed, 3d. No Drawing.]

HOGG, James, and NAPIER, John. — " Improvements in
" stereotyping."

The improvements relate to the formation of a matrix from an original, and the production of a cast from that matrix. For the former, a sheet of stout packing paper, cloth, &c., coated with a paste of red ochre and fine whitening, thin glue, starch, and wheaten flour, with a little alum, is laid on the original, previously oiled, and a single and very light "soaking" pull taken in a press, or a "planer and mallet" is used. The mould is weighted and left under the form to dry. Or the mould may be made in plaster of Paris, a coating being first run over the type, and a perforated plate then laid upon such coating, and cemented with it by pouring on plaster at the back of the said plate. The casting box consists of two plates of metal, varying in size according to the matrix, and each having a rectangular flange of five or six inches. The gauge and plates being heated in an oven of 450° Fahrenheit, the matrix, surrounded by the gauge, is laid between the plates, the sides of the matrix being allowed slightly to underlap the gauge, in order that the matrix may be held fast. The whole is then bound together, and is ready for the casting. A brick or slab is sometimes used as a substitute for one of the iron plates in the casting box, the brick and plate, with the matrix and gauge lying between them, being "cramped" together in the same manner as the two iron plates. Another modification of the casting box is formed by placing the matrix at the bottom of a stereotyper's "flat pan" with rather higher sides than usual, other matrices (if found convenient) being laid upon intermediate iron plates, kept apart by gauges, sufficient to form the thickness of the stereotype plates. An iron cover is then fixed on the "flat " pan," and the metal poured in "as in the ordinary flat pan used " at present in stereotyping, when not dipped in a bath of metal " or alloy."

[Printed, 8d. Drawings.]

A.D. 1856, April 5.—N° 830.

MORTON, ARNOLD.—"Improvements in the manufacture of " paints and pigments."

The invention consists in certain improvements on N° 1667 of 1853, simplifying the processes of that patent, and giving permanence to the colors produced by it. The specification is mainly a repetition of the former one.

[Printed, 5d. No Drawing.]

## A.D. 1856, April 7.—N° 842.

MORTON, ARNOLD.—" Improvements in the manufacture of
" paper-hangings for decorative purposes."

The invention consists in the use of dissolved soap and in the
compounding of various "vehicles" for reducing or resubduing
colouring matters employed in the manufacture of paints and pigments used in making paper-hangings.

Vehicle No. 1 consists of soap, skimmed milk, and alum, ground
together and added to china clay. A "saponaceous solution"
may be passed over the work when dry, as in N° 1667 of 1853.

Vehicle No. 2 is composed of soap, skimmed milk, alum, sulphate of zinc or acetic acid, ground together.

Vehicle No. 3. To the above-mentioned milky and saponaceous
compounds is added a quantity of pure or rough sulphate of zinc
or alum, or sugar of lead, such that the zinc, &c. shall be moderately in excess.

In paper-staining the colors are prepared and used according
to N° 830 of 1856. Grained papers have a saponaceous solution
spread over them to preserve them from dirt. For oak papers the
colors are used according to N° 830 of 1856, the light veins or
figuring being mixed with varnish, to impart a natural gloss to
the wood. " In graining marbles, granites, maples, mahogany,
" and all other grained papers, the chief thing to be observed is,
" to get in as much vehicle as possible, according to the affinities
" of the colors used, and in thinning the whole with water only,
" or diluted vehicles 1, 2, 3, or 5." To produce "a double egg
" gloss" a saponaceous solution is applied, and when dry brushed
" as usual with satin papers." In printing or blocking a great
advantage is obtained by mixing the vehicles with size "just on
" the run."

[Printed, 4d. No Drawing.]

## A.D. 1856, April 11.—N° 868.

NORMANDY, LEWIS.—(Communicated by l'Abbé Eugene
Cormier.)—" Improvements in the mode of writing and printing
" music, to facilitate the study thereof."

The stave lines are of several colors, "by which contrivance the
" reading of music is learned much more rapidly than heretofore."
They are (going upwards) green, black, dotted red, black, and red.
A drawing is given of a " common hand-printing press," on the

table of which is a compound printing plate, so arranged as to print at once the three required colors. This compound plate is separated, and inked with different colors, and subsequently reunited for each impression.

[Printed, 6d. Drawings.]

A.D. 1856, April 14.—N° 886.

COULON, Louis Pierre.—(Communicated.)—"A new type " distributing and composing machine."

The apparatus consists of a table or frame, on one side of which is the composing key-board. In the centre, and on the top, are placed vertically two cylinders, the upper one revolving upon an iron rod which passes through the lower, and rests on a pointed stud. The upper cylinder is the distributing, the lower the composing cylinder. The bottom plate of it is pierced with a number of oblong holes, which admit of the type passing to the upper plate of the lower cylinder, which is pierced with holes formed with different notches, which only admit types having corresponding projections. The type then falls upon the " guide rod " of the composing cylinder which belongs to it, and is thus conveyed to the distributing mechanism, consisting of a funnel having grooves made in it, down which the type runs to the trough, which brings it to the foot of the workman. In composing, the workman has simply to place the keys of the key-board in the order in which letters or type are required. This action causes the types to pass through the oblong holes in the bottom of the composition cylinder, where, by suitable mechanism, they are tilted into a trough which conveys them to the grooved funnel, and where they meet at the point where the letters are arranged in their proper order. While the workman is composing, he has only to move the pedal with his foot to perform " distribution." This pedal puts in motion a cam, and the distribution supplies the amount of types for the composition. A small instrument, by means of which the upper cylinder is filled, and which also permits of placing an entire line of type on each guide rod at one movement of the hand, consisting of a copper galley supported by steel arms fixed to the distributing cylinder. The return of the piston by which this is effected gives to the cylinder a slight rotatory motion, which successively presents each empty rod to the succeeding line of the distribution packet.

Another mechanical arrangement at the same time effects the separation of the lines.

[Printed, 10d. Drawings.]

A.D. 1856, May 3.—Nº 1050.

FONTAINE MOREAU, Peter Armand le Comte de. — (Communicated.)—" Improvements in electric telegraphs."

The improved telegraphic apparatus by which messages can be transmitted " with a rapidity hitherto unobtained " (placed one at each station) consists, first, of a motor or wheel-work arrangement wound up by electro-magnetism and having a continuous movement; secondly, in an improved alphabetical key-board current breaker for the transmission of the despatch; and thirdly, in a peculiar arrangement of the type, cylinders, and printing apparatus.

A ratchet wheel has fixed to it a barrel containing a clock spiral spring, and an ordinary toothed wheel, rather less than the ratchet wheel, is fixed over the barrel and gears with the pinion of another wheel. This sets in motion two rather smaller wheels, one of which gears with the pinion placed on the axis on which the fly wheel is fixed. As a further means of giving uniformity of motion, a flier is used. The pawl which works in the ratchet wheel is attached to a swinging lever. To the middle of the latter is fixed loosely the end of three levers, which form a T. The end of the middle lever is attached to an armature passing over two magnets, each movement of the armature causing the pawl to move the ratchet wheel round one tooth. At the bottom of each key is a small platina plate, which, when the key is pressed down, touches a plate of copper. A central wheel, with suitable pulleys affixed to its shaft, has a series of small oblong pieces of wood fixed to its circumference in such a manner that in plan they form a spiral or curve alternately. On each side of the central wheel is a pulley supported by suitable bearings. An endless band of laminated platina, pierced with small rectangular openings which fit the wooden projections on the central wheel, passes partly round these pulleys and over the central wheel. On this band oiled silk insulators are placed at equal distances, and in such relation to the central wheel and the key-board, that at each complete revolution of the wheel, one of such insulators being placed immediately below the first key to the right, it passes over the whole length of the key-board plus the distance of two consecutive keys. The revolution once effected, the insulator is replaced by the following one, which takes its place under the first key to the right. Between the metallic conducting band and the range of twenty-eight keys are disposed an equal number of flexible brass springs furnished at their extremities with small platina plates. At a suitable distance below the key-board two wheels are placed together on a suitable axis. On the circumference of each are engraved twenty-eight signals. Figures may be placed on one cylinder corresponding with those on the key-board. Near the centre of the machine are placed four magnets with an armature on each couple, and a square metal frame affixed to the armatures. Towards the cylinders the metal frame is extended till its extremity is over the printing cylinders. The extremity is covered with leather or caoutchouc, and acts as a press. Paper is fed in and regulated by suitable rollers, ratchet wheels, and other means.

[Printed, 1s. 8d. Drawings.]

A.D. 1856, May 10.—N° 1113.

BENIOWSKI, BARTHOLOMEW.—" Improvements in typogra-
" phical composition and the manufacture of logotypes to be
" used therein."

" Logotypes " are composed into lines and pages exactly as for printing, except that after each is placed a " separator " or space of the same body and shape as the types and usual spaces, " dis-
" tinguished, however, from these last either by a different nick or
" nicks, or by color, and also by making their feet completely flat,
" i.e. without the usual groove therein." 2. Between each line is put a " lad," which is in every respect similar to an ordinary lead of about small pica thickness. 3. The page so composed is justified, locked up as for printing, and corrected. 4. The whole is transferred to an air and water tight trough, and the type unlocked. 5. A thin solution of shellac or other similar varnish is poured into the trough, and the whole covered air-tight to prevent evaporation. 6. After a few hours the solution is drawn off. After standing uncovered for about ten minutes in a dry and warm atmosphere, the page is locked up and put for a few seconds on a sheet of blotting-paper.

[Printed, 11d. Drawings.]

A.D. 1856, May 12.—N⁰ 1116.

WHYTOCK, RICHARD.—" Improvements in apparatus to faci-
" litate the printing of yarns or threads."

The invention is designed to obviate the inconveniences attending the use of the large wheels and double cylinders usually
adopted for reeling hanks of yarns, which are printed to produce
figured fabrics, and consists in placing opposite to each other
two cylinders or open reels connected by bars so as to be moved
from place to place. These reels are covered with a continuous
coating of yarn or threads laid in as regular order as the threads
or yarns on a cylinder. These coils may be removed from the
reels and printed on tables or under cylinders for such patterns as
are termed "turned-over" patterns, or before removal of the yarn,
by means of traversing pulleys.

[Printed, 10*d*. Drawings.]

A.D. 1856, May 17.—N⁰ 1170.

SCHEURMANN, GUSTAV. — (Provisional Protection only.)—
" Improvements in printing music."

These consist, first, in the use of "solid and mathematical cha-
" racters, by which a very great saving of labour is effected in
" comparison with the modes hitherto in use, which characters
" likewise contain all declivities in a solid form necessary for
" printing music to any required length and angle, and which
" characters are cast partly in common moulds and partly in
" moulds specially constructed for this purpose." Also in a
press "so constructed that, by mechanical agency, the paper is
" brought in contact first with the rules (to produce the impres-
" sion of the lines) and then with the characters, or first with the
" characters and then with the rules. Or a stereotyped cast of
" the characters and lines may be taken so as to print the whole
" at one operation in any common press, or with the characters
" and rules at the same time."

[Printed, 3*d*. No Drawing.]

A.D. 1856, May 17.—N⁰ 1171.

CORNIDES, LOUIS.—" Improvements in ornamental window
" blinds and such like transparent decorations."

A lithographic or other impression made on transfer paper, and washed with purified ox gall, is, when dry, coated with a solution of pure gelatine, or gelatine in combination with sugar and water, and placed upon and transferred to the textile or wire-woven fabric or suitable perforated substance, stretched or otherwise held in a suitable frame. When the impression is perfectly dry, the paper is detached by wetting it with a solution of acetate of alumina or water. Surfaces thus ornamented may be protected from atmospheric influences by a coating of collodion or other transparent varnish.

[Printed, 3d. No Drawing.]

A.D. 1856, May 19.—N° 1179.

WILKES, JOHN, and WILKES, THOMAS.—"A new or im-" proved manufacture of rollers or cylinders for printing fabrics."

The invention consists in making fresh printing rollers from those already used. The former pattern having been effaced (by turning or otherwise), the roller is expanded by a bar passed through it longitudinally, and afterwards elongated and reduced in diameter by a drawing process. It is next placed upon a hollow cylinder of wrought or malleable iron, and the whole subjected to a drawing process whereby the copper becomes firmly fixed on the iron. The roller may be fixed upon its axis in the ordinary way.

[Printed, 6d. Drawings.]

A.D. 1856, May 19.—N° 1185.

WILKES, JOHN, WILKES, THOMAS, and WILKES, GILBERT. —"A new or improved manufacture of rollers or cylinders for " printing fabrics."

A hollow cylinder of copper, made " by any convenient process," is placed upon a hollow malleable iron cylinder and subjected to a drawing process, "similar to that by which metallic tubes are " drawn," by which it becomes firmly fixed upon the iron cylinder.

[Printed, 5d. Drawings.]

DUFRESNE, ALEXANDRE HENRI.—" An improved process of
" gilding and ornamenting steel and other metals."

The invention consists, first, in depositing by either chemical,
electro-chemical, or mechanical means one or several intermediate metals upon the surface to be ornamented. Iron or steel
is ornamented by depositing on it a coating of copper, which
is afterwards gilded or silvered " by the ordinary processes of
" amalgamation." They are damascened by being covered, as
before, with a copper coating, on which the design is traced with
varnish, bitumen of Judea, or other protecting substance, and
being immersed in chromic acid, which dissolves the copper not
protected by the varnish. The varnish is removed with hot
turpentine, leaving the design in copper on a steel ground. The
article is then finished off, and the gilding or ornamenting effected,
" the mercury being volatilized by heat after amalgamation in the
" ordinary way."

Platina articles are coated with copper, and have the design laid
on them as before stated. The unprotected parts of the copper
are then dissolved out by nitric, sulphuric, chromic, or other suitable acid, and the varnish being removed, the article is gilded or
ornamented by amalgamation as for iron.

On silver a triple metallic surface of copper, iron (or nickel),
and copper respectively is deposited. The reserves are formed on
the last coat of copper, and the unreserved parts of the superposed metals destroyed in succession, so that the iron which
presents itself on the removal of the upper coat prevents the
mercury from adhering to the first copper or silver surface during
the amalgamation. The iron is lastly removed by any suitable
re-agent.

Instead of forming the reserve by hand with protective varnishes,
the ordinary processes of photography, heliography, or impression
may be employed either directly or by transfer.

[Printed, 3*d*. No Drawing.]

BELL, ROBERT.—" An improvement in the manufacture or pro-
" duction of ornamental fabrics."

The invention relates to the making a cloth of cotton, having two printing surfaces and one or more filling wefts or warps between such surfaces, all woven into one as one fabric, which may be printed on one or both sides with different patterns or colors. (a) The invention is particularly adapted for the production of double-sided shawls, zebra dresses, and others. The filling warps or wefts inside between the outer plies or printing surfaces, while they prevent the colors on one side passing to the other, and thus procure beauty of coloring, give also thickness, softness, and the peculiar spongy feel necessary for such goods. Goods made in this way will have all the appearance and feel of a very much more expensive article " now made in the jacquard or " other harness and complicated loom, while the price will be very " much lower."

[Printed, 7d. Drawings.]

A.D. 1856, May 24.—No 1244.

ILLINGWORTH, WILLIAM. — " Certain improvements in " printing or coloring, and coloring and glazing china, earthen- " ware, or other ceramic manufactures, and in the machinery or " apparatus connected therewith ; and also improvements in the " subsequent treatment of such manufactures."

The invention is an improvement on No 2179 of 1855, and consists, first, in the preparation of colors by the use of animal and vegetable, mucilaginous, or amylaceous substances, deliquescent salts and other substances, such as the chlorides, nitrates, acetates, citrates, tartrates, saccharates, &c. &c., of zinc, manganese, lime, magnesia, &c.; also citric acid or lemon juice, secharic acid, phosphoric acid, arsenic acid, muriatic acid, together with all other deliquescent acids, either with or without saccharine matter as a substitute for oil. Secondly, in the use of " doctors " for cleaning flat printing plates, in a manner similar to that in operation for cylinder calico printing, and also, if preferred, in combination with the use of inking or coloring rollers for furnishing the flat plates. Thirdly, in the removal, in the subsequent treatment of pottery, of the transfer paper from the ware, by the application of diluted chlorides or acids to the back of it,

(a) See No 1191 of 1852.

or dipping the ware in water, or in water mixed with a little mucilage, chloride, or acid. Also in equalizing the power of absorption of the glaze in the body of the ware with those parts which are printed upon, by immersing the newly-printed ware in water, or water mixed with a little mucilage, chloride, or acid. Lastly, in improving the glaze employed by the introduction or admixture of mucilage.

[Printed, 4d. No Drawings.]

## A.D. 1856, May 27.—No 1267.

NEWTON, WILLIAM EDWARD.— (Communicated.) —" Im- " provements in printing machinery."

The invention relates to cylinder printing, and consists in a novel mode of securing the types on the cylinder, and " locking " up" the forms. The types are held in their places by means of wedge formed column rules, as described in No 12,216 of 1848. The lower edge of these column rules is provided with a projecting ledge, whereby they are held down by being placed in rebated grooves made in the type bed, and are further held by means of segmental pieces, made to rest on the said rebates or ledges of the column rules. These segmental pieces are let in spaces made in the type bed, and may be said to form part thereof. The columns of type are locked up by a novel arrangement of block pieces, instead of the quoins being shot along a channel in the form, as usual; or two metal bars, having a series of wedges formed on the face thereof, are employed, the pressure being thus more evenly distributed, while the types are held more securely and locked up with a less expenditure of power. These wedge bars are worked by means of screws or toothed gearing; or one of the bars may be dispensed with, and a set of quoins used by causing them to act against the wedges of the remaining bar.

[Printed, 7d. Drawings.]

## A.D. 1856, May 31.—No 1285.

BONVALLET, ADOLPHE.— (Provisional Protection only.)— " Certain improvements in printing woven fabrics, velvet, skins, " and other like materials."

These consist in the employment of a very narrow border or rim of a height proportionate to the effect to be obtained, made on the contour of the vignette, which is cut out. The border is obtained either by the galvano-plastic process, by raising the contour of the vignette plate, or by soldering, moulding, melting, or by pressure. It may be of metal, gutta percha, cardboard, plastic, or other similar materials. By placing the vignette on a long-napped woven fabric, and applying a slight pressure, the border is sunk into the thickness of the nap, by which divisions are made on different parts of the design, and the range of the liquid color is limited. The color is placed on the fabric with a brush, sponge, or by means of a furnishing roller supplied with color. For obtaining a variety of colors, several vignette plates are placed one after the other on the fabric, and allow of applying the colors with precision and clearness. In order that the impression may be satisfactory, the edges of the plates are pierced with small holes, through which pass markers fixed to the printing table. The fabric to be printed should be thoroughly cleaned from impurities on leaving the weaver's loom. When properly prepared and dried it is stretched on the printer's table by means of pegs. When a piece of the entire length of the table is printed, the fabric is well stretched and passed through a heated chamber. The fabric when dry is submitted to the steaming process for fixing the colors, and washed in the usual manner.

[Printed, 3d. No Drawing.]

A.D. 1856, June 3.—N° 1314.

MACKELCAN, George Josiah.— " Improvements in the " manufacture of rollers adapted to calico and other printing."

The invention consists in using " a simple cylinder of cast iron " or other metal adapted to the common printing mandril or other " spindle, covered with a shell of copper, brass, or other material " adapted to be engraved or embossed. The cylinder is first " coated with tin or solder on its external surface, and the shell " formed of such a size that when cold it is too small to go over " the prepared cylinder. The shell is then to be dilated by heat, " and raised to such a temperature that when passed over the " cylinder it shall contract upon and melt the solder, and thus " become effectually united or soldered to its entire length and

" circumference. The shell may be removed by raising the tem-
" perature of the whole mass sufficiently to again dilate the
" shell and melt the solder. I do not by the above description
" bind myself to the use of solder, it being possible that the hold
" which the shell will acquire by its contraction may be found
" sufficient for all practical purposes."

[Printed, 6d. Drawings.]


### A.D. 1856, June 10.—No 1375.

BROOMAN, RICHARD ARCHIBALD.—(Communicated by M.
Hermann.)—" Improvements in printing shawls and other fabrics,
" and in the machinery employed therein."

The invention consists, first, in printing shawls and other
fabrics by a single impression of a block of the same size as the
shawl or fabric itself for such color in which the pattern is
to be printed. Secondly, in improved arrangements for printing
fabrics by means of one or more engraved cylinders supplied with
color by distributing rollers, which receive the color from trough
rollers. Thirdly, in applying colors on shawls and other fabrics
by a cylinder, or by two plates of about the same size as the
fabric, one plate being engraved or carrying a block with the
pattern, and the other provided with felt, cloth, &c., and one of these
plates being made to advance towards and recede from the other,
the fabric is printed by being pressed between them. Fourthly,
in the employment of guides, which on being brought into contact
with the points of the block or engraved surface keep it in proper
position. Fifthly, in arrangements for supplying colors to the
engraved surface, either directly by a cylinder or cylinders in
connection with the color trough, or by transferring the colors
from a cylinder to a piece of cloth or other fabric mounted on
a frame, from which they are carried on to the engraved surface
or block, or to which the engraved surface is carried. And, sixthly,
in machinery for printing such fabrics.

[Printed, 7d. Drawings.]


### A.D. 1856, June 10.—No 1377.

PIETRONI, CARLO.—" Improvements in printing on cloths and
" other fabrics."

The apparatus (shown for printing in four colors) consists of one printing and two color tables, each composed of an upper and lower frame, the upper frame of the printing table (which is between the color tables) being so arranged that it can rise independently of its lower frame. The fabric is stretched on the upper frame or on a portable additional frame attached to it. The printing blocks are in two carriages, two to each carriage, and these successively are brought over the color tables, (each of which is furnished with two colors,) and over the cloth to be printed. A treadle raises both the color tables and printing table frames against the blocks, so as to furnish the blocks and print the material. The color surfaces are supplied by clothed rollers of sheet iron containing a reservoir of ink, which rollers are attached to the carriages. The cloth having been printed in two colors is raised by the depression of a treadle clear of the framework between each operation of printing, and the frame in which it is stretched turned a quarter of a revolution, when the same process is repeated four times.

[Printed, 10*d*. Drawings.]

## A.D. 1856, June 14.—N° 1409.

MACHARD, JEAN ETIENNE.—(Provisional Protection only.)—(Communicated by J. P. Vantravers, of Annecy.)—" Improve-" ments in printing or dyeing skeins, tissues, or other textile " fabrics of cotton, wool, flax, and other fibrous substances."

The invention relates to the employment of catechu and indigo in such processes, so as to obtain good and fast colors, and at the same time economize the indigo. The skeins, &c., are passed through a solution of catechu, and left for some hours or even days, and then dyed in the indigo by the ordinary processes; or they are first dyed in the indigo and afterwards immersed in the solution of catechu. Light or dark blues are thus produced. When white portions are required they are previously printed with a " resist," or subsequently with a discharge. A suitable resist is composed of a mixture of nitrate of lead, subacetate of lead, sulphate of copper, acetate of copper, gum arabic, and pipe clay. The resist acts both mechanically and chemically. By immersing the articles in a solution of chromate of potash or other chromate, the lead in the resist is converted into chrome yellow or orange.

[Printed, 3d. No Drawing.]

A.D. 1856, June 25.—N° 1489.

GARDISSAL, CHARLES DURAND. — " Improvements in en-
" graving glass and crystals."

The invention consists in engraving the above with hydrofluoric acid by means or with the aid of " reserves," " spares," or " resists," obtained by one of three processes :—1, by distributing fatty or resinous matter, reduced to powder, through fabrics or perforated tissues or substances on the surfaces which are to be acted on or engraved by the action of the hydrofluoric acid; 2, spreading a layer of fatty or resinous matter over the surface of the articles to be engraved, the layer being afterwards orna-mented by means of perforated vignettes or designs; 3, by the transfer of printings made of fatty or resinous matters on to the articles to be engraved.

1 and 2 are chiefly applicable to plane, 3 to either plane or curved surfaces.

[Printed, 4d. No Drawing.]

A.D. 1856, June 25.—N° 1499.

KENYON, JAMES, and KENYON, RICHARD.—" An improved
" fabric to be used in printing and other similar purposes, and a
" method of joining or connecting the ends of the same."

The invention relates to the endless aprons, sheets, or bands of cloth that form a bed for the calico or other fabric to be printed, and consists in forming the same of a linen fabric of sufficient strength or thickness, and woven at the ends in such a manner that a joint of equal thickness with the cloth aforesaid may be produced. It is woven in the ordinary manner, but with a suit-able length for a joint at each end woven in two parts or double. One of the parts of one end is then placed so as to overlap that of the other, and they are secured or held together by gum, paste, or other suitable adhesive or connecting substance. The other parts not required are then cut away, leaving a joint as set forth above.

[Printed, 6d. Drawings.]

CORNIDES, Louis.—" Improvements in ornamenting metal, " wood, leather, textile fabrics, and other substances."

The invention relates to ornamenting the above-named materials by a new mode of applying thereto plain or colored impressions, drawings, or photographs. If the article be of metal, the surface must be rendered bright by tinning; if of wood, it must be silvered or gilt. Leather or textile fabrics are prepared according to N° 745 of 1853. The materials being thus prepared, the metallic surfaces are coated with a solution of ox gall or transparent varnish. When dry a solution is applied thereto, composed of gelatine (4 parts), sugar (1), glycerine (1), and soft water (6 or 8). To this coating are transferred the ornamental, plain, or colored impressions, drawings, or lithographs, or such ornamental impressions made on a transparent, flexible, and elastic medium are attached thereto, or on the silvered, gilded, varnished, or japanned materials in common use; or the surface of the said materials is prepared by attaching thereto tin foil, foil paper, or silver paper, by means of the solution of gelatine or glue, " which " said processes of coating, transferring, as also the mode of pro- " ducing the transparent medium above referred to, and other " necessary processes, are set forth and described in the specifica- " tions of " (N° 2762 of 1853, N° 2066 of 1854, and 2112 of 1855), " or when leather, textile fabrics, and such like soft " materials having surfaces prepared as aforesaid are to be " ornamented, the ornamental device, plain or colored impres- " sion, may be printed direct thereon."

[Printed, 4d. No Drawings.]

MACDONALD, David.—" Improvements in printing textile " fabrics and other surfaces."

The invention relates to machinery more particularly suitable for printing from zinc patterns on muslins, to be afterwards embroidered, but also applicable to printing " according to either " the zincographic or lithographic systems." It consists in giving an impression during the backward as well as the forward motion of the table carrying the plate or stone upon one of two rolls of fabric alternately. For this purpose two pressure rollers and two counter pressure rollers are arranged near the centre of the framing, the former being alternately depressed, so that the plate passes in contact with each of them, and imparts an impression to the fabric passing round it. "Self-acting," damping, and inking apparatus, "supplied in any convenient way," may be employed in combination with the above, either between the pressure rollers or outside them.

[Printed, 11d. Drawings.]

### A.D. 1856, July 1.—Nº 1537.

SANDERS, FREDERICK GEORGE. — "Improvements in the "manufacture of ornamental floor and other tiles, bricks, slabs, "and other similar articles."

These consist in making squares or other forms of pulverized clay of different colors, and placing them together before being fired, so as to form a pattern, wholly or in part, in a metal or other strong mould, and consolidating the whole by pressure so as to form one tile, the said squares or other shapes forming either a part or whole of the thickness of the article. This tile, &c. is then fired "in the ordinary manner."

[Printed, 3d. No Drawing.]

### A.D. 1856, July 8.—Nº 1605.

PAGE, HENRY.—"Improvements in ornamenting or decorating "glass."

The designs are cut in relief on blocks, or out of thin metal or other suitable material, as in stencilling. The blocks receive the color from a sieve or roller, "as in paper staining," and the stencil plates are furnished with a brush. The latter may be applied at once to the surface of the glass after it is prepared. Calico, paper, or other material is coated with size, gum, or starch, and when dry has the design printed on it with colors made of varnish, oil, or spirit. The glass is prepared by roughing it with emery, &c., so that the first coat of varnish or cement will keep itself to the glass. A coat of white, hard varnish, japan, copal, or other suitable body varnish, is then spread upon it, and before it dries the surface of the printed design is turned down upon it and pressed evenly; the back is then wetted, thereby softening the size, which allows the fabric on which the design was printed to come away, leaving only the printed design on the glass. The whole is left to dry together, and any size that may have passed in the transfer removed by washing. The design is hardened by placing the glass in a drying stove, the heat being applied slowly. If the stencil mode is followed, the design not only can be applied at once on the glass, but can, like the block printing, be first applied on paper or any other suitable fabric previously coated with size, gum, or starch, and then transferred as before stated.

[Printed, 3d. No Drawing.]

## A.D. 1856, July 10.—N° 1634.

LANCASTER, CHARLES WILLIAM.—(Communicated.)—" An " improved method of, or apparatus for, inking, printing, or " stamping surfaces."

The invention consists in mounting an inking roller upon an arm or lever in such a manner that when the stamping or printing surface is at rest, the roller is held clear of it, and when the printing surface moves it acts upon the lever, presses it back, and causes the inking roller to traverse over and ink the printing surface. Upon the printing surface resuming the position from which it started a spring draws the lever and roller to their original position, and causes the inking roller in its course to travel a second time over the printing surface.

[Printed, 9d. Drawings.]

## A.D. 1856, July 11.—N° 1642.

CHEVALIER, JEAN BAPTISTE DÉSIRÉ, and O'SULLIVAN, NARCISSE RABONIN.—" A new or improved method of obtaining " or preparing printing surfaces, and in printing therefrom."

The invention consists in printing in one or more colors at the same time by means of permeable surfaces, such as linen or other " woven or suitable material," or a reticulated or perforated metal sheet. On this surface the design is drawn in an ink composed of lamp black, indian ink, gum, sugar, and salt; and a coating spread over the whole surface of gutta percha or other gelatinous matter. This coating holds to the fabric in every part, except where the ink intervenes, and on being washed the parts corresponding to the design are removed, leaving such parts the only pervious parts of the surface. The back part of the pervious substance is next coated with the color required to be printed.

The impression is then taken by pressure, the paper or surface to be printed being placed in contact with the face of the fabric or printing surface. Or instead of applying the ink or color to the back of the pervious material, the design in that material may be placed on a pad containing a reservoir of ink or color, by pressing it against which the color is supplied for the impression.

[Printed, 3d. No Drawing.]

## A.D. 1856, July 18.—Nº 1695.

GERBER, JEAN. — (Provisional Protection only.) — " Improve-
" ments in printing, dyeing, or impregnating fabrics, yarns, and
" threads, and in preparing metallic and other powders to be used
" for these purposes."

The invention " consists in printing woven fabrics with a me
" tallic powder mixed with a suitable vehicle, such as albumen,"
also " in a method of preparing certain metallic powders suitable
" for printing or dyeing fabrics and yarns."

[Printed, 3d. No Drawing.]

## A.D. 1856, July 21.—Nº 1724.

GREEN, WILLIAM.—" Improvements in treating, ornamenting,
" and waterproofing fabrics, and in machinery or apparatus for
" effecting the same."

1. Artificial leather is produced by combining a thin mem-
braneous material, composed of paper, pulp, or slivers of fibrous
substances and gelatinous and saccharine matter of the required
color to a woven or felted fabric.  2. Continuous lengths of such
paper or slivers are united to woven or felted fabrics by means of
gutta percha, or a solution of india-rubber and gutta percha
treated with sulphur or other vulcanizing matters.  3. Or gelatine may be used for the paper pulp or filamentous material, the
tannin being applied after the gelatine is spread on the fabric.
4. The fabric is partially or entirely coated on the wrong side with
paste or other matter not easily removeable, and which prevents
unctuous matters penetrating the fabric.  5. Patterns or designs
are produced in various colors upon leather, cloth, or oil cloth,
and afterwards treated with oil, composition, or varnish.  6. The
fabrics are coated with a flexible waterproofing matter, treated
with vulcanizing agents, then with a gelatinous and saccharine or

a farinaceous and resinous matter, and lastly with varnish, boiled oil, or other finishing composition. 7. Varnish, oil, and other adhesive matters are distributed by rollers made of printers' "composition" or vulcanized india-rubber. 8. In some cases vulcanized india-rubber rollers are used for drawing fabrics beneath a scraper or trough while being supplied with varnish or water-proofing matters, water or other fluid being, when requisite, applied to one of the rollers in contact with the waterproofing matters. 9. The varnish or other matter used in making japanned, painted, or leather cloth. 10. Surfaces similar to leather, cloth, oil cloth, or other pattern, may be produced upon portions only of plain, figured, or printed fabrics. 11. When fabrics are to be coated or ornamented over their entire surfaces with various colors, such colors are applied by engraved rollers or blocks previously to the use of the finishing composition. 12. When printing with stencil plates, hollow tables, provided with wire gauze or perfo-rated tops are employed, and are connected with another exhaust-ing apparatus. The perforated pattern plates are hinged to the side of the table, so as to fall always in the same position. 13. The fabric is distended and drawn to the drying room by means of bands and pulleys, and are also suspended side by side, or one above another, in such drying room by means of clip hooks or pins fastened to their selvages and running in or on grooves or guides. 14. Relief patterns are sometimes (as in the case of em-bossed felt table covers) produced by rollers or blocks engraved in relief. The waterproof matter is in some cases applied from the indented parts of engraved surfaces, such surfaces being cleaned off by suitable doctors, and the matter taken up by such fabric caused to adhere by pressure, as in calico or copper-plate printing.

[Printed, 5d.  No Drawing.]

A.D. 1856, August 4.—N° 1833.

GOTTGETREU, CHARLES GUSTAVUS.—(Provisional Protection only.)—"Lithographic printing in oil and varnish colours and "metal, on glass, wood, papier maché, marble, metal, porcelain, "or any other material that offers a suitable surface."

The invention consists in preparing paper to receive the print with various kinds of gums. The paper when printed is fixed by rubbing to the glass or other material. It is easily removed by being damped, and leaves the complete printing of colors and

metal sticking to the glass, &c.   " Hitherto only one black litho-
" graphic or copper-plate printing has been fixed to glass, &c., in
" the usual manner, with paste, and it has then been coloured by
" hand; instead of which my process transfers to glass, &c.,
" eight or ten printings all at one time, and produces a far supe-
" rior and novel article." The print " almost immediately after
" being transferred is so solid that any varnish or color for coat-
" ing may be applied to it with injuring the design."

[Printed, 3d. No Drawing.]

### A.D. 1856, August 8.—N° 1867.

LEESE, Joseph, Junior.—" Certain improvements in machinery
" used for printing calico and other fabrics."

The invention consists in the application of " doctors " to the
bowl itself, or the blanket or net of any kind used for covering the
bowl of the printing machine, by which arrangement a very short
blanket, or none at all, may be used.   Or, instead of applying the
scraper directly to the blanket, a roller is caused to revolve against
the face of the blanket or cylinder in a reverse direction to that in
which the blanket or cylinder moves.   The doctor is placed upon
this roller, and the colour recovered from it instead of from the
blanket direct.   A small stream of liquid, colored or otherwise,
may be caused to flow in front of the roller or scraper, " so that it
" may act as a lubricator, and so prevent injury to the bowl or
" blanket covering it."

[Printed, 3d. No Drawing.]

### A.D. 1856, August 8.—N° 1871.

NEWTON, William Edward.—(Communicated).—" Improve-
" ments in machinery for composing and distributing types."

In the composing machine the types are ranged upright in a case
divided longitudinally into compartments open at the top and
bottom, and to the front of which the types are pressed by " quods "
(plungers), which fit the several compartments, and are acted upon
by rods, the rear ends of which run in guides in the frame, and
which have bands attached to them, which pass once round a drum
which turns a short distance for each type composed under the
action of a pawl upon an arm connected with an excentric upon
the driving shaft by a strap " in the ordinary manner " The

quods in the compartments from which the types are not taken remain stationary, their bands slipping round the drum as it revolves. The types are withdrawn from their compartments by spring fingers at the end of levers connected with a series of finger keys. As each key and lever are depressed a single type is forced out by the spring finger entering a small opening in the type compartment into a trough or passage, through which it is transferred by a plate and slide and plunger with reciprocating motion to the composing stick. The finished line is moved on to the galley, between which and the table is a space sufficient for one of a series of leads (fed forward by a plunger), which is thrown up by a lever. There is a contrivance connected with the driving shaft for advancing the column of composed matter after the composition of every line.

In the distributing machine the galley used has a stationary side and a spring side. The latter is pivoted at one end, and at the other extends to within the breadth of a type of the edge of the galley. It is pressed up by a spring, and the column of type is thus held stationary, with the exception of the first line, which is left free to be fed along as the types are distributed. The types are selected from the extreme end of this line by a spring finger passing up and down through an aperture in the corner of the galley and attached to an arm on the end of a lever secured to the frame. The type thrown up is received between a case and a lever, one end of which is pivoted to the frame, the other being furnished with a cushion which permits the passage of the type, but holds it with a gentle pressure. The case that receives the type (called the "forwarding case") is furnished with compartments similar to those in the composing machine, and vibrates at intervals the distance between two contiguous types. In front of the forwarding case, and immediately over the case from the composing machine, is a stationary case, called the "trial case," also furnished with compartments similar to the other cases. The edges of the type are furnished with nicks, the position of which varies upon each letter, and the compartments of the trial case are furnished with pins, the position of which corresponds with the nicks upon the types, while each compartment of the trial case has a certain combination of pins corresponding to the nicks upon one of the types. The type is thus successively presented to each compartment of the trial case until it arrives at the one appropriated to it, when it drops through into the corresponding compartment of the case from the composing machine. As the single types are distributed in the composing machine case the line is pushed forwards by plungers actuated by suitable mechanism connected with the main shaft. The successive lines of type are brought up by means of a plunger which rests against the column of types and forces it forwards. A rod connected with this plunger is fed forward by a band which passes round a horizontal drum. A series of pins are made to project from the drum, against which a cam upon a short shaft strikes at the proper time, and thus the drum revolves a short distance, and the plunger is fed up, carrying with it a new line of type in line with the plunger, and the distributing continues as before.

[Printed, 1s. Drawings.]

## A.D. 1856, August 9.—No 1881.

REID, ARCHIBALD LOCKHART.—" Improvements in producing " ornamental figures or devices on textile fabrics and other sur- " faces."

The invention consists in depositing powdered coloring matter upon the surface to be ornamented through perforated patterns. The process is applicable to piece goods generally, and especially to "sewed " muslins." This is effected by a combination of rollers, which shake the powdered color through an endless pattern sheet from a color holder, and then fix the powder devices by an after treatment. The fabric is passed into the machine by an endless feed-cloth and rollers, and the powder is applied at the instant when it passes over or round the inner roller of the feed-cloth arrangement. The fabric then passes over a steam chamber or heated roller which sets the powder.

[Printed, 10d. Drawings.]

## A.D. 1856, August 13.—No 1895.

KAY, RICHARD DUGDALE.—" Improvements in machinery or " apparatus for washing, scouring, cleaning, preparing, dyeing, or " finishing woven fabrics, yarns, or threads."

The invention is " particularly useful for delicate textures," and consists, first, of a combination of three well-known systems, which although extensively used separately have not been hitherto applied in combination, the said systems being respectively known by the technical terms of "clapping or beating," "methodical washing," and "accumulation or advance."

For clapping or beating one or two clappers "of the customary "kind" are fixed on strong shafts "in the usual way" above a box or trough in compartments, the faces of such clappers being kept parallel while in motion.

For methodical washing a box is used, through which the water runs in an opposite direction to the motion of the piece. For accumulation or advance the material is drawn between solid or skeleton-formed rollers or instruments of a similar form to the clappers into one compartment of the box, where a certain length of it is allowed to accumulate in folds. From this it passes over the clapper nearest to the water, and over a bar furnished with pegs, eyes, or rollers, which keep it divided during its passage to the upper clapper. It then comes in contact with the rollers or other instruments as before, and is drawn into another compartment, where it accumulates as before, and so passes on from one compartment to another until it is sufficiently washed or cleansed. A modification of the above consists in drawing the material in folds through tubes, which pass it through several cisterns successively.

The invention consists, secondly, in an apparatus for washing, scouring, preparing, or dyeing yarns or threads. The skein of thread or yarn is supported by hooks at the end of a lever, which has given to it a rectilinear or circular alternate motion by hand or otherwise. Under the hook is a reservoir supplied with water either hot or cold. The levers are attached to shafts worked by excentrics from the driving shaft. To each of them is attached a spring, so that when, as the workman puts another skein upon the hook, the backward and forward motion is suspended, and re-commences as soon as the hook is released. Or one excentric wheel may be employed for any number of levers, such wheel working the lever shaft by means of an arm, which being attached to the shaft has alternate motion, and the shaft works the levers during its alternate motion by means of the cams through the action of two pins or flanges fixed on the levers one above the other below the shaft. Or the excentric wheels may act directly or through rods upon the levers. Or a steam cylinder may be used by attaching to the end of the piston a traverse motion to work the levers which support the hooks, or the levers may be dispensed with by fixing the hooks on a wheel or pulley.

[Printed, 1s. 11d. Drawings.]

### A.D. 1856, August 18.—No 1924.

TYTHERLEIGH, William.—" A new or improved manufacture
" of rollers or cylinders for printing fabrics."

A hollow iron cylinder of somewhat less diameter than the
cylinder to be manufactured is perforated with holes. It is
cleaned by acids or otherwise, and covered with fused borax or
other suitable flux. Copper, brass, or other alloy of copper is
then fused in another furnace, and the iron cylinder placed
therein, and turned so as to be coated. It is then taken and
while hot put in a hollow cylinder or mould closed at bottom.
A core is placed in the iron cylinder and adjusted in the axes of
the mould. The whole is then put into a furnace, and when
the coating on the iron cylinder begins to melt fused copper
or copper alloy is poured into the mould, and the heat kept up
until the copper or alloy is thoroughly incorporated with the coating
on the iron cylinder. The fire is then slackened and the whole
allowed to cool. The roller or cylinder is afterwards finished by
turning.

[Printed, 4d. No Drawing.]

### A.D. 1856, August 20.—No 1949.

STONES, William. — (Provisional Protection only.) — " Im-
" proved machinery for damping sheets of paper intended to be
" printed upon, so as to render the usual process of wetting
" unnecessary."

In place of steeping the paper in water, " as is now the case,"
jets of steam or a thin fine spray of water are thrown on one or
both surfaces of it. The paper is fed into the machine, and is
supported therein by endless tapes or bands, which pass over
suitable rollers or pulleys. "I propose to adapt my improved
" machinery to steam-printing machinery, so that the paper may
" pass from the feed table through my machine, and from thence
" direct to the printing cylinder." It may, of course, be employed separately.

[Printed, 3d. No Drawing.]

### A.D. 1856, August 21.—No 1952.

CROSSLEY, Joseph, and BOLTON, James.—" Improve-
" ments in apparatus or means employed in the printing of yarns
" for carpets and other fabrics."

To obviate the disadvantages resulting from the use of the oil-cloth which is usually placed beneath yarns when they are printed previous to being woven, such oil-cloths are, previous to their being so used, coated with oil paint (or cloth prepared by a coating of india-rubber or gutta percha may be used). After the yarns have been printed, and have been removed from the surfaces on which they have been printed, instead of being placed as usual on the shellings of oats or chopped straws, the yarns are, during the steaming process, supported upon an open-work of cords, metallic or fibrous, forming a sort of cradle, " or
" the said cradle may be a sort of creel formed by bars of wood,
" upon which may be placed a sufficient quantity of oat shellings
" to prevent the colors staining the wood. Cloths or other
" receivers are interposed to prevent droppings of the color from
" any one set of yarns during the steaming falling upon those
" below."

[Printed, 4d. No Drawing.]

A.D. 1856, September 5.—N° 2073.

HELRIGEL, CHARLES LOUIS FREDERICK.—(Provisional Protection only.)—" Improvements in lithographic printing-presses."

Motion is communicated to the table or bed carrying the stone by means of a toothed rack, driven from the first mover, and connected with adjusting stops and other gearing, so as to slide a certain distance before it is fixed to the table or bed, in order that the stone may remain stationary for a time till the scraper is brought down. The tympan is hinged to the table, and as the latter is run in comes under a roller, and is drawn down upon the stone. At other times it is kept up by a weighted cord. In order to bring down the scraper, the cog-wheel on the main axis is arranged to come into gear with the teeth of a sector-wheel on a third axis. Connected with this sector-wheel is a contrivance by which a pinion carried by it presents at all times a tooth to take into the cog-wheel on the main axis, so that when the sector-wheel has been moved to its greatest extent, the tooth of the pinion comes into gear, and causes the sector-wheel to be moved one tooth further, and then the pinion is unlocked, and is caused to revolve by the cog-wheel on the main axis; on reversing the action of the main axis the pinion is again locked, and by such means the sector-wheel is moved back by the cog-wheel on the main axis. A connecting rod attached to an arm of the sector-wheel gives motion to a lever, which is pin-jointed to a connecting rod on the lever which carries the scraper, and the scraper is suspended to the last-mentioned lever. The cog-wheel on the main axis is caused to gear with the sector-wheel by means of an adjustable stop on the bed or table acting on a lever, which moves the arm on the sector-wheel a distance so as to bring these wheels into gear.

[Printed, 3d. No Drawing.]

A.D. 1856, September 8.—Nº 2087.

ESTIVANT, FELIX.—" Improvements in casting metal tubes."

The invention consists in forming the above " perfectly neat, " homogeneous, and without bubbles," by casting them in a mould of metal of varied dimensions with a core of sheet iron or other metal filled with sand to prevent intrusion of the metal, which would impede the removal of the casting. The interior of the mould is of a conical form, to allow the casting to be easily removed. The shell is of rolled sheet or cast iron, "inverting " the form of a cone, whose edges being cut through the genera-" trix are then closely jointed." To obviate the formation of " blebs " or bubbles, the mould has two channels, through which the metal is poured by means of iron spoons. The shell is suffi-ciently thin to be compressed by the melted metal. Its lower part is bevilled, so that the metal cooling more rapidly at the bottom, causes the shell to slide up a little into the tube, thereby leaving a space between the shell and the tube, which is also to be filled up with sand.

[Printed, 10d. Drawings.]

A.D. 1856, September 11.—Nº 2123.

HUDSON, JAMES. — " Improvements in whetting or setting " printers' ' doctors', and other straight-edged tools or instru-" ments."

After observing that theretofore the whetting or setting of such blades had been effected by filing and rubbing with oil-stones by hand, the Specification proceeds :—" My improve-" ments consist in the employment of a rotating grindstone, " instead of files, supported in suitable framework, and a car-

" riage or apparatus for holding the blade or 'doctor,' capable
" of sliding or travelling to and fro, or reciprocating upon a
" true rectilinear bed in connection herewith, and operated by
" suitable driving apparatus. The blade is caused to traverse
" in contact with the edge of the rotating grindstone from end
" to end of the said blade, whereby I obtain a true straight edge,
" and the apparatus being capable of adjustment, I can set the
" blades to any required angle or bevil of edge. I also mount a
" number of oil-stones on the ends of spindles, to which I give
" simultaneous rotary motion, and apply them in such way or
" manner that the said blade or 'doctor' may reciprocate or
" traverse in contact therewith, same as on the grindstone. This
" apparatus may be driven by hand or power, and applied to the
" grinding any straight-edged tools or instruments."

[Printed, 1s. 2d. Drawings.]

A.D. 1856, September 17.—N° 2175.

BARBER, JOHN.—" Improvements in machinery or apparatus
" for mill and other engraving, punching, dividing, and ruling
" rollers, either for hand or machine engraving, and an improved
" maundril, used in mill, eccentric, and other machinery employed
" in engraving rollers for printing and embossing calicoes and
" other fabrics."

The invention consists, first, of a machine for dividing and
punching the pitch-pins or rollers for engraving by mill and
other machines, and for cutting the gauges and dividing the
sketches. The chief peculiarity consists in fastening the roller
to the maundril by "bell chucks," formed so as to grip the
whole outside coned circle of the roller. The roller and maundril are placed between antifriction wheels on pedestals on the
adjusting table. The maundril has two collars at the index
end to prevent end play of the maundril and roller, "which
" working on its own bearings, and the shanks of the maun-
" dril in the grooves of the headstock rising and falling only with
" the different size of the rollers, must divide correctly." The
pedestal, headstocks and indexes all move with the adjusting
table, independently of the rest of the machine, the table turning
on a pivot in the centre of the machine. The other peculiarities
in the invention consist in a certain arrangement of levers and
a ball lever and screw as applied to engraving machines; in an

" indicator" attached to the carriage of a machine for " bumping,"
and applied to the roller as an indicator for fitting in; in a driving
and reversing motion for " bumping" and " straight-round
" work;" in a direct application of a steam-engine to the machine,
instead of the secondary motion from shafts and straps; and in
the application of springs in the steps to give the necessary
elasticity and balance to the mill.

The drawings represent a " top pressure mill engraving ma-
" chine," in which the dividing apparatus and turning handle are
placed on the mill carriage; a " side pressure mill engraving
" machine," in which the maundril and roller can be reversed at
pleasure, and when the coupling box is out of gear the roller can
be easily brought round by a handle, the indicator being under
the workman's eye; a " dividing, punching, and engraving ma-
" chine," fitted with the improved maundril and an indicator
attached to the carriage for bumping and fitting in; and a " mill
" engraving machine," in which the mill acts on the under side
of the roller.

[Printed, 4s. 10d. Drawings.]

A.D. 1856, September 19.—N° 2197.

SMALE, JAMES.—(Provisional Protection only.)—" Improve-
" ments in the mode, means, or apparatus for printing or trans-
" ferring designs or letters on to glass."

The " job" having been prepared in " the usual manner,"
an impression is taken on a glazed, oiled, or otherwise prepared
paper. This is then placed upon a glass, and pressed or rolled
until the colors are transferred. Powder of any color may be
added to give the letters or design the appearance of body. The
blanks may be filled up with color, metal, or any appropriate
material. A coat of varnish may then be given to the whole back
of the job.

[Printed, 3d. No Drawing.]

A.D. 1856, September 19.—N° 2206.

UNDERWOOD, JOHN, and BURT, VALENTINE. — " The
" manufacture of copying inks for printing."

Many ingredients may be used for such inks. A black is made
of nutgalls (14), sulphate of iron (6), gum senegal (12), treacle (6),

soap (3), lamp black (6), prussian blue (3), and filtered rain water 15 gallons, or nutgalls (12), and sulphate of iron (6), to which the requisite coloring matter is added.

[Printed, 4d. No Drawing.]

### A.D. 1856, September 26.—N° 2264.

BOYD, JOHN.—" Improvements in letter-press printing ma-" chines."

The invention consists of a machine capable of printing any bill, poster, or other matter in as many primitive and compound colors, "not in a general way" exceeding three, as there may be inks and inking apparatus applied to such machine. Two or more (the drawings represent a machine with two only) type tables are driven by rack and pinion with reciprocating movement, so as to pass under a pressing cylinder in the centre of the machine, and under separate inking rollers, each in connection with its inking apparatus. The pressing cylinder revolves continuously in one direction. It is raised on the return of the type tables by a cam action, which also brings down the laying-on table, from which the sheet is received on to grippers on the cylinder. The inking rollers rise and fall so as to ink their own forms only. The ink ducts are sometimes divided into two or more compartments containing different colors, in which case a beautiful blending of these colors is caused by the lateral motion of a distributing roller in screw bearings.

[Printed, 11d. Drawings.]

### A.D. 1856, September 27.—N° 2271.

ORMEROD, JOHN.—(Provisional Protection only.)—" Improve-" ments in machinery or apparatus for bleaching and washing or " cleansing textile fabrics and materials, applicable also to the " ' soaping ' of printed fabrics."

The invention relates to improvements upon N° 923 of 1855 (Wallace's), and other machines, in which the goods are placed within rotatory chambers with or without steam. Its object is to prevent the entangling or massing together of the said goods, for which purpose they are placed in separate portions upon pegs, rods, or other such apparatus adapted to the revolving chambers.

Another arrangement consists in causing the goods applied in separate portions, as above described, to revolve within stationary chambers, the processes being conducted with or without steam.

[Printed, 3d. No Drawing.]

## A.D. 1856, October 8.—N° 2352.

WHITEHEAD, FRANCIS.—" A method of, and apparatus for, " producing devices in or on wood, leather, and other similar sur- " faces, whether for ornamenting the same or for the production " of printing and embossing surfaces therefrom."

The apparatus consists of an upright holder, through which the forefinger is inserted, and from which the rest of the apparatus is suspended in such a manner that the tool may be rotated or moved about it by the remaining fingers and thumb. At the bottom of the apparatus the tool, or the metal containing it, is surrounded by one or more stationary gas rings, jets, or burners. Between the burners and the collar, connected to the apparatus just below the holder, and on which the fingers and thumb rest to work the tool, are guards to keep the hand cool, and certain contrivances for regulating the depth to which the tool may be pressed into the block. In some cases the tool is mounted upon a rod, plate, or frame so as to be moved over a fixed block, in which cases it is returned by a spring after being depressed, the spring serving also to release the tool when it is required to change it. When this apparatus is used in connexion with a pantograph, the device may be produced without any previous drawing on the surface operated upon. One apparatus without heat is em- ployed in place of the tracer, and a similar one with heat sub- stituted for the pencil, an endless tape or other similar agent being used to ensure simultaneous motions in both apparatus. A lever or separate operator may be necessary to depress the working of the apparatus substituted for the pencil. If the apparatus are connected on a parallel frame, and the tracer apparatus be directed over the pattern, then the pencil apparatus used with heat will produce a device of the same size as the pattern. Another applica- tion, whereby curved and elongated lines may be produced, consists in mounting the apparatus upon a swinging arm or lever pro- jecting from a fixed upright, and on which the apparatus is free to slide, the depression of the tool being effected by the rotation of an excentric bar or other suitable depressing agent.

[Printed, 9d. Drawings.]

A.D. 1856, October 11.—N° 2390.

SCHEURMANN, Gustav.—" Improvements in printing music
" when type is employed."

The invention consists in so constructing music type as to admit
of a page being set up in two forms, one consisting of such type,
and the other of full-length lines, separated by moveable spaces
in such manner that the same lines or rules may be used with
different spaces, the impression being taken in succession from
the two forms. The register of the lines, notes, and signs is
obtained by the two chases being fixed on a sliding bed or table.
The " tie " lines are each cast in one piece, together with several
" spaces," according to the number of notes to be tied thereby, and
the spaces or bodies formed with such " tie " lines in each case are
arranged step by step on each other, the greater or less inclination
of the " tie " lines being obtained by the " spaces " combined or
cast together overlapping each other to a greater or less extent.
In the dies employed for casting such " tie " lines with their step-
by-step bodies or " spaces," there are sliding or adjusting plates
used, which are adjusted to overlap, to correspond with the angle
of the groove in the matrix used. The dots or notes are usually
each formed into a type, together with its tail. The slurs are each
formed into a type, excepting in cases of irregular slurs, which pass
under as well as over the lines (stave), in which cases strips of thin
metal are used, bent to the desired form, and fixed at intervals to
spaces. The smaller signs, such as sharps and flats, and others,
are either cast into a separate type, or two or more of them are cast
on the face of one type. The stave-line form is composed of a
series of thin plates, with spaces of proper thickness to keep them
apart. The lines and notes may be printed in different colors.
The press used has an upper sliding bed or table, which slides in
the ordinary table or bed of a hand-printing press; the frisket
and tympan are hinged to the ordinary bed or table, and move
with it under a platen. The forms are fixed on the upper sliding
table, and an impression taken from each form in succession on
the same paper.

An electrotype copper plate for use upon a cylinder may be
obtained from two forms, such as above described, by obtaining a
reverse impression of the same in a sheet of lead in a suitable press.
The lead may be used as a printing surface, or form the matrix
for a plaster mould for reproduction in stereotype.

[Printed, 11d. Drawings.]

### A.D. 1856, October 16.—Nº 2417.

STURGES, Richard Ford.—" A new or improved manufacture
" of rollers or cylinders for printing fabrics."

The invention consists in placing vertically a tube of copper
or alloy of copper, ¼ inch thick, and of an external diameter somewhat greater than the finished roller is to have, and furnished
with an iron axis or a hollow mandril. The space between the
tube and axis or mandril is closed at the bottom, so as to form an
annular vessel, into which zinc or other hard metal is run.
When this has cooled, the whole is placed in a lathe, and the
cylinder finished " in the usual manner." The inner surface of
the tube and the outer surface of the hollow mandril or cylindrical
surface of the axis may be coated with zinc, prior to the casting of
zinc between them.

[Printed, 5d. Drawings.]

### A.D. 1856, October 17.—Nº 2439.

MAGNAY, Frederick Arthur, and WHITEHEAD, Ralph
Radcliffe.—" Improvements in damping paper for printing."

1. The paper is piled in sheets alternately with felts saturated
with water, and a board and weight or pressure is applied on the
upper layer of felt. 2. An endless felt moves over rollers, the
lower roller being immersed in a trough of water. The paper (in
quires or other number of opened sheets) is fed on to the upper
surface of the felt, and carried between two pressing rollers, the
upper one being of wirework, " similar to a dandy roll used by
" paper-makers."

[Printed, 6d. Drawings.]

### A.D. 1856, October 18.—Nº 2444.

DELCAMBRE, Isidore.— " Improvements in machines for
" composing and distributing type."

The improvements in the latter consist, first, in an arrangement
permitting the machine to hold an increased quantity of type by
prolonging the " furrows " of the compartments in which the
type are stored. Secondly, in causing the types to fall into
grooves of the incline by means of a curved lever connected by
rods with the key-board. Thirdly, in adding a hook to the con-

necting rod, by which means the type are kept in their proper position in the grooves. Fourthly, in causing the types to range themselves side by side at the end of the grooves by means of a hammer, which, under the action of an eccentric, forces the types into a "guide canal," while a smaller hammer pushes against their front side. The "crossbar," which "formerly was fixed to "the frame," is made moveable, and raised to a height which enables the workman to watch the types in their progress.

The distributing machine may be either separate from or in connexion with the composing machine. It consists of an inclined plane of a triangular form, provided with grooves serving as guides for the types to glide in. The types being placed on a table at the top of the machine, the lines are separated one after another by a knife turning at one end on a pin. The letters of each line are then read from the printed sheet, and caused to fall into their respective boxes as follows. There are three keys, the actions of which upon levers raise a "trap" the height requisite for letters as thick as $i$, $n$, and $m$ respectively. The levers are also so combined as to push forward at each lifting of the trap one type into a canal in the middle of the machine containing a series of lateral canals furnished each with a door opened with a key, as the type corresponding with each canal arrives at the entrance of it. The workman has thus "only to "lower with one hand the key for opening the trap hole at the "height required for the size of the type to pass under it," and with the other to "lower the key for opening the lateral canal "corresponding with the box for the type he has caused to pass "under the trap door."

The composing machine consists of an inclined plane, with guiding grooves for the types, which are moved by means of suitable levers acted upon by the keys of the key-board, whereby the types are thrown in a suitable hole corresponding with one of the guiding grooves, and from thence are brought into lines, each type coming to stand close against the preceding one on a "justificator."

[Printed, 10d. Drawings.]

A.D. 1856, October 25.—N° 2507.

ERNST, Gustavus, and LORBERY, William.—(Provisional Protection only.)—"An improved mode of raising or producing

" designs, patterns, or impressions of the surfaces of plates,
" blocks, or rollers, and transferring or imparting the same to
" paper, parchment, woven fabrics, leather, or other similar
" materials."

Designs are executed on a metal plate either directly or on
transfer paper with chalk composed of wax, soap, tallow, suet,
saltpetre, or other alkali, with coloring matter, or lithographic ink
of wax, tallow, soft soap, varnish, Venice turpentine, and coloring
matter, or wax, suet, soap, shellac, pitch, asphaltum, and
coloring matter. The transfer paper is made of jelly, starch,
gamboge, or starch, gum tragacanth, glue, chalk, gamboge, and
water. "If copies only are required, we transfer them with the
" transfer ink to the metal plate." The metal plate is cleaned by
passing it through a solution of some alkali or acid, and the back
being protected by some common varnish made of wax, tallow, &c.,
is placed in a solution of the same metal as itself, and connected
to a galvanic apparatus. By this process the unprotected parts
of the plate are quickly dissolved, leaving the design or subject
untouched in relief on the surface of the plate. The raised plates
and blocks thus made may be set up and worked with letter-
press like woodcuts. A stereotype is also at any time obtainable
from a copy of the work preserved on the transfer paper. "In
" printing woven fabrics by blocks or rollers with raised surfaces,
" the present machinery may, perhaps, require alteration in the
" construction, to which alterations we lay no claim; but if it is
" found by experience that the raised design is objectionable,
" we can sink or etch it by the process herein described."

[Printed, 3d. No Drawing.]

A.D. 1856, November 3.—N° 2576.

TEARNE, Samuel, and RICHMOND, George William.—
" Certain improvements in producing ornamental designs on the
" faces of fancy and other goods made of papier maché, wood,
" glass, china, earthenware, tin, iron, or such like materials, the
" surfaces of which when made up are usually finished by
" staining, varnishing, painting, or japanning."

The invention consists, first, in coloring, graining, or marbling
the above with a distemper or water color, and afterwards transferring thereto a design printed in an oily material, so as to
protect part of the surface while the graining or marbling is

washed from the remainder, the process being repeated as often as may be necessary. Secondly, in coloring the above with an oil color, and transferring thereto a design in distemper or water color, so as to protect while the graining or marbling is removed from the remainder by a suitable solvent, the process being repeated as often as required. Thirdly, in ornamenting pearl and other surfaces, which may be acted upon by acids, by transferring to the said surfaces a design printed in some material not acted upon by the acid employed for the purpose of defending a portion of the surface from the action of the acid. Fourthly, in ornamenting glass by transferring thereto a printed design, so as to defend portions of the surface while the stain or ground colour is poured or floated upon the said surface, and afterwards drying the stain or ground color and burning, the stop being previously removed or burnt off by the heat applied. Fifthly, in ornamenting glass and other vitreous surfaces by transferring thereto designs printed in an oily or greasy stop, so as to protect the surface. The proper stain or color for the ground is poured on after the removal of the transfer paper. When dry the stop is removed with oil, turpentine, or other solvent, and the article being heated on a "muffle," the stain or ground color is burnt in.

Coloured prints, in which the colours have been laid on in the reverse of the ordinary manner, can be similarly transferred to glass or opaque bodies by one process. The design is afterwards varnished, and finished "in any desirable manner." "We some-
" times print the color print in vitrifiable colors, and fix it on
" the glass by burning." (a)

[Printed, 3d. No Drawing.]

A.D. 1856, November 10.—N° 2640.

DOLBY, EDWIN THOMAS.— (Provisional Protection only.)—
" Improvements in printing several colors at one time from a
" single stone, plate, or block."

The invention consists of applying several colors to the same stone, plate, or block by means of perforated plates in the nature

---

(a) By a disclaimer filed on the 3rd day of November 1857, by Martin Billing, assignee of the above Patent, the words " we sometimes print the color print " in vitrifiable colors, and fix it on the glass by burning," were disclaimed.

of stencil plates, and of rollers having recesses or cells therein to receive the various colors, the cells or recesses being of such forms as to correspond with the required parts of the design to be colored thereby.

[Printed, 3*d*. No Drawing.]

A.D. 1856, November 10.—N° 2646.

JOHNSON, JOHN HENRY.—(Provisional Protection only.)—(Communicated.) — "Improvements in apparatus for printing " electro-telegraphic despatches."

The invention is "more particularly applicable to dial-indi-" cating or recording instruments." The dial contains all the required letters and signs. The needle or indicator is actuated by the make and break of contact in the ordinary manner. A local battery is employed for working the printing mechanism. On the arbor of the escapement wheel of the clockwork for working the dial-indicating mechanism is fitted a type wheel, having its letters and signs raised upon its periphery. Two electro-magnets or coils work a lever, which presses the strip of paper upon which the despatch is to be printed on to the surface or periphery of the type wheel. A catch on the impressing lever turns a feed wheel for moving the strip of paper forward at each stroke of the lever. On the armature of the magnets which actuate the dial mechanism are two springs, which move with it, and serve to establish the circuit from the local battery through the magnets which work the printing mechanism. Each time the indicator passes in front of a letter on the dial a certain amount of attraction is exerted upon the armature by the magnets of the dial mechanism; as the two springs are attached to this armature, spring N° 1 comes in contact with a stop or screw carried by a fixed piece between the coils. Spring N° 2, which establishes the circuit of the local battery when it comes in contact with its own particular stop, has the same movement as spring N° 1, only that spring N° 1, by striking its stop, prevents spring N° 2 from coming into contact with its own stop when the manipulator does not stop the indicator in front of the letter which is to be printed, since there is not sufficient time requisite to magnetize the coils; but when the indicator is stopped, magnetic attraction is effected, and spring N° 2 comes into contact with its stop, thereby establishing the circuit of the local battery. One peculiar feature in this system is the arrangement of the two springs, and the magnetizing of the supplementary coils of the printing mechanism. As these coils are of considerably larger diameter than those of the dial mechanism, they naturally require a longer time to become excited.

[Printed, 3d. No Drawing.]

A.D. 1856, November 11.—N° 2649.

JONES, JOHN FELL.—" Improvements in the manufacture of " rollers or cylinders for printing fabrics, and in machinery to be " used in manufacturing the said rollers or cylinders."

The invention consists, 1, in casting the "liner" (the hollow cylinder which is placed between the axis and the copper shell), in metal moulds, with mandril inserted of such a figure as to leave the "liner" of the required size taper, and with a "nib" formed longitudinally in the interior; and also in cutting or shaping the interior of the liner to the required form by means of a " sliding cutter bar," travelling longitudinally in the interior of the iron tube or cylinder, the said iron cylinder having a slow rotatory motion. Or the cutter may be fixed, and the iron cylinder may perform both a reciprocating longitudinal motion and a rotatory motion. 2. In securing the copper shells to the liners by soldering, tinning, zincing, or by depositing zinc or other suitable metal, and by screwing one upon the other. The pattern is formed on the copper cylinder by pressure applied from within, forcing the copper into metal dies or moulds.

[Printed, 10d. Drawings.]

A.D. 1856, November 12.—N° 2667.

BOULAY, JEAN CHARLES.—(Provisional Protection only.)— " An improved method of printing in various colors simul- " taneously."

The inking table is composed of a frame similar to the chase of the type form, arranged with pieces of wood and rules or reglets of metal corresponding with the various lines of color required to be printed. A proper quantity of ink is laid on each of the rules, and distributed by means of an ordinary inking roller, provided with guides or runners at each end, which run along the sides of the inking table. The roller is then charged with the colors placed upon the various sections or rules, and applied to the form in the same relative position as it was applied to the inking table, the guides on the roller running in grooves at the side of the form, by which means the ink taken from each section or rule of the inking table is transferred to the corresponding line or section of the type form.

" The above applies simply to printing in various colors
" arranged in lines parallel to each other, but by a slight modifi-
" cation of my apparatus I am able to print various colors in the
" same horizontal or perpendicular line, and to alternate and
" arrange them so as to produce check or plaids in many colors
" and in any proportions simultaneously. I also print two, three,
" or more colors on one line of type, block, &c., in such a manner
" a that they may intermingle at the edges, and produce a shaded
" or rainbow tint. I can also, simultaneously with the printing,
" rule the paper with what are called ' feint,' red, or other lines.
" In applying my process of simultaneous printing to fabrics,
" oiled and painted cloths, paper-hangings, &c., I cover the sec-
" tions or rules which receive the color with flannel, felt, or other
" similar fabrics."

A modification of the above for printing circular objects, such as fans, lamp shades, &c., consists in arranging the printing form and inking table to the required curves. The inking roller is conical, and is kept in its proper position on the inking table, as well as on the form, by means of a guide acting on its smaller end.

[Printed, 3d. No Drawings.]


## A.D. 1856, November 18.—N° 2722.

MAGNAY, FREDERICK ARTHUR.—" Improvements in damping
" paper for printing."

" In the Provisional Specification to" N° 2439 of 1856, "paper
" was to be damped by being carried on an endless wet felt and
" pressed between rollers. Now this invention consists in adding
" to this machine two perforated pipes or other suitable apparatus
" for throwing jets of water on to the upper and under surfaces
" of the paper before it passes under the pressing roller."

[Printed, 6d. Drawings.]

A.D. 1856, November 28.—N° 2817.

CELLIER, Auguste.—"An improved mucilage, applicable to " the sizing and printing of textile materials."

A paste is formed by boiling lichen or pearl moss in water and straining off the liquid. Various proportions are given. When the composition is employed for printing the salts required for each color are added. This composition can be combined with all kinds of gums, potato flour, starch, and their compounds. The composition may be employed on the fabric when made, or on the woollen, silk, or cotton thread.

[Printed, 3d. No Drawing.]

A.D. 1856, December 2.—N° 2857.

DRYDEN, Robert, and MILES, Stephen.—"An improve-" ment in the construction of cylinder printing presses."

The invention relates to cylinder perfecting machines in which the paper is fed into the machine by tapes, and consists in using an additional feeder for placing under the sheet to be printed (as it comes on to the second cylinder) a second sheet which shall take the " set-off " from the printed sheet. This is effected by an arrangement of tapes which carry the set-off sheet from the feeding end of the machine, pass it under the first cylinder, and interpose it between the second cylinder and the sheet at the moment of the reiteration.

[Printed, 6d. Drawings.]

A.D. 1856, December 3.—N° 2871.

CHEETHAM, James Kinder.—"Improvements it the appli-" cation of photographic pictures to metal and other surfaces, and " in rendering the same applicable as printing surfaces."

1. A photograph taken by any ordinary means, and the reduced silver or other substance composing it transferred to the copper or other surface, which is coated with mercury in such manner that it is free from the film which supported it, and in direct contact with the metal. Another mode consists in obtaining the silver picture on the copper surface as before, and then treating such plate with nitric acid or similar substance which etches one part of the surface and leaves the other in relief. Another consists

in depositing a coat of copper on a stone, transferring the design to the copper, and then eating away the bare portions of copper. " The stone which was beneath this is then run over with the " inking roller, and the metal picture subsequently removed, " leaving a clear surface of stone for the light portions. 6. This " operation may be reversed."

[Printed, 3d. No Drawing.]

### A.D. 1856, December 3.—N° 2872.

NEWTON, William Edward.—(Provisional Protection only.) —(Communicated by Charles Nègre, of Paris.)—" Improved pro- " cesses for ornamenting metallic surfaces, and for producing " surfaces in intaglio or in relief for printing purposes."

The invention consists also in producing upon such surfaces " damascened " designs, " nielle," and inlaid work, by means of heliography. A layer of sensitive matter is spread over the metal, and an impression taken upon it by the camera or a copying press. To produce an intaglio-engraved plate this layer may be acted upon in a camera or through a negative reversed proof. For a block an ordinary positive proof is employed, and for damascening an ordinary negative. The parts of the layer which have been protected from the action of the light are then removed by a solvent, and a galvano-plastic deposit of a metal less oxidizable than the original plate made direct upon all such parts, and in the case of damascene work of a different color. The layer and heliographic picture are then removed, leaving on the metal plate an incrustation reproducing the original. A shaded incrustation is obtained by forming an oxide or metallic sulphuret and filling in the parts not protected by the deposit with dilute acid or a galvanic current. Inlaid work may be obtained from the above by covering the parts in relief with a ground, and immersing the plate as a cathode in a solution of one of the soluble salts of the metal to be obtained. " Nielle " work is obtained by filling up the hollow parts with a substance which will melt into an enamel by fire. An engraving in relief may also be obtained by printing through an ordinary negative, the layer of bitumen placed upon a plate of copper, silver, &c. After the action of the solvent the plate is immersed in a bath of sulphate of copper, and an electric deposit made upon it. The separate parts of the design are then united by wires, and detached from the plate when the deposit has attained a sufficient consistency. In order to reproduce in copper an engraved steel plate, the surface of the engraved plate is covered with gold or platinum, and copper deposited thereon by galvanic agency. This deposit is then removed, and a fresh galvanic deposit made upon it, which forms an exact copy of the original plate. Engraved plates in intaglio and in relief may also be obtained from photographs, drawings, &c., by chemical and galvanic operations without the employment of the organic matters above mentioned, by reducing the metal in the parts of the sensitive layer acted upon by the light, when this layer consists of a salt of silver or any other metallic salt sensitive to light. The reduction of silver is effected by allowing the photograph to remain in a bath of gallic acid and nitrate of silver.

[Printed, 3d. No Drawing.]

A.D. 1856, December 8.—N° 2910.

MILLER, ROBERT FREDERICK.—" A mode of printing tables of
" fares, advertisements, notices, tablets, ornamental designs,
" figures, and other like announcements on painted or other
" surfaces to supersede writing."

For this purpose the surface is coated with gold leaf or a composition of turpentine varnish, and gold size, or " flattened " colors of any kind. The types are set as for ordinary printing, and furnished by rollers charged with paint instead of ink. " The
" prepared surfaces being impressed on these types will receive
" the required prints, and the surface may then be printed and
" varnished."

[Printed, 3d. No Drawing.]

A.D. 1856, December 13.—N° 2968.

LITTLEWOOD, GEORGE. — " Improvements in printing geo-
" metric patterns."

The invention consists in printing " Berlin work," &c. from type. In connection with the type for this purpose are short pieces of metal, circular in section, called "raising pieces," and these have pins projecting from their upper ends which fit into the bottom of the types. A raising piece is placed under each of the types intended to print any one color. The whole is then clamped together, and after the impression has been taken the whole is again unlocked and the types re-arranged for another color.

[Printed, 6d. Drawings.]

### A.D. 1856, December 16.—N° 2980.

GERHARD, FREDERICK WILLIAM. — " Improved means of " obtaining aluminium metal and the adaptation thereof to the " manufacture of certain useful articles."

The metal is reduced from its fluoride by placing the latter (powdered) in dishes in an oven, and surrounding such dishes with other dishes containing iron filings. The oven is then tightly closed and luted, and the heat increased to redness, after which a stream of hydrogen gas is turned in and allowed to remain in the oven for about an hour. " By this means aluminium is " rendered capable of being used without being alloyed or mixed " with other metals in and for the manufacture of various useful " and ornamental articles, such as small or delicate weighing " weights, bells, pens, penholders, musical wind instruments, " the strings of musical stringed instruments, printer's type, " medals, coins, plated goods, and articles of vertu, and all " articles required to withstand the corroding action of the " atmosphere and acids."

[Printed, 4d. No Drawing.]

### A.D. 1856, December 16.—N° 2984.

NEWTON, ALFRED VINCENT.—(Communicated.)—" Improve- " ments in printing presses."

This invention consists, first, in the employment of "twin " fingers" upon the pressing cylinders, so constructed and operated, that the sheet after being printed on one side by the machine is seized and returned to the types for reiteration. Secondly, in the use of a second cylinder furnished with similar fingers, and placing such second cylinder behind or at any other convenient point in proximity to the impression cylinder, the arrangement being such that the sheet will be drawn around a part of the circumference of the second or extra cylinder and delivered to the impression cylinder to receive a second impression.

[Printed, 1s. 1d. Drawings.]

## A.D. 1856, December 23.—N° 3048.

VAN ABBOTT, George Washington. — (Provisional Protection only.)—"An improvement in bank notes, which is also " applicable to share certificates and other similar documents."

The invention is designed to prevent forgery, more particularly by photography, and consists "in printing the notes, certificates, " and other similar documents upon both sides instead of on one " side only, as at present."

[Printed, 3d. No Drawing.]

## A.D. 1856, December 24.—N° 3054.

WILLIAMS, Taylor.—"Improvements in producing various " ornamental effects upon fabrics, paper, and other surfaces."

The invention consists, first, in printing corresponding patterns on both sides of lace and other open fabrics. The designs are formed on an elastic material, (india rubber, gutta percha, leather, felt, cork, &c.,) and applied to two cylinders rotating at equal speed, which print the material (formed in two parts) as it passes between them. The impressions may be taken in ordinary inks, flock, bronze, gold, &c., as usual. Secondly, in coating lace or other open fabric with coloring or other matter, and then by pressure causing the same to set off upon the surface of a closer fabric. A double set of color apparatus is employed, each consisting of a trough ductor, distributing and coloring rollers, and the open fabric is passed down between a pair of pressure rollers. Thirdly, in producing patterns from a series of cylindrical printing surfaces acting in succession and in register, aided by impressing cylinders with inks of different colors. Fourthly, imparting various effects to lace or other open textures, and simultaneously to fabrics of a closer character, by causing the two fabrics temporarily to adhere whilst under pressure, or other coating or partial coating is applied thereto, and then separating such fabrics. Fifthly, in producing metallic effects upon the surfaces of thread, by causing the same, when coated by varnish or other adhesive matter, to be passed under pressure between the surfaces of gold or other metallic leaf, or to be subjected to a coating of bronze or other metallic powder. Sixthly, in printing imitations of costly woods and imitations of inlays on wood, cut in thin slices "from " the round," and strengthened by the application of paper or woven fabric. Seventhly, in producing metallic effects to one surface of a series of threads, and in stripes to other fabric or material, by laying the threads, side by side in series, at intervals, on the surface of the fabric or material, to which they are caused temporarily to adhere. Metallic leaf or powder is then applied over varnish to the whole surface, and on the threads or tapes being removed the effect of the metal will be seen on the other fabric in stripes. Eighthly, in coating lace and other open fabrics by means of flock, bronze, or other metallic or other powder and gold, or other metallic leaf, the same being caused to adhere to such open fabric by the application of varnish or other adhesive matter applied as in (4).

[Printed, 2s. Drawings.]

A.D. 1856, December 26.—N° 3068.

CLAY, JOHN.—(Provisional Protection only.)—"A new or im- " proved portable printing or impressing instrument."

The inking apparatus is a perforated metallic cylinder, surrounded with cloth, into which the ink is poured. The printing apparatus is a metallic cylinder, on one half of which is hard soldered or cast a piece of metal nearly three-sixteenths of an inch in thickness; in the other half of the cylinder are parallel slits, in which moveable letters are held together by a screw. One or more pieces of steel, about one-sixteenth of an inch wide and one-eighth of an inch in breadth, are soldered on to the exterior of the cylinder, and form a part of the "stop."

The "stop" is a rod of steel with a spring, which, when pressed down by the thumb on the printing cylinder, comes in contact with the projecting pieces of steel above described, and stops the further revolving of the cylinder. When the pressure of the thumb is taken off the spring restores the rod to its original position.

The inking and printing cylinders are fixed into a forked metallic framework, and are placed in opposition to each other. The inking and printing cylinders revolve in circular holes cut in the framework. The whole is fixed to a hollow handle of a convenient size, down the centre of which the rod forming the stop is passed, connected at the top of the handle with a button to facilitate the pressure with the thumb.

The action of the instrument is as follows:—When an impression is to be made, the printing cylinder is pressed on the surface to be impressed with moderate firmness, and moved to and fro, and as the cylinder revolves the impressions are left on the surface to be impressed.

[Printed, 3d. No Drawing.]

A.D. 1856, December 29.—N° 3089.

ALDEN, TIMOTHY.—"Setting and distributing printing types."

The invention consists in an automatic type-distributing machine, the same machine being used for setting type by the aid of an attendant. Both setting and distributing may be going on at the same time. The machine consists principally of a type-carrying wheel supported in a horizontal position above a suitable bed-plate or table of a horse-shoe form, around which the type cases are arranged. These cases consist of a series of channels, type wide, pointing toward the centre of the wheel, the inner ends of the channels terminating near its circumference. The square part of the bed-plate forms a table, the right-hand half of it being occupied by the distributing, and the left by the composing apparatus. Upon the extreme left is the galley, and immediately adjoining it a series of keys consisting of buttons, the shanks of which pass vertically through the table and actuate a series of levers leading to the inside of the carrying wheel, where they effect the set of the indicator, by which the proper type is taken from its case and brought round to the setting table, where they are deposited in a channel and fed along towards the galley, to be formed into columns. At the head of the galley in the distributing machine is a channel which terminates at about the centre of the table at a tangent to the periphery of the carrying wheel. By the operation of suitable mechanism each line of type is forced along the channel towards the carrier, so that as the type is picked off and distributed the column is fed up and another line is taken off, and so on until the whole is distributed into the cases. The types have nicks upon their shanks, whereby, before leaving the channel and being taken up by the conveyor on the carriage wheel, certain parts are set in a given position, which indicates the proper case into which the type is to be deposited, so that the wheel holds on to the type until, by its revolution, the type arrives opposite the mouth of the appropriate channel of the set of cases first mentioned, when it is deposited therein, the type maintaining always its erect position. Upon the face of the carrying wheel are two sets of "conveyors," one set being for distributing and one for setting. These are plates so constructed and fixed to the carrying wheel, that while the latter has a constant and unvarying motion, the former may be permitted to stop for a period and then go on with the wheel, and also to overtake and assume the former position. On each conveyor is a pair of fingers to grip the type, and also certain parts which affect the opening and closing of the same, together with means for thrusting the type out of the conveyor. In the case of distributing this is accomplished automatically by means of the nicks on the type; but in composing the time for these operations is regulated by the compositor who plays upon the keys. These conveyors are arranged around the carrier alternately, that is, first a setting conveyor and then a distributing conveyor, &c. There may be eight or ten of each kind to the wheel. These conveyors, when the machine is both composing and distributing, stop twice at each revolution of the carrying wheel, as follows :—The distributing conveyors always stop at the end of the channel leading from the column of type being distributed, and, having taken a type, stop again at the proper channel in the case for that letter. The composing conveyors stop at the channel indicated by the compositor through the keys, and stop again to deposit their types at the mouth of the channel leading to its column on the galley. The machine has also this peculiarity, that the compositor can compose faster than the type is delivered by the wheel. There is a twofold object for this ; the one is, that the carrying wheel shall have a constant and unvarying motion without regard to any exactness of time in the compositor's playing with the keys; the other, to enable the compositor to look occasionally to the working of the distributing part, as also to justify his lines and set the same into columns upon the galley.

[Printed, 3s. 9d. Drawings.]

# 1857.

---

LORIMIER, ANTHONY.—" An improvement in preparing the
" surfaces of printers' inking rollers and other articles when vul-
' canized india-rubber is used."

The invention consists in subjecting the surfaces to heat, so as
partially to melt the same, the most convenient mode of so doing
being by causing heated iron or other metal to pass over them

[Printed, 3d. No Drawing.]

HILL, HENRY CHARLES.—" Improvements in screw and lifting
" jacks, and in machines for lifting, pressing, and lowering."

The invention (which is stated to be suitable for " stationers',
" printers', bookbinders', and embossers' presses ") consists in the
use of one or more sets of a combination of levers known as
" lazy tongs." Motion is given to these levers by screw rack and
pinion lever, steam, or any other power.

[Printed, 1s. 5d. Drawings.]

SCOTT, URIAH, and HOLDWAY, FREDERIC.—(Provisional
Protection only.)—" Improvements in the manufacture of metal
" type and the arrangement of the same for various purposes."

The invention consists, first, in using type carrying pins upon
their surface, such as when impressed on paper, &c., to leave the
form of the character in perforations, and if used with ink, to
leave both a perforated and colored impression; and, secondly, in
" making a drum or wheel combined with an ink roller or brush,
" so as to ink the type round the wheel or drum and the printing
" surface of the type forming the periphery of the wheel or drum,
" and rolling it over the paper or other material; it will print and
" perforate at the same time when ink is used."

[Printed, 3d. No Drawings.]

A.D. 1857, January 19.—N° 155.

MITCHEL, William Haslett.—" Improvements in means for
" distributing and composing types."

1. The distribution is effected by means of an inclined check
block, in combination with notches in the sides of the type, so
placed that the notch of the first type comes in contact with the
inclined check block when the type is projected its thickness
beyond the end of the slide containing the line of types, so that
one type is separated at a time from such line. 2. By means of
studs or pins uniformly placed to take notches variously placed
in the types, thereby sustaining the types in various positions,
to be dropped or distributed when the types reach receptacles
adapted to the peculiar position of the types. 3. By means of
a revolving wheel with grooves and pins, when combined with
stationary inclines or " disengagers." 4. By means of two notches
combined with their respective inclines and offsets or disengagers,
thereby providing for distributing greater varieties of types without
requiring extreme accuracy in the position of the machine. 5. There
is an arrangement for stopping the machine in case of the revolving
wheel being accidentally arrested by a misplaced type.

The composing machine is an improvement on N° 1287 of 1853
(Mitchel), and contains an arrangement for dropping one type at
a time from the line of types in the " conductor," by the combined
operation of pushers or stop and " fingers." A composing wheel
is used, constructed of thin circular plates with teeth in them,
to receive the type from the conductor, in combination with other
plates which pass beween the circular plates and receive the types,
preventing their further descent, and passing them in line into the
receiving slide. The composing wheel is used in connection with
the inclined shoot or conductor and fence on the lower side only
of the inclined composing wheel.

Compositors' grab, formed of a slightly arched piece of metal of
length corresponding to the width of the page, and furnished
with a lip and finger piece. The compositor, holding his stick in
his left hand, with the top of the page or column next him, takes
the grab in his right hand, and seizes the length of one line of
types by pressure from the thumb, arching the types to the curved
form of the grab, and transfers them to his stick, where he justifies
them.

[Printed, 1s. Drawings.]

CONSTANCE, François.—(Provisional Protection only.)—"An
" improved apparatus for casting and finishing types and vignettes
" used for printing."

The metal is melted in an additional reservoir, communicating
with the ordinary one in such a manner that as the metal is drawn
off from the latter a proportionate quantity is supplied to it from
the former. It is injected by a piston connected with a chamber
leading from the ordinary reservoir into a horizontal mould. The
casting is then, by the action of the apparatus, carried forward
between two cutters, which remove the burrs from two of its faces,
and polishes it. It then passes under a cutter which removes the
jet, between two cutters which remove the burrs from and polish
the remaining sides, and lastly, under other cutters, which "act
" upon and dress the respective ends." The finished castings fall
into a drawer or other receptacle.

[Printed, 3d. No Drawing.]

A.D. 1857, February 4.—N° 321.

LEWIS, Edward and BÖHM, Gideon.—(Provisional Protection only.)—"Improvements in printing in colours, called an
" improved photogalvanographic chromographic process."

The invention consists in the use of plates or impressions from
plates prepared by the "photogalvanographic" process, in color
printing, or "chromography." The first-named process, which
forms the subject of Letters Patent granted to M. Pretsch, consists in the peculiar adaptation of the photographic process to the
production of printing plates in copper and other metals. " Now,
our invention consists of the use of these plates or impressions
" therefrom as a basis, outline, or groundwork for pictures printed
" in colours on wood, stone, metal, or other substance."

[Printed, 3d. No Drawings.]

A.D. 1857, February 6.—N° 346.

POISSON, Pierre.—" Improvements in preparing and applying
" surfaces for painting."

A linen cloth or canvas is coated with a layer of an equal thickness of glue or size, and when dry with a layer of gum copal and
water, to which may be added white of egg or albumen, and when

the second coat is dry, with oil paint equal to forty or fifty ordinary coats of paint. To separate this thickness of paint, a piece of muslin or permeable paper, unsized, is gummed over it. The first cloth is then wetted with water, and may then be readily detached from the paint, carrying with it the two layers of size and gum, leaving simply the coating of paint gummed on the muslin or permeable paper, when it is fit for use. The painting or artistic work having been applied to this surface, another thin piece of muslin is gummed on it above the painting.

To apply this painted sheet on a wall, wainscot, cloth, metallic, or other surface, &c., such surface is coated with oil paint, and on this is applied the painted sheet or surface, it being previously deprived of the muslin first applied by soaking it in water. There remains then but to separate the second muslin which covers the work, which is effected by applying water as before.

" The product or painting surface above described, which I
" apply as a ground or support on paper, instead of muslin,
" obviates the difficulty of obtaining an exact registering of the
" different colors applied, and rendering xicochromy (or painting
" by impression, or printing in oil colours,) a process easy of
" attainment, as the above-described painted surface or founda-
" tion is capable of being worked off as many as fifteen times with
" different colours without being put out of form."

[Printed, 6d. Drawings.]

## A.D. 1857, February 18.—Nº 481.

FOUCHER, LOUIS LÉON.—" Improvements in apparatus for the
" manufacture of type and other articles used in letter-press
" printing."

The mould is formed of two parts, one stationary, the other moveable on a fulcrum; the latter is caused to move sidewise and upwards a little, leaving a space between the parts. The bottom of the mould is formed in the solid metal of the main part, and one side of the mould in the other part. The second side of the mould is formed by a sliding piece fitted in the stationary part, and the top of the mould by a sliding piece fitted in the oscillating part; these two sliding pieces are forced towards each other for the casting by springs, their positions being adjustable by nuts and screws for the different thicknesses of type. The springs afford sufficient resistance to the pressure of the metal, but recede in case of anything rigid getting accidentally between them.

The oscillating part receives motion from a cam acting on an extended arm furnished with a spring to obviate rigidity and permit the adjustment mentioned. The channel from which the metal flows is, while casting, held close up to the get or entrance aperture to the mould. A plate with a small hole is placed between the injecting pipe and the mould. One side and the top of the get is fixed to the oscillating part, while the bottom is fitted to the stationary part. The fourth side of the get is a sliding piece which is fixed in the stationary part, and serves to throw the cast type out of the mould. Another sliding piece acts similarly on the side of the eye of the type, which is thus simultaneously pushed at either end. When so ejected, it drops between the main parts of the mould and descends by a shoot. The matrix is on a slide, and advances towards the mould when closed ready for the casting. It is adjusted sideways by a screw in its carriage, and is further adjusted each time it advances by parts attached to the mould.

Instead of making the parts of the mould adjustable, separate pieces may be fitted and removeable to change the size of mould. In this case the bottom and one side are stationary, as before, while the top and opposite side are moveable. These parts, when closed, overlap each other, leaving the cavity of the mould between them. The several moving parts of the mould and matrix are moved by cams on a rotating shaft.

The invention consists, secondly, of cutters fixed on two surfaces mounted on an oscillating shaft, which pare the type to a uniform thickness.

There is a peculiar arrangement for scraping letters such as *f* and *g*, or where the eye projects beyond the type.

[Printed, 1s. 11d. Drawings.]

A.D. 1857, February 21.—N° 511.

BARBER, John.—" Improvements in compound printing maundrils."

The invention consists in the general composition and arrangement of the mandril. Instead of employing the usual taper shaft, the roller is placed between two chucks or circular cone projections upon a strong shaft, the ends of the roller being grooved or indented " the same as in my improvements for holding rollers for turning

" and engraving," so as to fit the chucks, one of which forms part
of the shaft. The other has a long barrel fitting the shaft, thus
forming a complete bearing and bounded by a washer, and kept
up to the end of the roller by a screw on the shaft and nut on the
boss of the pulley or toothed wheel which drives it. The thread
of the nut and screw being right or left handed, according to the
course of the roller, so as to cause a tightening of the chucks or
cones against the ends of the roller by the resistance of the work
against the moving power, and also preventing the possibility of
slackening so long as the machine is in motion. The vibration or
deflection of the centre of the roller is prevented by the force of
the screw compressing and strengthening the centre of the tube or
cylinder between the chucks. "The roller, as it becomes thinner
" by repeated turnings off for new engravings, will be more
" strengthened in proportion by the force of the screw upon the
" chucks acting more upon the centre of the roller and keeping it
" firm in the chucks, as if the roller and maundrill were one solid
" body, and working true on its axis will require less tapping and
" driving power."

[Printed, 1s. 6d. Drawings.]

## A.D. 1857, February 23.—Nº 524.

BROWN, James.—"A method or methods of preparing paper
" to enable it to receive an impression from an engraved block
" or plate type or other printing agent while in a dry state."

In order to obviate the inconveniences arising from the contraction of paper damped for the purpose of printing maps, charts,
engravings, &c., the paper is coated or impregnated with glycerine
during or after its manufacture.

[Printed, 3d. No Drawings.]

## A.D. 1857, February 23.—Nº 526.

DEVINCENZI, Guiseppe. — "Improvements in producing
" figures and designs upon plates for printing from."

Lithographic ink or chalk, or other oily, greasy, resinous, or
bituminous matter held in suspension by alcohol or ether, or
other liquid, is used to obtain upon the surface of the plate either
a regular grain or some accidental figures or designs, either by
simply covering the plate or by the aid of brushes or other agents.

The plate is then prepared as for lithographic or zincographic
printing; strong varnish is applied instead of ink, and the plate
etched by chemical or electro-chemical action. The plate may
be drawn on with lithographic ink or chalk before being prepared, and granulated in any design, when varnished, by drawing
with a varnish to which alcohol or ether is added. Secondly,
a piece of stained or marbled paper, "produced in the ordinary
" manner in oil colors," or other greasy, resinous, or bituminous
matter, is transferred upon a metallic plate. When resinous or
bituminous matters are employed, the printing plate may be engraved without any farther preparation. Thirdly, the plates are
prepared for engraving by powdering them with some resinous or
bituminous substance, instead of varnishing them. Fourthly,
" an endless variety of stained fancy paper " may be obtained by
the application to the plate of strong varnish and alcohol or ether
by means of brushes, combs, &c. Heat may also be used to produce variety. The plates thus prepared are etched in the way
above described. Fifthly, a metallic plate has the drawing made
directly upon it with a varnish, and is engraved by galvanic
action. Sixthly, the means specified in the first, second, third, and
fourth paragraphs are employed to produce similar drawings and
figures upon stones, which are varnished, " as described," and
engraved by chemical action.

[Printed, 4d. No Drawings.]

A.D. 1857, February 28.—Nº 597.

JENNENS, THEODORE HYLA.—"A new or improved manufac-
" ture of rollers or cylinders for printing fabrics."

A papier mâché core for such roller or cylinder is compressed in
a suitable mould with or without a metallic tongue for sliding in
the groove of the spindle. A seamless casing of copper or copper
alloy of any desired thickness is formed over the core, and this
being drawn down to the desired size on the papier mâché or pulp
base, " a perfect union will be effected, and the pressure conse-
" quent on the process of drawing will be such as to compress the
" papier maché or pulp into a solid and compact mass."

[Printed, 6d. Drawings.]

A.D. 1857, March 7.—Nº 664.

PAGNERRE, ELEONORE AUGUSTIN.—(Provisional Protection
only.)—"A machine for connecting, cutting, and inserting wire

" in blocks of wood for the purpose of printing and stamping
" on linen, calico, silk, cloth, and paper, and for all printing
" purposes."

The machine (two feet high and six inches broad) is screwed on
a table, under which is a pedal communicating with the upper
part of the machine by a lever placed above a reel, upon which
wire is rolled, and then the wire, by means of pliers and six
springs,—two of which are placed horizontally, two perpendicularly,
and two in an inclined plane,—compels the wire to enter into a
tube, which traverses the whole of the machine to the bottom, and
there the wire is forced into the block, which the workman weaves
according to the design, then by the movement of the pedal and
action of the two inclined springs the wires are cut by a pair of
flat scissors, according to the height of the block. Between the
reel and the communicating pedal is placed a small crank, close
to which the wire is obliged to pass into the tube, and then, by its
friction, causes a hand, similar to one in a watch, to indicate on a
dial the number of turns which the pedal performs, and which is
equal to the number of wires inserted in the blocks.

The whole of the machinery, with the exception of the pedal, is
enclosed in a tin case, and is portable, and it can be used for wire
of every size and description.

[Printed, 3d. No Drawings.]

## A.D. 1857, March 9.—No 679.

DAVIES, George.—(Communicated by William H. Elliot, of
Plattsburgh, in the State of New York.)—" An improved self-
" inking stamp for printing cards, labels, and other articles."

The stamp carrying the die at its lower end is supported by the
frame or bed of the apparatus below, and an arm or link above.
The inking and impression pads are for this purpose symmetrically disposed at an angle of 45° to the horizon, on either side of
a crank at the foot of the stamp. The stamp recovers itself by a
spring, the recoil of which throws it from one side of the crank to
the other. The stamp being inclined towards the inking pad, a
smart blow is struck on a hand-piece at the upper end of it, which
brings it down and furnishes the die. The recoil carries it over
the crank so as to present itself to the impression pad, upon which
it is brought down by a smart blow administered in the same way
as the first.

[Printed, 7d. Drawings.]

## A.D. 1857, March 11.—N° 710.

COOPER, JAMES DAVIS. — (Provisional Protection only.) — " Improvements in producing engraved surfaces for surface-" printing."

The design is drawn on a block as for ordinary wood engraving, but instead of cutting away the whites, as in ordinary wood engravings, the whites are left in relief. The block is then carefully varnished with coat after coat until the desired thickness is attained, care being taken that the varnish does not come into the engraved lines. The broad whites are then built up with cement. An electrotype cast is then taken from the block to serve as a printing surface ; but before being so used, the cast requires to be ground to an even face, the grinding being continued until the shallowest lines of the original block begin to appear. The cast then mounted and used " as an ordinary wooden block is used."

Blocks for surface-printing are also prepared from line-engraved plates by obtaining a copy in reverse by electrotype and grinding away such " electrotype or reversed copy of the original plate until " a surface suitable for surface-printing is obtained."

[Printed, 3d. No Drawings.]

## A.D. 1857, March 12.—N° 711.

DERRIEY, JOSEPH JULES.—" Improvements in machines for " manufacturing lozenges, wafers, or pastilles of pasty ma-" terials."

The paste is carried forward by rollers, and thus formed into a sheet of the required thickness, from which the lozenges are cut out by means of cutters fixed in holes on the outside of a revolving cylinder and pushed outwards by suitable springs. The sheet of paste resting on a sliding piece, in which are suitable dies flush with the surface, each exactly opposite the cutters travelling between the cylinders and the sliding piece, has thus the lozenges cut out by the cutters and dies. The whole receives motion from any suitable prime mover. As by this means certain parts of the paste are not acted upon by the cutters and dies, a hollow cylinder is added, in which the paste is pushed forward by a piston, so that at each time a certain portion of the paste is caused to protrude through a hole corresponding in form with that to be given to the lozenge. A cylinder revolves before this opening, and is provided with hollow dies, pushed forward by suitable springs. At each time the cylinder makes one half of a revolution, a suitable quantity of the paste is pushed in the die which is at that moment opposite the opening of the paste-holder, and this portion of the paste is cut off by a knife.

[Printed, 1s. 1d. Drawings.]

### A.D. 1857, March 13.—N° 725.

JUVIN, EDMOND JOSEPH NICOLAS.—(Provisional Protection only.)—"Improvements in producing printing surfaces."

The invention relates to letter-press and music printing, and is adapted to supersede surfaces composed and set up in separate characters. It is also available for printing drawings and writings, &c. The characters or designs being arranged and engraved on a sheet of tin by punches or otherwise, gutta percha is poured or impressed upon the plate, thus producing a block in relief, which serves to prove the work. The sheet of tin is then placed in a galvanoplastic bath, where a deposit of copper on its engraved surface takes place, equal to the thickness of one-fiftieth of an inch. This thin film of copper is then separated from the tin, which, on the relief side (the printing surface), presents a counter-part of the gutta percha cast before taken; a mixture of lead and antimony is then cast on the back part of the copper to give it substance and body. A stereotype in lead may be cast at once on the engraved plate of tin. Or the sheet of tin is engraved and proved by gutta percha as above; a plaster cast is taken of the gutta percha surface, furnishing a mould from which a lead stereotype is cast. Or, thirdly, the lead block in relief obtained as last described may be used to produce a concave cast in gutta percha, which is submitted to a deposit of copper by electrical agency. The film of copper so deposited is then backed up with lead to form a block to print from.

[Printed, 3d. No Drawings.]

### A.D. 1857, March 21.—N° 807.

DOLBY, HENRY, and DOLBY, EDWIN THOMAS.—"Improve-
"ments in machinery used when printing several colors in suc-
"cession on the same surface."

The several blocks or printing surfaces are fixed to a suitable table or frame having on the sides rails for guiding a carriage

from end to end of the machine. The material to be printed is
placed round a roller, and attached thereto by points or suitable
instruments. The roller is carried by a frame or carriage moved
to and fro on the rails by suitable means, in such manner that it
may roll correctly, without slipping, over the succeeding blocks
or printing surfaces, on which are respectively portions of the
whole subject to be printed. Or the bearings of the roller may
be stationary, and the table or machine move past the roller,
thus causing the several blocks in succession to give off their
impression. The arrangement of the apparatus at the ends of
the table and on the roller is such that the material is, after
receiving the several impressions, delivered from the roller, and
a fresh piece placed thereon. In order to supply color to the
several blocks or printing surfaces on the table, as many color
apparatus are used as there are blocks or printing surfaces, and
each color apparatus consists of a trough containing the color,
in which a roller revolves, having a suitable doctor or scraper.
This roller at its upper surface delivers color to an endless apron
of vulcanized india-rubber, or other suitable material, carried
by two rollers. The endless apron passes over a table, on which
there is an inking roller, which at suitable intervals is moved
over the apron on the table, and then over its block or printing
surface. In place of applying the several blocks or printing surfaces on a horizontal table, as above explained, they may be placed
on a cylinder.

[Printed, 1s. 9d. Drawings.]

### A.D. 1857, March 25.—N° 832.

HILL, PEARSON.—" Improvements in machinery for stamping,
" marking, or printing and arranging papers, letters, and other
" articles."

The invention is adapted for post-office and other purposes.
The position of the letter, &c., introduced by hand or otherwise
into the machine, is regulated by a stop, and the stamp furnished
with color by an inking apparatus or otherwise, is pressed against
it, so as to produce the required mark. The letter is carried by
fingers or nippers or other means, to a trough or case, into which
it is forced by a presser or plunger, or by fingers, which propel
forward the column of letters as they accumulate in any required
direction, when the column of letters is propelled in an inclined or

curved open trough. A moveable plate or board serves to press them into the trough, and prevent any danger of their shuffling out. A ratchet may be also employed to prevent any accidental recoil of the letters as they advance. The letters are counted by a self-acting counting apparatus, so arranged as to act only when a letter is placed in the machine, and to cease acting when no letter is introduced, notwithstanding that the motion of the machine may be continued. The printing pad is either made of elastic material, or an arrangement is made in the stamp, in order to accommodate the varying thickness or irregularities of the letter.

" The various motions are produced by cams and excentrics or " cranks, and other well-known mechanical means, and the " machine may be driven by hand or by the foot, or by power, as " may be most convenient."

[Printed, 3s. 9d. Drawings.]

## A.D. 1857, April 1.—Nº 898.

LEE, RICHARD EGAN.—(Provisional Protection only.)—" A " portable printing apparatus adapted alike for moveable type, " lithography, and copper-plate."

The invention consists of a cylindrical press and an improved case for amateurs, " so constructed that both the said press and " case, together with the usual requisite materials for printing from " type, or stone, or copper, or steel, may be enclosed and carried " from place to place in an ordinary work-box or dressing-case." The type is laid on the bed of the press and a cylinder is driven over it to give the impression by the revolution of two longitudinal screws, which pass through the ends of the cylinders (or a lithographic scraper may be used for the cylinder).

[Printed, 6d. Drawings.]

## A.D. 1857, April 16.—Nº 1087.

SCHAUB, GEORGE. — " A new or improved manufacture of " types for printing."

The invention consists in making the heads of the types of copper, zinc, nickel, or other alloys, either by electro-deposition or embossed by dies and pressure, " according to the well-known " process of raising metals." The heads are formed in sheets or series side by side, there being depressed divisions between them, so that they can afterwards be readily divided. Solder is attached to the back of the sheet, which is placed in a mould so constructed that type metal run into the said mould forms the bodies of the types. The type heads are afterwards separated by sawing or otherwise.

[Printed, 7d. Drawings.]

### A.D. 1857, April 20.—N° 1112.

UNDERWOOD, John. — " An improved method of printing " and of preparing materials employed therein."

The invention consists in printing, writing, or marking upon any suitable material with a solution of extract of logwood, or with a material or varnish soluble in water or other like suitable vehicle; and when with the latter, in dusting or throwing over it extract of logwood in powder. The paper, &c., to be used is treated with a solution of neutral chromate of potash or other agent, which will have a like effect in absorbing the extract or powder of logwood, and the paper so treated is used in a damp state; or instead of logwood and chromate of potash, other materials which have a strong affinity for each other, and which, when acted upon in the manner above described, throw down colored precipitates, as, for instance, sulphate of iron and infusion of nutgalls.

[Printed, 3d. No Drawings.]

### A.D. 1857 April 22.—N° 1128.

BURTON, Thomas, and LORD, Simeon. — " An improved " self-acting steam regulator, which is applicable to drying " cylinders and other similar purposes."

The invention relates, among other things, to printing machines, drying stoves, print works, dye works, and bleach works. For the purpose of carrying off the air and condensed steam or water from steam pipes or vessels without the usual loss attendant upon their escape, a chest or chamber is connected to the pipe or vessel containing the air and condensed steam or water. At the upper part of the chest is placed a small ball valve which opens inwards, so that when the chamber is in operation the air may be forced out of the chest or chamber. At the lower part of the chest or chamber is placed an outlet or delivery pipe communicating with the interior of a barrel valve, the passage being open at both ends, and also having an aperture which can open to or be closed from the outlet pipe by turning on its rest. Within the chamber is a float, which rises as the air is expelled, and the tap thus gradually opens; and when the float is at its full height, the aperture in the barrel is full open to the outlet pipe.

[Printed, 7d. Drawings.]

## A.D. 1857, May 11.—Nº 1318.

MYERS, JAMES JOHN.—" A new method of regulating paper " laid on to be printed on one or both sides at and by cylinder " printing machines by means of guides."

These guides are plates fixed on a rod or spindle, each end of which rests upon a carriage centre or bearing fixed to the side frames of the machine. The edges of the paper are laid from the laying-on board to the inside of the guides, as is done in the case of " grippers " or tapes, and the paper having passed along to the extreme end of the guides, is taken hold of and becomes attached to the cylinder of the printing machine by the " grip- " pers " or tapes, and immediately thereupon the guides are thrown back by means of a lever which allows the paper to pass freely beneath them from the laying-on board round the cylinder.

[Printed, 4d. No Drawing.]

## A.D. 1857, May 15.—Nº 1371.

VANDERBORGHT, MICHAEL JOSEPH.—(Provisional Protec- tion only.)—" A new system of machinery producing simulta- " neously the three-fold effect of casting, breaking off, and rubbing " (smoothing) of printing characters."

The invention purposes to remedy the defects arising from the types being too large for average, thick, and out of line. " Fol- " lowing out the principle of the old mould, I combine and " arrange my new mechanical mould. Instead of the two pieces " forming the body of the letter being moveable, and those called " blanks, which form the thickness, firmly attached to the move- " able pieces, I propose to attach the two pieces forming the body " of the letter, and to render moveable the blanks. The two " pieces which form the body of the letter will each carry its " break piece ('jet'), with this difference, that by the hand

" mould each break is of one piece with its side, while with my
" mould the sides of the breaks, being each for its own part of
" one piece with the two blanks, are made to move with them.
" With the hand mould the operater (caster) before each casting
" shuts the mould between the two registers by means of a
" circular spring, which sustains its bearing on the mould.    I
" propose to do without these registers, and to attach a mould
" carrier, whose free circular motion will not fail to bear or press
" the matrix with exactitude against the mould.    I propose to
" break or smooth off the beards from the types by means of an
" instrument, across which the type will pass when it is pushed
" from between the blanks of the mould at the moment the type
" leaves the blanks.    This instrument will be formed of two file-
" shaped cutters placed opposite each other, provision being made
" for the exit of the beards when cut or smoothed off the types."

[Printed, 3d.  No Drawings.]

A.D. 1857, May 19.—Nº 1400.

VASSEROT, CHARLES FREDERIC.—(Communicated by Auguste
Trouillet, of Paris.)—" A typographical numbering apparatus."

The apparatus may be used by hand or with the press, either
for numbering or putting control stamps on vignettes, or it may
be employed concurrently with a test or fixed stamp.

1. The " numerical apparatus" consists, 1st, of a fixed steel
axis on which metallic type wheels revolve.  2ndly, of these type
wheels to the number required by the notation engraved with
the successive numerals from 0-9.  Besides the hole made for the
passage of the axis, each circle has a small hole " perfectly con-
" centric with the one through which the axis passes " (made
in the direction of the axis) to receive a piston with a spiral spring.
3dly, of a steel ratchet-wheel, with ten teeth fixed to the side of the
unit circle.  This wheel has the same holes as the engraved
wheels.  4thly, of steel wheels with ten circular teeth and holes
near the periphery concentric with such teeth to receive the piston.
One of these wheels is fixed to every type wheel except the units
wheel.  5thly, of an inclined spring catch on the axis gearing
into the ratchet of the units wheel, and connected with a lever and
button for working it.  6thly, of springs screwed on one of the
sides of the case bearing upon the steel wheels to keep the figures
in line with each other.  7thly, of spiral spring pistons lodged

in the thickness of the type and steel wheels. The head of the pistons on the units wheel passes beyond its ratchet wheel sufficiently for to come in combination with the catch. 8thly, of a brass or other metallic case to contain the mechanism. The lever being worked by the button causes the units wheel to advance one step until it reaches 9, at which time the catch meeting the piston of the units wheel forces it into the steel wheel, or fixed to the tens wheel, and causes it to advance one step, and so on until the tens wheel reaches 9, when a similar effect is produced on the hundreds, and so on for the other wheels. For numbering by two and two, the wheels have either the even or odd numbers repeated twice. For numbering by 5 and 5, 10 and 10, 100 and 100, and so on, the wheels are similarly arranged. Four arrangements are shown for causing the momentary disappearance of the non-expressive ciphers, as it " would be " impossible with the numbering apparatus above described to " number one or several orders of units without preceding them " with the ciphers representing the several orders of superior units." I. by the use of moveable ciphers screwed and unscrewed alternately in order. II. by lowering successively the type wheels by means of a shaft or axis nearly double the total length of the apparatus. III. by lowering the ciphers, by adjusting in the centre hole of the type wheels an excentric circle, which acts freely in the hole IV., or by adjusting a peculiar piece of mechanism inside them.

" Vignette stamping apparatus," the mechanism of which differs from that of the numbering apparatus only in having ten vignettes entirely different from each other in place of the numerals.

" Stamping apparatus with free changes." This consists in various additions to or substitutions for the vignettes or numerals, (1) of signs of punctuation, (2) of words, and (3) of signs, drawings, or figures.

" Formation of the typographic circle " (type wheel). Instead of engraved wheels, "cast circles," "circles with moveable figures," " stamped circles," "milled circles," and " circles and cylinders " with galvanic rings or envelopes " are employed.

" Cylindrical printing." The above process is " applicable to " the galvanic stereotyping of cylinders similar to those used for " printing textile fabrics. Thus the typographical printing on a

" plane could be done by means of cylinders, which would
" greatly increase the number of proofs of one type in a given
" time. With the same printing-press several copies could be
" obtained, showing the same or different colors, and even the
" colors could be varied in the different parts of a same model,
" for there is no other limit with regard to colors and number
" of proofs than the number of printing cylinders. A small
" number of cylinders corresponding exactly to the sizes used in
" typography, could be used undeterminately to work off proofs
" of several models, owing to the same cylinder being easily and
" indefinitively coverable with any number of typographical
" impresses."

Numbering apparatus with a fixed text or stamp, differing from
the others by being furnished with a fixed text or drawing engraved on a plate in which it is enclosed, so that the fixed text or
drawing is printed at the same time as the moveable figures or
vignettes of the wheels. Its sides are closed by means of two
fixed plates.

Numbering apparatus worked by hand.

Vignettes stamp worked by hand.

" Numbering apparatus and vignettes stamps adapted to a
" special press," consisting of a piston, with or without a fixed
text or drawing at the end of it, sliding in a hollow cylinder,
and furnished with an inking apparatus.

" Numbering apparatus applied to ordinary printing," which
consists in the application of the moveable apparatus " to the
" typographic impression on the presses usually employed, with
" or without addition of text or vignettes, the said application
" being principally useful for numbering shares, bank notes,
" tickets, &c., &c., and for the impression of guarantee marks of
" any kind resulting from the employment of the vignettes
" stamping apparatus." The numbering apparatus may be used
as a " controler " for counting the number of movements of any
machine whatever.

[Printed, 1s. Drawings.]

A.D. 1857, May 27.—N° 1485.

CLARK, WILLIAM STETTINIUS.—(Provisional Protection only.)
—(Communicated.)—" Improvements in printing presses."

The invention relates to small portable presses in which a conical roller is used for the impression, and consists in means of adjusting the roller so as easily to adapt it to the surface of the type. In connexion with the conical roller is a spring so arranged that, on turning the roller in the direction of the tympan, the latter will be depressed over the type, and on turning the roller away from the tympan the latter will be raised by means of its spring, and thus allow the paper to be readily placed upon the type.

[Printed, 3d. No Drawings.]

## A.D. 1857, May 29.—N° 1518.

FLEET, CHARLES.—(Communicated by George Matthews, of Montreal, Canada.)—" An improvement or improvements in the " manufacture of printing ink."

Calcined green oxide of chromium is mixed with oil, varnish, or other ordinary ingredients used for the different kinds of printing. Ink thus composed is unalterable by the action of air, light, or sulphurous vapours, and insoluble in nitric, muriatic, and most other acids, and caustic alkalies, and only soluble in boiling or hot oil or vitriol, and is thus adapted for printing bank notes, bills, and similar instruments. Green oxide of chromium may be substituted for or used in combination with lamp black or other coloring matters in making ordinary inks.

[Printed, 3d. No Drawings.]

## A.D. 1857, May 29.—N° 1519.

SALLES, JEAN.—(Provisional Protection only.)—" An improved " apparatus for printing or stamping."

The invention is intended chiefly for the use of post-offices. It consists of a piston rod free to move up and down in a cylinder with slotted sides. The piston rod carries at bottom the stamp, and at top a strong spring bears on the head of the rod. A cross piece fixed to the rod protrudes through the slot in the side of the cylinder. An inclined or curved lever, worked from a crank upon a pinion driven by a toothed wheel coated to rotate through a crank handle fitted thereto, comes under the cross piece, and upon the rotation of the toothed wheel raises the piston, and with its stamp or die, until it reaches the top of its stroke, when a flap pressed by a spring is brought under the cross pieces and keeps it up. At the time the piston and stamp are so raised, an inking roller connected to the back of the elevating lever is brought under the stamp, and the fore end of the lever is at the mouth or fore part of the apparatus. The lever has connected to it points or small pins, and the letters or papers to be stamped having been previously arranged on an inclined feed plate, each time the fore end of the lever reaches the feed the points seize a letter or paper, and carrying it down an inclined guide plate bring it on its return stroke under the stamp, when a projection on the side of the lever turns back the flap before mentioned, whereby the piston is released, and the spring being now free to exert its pressure forces down the stamp upon the letter brought under it, as before named. In a moderately sized apparatus every complete rotation of the main proportion of strokes in the stamp may be obtained.

Where an impression is required to be struck upon paper the inking roller may be dispensed with.

[Printed. 3d. No Drawings.]

A.D. 1857, June 5.—N° 1583.

SCHIMDT, Henry.—(Provisional Protection only.)—(Communicated.)—" The new cork roller for printing."

A thin sheet of cork is placed over a wooden roller, with a handle at each end. Over the cork is rolled a coating of woollen cloth, and the cloth is then covered with leather, the latter being kept in its place by brass plates screwed on the ends.

[Printed, 5d. Drawings.]

A.D. 1857, June 9.—N° 1620.

BAXTER, George.—(Provisional Protection only.)—" Improve-" ments in printing in colors."

The invention consists in producing gradations in the color applied by each block in the same way as that effect " is now " usually obtained in copper or other plate printing, and sometimes, " also, in surface printing, where one plate or block produces a com-" plete impression, that is to say, by ruling a series of fine lines on " the surface of the block by machinery in those places where a " lighter tint is required. The machine ruling is effected in a " similar manner to that in which machine ruling is now produced " on copper and steel plates, by applying an etching ground to

" the block, which is then removed in lines by the machine, and
" these lines are then bit in by acid." The same effect is stated
to have been hitherto " imperfectly " produced by carefully inking
the parts to a greater or less degree, and when any considerable
difference of tint was required, using a separate block for each
color.

[Printed, 3d. No Drawings.]


A.D. 1857, June 10.—N° 1625.

JARRETT, GRIFFITH.—"Improvements in apparatus for printing
" or endorsing in colors on paper or other surfaces, being improve-
" ments upon the invention secured to me by Letters Patent dated
" the 29th of July 1853."

The object of the invention is to render the working parts of
the press more compact and less liable to accident. A vertical
slide, carrying the die at its lower end, is worked by a cam lever
" as heretofore," and returned by a lever acted by an elastic spring.
Immediately above the die the slide carries two brackets, which
support two small rollers, around which is passed an endless band
or ribbon carbonized or otherwise suitably prepared with coloring
matter. One end of one of the rollers is furnished with a ratchet
wheel, which is acted upon by a pall (attached to the frame of the
press) in such a manner as to advance the endless band or ribbon
slightly at every movement of the press. The impression pad or
counterpart is also made capable of easy adjustment and renewal,
being formed of a plain piece of leather or other suitable material
bevilled at the edge and slipped horizontally between two metal
slides having their edges similarly bevilled and placed parallel to
each other, or nearly so.

[Printed, 7d. Drawings.]


A.D. 1857, June 10.—N° 1635.

NEWTON, WILLIAM EDWARD.—(Communicated.)—" Improve-
" ments in printing machinery."

The invention relates, first, to machines in which the sheet is fed
in by means of " drop rollers " and tapes. " It has been customary
" heretofore upon starting the machine to set the drop rollers in
" motion by hand, and then to allow them to derive their impetus
" from their brief contact with the feeding cylinder, and the result

" has been unsatisfactory, inasmuch as during its elevation or
" detachment from the feeding cylinder its velocity is reduced by
" natural causes, so that upon resuming its contact with the feed-
" ing cylinder it has a tendency to retard the sheet more or less in
" an increased ratio to the varying speed of the machine, thereby
" causing an imperfect register." To obviate this difficulty, the
drop roller is, according to the first part of the present invention,
driven at all times at a velocity corresponding to that of the impression and type cylinders so as to obtain register.

The second part of the invention relates to an improved mode
of working the fly frame, into which the printed sheets are delivered and deposited on the receiving table. "As now constructed
" the cam shaft carrying the fly cams is placed under the centre of
" the press at the greatest possible distance from the fly frame, to
" which it is intended to give motion by the intervention of geared
" levers, connecting rods, intermediate levers, bell cranks, and
" other complicated contrivances." To obviate the wear and tear
and other inconveniences of this arrangement a fly cam shaft is
placed at each end of the press, and such shaft is actuated by
toothed gearing on side shafts geared to a central main shaft,
" causing the cams on the main shaft to act more directly on the
" fly frames than heretofore."

[Printed, 1s. 3d. Drawings.]

A.D. 1857, June 15.—Nº 1670.

SMITH, WILLIAM.—(Provisional Protection only.)—(Communicated by A. E. Rochette.) — "Improvements in chromo-litho-
" graphical printing presses."

"With this improved typographical press I can print several
" colors at once in the same form, which press is divided into four
" compartments, each compartment containing characters of a
" different color. The sheet of paper to be printed is laid securely
" on a moveable tympan, which is made to revolve by quarters of
" a revolution after each stroke of the press. Four proofs by this
" process are printed simultaneously on a sheet of paper, each
" proof with a different tint or color, and successively each one
" with four colors. After receiving four impressions, the sheet
" becoming loose, is taken out, and a new one replaced on the
" tympan."

[Printed, 5d. Drawings.]

### A.D. 1857, June 22.—N° 1744.

SEROPYAN, CHRISTOPHER DICRAN.—"A mode of preparing
" bank notes, bills of exchange, and other papers, to prevent
" counterfeiting by photography, and its kindred processes, and a
" mode of preparing an ink for the same."

This invention consists in using two or more colors which do
not reflect nor transmit, but absorb the chemical rays of light,
one of which is applied to the paper or other material either by
printing, staining, or tinting, so as to cover the surface with a tint
or ground of a red, orange, or yellow shade or color, while an ink
of a different color or shade from the tint or surface color is
used for printing the other parts of the note, that is, the obligatory
and ornamented parts upon the said surface; the said ink consisting of such ingredients as will render it equally or more fugitive
than the color forming the tint or surface color of the paper.

[Printed, 3d. No Drawing.]

### A.D. 1857, June 26.—N° 1794.

HATTERSLEY, ROBERT.—"Improvements in machinery for
" distributing and setting up type."

A type table attached by fixed screws to the framing of the
machine is furnished through nearly its entire length with metal
partitions, not quite the height of the types, in which the types
can move freely. Two or three of these tables are used, one
being charged with type, while others are being worked out on
the machine. At the back of the rows of type are " followers,"
or propellers, which by means of a vulcanized india-rubber spring
press the type against a fixed plate. The last type of a row is
depressed by one of a series of pistons into a guide plate, the
types being prevented from rising with the piston by an angular
strip of metal extending over the last row but one, and furnished
with adjusting screws, which serve to keep the pistons over the
top of the last types. The pistons recover themselves by wires
and elastic bands. They are made in two parts, the bottom ones
being thin and bent, so that two of them pass through one slot
in the guide plate. The guide plate is furnished with a number
of grooves, all conveying to an outlet at the bottom. An outer
plate and springs prevent the types turning in their descent. The
compositor's stick (a piece of angle iron long enough to have two

or more lines set up along it) slides on a bracket fixed to the
framing. It is moved forward as the composing proceeds by a
lever acted on by an elastic band. By depressing any one of the
several keys on a key-board a lever is acted on, which raises one
end of a second lever which rests upon a bowl, thus drawing
down the other end, and thus giving motion to certain guide
pulleys and cords which work the pistons by which the type is
thrust out on to the guide plate.

Two forms of the improved compositor's sticks are shown.

[Printed, 10d. Drawings.]


### A.D. 1857, July 1.—N° 1835.

NEWTON, WILLIAM EDWARD.—(Communicated by Charles
Negre, of Paris.)—" Improved processes for ornamenting metallic
" surfaces, and for producing surfaces in intaglio or relief for
" printing purposes."

The object of the invention is to reproduce copies of photographs " by obtaining from them by the action of light, in con-
" junction with the employment of chymical and galvanic opera-
" tions, engraved plates either in intaglio or in relief, upon iron,
" steel, copper, and its alloys zinc, silver, tin, aluminium, gold,
" and other metals; also to produce damaskened designs formed
" by metals of various colors; also designs formed of different
" colors by means of several engraved plates resistering one with
" the other; also designs of different colors, gold and platinum,
" upon porcelain, earthenware, stoneware, &c.; also enamel or
" ' nielle ' work, and inlaid work upon metals, marble, stone, &c.
This is effected by producing,—1, by means of electricity, direct
deposits or metallic images of gold, platinum, copper, &c., upon
the surface of another metal, such as steel, iron, copper, &c.,
partially covered with a photographic varnish, insulating and
utilizing this superposed metal as a reserve or ground for the
purpose of attaching or biting into the more oxidizable metal,
forming the foundation or back either by means of an acid or
by electricity. 2. By effecting, by means of electricity, direct
metallic deposits upon photographic images obtained by means
of a metallic salt.

[Printed, 5d. No Drawing.]

## A.D. 1857, July 8.—N° 1898.

NISSEN, Hilary Nicholas.—(Provisional Protection only.)— " An improved method of making impressions similar to water- " marks upon paper."

The invention consists in taking paper after it comes from the mill, damping it to such an extent as will not deprive it of its size, and then subjecting it to pressure under metal letters, types, or devices, in an ordinary hand or other printing press. " But in " order to obtain a perfect and lasting impression, I remove the " tympan, and thus the paper is exposed to the metal type or device " on one surface, while the other surface is in contact with the " platten or with the cylinder."

[Printed, 3d. No Drawing.]

## A.D. 1857, July 15.—N° 1969.

JOHNSON, John Henry.—(Communicated by S. W. Francis, of New York.)—"Improvements in machinery or apparatus for " marking or imprinting characters on papers and other fabrics."

The invention relates to the use of an apparatus as a substitute for the ordinary process of writing, such apparatus combining great rapidity of action with the neatness of printing. The apparatus is composed of a number of hammers placed in a circle in such a manner that they will strike upon one central point, upon the face of which hammers the letters of the alphabet are cut in relief. These hammers are put in motion by means of keys similar to those of a pianoforte key-board. The paper, borne upon a carriage, is constantly drawn from right to left by a spring, which is recoiled by drawing back the carriage by hand at the conclusion of each line. A detent mechanism causes the paper to move the length of one letter each time that one of the keys is depressed. The movement of the paper necessary for commencing a new line is imparted to it by rollers carried by the chariot, which are in their turn acted on by an apparatus attached to the framing of the machine at the required time. Certain small pieces of mechanism are also arranged beneath the keys, the object of which is to prevent two keys from being pressed down at the same moment, and the hammers from being injured by being struck against each other. The inking of the hammers is accomplished by means of a silk band passing over pulleys, which are capable of sliding vertically in grooved bearings, and are raised by separate keys placed for that purpose at each end of the key-board. The band is raised with the pulleys, can thus be easily worked without soiling the machine. By pressing upon the pulleys, they easily reassume their former positions.

[Printed, 11d. Drawings.]

A.D. 1857, July 17.—N° 1982.

BARWELL, WILLIAM.—(Provisional Protection only.)—"An " improvement or improvements in casting metals."

" I make a mould of a suitable form for casting a cylinder, and " I support in the axis of the mould a core or cylinder, and " between the interior of the said mould and the said core the " molten metal is poured in in the usual way. I make the said " mould of coarse sand, mixed with horse-dung or chopped straw " or hay, or other suitable matter; and I make the core of a " cylinder of the same materials, in the interior of which I prefer " inserting a metal rod or cylinder for the purpose of strengthen- " ing the same. In order to make the mould and core more " porous, I pick small holes therein." The metal being poured into a mould of this description, "the air escapes freely throug. " the pores or perforations in the mould and core."

[Printed, 3d. No Drawing.]

A.D. 1857, July 17.—N° 1983.

ROBERTS, THOMAS, and DALE, JOHN.—"Improvements in " obtaining pigments from dye woods, and in the application of a " pigment to printing paper-hangings."

The dye woods are immersed in a fluid containing substances which take up the coloring matter as it is dissolved. For instance, if the substance be barwood, it is ground and immersed in a fluid, to which a salt of tin is added. The invention consists also in the use of barwood itself as a pigment, for which purpose it is ground fine, and immersed in any liquid which will develope its tinctorial quality. " This will be found to have taken place by " the use of the first part of the invention, and the two may there- " fore be used as a combined operation." The invention also consists in the application of a pigment obtained from barwood to the purpose of printing paper-hangings, "which pigment may be " obtained as above described, or by other means."

[Printed, 3d. No Drawing.]

A.D. 1857, July 28.—N° 2050.

CLARK, WILLIAM STETTINIUS.—(Communicated by S. W. Wood and H. A. Bills, of the United States.)—" Improvements " in automatic feeding printing apparatus."

A series of rotating surfaces, upon which the flat columns are secured, are affixed alternately upon two many-sided rotating beds, in order that the ordinary type may be employed, and set up in flat forms in the usual manner. The matter is contained on the two series of beds in alternate columns. The first series of rotating beds, or those nearest the coil of paper, leave every alternate column blank, which blanks are printed by the second set of type beds. To press the paper upon the type, a wheel of the proper size to correspond with the type bed is placed for convenience above the type, and secured in bearings. In the periphery of this wheel are secured segments of wheels arranged alternately, corresponding with the columns of type, and also corresponding with the spaces formed by setting the columns of type in flat forms. Hence as the paper is carried through between the type and wheels, and by its margin, the segments of the wheel roll upon the face of the columns of type in a line perpendicular with their centres. To secure the type upon the cylinders, the column lines are grooved to receive the ends of the keys, the type being notched to receive the keys flush with their surfaces. The paper, in a roll of any required size, is laid on an endless belt of felt, leather, or other material moving at the same velocity as the types. The ends of the shaft carrying the paper extend into slotted guides formed in the frame of the machine to retain it in a proper position when revolving. A knife is secured to a revolving framing for severing the sheet in any desired size. The paper is damped by passing under a roller clothed with absorbent material.

[Printed, 1s. 4d. Drawings.]

A.D. 1857, July 29.—N° 2066.

KENYON, HARTLEY.—(Provisional Protection only.)—" Improvements in the treatment of certain compounds of silica, " alumina, sodium, or potash, and the application of such com-" pound in the processes of printing, dyeing, tawing, paper-" making, or in any other process in which the alumina of com-" merce is employed.

" I take ordinary clays or spars (such as fluorspar and felspar),
" compound of various quantities of silica, alumina, water, and
" as little iron or lime as possible. The clays are dried, ground,
" and calcined. The spars are ground and calcined before being
" used."

" I take two parts of clay or spar, or both combined, and add
" 1 part of marine salt, muriate of soda, or nitrate of soda, 1½ parts
" of boiling water, and dissolve ⅛th part of Glauber's salts, or
" acid sulphate of soda, or sulphate of potash, and add to it the
" above-named spars or clays and salt." It is then mixed with
sulphuric acid and the hydrochloric acid, or (if nitrates are used)
the aquafortis driven off. The residue is submitted to a furnace
" as used by soda-ash makers, heated by the residue of heat from
" the pot, or any other kind of furnace, until the whole of the
" hydrochloric or nitric acid gases are driven off."

[Printed, 3d. No Drawing.]

### A.D. 1857, August 1.—No 2092.

AVRIL, CHARLES.—(Provisional Protection only).—"Improve-
" ments in the mode of forming the printing surface of blocks,
" plates, cylinders, lithographic stones, or other similar bodies
" made use of for printing in colours."

The object of the invention is to give with two or more plates a
greater variety in colors and tints of colors "than was hitherto
" possible with the same number of plates." The outlines of the
various colors are established on two or more plates or printing
surfaces, its own color is then applied to each plate so as to make
the latter take only on those spots of the plate as require the said
color, in such mode that by printing over the same outline, printing with each of the plates in succession, certain parts of the
colors of these latter are caused to mix together, and thus make
the colors in these spots differ from those on the plates.

[Printed, 3d. No Drawing.]

### A.D. 1857, August 10.—No 2141.

GEDGE, JOHN.—(Provisional Protection refused).—(Communicated by Adolphe Barthélemy Elbena, of Toulon.)—" Improve-
" ments in carriages of printing presses."

" I make a framing in and on which the assemblage of wheels
" drum, and other mechanical parts, called the carriage, rest and

" work. An axle situated about one-third of the distance from
" the back of the frame is worked by a winch, on this axis I place
" two wheels and a drum (the latter to contain the motor or
" driving spring); the larger of these two wheels being toothed,
" gears into a pinion wheel, supported by a shaft passing from
" side to side of the frame; this pinion causes another wheel
" placed on a lower shaft to rotate, and the last-mentioned wheel,
" by means of a second pinion fixed on a third shaft, causes a
" toothed wheel fixed on the same shaft also to rotate, it being
" driven round by the wheels and pinions aforesaid; this wheel
" gears into a pinion wheel fixed on the second or middle shaft,
" thus communicating motion to a wheel placed beneath the
" framing on two supports or iron. A crank, called the carriage
" crank, carries the arm of the balance which is attached to the
" carriage, and also the flyer, which is placed to retain power at
" command."

[Printed, 3d. No Drawings.]

### A.D. 1857, August 19.—Nº 2195.

ROSENTHAL, SIGISMOND.—(Provisional Protection only.)—
" Printing on both sides of a sheet of paper by a single impression
" on an ordinary lithographic or other press."

" Take two zinc or other plates and connect them together by
" hinges, so as to allow them to face each other, the same as the
" covers of a book, each plate to have on it the drawing or writing,
" and when inked in the usual way, the paper to be placed on one
" of the plates and the other folded over it; they are then to be
" pressed in the usual way, when the paper will receive impressions
" on both sides. Lithographic stones and other materials will
" also do. By this invention neither tympan nor backing sheets
" are required. A great saving of time is effected, as double the
" quantity of printing may be done by this than in the ordinary
" process."

[Printed, 5d. Drawing.]

### A.D. 1857, August 27.—Nº 2268.

THOMPSON, CHARLES, and THOMPSON, JAMES.—" Im-
" provements in apparatus for discharging condensed water, air,
" or other fluids from steam pipes, drying cylinders, and other
" apparatus where steam is used."

At any part of the steam pipe near its outlet or between the ends of the steam and outlet pipes is placed a tap or cock, to the plug of which is attached a toothed pinion or wheel. The pipe or pipes work within guides, so that with the tap they can move to and fro according to their expansion and contraction from the change of temperature. The pinion on the plug of the tap gears into a stationary rack, thereby giving a rotary or turning motion to the pinion and plug as the pipe or pipes move to and fro by means of expansion and contraction, which rotary or turning motion opens or closes either partially or entirely the apertures of the plug, either discharging the condensed water or closing the aperture against the escape of steam as may be required, the length of expansion and contraction of the pipes depending upon their length, and consequently giving a corresponding effect to the plug of the tap. If it be more than sufficient to close and open the aperture, the pinion will disengage itself from the rack and allow the contraction to go on without closing the aperture. Instead of a tap a slide surface or mushroom valve can be used, acted upon either by a lever or inclined plane as a substitute for the rack, or one cylinder sliding on the inside of another, the outer cylinder having an aperture at right angles with the axes of the apparatus, and the inner one sliding to and fro over the aperture.

[Printed, 10*d*. Drawings.]

A.D. 1857, September 22.—N° 2453.

THEILER, MEINRAD.—(Communicated by Franz Theiler, of Einsiedeln, in Switzerland)—" A direct printing telegraph without " relais and local battery."

" In this, as in Morse's apparatus, a strip or tape of paper is put " forward in a slow and regular motion by means of a series of " wheels actuated by weights or springs. On this strip or tape " of paper are imprinted with a needle the despatches in points " and lines, whereby the writing lever is set in motion by an " electro-magnet. Now this invention relates to an improved " arrangement by which the writing lever is acted upon by " mechanical power of the wheelwork, and consists in the appli- " cation of a mechanical resistance to a wheel, lever, or other part " of the mechanism moving at a sufficient velocity. This resist- " ance, which may be modified or reduced in its strength according " to circumstances, causes the axle of a wheel or lever which is

" fitted in the writing lever to make a particular movement in the
" direction of the writing lever besides the general one round its
" axis. The establishing, modifying, or breaking off of this
" mechanical resistance is effected by one or more electro-magnets,
" which are effected through the direct current of the line, without
" having recourse to a local battery."

[Printed, 1s. Drawings.]

## A.D. 1857, September 23.—N° 2465.

FONTAINE MOREAU, Peter Armand le Comte de.—
(Provisional Protection only.)—(Communicated.)—" An improved
" method of marking paper for postal purposes."

"The invention consists in the application of a stamp or mark
" to every sheet of letter or other paper, whether written or printed,
" so that every such sheet of paper, envelope, or wrapper will
" indicate the weight of postage, and thus save much trouble,
" and the doubt as to postage dues on the transmission of letters
" to any country. The stamp or mark can be affixed either on
" each sheet of paper separately, or upon the envelopes of packets
" containing sheets of paper, the marks on such envelopes
" denoting the different weight of the sheets contained therein."

[Printed, 3d. No Drawing.]

## A.D. 1857, September 25.—N° 2474.

BARBER, John.—" Improvements in machinery or apparatus
" for manufacturing rollers or cylinders used for printing and
" embossing woven fabrics, paper, leather, and other materials."

The rollers or cylinders are made of two separate tubes, the
inner one of iron or " other suitable metal," the outer one of
copper or other metal, " similar to those now in general use.
The invention relates to former Patents (N° 511 of 1857 and
N° 2175 of 1856), and consists, first, in an expanding cutter for
boring the roller or cylinder, so as to leave the end bearing the
required form. Secondly, in a compound boring head for holding
two or more cutters for boring " seven-eighths " or " nine-
" eighths " rollers. Thirdly, in machinery for making these
cutters. Fourthly, in the construction of a compound boring
maundril and head for boring large cylinders. Fifthly, in
machinery for putting iron or other metal or composition tubes
into the copper rollers, by means of contraction and expansion,

and the employment of water or other fluid for the purpose of keeping the inner tube cool, and preventing expansion of metal. Sixthly, in cutting the grooves of iron or other cylinders square or dovetailed. Seventhly, in cutting the same in waves. Eighthly, in making the same equidistant, similar to right and left hand screws. Ninthly, in the use of short tubes to support the ends of the rollers; and Tenthly, in the general arrangement of the machinery employed for manufacturing the said rollers.

[Printed, 4s. 2d. Drawings.]

### A.D. 1857, October 1.—N° 2523.

NAPIER, JAMES MURDOCH.—" Improvements in printing " machines."

The invention relates to machines for printing from type or other raised surfaces in which platens are used to obtain the impressions, and is " peculiarly applicable to machines in which " the type tables have horizontal motion." The improvements consist in the arrangement of knuckle joints actuated by a crank or excentric action, by means of which the necessary rising and falling motion is imparted to the platen, and the friction and torsional strain common to the machines " now in use " are very much reduced. The platen is counterbalanced by a weight below the table.

[Printed, 1s. 10d. Drawings.]

### A.D. 1857, October 6.—N° 2565.

APPLEGATH, AUGUSTUS.—" Improvements in printing ma- " chines."

The invention consists in arranging the whole of the form on one printing cylinder in such a way that every side of each column is as accessible as it was when arranged on two. For this purpose the form is separated into two parts, as before, and placed one after the other on one cylinder, so as to be at a third of its circumference apart. The other third of its surface is used as a distributing surface. In contact with the type cylinder a series of printing cylinders revolve, each one-third of the diameter of the type cylinder. On to these cylinders the paper is fed, and has to remain while its cylinder makes two revolutions before the impression is complete. The paper is held to the cylinder by clamps instead of tapes.

[Printed, 1s. 6d. Drawings.]

### A.D. 1857, October 14.—N° 2626.

**JOHNSON, John Henry.**—(Communicated by Leon Louis Honoré Berton, of the firm of Berton and Pottier, Paris.)—" Im-" provements in producing figured paper to be used in teaching " writing and drawing.

The invention relates to a system of producing letters, figures, devices, or designs to be used as a means of conveying elementary instruction in writing or drawing, and consists in placing the paper to be operated upon with its face upon a zinc plate, such plate having the described letters, figures, devices, or designs engraved thereon, either in relief or intaglio. A second metal plate, having a smooth surface, is then placed upon the back of the paper, and the whole is passed through a press. The paper on being removed will be found to bear upon its surface an exact copy of the device engraved upon the plate. The mode of using these prepared sheets of paper consists in simply tracing or following the lines or marks of the design or device with a lead pencil or other marking instrument.

[Printed, 3d. No Drawing.]

### A.D. 1857, October 18.—N° 2654.

**CHADWICK, James.**—(Provisional Protection only.)—" Im-" provements in rollers or cylinders for printing or staining the " surfaces of woven fabrics, yarns, paper, and other materials."

The invention consists in etching or engraving the relieved parts in lines or cells, " as with ordinary engraved printing " rollers," so that the lines or cells will carry more color than felt or other absorbent substances, besides giving finer impressions. Secondly, the roller engraved or etched, and polished as for ordinary printing, is put into a solution of copper, lead, tin, or other suitable material, and electroplated.

[Printed, 3d. No Drawings.]

### A.D. 1857, October 23.—N° 2703.

**HARRILD, Robert, and HARRILD, Horton.**—"An im-" provement in the manufacture of the composition used for " printers' rollers."

The invention consists " in reducing the glue to a proper state " for combining with molasses and the other ingredients usually

" employed in the manufacture of the printers' rollers composition
" by the application of high-pressure steam instead of by soaking
" it in water." The water into which the steam condenses will,
after the operation is conducted in a close vessel, be "apparent,
" floating on the surface of and unmixed with the glue," and may
be drawn off by any suitable means, leaving the glue ready for the
manufacture of the rollers, as "now ordinarily practised."

[Printed, 3d. No Drawing.]

A.D. 1857, October 30.—N° 2754.

EVANS, JOHN.—(Provisional Protection only.)—" Certain im-
" provements in the method or methods of affixing or securing
" patterns and designs upon rollers and blocks used for imprint-
" ing on paper and other substances."

The invention consists in enveloping the roller with felt or other
substance to the eighth of an inch in thickness, driving the metal
through the felt into the wood below, and then, by clearing away
the superfluous felt or substance, leaving the figure in relief
already fitted in, "thus securing accuracy of fitting and saving a
" great amount of labour and time."

[Printed, 3d. No Drawing.]

A.D. 1857, October 30.—N° 2758.

SHIELDS, WILLIAM.—" Improvements in machinery or appa-
" ratus for etching, engraving, and cutting cylinders and other
" surfaces to be used in printing and embossing."

The invention refers to machines in which the motion of a tracer
is copied by an etching or cutting tool, and consists, first, in a
method of varying the dimensions of the copied design in proportion to those of the original. For this purpose the tracing instruments communicate motion to the tool through the intervention
of inclined planes, the inclination of which determines the proportion. A similar apparatus is employed for communicating motion
to the cylinder or other surface to be operated upon. Secondly,
the invention consists in the application to machines of the above-
mentioned class of revolving tools, which, as they copy the design,
may by such revolutions be caused to cut or drill into the material in order to produce raised or deeply sunk surfaces for printing
and embossing.

[Printed, 1s. 9d. Drawings.]

## A.D. 1857, November 10.—N° 2840.

**PARKES, Alexander.**—"Improvements in the manufacture of " tubes and cylinders of alloy and copper."

For these purposes, when using ingots or masses cast hollow in place of casting the same in close moulds, " they are cast in " like manner to that practised when casting ingots, that is, in " open moulds, so that the metal ' poured into the mould is " uncovered on its upper surface." The mould is rectangular, and its ends are so constructed as to support a core by its two ends in such a position that when the melted metal is poured into the mould the metal may, when the mould is filled to the desired extent, be as thick above as below the core. Or the ingots or masses are cast solid, and a hole drilled, and a saw cut made through each. They are then rolled out, and " extended or opened as heretofore." The casting of such hollow ingots or masses is stated to be " greatly improved by employing " reducing alkaline fluxes when melting copper, or copper and its " alloys, preparatory to casting the same into hollow ingots or " masses suitable for making cylinders or tubes." When using sheet copper for making cylinders or tubes for printers, silver or silver solder is employed for joining the edges. Instead of using the ordinary draw plates or dies for extending hollow masses or ingots of copper or alloys of copper, dies or plates having an inclined screw thread on the interior are used, such die or plate revolving as the tube or cylinder is passed through it.

[Printed, 4d. No Drawing.]

## A.D. 1857, November 16.—N° 2872.

**DEBAX, Talabas Casimir.**—(Provisional Protection only.)— " Improvements in lithographic printing presses."

The invention is intended to increase the performance of the machine about one-third without entailing extra labor on the workman, and consists in reducing the number of motions necessary for printing. With the press " in actual use," these motions are said to be, 1, lowering the moveable frame over the sheet; 2, lowering the squeezing bar-holder (porte-rateau); 3, bearing upon the foot-board; 4, driving the hand windlass; 5, unhooking the moveable frame; 6, raising up the same; and, 7, raising up the squeezing bar-holder. By these improvements the following movements only are required : First, when bearing upon the foot-board, the moveable frame and squeezing bar are both lowered at once; secondly, when driving the hand windlass the moveable frame is unhooked at the moment when the stone carriage reaches the end of its useful motion; and, thirdly, when the foot is lifted from the foot-board, the squeezing bar and moveable frame are raised up at once by the action of a counterpoise fixed upon a transverse lever under the main frame of the press.

[Printed, 6d. Drawings.]

## A.D. 1857, November 18.—N° 2894.

CLEGG, ROBERT.—" Improvements in registering or indicating " apparatus applicable to the registration or indication of fares, " the distances passed over by vehicles, the revolutions of " machines or parts of machines, and other similar purposes."

A pin or stud upon the axle or other rotating part of a machine acts upon a lever attached to some fixed part of it, and thereby gives motion to a ratchet wheel, which, by means of other wheels, transmits intermittent motion to a hand on a dial plate. The lever recovers itself by a spring.

[Printed, 10d. Drawings.]

## A.D. 1857, December 10.—N° 3052.

BEST, ISAAC ARROWSMITH.—(Provisional Protection only.)—" A new or improved mode of manufacturing printing types."

The invention consists in forming the type of two parts; one of copper, brass, or other suitable metal; the other of ordinary type metal. The heads of the types are made by electro deposition of copper, &c. in suitable moulds. The superfluous metal is then clipped away with clipping tools and press; the deposited portion, thus finished, is placed in the matrix, and the common type metal portions cast upon it, the latter becoming firmly united to it by the rough interior of the deposited portion of the body."

[Printed, 3d. No Drawings.]

## A.D. 1857, December 12.—N° 3063.

PULS, FRANCIS.—(Provisional Protection only.)—" A new com-" bination of mineral substances for the production of artificial " stone."

The artificial stone to be employed in the manufacture of grind-stones, whetstones, oilstone, hones, or the like, as also of lithographic stones and stones for ornamental purposes, and as a substitute for meerschaum, consists of a combination of powdered emery, flint-glass, ruby, diamond, melted alumina, oxide of iron, or similar hard mineral substances, with proportionate quantities of lime, barytes, plaster of Paris or chalk, and silicate of potash or soda, or potash and soda powdered in solution, or in a semi-fluid state. " For production of stone for lithographic or ornamental pur-" poses, I combine lime or chalk powder with silicate of potash " or soda, or otherwise, as aforesaid, to which colouring matter " may be added as required; and for meerschaum, I mix " carbonate of magnesia or oxide of magnesia, or a mixture of " both, with silicitate of potash, soda, or otherwise, as above, to " which may be added small proportions of slacked lime, chalk, or " clay. Either of the above compositions may be pressed into " moulds either warm or cold, to give it the required shape and " render it close and compact."

[Printed, 3d. No Drawings.]

### A.D. 1857, December 15.—No 3076.

SMITH, WILLIAM. — (Communicated by A. E. Rochette.)— " Improvements in chromo-typographical printing presses."

The Drawings annexed to the Specification show the improvements specified in No 1670 of 1857 for hand printing presses, as applied to presses driven by steam or other power. Pressure is applied by a counterpoise platen, actuated by two excentrics. The table is driven to and fro by a crank and connecting rod, " as in " ordinary presses," one direction for inking the form and in the other for receiving the pressure. The sheet, taken from a pile above the platen, is held by clasps upon a frisket frame, which after each impression retires in an opposite direction to the form, and while the latter is being inked turns upon its centre one-quarter of a revolution, and is released after the impression from the claws or nippers which hold it, and which are attached to the frame. The frame is included within a toothed ring or wheel, which is actuated by a rack driven by a toothed segment, which segment causes the circle to rotate a quarter of a revolution, whilst in its back motion the rack does not gear with the wheel. The table is divided into as many compartments as there are colors, and the inking rollers (placed in comb-shaped stands) ink only when passing over their own compartments, being at other times raised by double crescent-shaped lifts. The ink is spread on the rollers by circular or cylindrical tables and inkholders, each of which contain two colors.

[Printed, 1s. 10d. Drawings.]

A.D. 1857, December 15.—N° 3079.

CHADWICK, James.—"Improvements in rollers or cylinders " for printing or staining the surfaces of woven fabrics, yarns, " paper, and other materials."

The invention, which is an improvement on N° 2654 of 1857, consists in improved modes of employing the metal types "at " present used in block or surface roller printing, which types " have been hitherto nailed or otherwise fastened to wooden " blocks or wooden surface rollers." The types are screwed, soldered, or cemented to metal rollers. To arrange them with perfect accuracy and in register, a machine is made use of which has four steps so adjusted that two rollers, placed thereon, shall be perfectly parallel. It is also fitted with a slide, moving longitudinally, and furnished with adjustable points placed over the centres or other desired portions of the rollers, so that a perfectly parallel line can be made on each roller at the same time, and also various points or positions determined parallel to each other, whereby the types can be accurately placed on the roller, and other measuring, setting, and adjusting operations performed.

[Printed, 7d. Drawings.]

A.D. 1857, December 15.—N° 3085.

EVERITT, George Allen,—"Improvements in the manufac- " ture of tubes or cylinders of copper or alloys of copper."

The improvements relate, first, to casting of cylinders of copper or alloys of copper under pressure. Cores of any suitable description are employed, the moulds or ingots being somewhat similar "to those now in use," but having, when ready to receive the molten metal, a larger sectional area than that of the tube required to be produced. For this purpose, between the edges of the several parts of the mould, spaces or grooves are left to be filled with sand or other compressible material which will act as a cushion in preventing immediate contact of the edges of the mould. Directly the tube or cylinder has been cast, pressure is applied to the outside of the mould, closing its parts together. The sand is thus forced out, and the sectional area of the mould being thereby reduced, great compression of the molten metal takes place and a sound cylinder is produced. The cushions or fillets of sand may, if requisite, be pierced with small apertures to enable the air to escape more freely. Secondly, to the alloying of copper for subsequent manufacture into cylinders. The alloy consists of about eight parts of copper to one part of good yellow brass. The cylinder, thus produced is of the color of copper and free from the flaws or air holes to which tubes of pure copper are liable. It is afterwards drawn down as a solid or unbrazed tube. Thirdly, the invention consists in cleansing or pickling such cylinders prior to the first operation of drawing, and also prior to every other drawing operation, except the last, by immersing them in a solution of soft soap and water and applying the same solution to the outside of the tube whilst it is being passed through the dies.

[Printed, 3d. No Drawing.]

## A.D. 1857, December 17.—N° 3098.

DAVIS, John James.—" Improvements in presses for printing " and endorsing or embossing."

The lever of this press is mounted on an arbor carrying a double cam. On being moved in one direction, one cam acts on the slide carrying the die or printing surface, causing it to descend and emboss or print, and on being moved in the opposite direction the other cam is brought into action, by which means the die is also made to descend, but at the same time the shaft on which the pressure pad is fixed turns so as to present a color pad to the die. The slide and shaft recover their original positions by means of springs.

[Printed, 10d. Drawings.]

## A.D. 1857, December 17.—N° 3099.

MASON, Mark, and MARKLAND, Thomas.—(Provisional Protection only.)—" Improvements in machinery or apparatus for " printing."

The invention relates to railway tickets, postage stamps, cards, and small devices on paper, leather, &c., and consists of a roller partly covered with caoutchouc or other elastic material, and turned by an endless band or chain. Over this roller is a cylinder containing the type or device, another containing the necessary inking apparatus, and above that a vessel formed so as to constitute a self-acting feeder to supply the ink.

[Printed, 3d. No Drawing.]

## A.D. 1857, December 18.—N° 3113.

NAPIER, James Murdoch.—" Improvements in letter-press " printing machines."

The invention consists in the use of two or more friskets, with each form in platen machines, the friskets acting alternately so as to give more time to the layers on, and increase the productiveness of the machine. The form passes twice under inking rollers for each impression. Where still greater productiveness is required rising and falling platens are used, there being two friskets to each platen, and the form travelling backwards and forwards from one platen to the other. "When two colors are required to be printed in register
" upon the same side of the same sheet of paper, I employ a ma-
" chine somewhat similar in general principles of arrangement to
" that which is now in common use for printing from two separate
" forms of matter with one platen, in which the forms of matter
" pass alternately under the platten, each delivering its impress to
" a separate sheet of paper; but instead of using two complete
" forms of matter, and feeding a sheet of paper for every impres-
" sion given by the machine, I place the two forms of matter
" which are to be inked with different colors in the same relative
" positions as two ordinary forms might be placed in, and I
" arrange that part of the machinery which supplies the sheets in
" such a manner that each sheet is caused to remain under the
" platten until it has received two impressions, one from each form
" of matter. The sheet then printed with two colors retires from
" under the platten, and makes room for the next incoming sheet."
If more than two colors are to be printed register points should be used. The above machine may also be used for ordinary one-color work by slight modification in detail. "The ordinary worm-barrel
" movement may be used for actuating the travelling tables of the
" various modifications of platten machinery above described, the

" form of the worm being modified and suited in each case so as
" to give the proper times of rest and motion. The plattens may
" be actuated in their rising and falling motions by any of the
" known methods, but I prefer to employ an arrangement in which
" knuckle joints are used, as described in the Provisional Specifica-
" tion of my Patent, dated the 19th day of August 1857." (a)

[Printed, 2s. 8d. Drawings.]

A.D. 1857, December 19.—Nº 3118.

FURNIVAL, RICHARD.—" Certain machinery or apparatus for
" cutting paper, cardboard, and other similar articles."

The invention consists in cutting through a pile or thickness of
paper or other substance with an easy and clean cut, by imparting
to a knife or blade a reciprocating lateral direction across the pile
simultaneously with its descent through such pile. This is effected
by a vertical excentric or vertical heart-shaped shaft or other
equivalent connected with the knife, " connected with and actuated
" by the shaft employed to cause the descent of the knife through
" the paper or other material."

[Printed, 9d. Drawings.]

---

(a) 1st October 1857, supra (?), No. 2523.

# APPENDIX.

A.D. 1844, October 3.—N° 10,338.

NEWTON, William.—(Communicated.)—" Improvements in " machinery for letter-press printing."

The invention consists of a rotary press, in which a horizontal centre axle with carrier arms supports several (in the drawings, six) pressing cylinders, furnished with clips. The form of types is flat, and is placed horizontally at the lower part of the press, its surface forming a chord to the circular path of the outer surface of the pressing cylinders. The carrier arms are peculiarly fitted so as to admit of the axles of the pressing cylinders adapting themselves to the position in which they are required to pass over the form. Four feeding tables are shown. The sheet is laid on either of them, with its edge against a hook-formed stop, and as one of the pressing cylinders comes round peculiar arrangements cause the feed table to be slightly raised, and a further contrivance, consisting of a sliding horse-shoe piece and certain cams or guides, causes the spring clips on the cylinder to open and seize on the sheet, which is by the further rotation of the cylinder wound round it, and thus carried to the impression. After the impression the clips open and the sheet is drawn off by a second set of clips, mounted on horizontal bars, which are jointed to two rocking lever arms, a current of air being at the same time directed against the sheet. The sheets are thus suffered to fall severally upon a fly-board, so contrived as to sink gradually as the pile of printed matter grows. The sheets are secured on the fly-board by spring holders, which turn sideways previous to each deposit. The ink trough is at the bottom of the press. A ductor roller having taken from it its supply, communicates it by means of certain intervening rollers to a distributing drum, from which it is furnished to several sets of inking rollers, which, by means of endless chains, pass (alternating with the pressing cylinders) over the form.

[Printed, 2s. 2d. Drawings.]

A.D. 1852, November 19.—N° 793.

JOHNSON, John Robert. — " Improvements in the manu-
" facture of type or raised surfaces for printing."

The invention consists in the use of zinc and the alloys of
zinc more fusible than that metal for casting type and other
raised printing surfaces. For type of great hardness, 33 parts of
zinc are added to 59 of tin, and used either alone or combined
with from two to five per cent. in weight of antimony. For
type of inferior hardness, this alloy is mixed with ordinary type
metal, in proportions varying with the hardness required. Zinc
redistilled, or otherwise purified, zinc and lead, zinc and tin (in
other proportions than above), zinc, lead. and antimony, zinc, tin,
and antimony, zinc, tin, and lead, and zinc, lead, tin, and antimony, may also be used for the same purpose. When zinc alone
is used, or such a proportion of zinc as to raise the melting point
considerably above that of the ordinary type metal, the jet or
break of the mould is made of earthenware, or if of metal is
covered with white-lead ground in drying oil or putty to render
it imperfectly conducting. The surface of the fused metal is, to
prevent oxidation, covered with sheet iron, having an aperture for
admission of the ladle. Oxidation of the type from the use of
the cleansing ley is stated not to occur when the alloy of zinc
does not exceed ten per cent. of the whole, and may be altogether
avoided by the use of soft (potash) soap.

Raised printing surfaces may be also formed of the alloys of
zinc by the cliché or "dabbing" process "by adopting the well-
" known apparatus and manipulations at present employed," and
the alloy of zinc first described.

Printing surfaces may also be formed by stereotyping with the
ordinary alloy of lead and antimony, with the addition of five to
ten per cent. of the alloy of zinc and tin first described.

[Printed, 3½d. No Drawing.]

# INDEX OF SUBJECT MATTER.

The Numbers refer to the page in which the notice of the subject referred to commences.

# INDEX OF SUBJECT MATTER.

Dies :
Clayton, 136.
Mabley, 224.
Wilkinson, 410.
Johnson, J. H., 506, 507.
Printing lozenges with ;
Derriey, 580.

Discharging printed sheet :
Church, 160.
Bold, 161.
Parkin, 171.
Church, 174.
Smith, A., 195.
Archer, 445.
Newton, 591.

Distributing :
Ink ;
Schnebly, 253.
Rose, 299.
Machine (type) ;
Gaubert, 215.
Clay and Rosenborg, 233.
Beniowski, 265.
Mitchel, 360, 453, 573.
Boulé and Caillaud, 366.
Poole, 382.
Delcambre, 397, 557.
Simencourt, 412.
Wiberg, 444.
Coulon, 528.
Newton, W. E., 545.
Alden, 579.
Hattersley, 593.

Dividing printed sheet :
Hansard (Serrated tympan), 137.

" Doctor "
Grinding and setting ;
Sington, 379.
Whetting and setting ;
Hudson, 551.
Jones (Paperhangings), 498
Of increased width ;
McNicol, 508.
With flat plates ;
Illingworth, 524, 534.
Applied to the bowl ;
Leese, 545.

Donatus, 14.

Double cloth :
Printing on ;
Lord, 435.

Drawing :
Mechanical mode of perspective ;
Worcester, Marquis of, 19.

Drying :
Fabrics ;
Bourlier, 237.
Smith, L. and M., 317.
Johnson, W., 447.
Burton and Lord, 584.
Cylinders, discharge of water from ;
Thompson, 599.

Dunging :
Chemical substitutes for ;
Higgin, 360.

Duplex machine :
Rose, 299.
McNaughton, 358.

Early Printers :
Protective policy as to, 37.

Earthenware :
Printing on ;
See China, glass, &c.

Elastic :
Tympans ;
Lewis, 257.
Fabrics, printing ;
Ball, 435.

Electro printing :
Wright and Bain, 231.
Bain, 242.
Brett, 259.
Mapple, 384.
Johnson, J. H., 432, 522, 561.
Whitehouse, 438.
Varley, 491.
Humaston, 511.
Fontaine Moreau, 529.
Theiler, 600.

Electrotype (and see Printing Surfaces, metal (electro-deposited) ;
Mabley, 223.
Palmer, E., 229, 231.
Morse, 283.
Johnson, J. H. (Underwood), 402.
    (Besley), 506.
Wilkinson, 410.
Perkins, 423.
Pretsch, 464, 497.
Newton, A. V., 508
———, W. E. 565, 504.
Bergner, 515.
Schaub, 583.
Chadwick, 603.

Embossing :
Perkins, 144.
Mabley, 223.
Palmer, E., 229, 231.
Knight, H., 296.

R R

SUPPLEMENT

# SUPPLEMENT.

PAYNE, DANIEL BEAUMONT.—"Method for more accurately
" and expeditiously expressing and ascertaining the numbers,
" dates, and sums, in bank bills, notes, and other securities
" for money, and preventing forgeries, frauds, and losses by
" defacing or altering the same."

Characters, consisting some of a single curved line, others of
two or of three curved lines united, others of curved or of
straight lines united so as to form figures, are " separately cast
" by a letter founder." The characters of the same description are "longitudinally cemented with soft solder until they
" form continued lines of characters of the same denomination
" proportioned in extent to the general length of bills, notes,"
&c. Among the characters and "equidistant from the extremes
" of each type line," are cemented " the old numerical figures
" of the same signification as the said characters." When the
lines of characters are arranged close one above another, the
lowest line represents units, the one next above it tens, and so
on, "repeated as many times as there are characters and
" figures in each horizontal line." In addition to the common
mode of dating bills, &c., the date may be "composed in hori-
" zontal lines of the aforesaid characters." Usually ten bills,
&c. "numbered in regular arithmetical series," are set up in
one chase, "and as many impressions taken off as may be
" required." The numbers on the form will of course require
alteration after each series of impressions.

[Printed, 6d. Drawing.]

A.D. 1810, July 18.—No. 3362.

WEDGWOOD, RALPH.—"A new character for language,
" numbers, and music, and the methods of applying the
" same."

This invention consists in the use of characters, notes, and
types, different from those hitherto employed.

"The architype of the character may be of any regular
"figure," the patentee preferring a square. "The different
"parts of this square figure are made to signify all the various
"letters of the alphabet, figures, notes, and points." This is
effected in printing "by making three types," one of which
will make "a line equal to the whole side of the square figure,"
the second "a line equal to one half" of the side of the square
(this type is distinguished by adding a point to it), and the
third a line "equal to half the length of the side of the said
"square." To multiply the power of each type, both ends
"make a similar figure, distinguishing the one end by causing
"it to make a double line thus ══, by which it may signify
"a capital letter of the same kind as that described at the
"other end." One end of each type is also distinguished "by
"adding a beard or hair-line thereto," or by an extra breadth.
The shank of each type "forms one half part of a square,"
so that two of them united make "a compound square
"type capable of being used at both ends." From a combination of any two of these three types there result "eight dis-
"tinct marks or letters," from which are selected such as "are
"best calculated to signify letters, notes, figures, or points."
The ends of the types are "wedge-like in every direction," and
can be securely locked in "the line frame." The lines are
made fast in the page frame by screws, and the page frames
are fastened on the bed of the printing press.

To understand this invention, the reader must consult the
drawing annexed to the Specification.

The part relating to musical notes is described in the series
entitled "Music and musical instruments."

[Printed, 1s. 4d. Drawing.]

A.D. 1811, April 27.—No. 3439.

CASLON, WILLIAM, the younger.—"Improvement in the
"register belonging to a mould for casting types."

[No Specification enrolled.]

A.D. 1820, October 20.—No. 4500.

GILMOUR, JAMES RICHARD, and BOLD, JOHN.—"Improve-
"ments on printing presses."

[No Specification enrolled.]

A.D. 1822, December 10.—No 4731.

ROBSON, WILLIAM.—" A method to prevent or protect against
" fraudulent practices upon bankers' checks, bills of exchange,
" and various species of mercantile, commercial, and other
" correspondence."

The method proposed is either "the application of any suit-
" able vegetable colour or colours upon one or both sides of
" the paper," the colour being applied "by ruling any appro-
" priate lines " with a pen or ruling machine ; or the printing
on the paper any device with a mixture of "any proper vege-
" table colour or colours with any suitable vehicle," to give
the colour sufficient viscidity to be used as a printing ink.

The prepared paper is to be written on with common writing
ink ; any attempt to remove the writing with acid or other
chemical means "will produce such a change in the vegetable
" colour as to prove by mere inspection that a fraud has been
" attempted."

The patentee prefers the use of "saffron, Brazilwood, log-
" wood, and turmeric," adding that "any of the vegetable
" colours commonly used as chemical tests will produce the
" same advantageous effects."

[Printed, 9d. Drawing.]


A.D. 1825, June 21.—No. 5195.

BROOKES, PHILIP.—"An improvement in the preparation of
" a certain composition, and the application thereof to the
" making of dies, moulds, or matrixes, smooth surfaces, and
" various other useful articles."

The composition consists of a "combination of siliceous,
" argillaceous, calcareous, vitrescent, and barytic earths, or
" other natural earthy compounds ; " it is made into dies, and
these after undergoing "a certain degree of vitrification by
" heat," are applicable "for the purpose of embossing by
" stamping or otherwise."

The composition is made also into "tabular plates with
" smooth surfaces," and these after a similar vitrification are
" applied for the purpose of drawing, writing, printing, and
" painting upon."

[Printed, 3d. No Drawings.]

A.D. 1834, November 15.—No. 6716.

GILES, EDWARD GALLEY.—"Improvements on apparatus for
" engraving on copper and certain other substances."

By means of the following two improvements on the ordinary
pantograph the operator has "the power of reversing the
" subject to be engraved, whether reduced or of the same size
" as the original, on a plane or level surface, and without
" inverting the copper plate or other substance engraved
" upon."

The first improvement is the addition to "the principal
" centre round which the instrument turns" of a leaden
weight provided with "points which fix the lead firmly to the
" table." The inner end of the weight may be raised or
lowered by means of a screw.

The second consists of the addition to the pantograph of
four hollow bars of equal size, joined at their extremities by
centres, and forming a parallelogram in whatever position
they are placed. "Beneath two of the opposite centres" are
pulleys "respectively formed with an angular groove" which
rolls on a semicircular bar. The pulleys are prevented from
sliding off the bar by means of a circular leaden weight carried
by a plate above each of them, and when they are adjusted
by screws, &c. they are prevented "from having any motion
" endways." One of the other centres "receives the tube in
" which the point that traces the outlines of the subject
" slides;" the other connects this apparatus to the pantograph
by means of a steel pin.

Both parts of the apparatus are used "to engrave the subject
" smaller than the original;" the second part alone to engrave
the subject "the same size as the original."

"The instrument is supported by friction rollers or castors."

[Printed, 7d. Drawing.]

A.D. 1835, January 17.—No. 6747.

HOUSTOUN, WILLIAM.—"Improvements in type-founding."

[No Specification enrolled.]

A.D. 1835, May 13.—No. 6830.

VALOIS, ALPHONSE HUMBERT JEAN FRANÇOIS.—"Improve-
" ments in the mode or method of producing engravings,

" etchings, or reliefs on metallic plates, for producing im-
" pressions therefrom, and in the apparatus used in the
" same."

The metallic plates are obtained "by casting or pouring
" fluid metal of suitable qualities" on to "an original or
" model carving, engraving, or etching, produced in plaster"
or similar substance. The castings are afterwards "dressed
" and finished, ready to be used for producing imprints or
" impressions."

Duplicates in metal of these plates are obtained by taking
impressions from them in plaster, "which after being dried
" form the mould or matrix to produce other metal plates"
by casting, &c. as before stated.

To obtain metallic plates "with sunken or depressed figures
" or designs thereon," a plate of fine plaster (in a suitable
frame) is covered with a composition of pure wax and hard
resin ; the composition is absorbed by the plaster; the surface made perfectly smooth is then ready to be worked on
with the etching or tracing point or graver ; when the design
is completed, a rag steeped in a mixture of oil and alcohol is
passed over the surface, the mixture "being allowed to
" penetrate into all the lines" of the design ; a second frame
is placed over the first ; fluid plaster is poured upon the
plaster design, and thus "a plaster cast is taken in relief of
" the lines of the pattern or drawing." This cast forms the
mould for producing the plate required.

The apparatus used by the patentee for producing the
design "on the original plaster" is composed of (1) four bars
pinjointed so as to form a parallelogram ; (2) a small pulley
on each pin ; (3) a cord passed round the four pulleys; (4) a
larger pulley mounted on one of the pins or spindles, which
pin or spindle is actuated "by a train of wheelwork" or other
contrivance ; (5) a drill placed in the hollow spindle which
forms the pin joint opposite to the last-mentioned one ; and (6)
a handle to guide the drill as required. The patentee remarks
that it "is not absolutely necessary to use this apparatus."

[Printed, 8d. Drawing.]

A.D. 1835, October 15. —No. 6906.

BIRD, JOHN.—"An improved method of making and com-
" pounding printers' ink, paints, and other pigments."

The base of this ink is a mineral earth "found in great
" abundance " on the patentee's estate in North Wales ; it is
composed of about " silicia, forty-six ; alumina, forty-two ; and
" coaly matter, twelve." The earth is washed clean from "slate
" or other debris," when it "becomes a very fine black
" impalpable powder if dried, or a very fine paste if wet."

Printers' ink is made by grinding up as large a quantity of
the prepared earth as is considered necessary "with boiled oil
" or prepared oil usually used in the making of inks."

To make ink used in copper plate printing, the patentee
adopts "the method now in use," substituting the prepared
earth for "Francfort black or what is usually designated by
" that name."

[Printed, 3d. No Drawings.]

## A.D. 1837, November 7.—No. 7462.

AULAS, CHARLES FRANÇOIS EDWARD. — "Improvements in
" preparing writing paper so as to prevent the discharge of
" the ink therefrom without detection and to prevent the
" falsification of writing thereon."

The paper is covered with "an engraved or printed design
" composed of minute figures perfectly identical and capable
" of being on near inspection compared with one another, yet
" so minute and systematically arranged as to give at a
" distance only one uniform tint to the whole surface." With
this design there is blended or united, "by engraving on the
" same plate or cylinder, another design of a bolder character,
" presenting so many points of intersection with the original
" design as to render an accurate imitation almost if not
" absolutely impossible."

When the design is applied to paper "intended for ordinary
" writing," it is printed with "a delible colour which would
" disappear under the action of any chemical agents which
" may be used to take out the common writing ink." When
the only object is "to prevent the counterfeiting of certain
" printed instruments," the design may be printed with
" indelible ink." For delible ink the patentee prefers a
mixture of "pyrolignite of iron and gum dragacanth," but the
paper ought previously to have had "an infusion of nut
" galls " introduced into its texture.

The impression of the combined designs may be "in the

" interior" instead of on the surface of the paper ; for this purpose the paper is composed of two thin leaves which are united after the impression has been made "upon the interior " surface " of one of the leaves.

The patentee describes (but does not claim) the process of engraving the plates or cylinders.

[Printed, 4d. No Drawings.]

A.D. 1838, January 25.—No. 7552.

HANCOCK, CHARLES. — "Improved means of producing " figured surfaces, sunk and in relief, and of printing there- " from, and also of moulding, stamping, and embossing."

The patentee describes eleven methods with modifications of some of them.

1. He roughens the surface of a metallic plate, transfers on to it "the outline of the subject," and then removes "the " superfluous parts of the surface so as to obtain the required " forms and variations of light and shade." To print from this plate, he cements the edges of a sheet of india-rubber to a piece of stout canvas, fixes the canvas in the tympan frame ("dispensing wholly with the blanket"), and interposes a sheet of very thin paper between the paper to be printed on and the india-rubber.

2. "To produce certain parts of a subject in high or bold " relief," he cuts out separate pieces of metal of the shape of those parts and solders or cements them "in their proper " places to the principal plate."

3. He prepares a plate "with an ordinary etching ground," lays over this ground a "fabric of such a texture as will by " pressure break up uniformly the whole surface of the etch- " ing ground into minute particles,".and transfers the subject " in the usual way" to the ground so obtained.

4. He covers the surface of the plate with a solution of india-rubber "mixed with etching ground diluted to a suitable con- " sistence," removes all the parts which are not intended to be in relief, and immerses the plate with its face downwards into " acid liquor" which he allows "to operate until the desired " effect is obtained."

5. He covers the surface of the plate with a " composition " that will mix with water," draws in the subject "through

" the composition down to the surface of the metal," fills up
the incisions and spaces so made with a "composition in-
" soluble by acid," and when the whole is hard submits the
plate " to the action of acid."

6. " For obtaining a very bold relief " he uses (by preference)
lithographic stones, and the acid used is " the nitric diluted."
He takes "sunk impressions from them in plaster," and then
casts in relief from the plaster moulds in stereotype metal. He
deepens "the spaces between the lines " by "cutting with a
" graver."

7. He draws on a metallic plate with water colour, treacle,
or material which dilute acids will act on, brushes the surface
with a resinous varnish or wax, plunges the plate into hot
water "to soften and loosen the treacle, &c.," and afterwards
applies "the diluted acid in the ordinary way."

8. To "produce figured surfaces, sunk and in relief, upon
" thin plates " of ductile metal, he smooths the surface,
indents thereon the subject with a hard point (or impresses
with a die, stamp, or roller) and fixes the plate " with either
" surface upwards " to a block or frame.

The other methods belong to other series.

[Printed, 4d. No Drawings.]

A.D. 1839, May 25.—No. 8078.

GRIFFITHS, HENRY.—"Improvements in the process of
" producing prints or impressions from steel, copper, and
" other plates."

The object of this invention is the production of "imita-
" tions of drawings by several successive operations of print-
" ing different colours or tints " upon paper, so that the whole
shall have the effect of a picture "delineated in its various
" tints or colours with a camel's hair or other pencil."

As many plates are used as are required "to produce the
" different gradations of tints or of colours in the drawing
" to be imitated." On these plates are produced severally by
the ordinary process of etching, &c., "the selected parts or
" portions of the drawing which are to be represented by the
" particular tint or colour printed from each individual plate."
When the plates are thus engraven, "there must be lines or
" registering points marked upon all the plates accurately
" corresponding," in order that the first impression upon the

paper "may exactly register with the parts of the subject
" upon the successive plates."

[Printed, 6d. Drawing.]

A.D. 1839, July 3.—No. 8142.

YATES, JAMES.—"Improvements in making, forming, or
" producing raised or projecting letters, mouldings, figures,
" or other ornamental work for external decorations of build-
" ings and other purposes."

The patentee claims *inter alia* "the making of reversed
" letters, figures, or types for printers' use, from earthenware
" or potters' clay."

The press which he uses consists principally of (1) a table
having an "interrupted rotary motion," and divided into
compartments each carrying a receptacle for a mould, (2) a
follower or presser moved up and down by any suitable agent,
(3) means for giving motion to the table and stopping the table
during the pressure.

Round the table is a toothed wheel in gear with a wheel "of
" only half the diameter" of the toothed wheel and having
only half of its periphery toothed. A bolt, rising by means
of a weighted lever, enters holes in the underside of the table
beneath the receptacles. The bolt is lowered by a tappet (on
the shaft of the presser) acting on one end of a lever which is
connected by a rod to the weighted lever.

The patentee does not limit himself to the description of
press represented in the sheet of drawings, nor to the use of a
revolving table, "as an oblong table having an interrupted
" horizontal reciprocating motion given to it may do equally
" well."

[Printed, 7d. Drawing.]

A.D. 1839, August 1.—No. 8172.

FEUILLET, LOUIS FRANÇOIS.—"Improvements in casting
" type for printing."

The patentee claims " the mode of applying moulds on a
" rotatory axis for casting type," and the "arrangement of
" apparatus for pouring the melted metal into the moulds "
" and for opening the said moulds and separating the
" characters."

1. The moulds (the patentee does not restrict himself to any particular number in one machine) are fixed to the ends of two arms, which are joined to a cross piece attached to a shaft; and the shaft revolves by means of toothed gearing and a handle. Each mould is "similar to an ordinary mould;" the parts "slide one over the other;" and it is furnished "with " the means of forcing out" the character when cast. The means consist chiefly of (1) rollers carried by the moveable part and "placed at opposite points to each other"; (2) "a curved " piece," over which the rollers roll; one part of this piece " regulates the opening of the mould"; (3) "a square piece" carried by the moveable part; it "passes behind the fixed " part," and to it "is attached a pin which traverses the fixed " part and corresponds to the casts." The pin "also de- " taches the cast" and "forces out the letter from the other " side." To ensure the fall of the letter "there is placed " upon the same curved piece an inclined plane" which moves a lever that "forces the character through the side, so that it " is forced out of the mould either one side of the mould or " the other."

2. " A long rectangular cast-iron or other metal trough" is placed over a stove fixed in an iron framing. "Small metal " cases" are attached to the trough, being each provided with a slide. In each case is a weighted valve for regulating the flow out of the melted metal; the valve is raised by a forked lever which has "an excentric piece" at one end.

The patentee explains the method of working the machine, an arrangement for ensuring the forcing out of the cast letter, " when the eye of the character is very deep and the character " fine," and a swing trough "which receives the metal before " it is poured into the moulds," to be used when the charac- ters are composed of fine lines or of "lines crossing one " another."

[Printed, 9d. Drawing.]

A.D. 1839, November 9.—No. 8266.

EDMONDSON, Thomas. — "Improvements in printing ". presses."

[No Specification enrolled.]

A.D. 1840, January 18.—No. 8344.

WALKER, ARTHUR ELDRED.—"Improvements in engraving
" by machinery."

Instead of engraving by hand with a graver, the patentee
employs "hardened plate type" having thereon the letters,
figures, or designs, to be engraved on the copper plate or other
printing surface.

The types are of steel; the patentee describes "the mode of
" preparing the type" which he adopts, adding that he makes
no claim thereto, "steel for engraving purposes having been
" subjected to like processes before." Care must be taken
that the types are all "of the same size and thickness in
" order to their all filling the same instrument by which they
" are used."

" The machine stands on three feet;" it comprises (1) a
weight which "rests on the upper part of the frame of the
" machine;" it is raised by means of a treadle; when raised
the workman "can readily move the machine in any direction,"
and when lowered "the machine will be kept secure from move-
" ment"; (2) a table whereon the copper plate is placed; (3)
a type holder adjustable as to the height to which it can be
raised and "formed at the under surface to receive and work
" with one type at a time"; (4) a sliding bar "at the under
" part of the frame;" on it are uprights, the one carrrying a
magnifying glass, the other a spring hammer; (5) "a pointing
" plate" hinged to the lower end of the type holder (which
" beyond its axis is turned downwards") and capable of adjustment as to "correct placing" by the aid of the magnifying
glass; (6) "a train of wheels with a dial plate and hands" set
in motion by a catch or tooth "affixed on the axis of the
" hammer" and indicating the number of letters, designs, &c.
" which the machine has engraved." The hammer gives "the
" requisite blow to the projection on the upper surface of the
" type holder."

The patentee does not confine himself "to the precise
" arrangement of the mechanism shown and described;"
provided that the "holding and directing of the type correctly
" to the proper point or locality" be obtained, "variations of
" the mechanism" may be used.

[Printed, 1s. 3d. Drawings.]

A.D. 1841, June 23.—No. 9003.

LE KEUX, John Henry.—"An improvement in line engrav-
" ing and in producing impressions therefrom."

Two steel or copper plates are employed ; a portion of the
subject or picture is engraved on the one, and the remainder
on the other, in such manner that, "when printed one upon
" the other on the same surface, the combination of the two
" impressions shall produce the representation required."

On the one plate is put "a tracing or rolling off of any given
" subject ; " then the "necessary outline and dark shadows"
are etched thereon, and then the etched portions are finished
" by the usual process of line engraving." On the other
plate (called the ground plate) is placed "a tracing or
" transfer " from the first ; "a tint of lines" is ruled all over
the subject ; the lights are stopped out; "the under-tints or
" shadows " are produced "by biting in ; " and "any etching
" or graving to deepen the shadows or burnishing to brighten
" the lights if necessary " is done.

An impression is printed from one plate ; the paper before
it is removed is marked "to correspond with the register
" lines ; " it is then taken off and properly laid on the other
plate ; an impression being taken, " the process is completed,"
and the effect is produced. Colour may be applied to each
plate. More than two plates may be employed.

[Printed, 11d. Drawings.]

A.D. 1842, January 27.—No. 9233.

BAGGALY, John James. — " Improvements in making
" metallic dies and plates for stamping, pressing, or em-
" bossing."

These dies, produced "from flat plates of steel or other
" metal," are intended as substitutes for "the steel-faced dies
" commonly produced by welding steel on to the body of a
" wrought-iron block and afterwards cutting or stamping the
" subject thereon."

From a model in relief of the subject required to be sunk in
a die a matrix is produced in plaster or other material. The
figure of the back of the matrix must nearly correspond to
that of the face, and from the back ("including the thickness

" of the edges ") a cast iron die or block is obtained of substance and dimensions suitable "for sustaining the blow or
" pressure in the operation of stamping." From the face of
the matrix is obtained " a model for casting in iron a hub or
" sinker, containing the raised part of the subject," and the
sinker should have at its back a staple or stud for attaching it
to the press or stamp hammer.

The die block and sinker being adjusted in the press, a plate
of steel or other metal is made red hot and laid upon the upper
surface of the die block; the sinker is struck down on the
plate, and after several strikings and heatings, the plate is
brought "into the form of the die block on the under side and
" of the sinker on the upper side." The feather edges, &c.
of the plate are removed; the plate may be hardened if required; the back and edges are then cleaned and "tinned
" over;" the face of the die block also is cleaned and tinned,
and the plate is fixed into the block by hot solder and pressure.
The die, when worked up with the customary tool, is ready for
use.

" The figures in the face of the matrix" may be produced
" by casting them from molten steel."

[Printed, 3d. No Drawings.]

A.D. 1843, June 10.—No. 9771.

NEWTON, WILLIAM. — (A communication.) — " Improve-
" ments in the preparation of paper designed for bank notes,
" government documents, bills, cheques, deeds, and other
" purposes wherein protection and safety from forgeries or
" counterfeits are required."

The paper to be used is only such as is "manufactured by
" hand with rags naturally white and not bleached by
" chlorine." Both sides of the paper are covered "with
" designs arranged and printed in such a manner that they
" cannot be imitated by the hand of man or the agency of
" machinery, nor transferred upon stone and then repro-
" duced" by lithography.

The first design must be "composed of regular parts," and
the "type, figure, or device, be geometrically regular;" in
the composition there should not be "straight lines, because
" they are too easily made with a rule, nor any curve which

" may be traced at once by a compass." The second design, which is to fill up "the spaces left between the regular "elements," must be of "a different aspect and description, "but no confusion with the regular elements must take "place;" it should be "produced by chance, so that it is "impossible to obtain two similar drawings by using the same "means or any other;" it should also be "microscopic."

Two inks are used (by preference) "delible" :—The one is composed of "balm capahu, Venetian turpentine, and chalk," ground together to the consistency of ordinary printing ink. Half of this forms the first ink. The other is made by adding to the other half "ordinary ink reduced to powder by "evaporation" or "other colouring substance which is equally "delible."

An impression is made on both sides of the paper with the first and then with the second ink.

[Printed, 5d. No Drawings.]


A.D. 1843, December 8.—No. 9976.

HILL, JOHN REED.—Improvements in presses for letter-press printing.

[No Specification enrolled.]


A.D. 1844, October 3.—No. 10,338.

NEWTON, WILLIAM. — (A communication.) — "Improve-" ments in machinery for letter-press printing."

The invention consists of a rotary press, in which a horizontal centre axle with carrier arms supports several (in the drawings, six) pressing cylinders, furnished with clips. The form of types is flat, and is placed horizontally at the lower part of the press, its surface forming a chord to the circular path of the outer surface of the pressing cylinders. The carrier arms are peculiarly fitted so as to admit of the axles of the pressing cylinders adapting themselves to the position in which they are required to pass over the form. Four feeding tables are shown. The sheet is laid on either of them, with its edge against a hook-formed stop, and as one of the pressing cylinders comes round peculiar arrangements cause the feed table to be slightly raised, and a further contrivance, consisting of a sliding horse-shoe piece and certain cams or

guides, causes the spring clips on the cylinder to open and
seize on the sheet, which is by the further rotation of the
cylinder wound round it and thus carried to the impression.
After the impression the clips open, and the sheet is drawn
off by a second set of clips mounted on horizontal bars, which
are jointed to two rocking lever arms, a current of air being
at the same time directed against the sheet. The sheets are
thus suffered to fall severally upon a fly-board, so contrived
as to sink gradually as the pile of printed matter grows. The
sheets are secured on the fly-board by spring holders, which
turn sideways previous to each deposit. The ink trough is
at the bottom of the press. A ductor roller, having taken
from it its supply, communicates it by means of certain intervening rollers to a distributing drum ; from this it is furnished
to several sets of inking rollers, which by means of endless
chains pass (alternating with the pressing cylinders) over the
form.

[Printed, 2s. 2d. Drawings.]

A.D. 1846, January 29.—No. 11,060.

HALL, GEORGE FREDERICK.—"Apparatus for writing and
" booking, numbering, cutting, checking, and expediting
" the delivery and receipt of pawnbrokers' duplicates, pass
" tickets, and other like documents."

The patentee claims the invention of (1) "a numbering and
" cutting machine;" (2) "a triplograph, whereby the three
" written parts of the three copies of each pawnbroker's
" ticket " are produced by one mechanical movement; (3) "a
" diplometer, whereby an exact registery is kept of all
" redeemed pledges."

1. An upright plate on a sole plate is supported at the back
by a standard. On the face of the upright is mounted a
toothed driving wheel, which has at the back end of its axle
" a double-armed handle " weighted with two knobs. Above
and below this wheel and in gear therewith is a toothed wheel,
turning on a pivot passed through the plate and standard, and
pinned to the face of these wheels is the shaft of the numbering
box. On the upright, on one side of the driving wheel, is a
third toothed wheel, "the pivot of which carries at the back
" of the plate a small pinion of six leaves." The leaves take

into a sliding rack connected at its lower end to a knife carriage, and to the carriage are screwed two cutters set at right angles to each other. The teeth of the driving wheel are in the proportion of 30 to 24 of the upper and lower wheels and of 30 to 16 of the side wheel. In the sole plate are (1) "an " ink pan," (2) "a stamping bed," (3) "a guide for the " tickets," (4) "a fender" to keep the tickets down "after " they have been numbered and cut," and (5) "two steel " edges" for the reception of the cutters. The axle of the numbering box carries an arm which is so acted upon by a spring lever as "after each operation of the numbering box " to move the numbers therein "one forward."

"A strip of six" tickets being placed with the first over the bed and with the bottom part against the guide, a push of the handle "over to the left" will set the machine in motion and cause the first ticket to be numbered and to be cut "length- " wise and crosswise."

2. This apparatus will be found described in the series entitled "Writing instruments and materials."

3. This apparatus "is locked up in a box," except a "slid- " ing tablet to lay the ticket upon;" it is worked by an inward pressure of the tablet. A date box is suspended on the axle of a crank between two side standards on the sole plate and on a shaft which passes through a "gimballed ring" in a back standard. A frame (of which the tablet forms the outer end) slides to and fro on the sole plate within the side standards by means of racks and pinions. The date box rests on an ink pan "when out of action;" the pressure causes it "to spring " forward in a semicircular sweep" to the stamping place (the part next the tablet), and a coiled spring restores the parts to their places. Inside the date box are five wheels mounted on one square axle; the one on the left has engraved on it the first 12 letters of the alphabet representing the months, each of the others the numerals, which are changed in due order by means of pins, spring detents, a wheel (alongside of the unit wheel) carrying a projecting tappet, a click and a cam. The month wheel does not revolve with the others, the axle "being " rounded" at the part where it passes through that wheel; it is moved forward when required by loosening a screw. "A " counter check which consists of a single disc and spokes"

revolves with the spokes pointing downwards "on a pivot
" stepped in the sole plate;" the revolution is effected by a
long spring "which projects from the front end of the rack of
" the traversing frame" and another spring "screwed to the
" face of the sole plate." A "lifting lever" is "connected at
" one end of the axle of the date box and linked at top to a
" strong spring" which is screwed to the sole plate.

In a less expensive diplometer "there is no month wheel,"
and the numbering wheels merely register "the number of
" strokes made by the machine." The types which imprint
the date are enclosed in " a chase" which is brought down at
each stroke upon the stamping place of the tablet; they must
be changed daily "to indicate the day, month, and year."

[Printed, 1s. 5d. Drawings.]

## A.D. 1846, March 11.—No. 11,122.

WOONE, GODFREY.—"Improvements in the art of engraving
" in relief."

The engravings, "having the character of wood engravings
" or types," are applicable *inter alia* "to the production of
" prints, illustrations to books," &c.

The patentee divides his improvements into three heads :—
1. "Direct modes," by which the engraving "is formed imme-
" diately on the plate from which the impressions are to be
" taken." 2. "Indirect modes," by which "an engraved sur-
" face in relief is obtained," but on a material not sufficiently
hard to print from, "from which casts are to be taken fit for
" printing." 3. "The intaglio mode," by which "the print-
" ing surface is obtained from a mould."

He uses "five different tools" or plates "for bruising or
" breaking up a protecting surface or etching ground" :—One
is a plate whereon is laid "a mezzotinto ground;" one a plate
into which an aquatinta ground is bitten; one has bitten into its
surface "two sets of lines at right angles diagonally across,"
" leaving a surface of mere dots;" one is an electrotype cast
from the last-named, "which will present on its surface a kind
" of square network;" and one "consists of wire gauze" of
about "eighty squares to the inch." The operator "must
" select one of them for each plate to be engraved," being

guided "by the nature of the subject to be engraved, and the " peculiar character desired to be given to it."

1. An etching ground is laid on a copper plate. "The " granulated side" of one of the plates slightly blackleaded is placed in juxta-position with the etching ground, and the two plates are passed through a copper-plate press. A tracing of the design is made on the prepared copper plate; the parts " intended to print entirely black" are protected with diluted Brunswick black; the plate (perfectly dry) is put into the cell of a galvanic battery and kept there from 5 to 20 minutes; the protecting, drying, and immersion are "repeated for each " shade required." The patentee describes a modification which produces an "imitation of tinted lithography," and one which consists "in reversing the ordinary mode of stipple " engraving."

2. One of the plates is heated and covered with white wax; the design is traced thereon, and the subject is drawn "with " vermilion mixed with gum water;" when dry, the ground is removed, and from the prepared plate a cast is taken, which " will produce black lines on a middle tint."

3. This consists in "throwing a middle tint entirely over " grounds in the methods lately introduced of producing a " printing surface in relief by casting or taking an electrotype " impression from moulds formed by drawing through a com- " position down to a base of metal." This may be done by employing one of the "new tools for throwing a tint over the " entire plate."

[Printed, 4d. No Drawings.]

A.D. 1846, October 15.—No. 11,416.

MILLWARD, ARTHUR.—"Improvements in producing figured " surfaces sunken and in relief."

The patentee claims eight improved processes, the eighth of which is the production of engraved surfaces "from which " impressions may be afterwards taken on paper, cloth, or " any other suitable material, by any of the modes of printing " or embossing in ordinary use."

If the design is to be sunk in, it is painted or otherwise depicted on a plate of metal, and "a thin coating of any other " suitable metal" is deposited on the uncovered parts "by

" the agency of voltaic electricity or otherwise." The colour
employed in making the design is then cleared away, and the
plate is immersed "in an acid or alkaline or other saline solu-
" tion," whereby the parts now left exposed "may be decom-
" posed and removed to any depth required."

If the design is to be in relief, a coating of any suitable metal
is deposited on the plate as aforesaid; the design is painted on
the deposited metal; the plate is then subjected "to the action
" of the negative pole of a voltaic battery, or electro-magnetic
" machine," or is immersed in a solution (such as before stated),
" whereby the deposited metal on all those parts not covered
" by the figure or design are decomposed and removed," and
the design is left "standing out in strong and clear relief."

[Printed, 4d. No Drawings.]

A.D. 1847, August 5.—No. 11,832.

BIRCHALL, Thomas.—"Improvements in folding newspapers
" and other papers."

This machine, which may (or not) be connected with a printing machine, folds the printed sheet four times, "each time at
" right angles to the former fold."

On an axle (to which motion is given in any suitable manner)
is a pinion; this sets in motion a toothed wheel "which gives
" motion to the other parts." The sheet to be folded is laid
on a bed plate, and above is a bar carrying the blade "by
" which the first creasing for folding is effected." The bar and
blade have an up-and-down movement, and in descending press
the sheet down between a pair of rollers. One of these rollers
has on its front end a pinion which receives motion through
intermediate wheels from the toothed wheel, and the sheet is
conducted by means of these rollers down to between a second
pair of rollers, when it is in a position to be acted on by a
second blade projecting upwards from a slide that moves to and
fro between guides. The blade causes the sheet to be again
folded by causing it to pass between the second pair of rollers,
and forces it between springs and a third pair of rollers. The
springs are provided on their inside with felt for the purpose of
better holding the sheet whilst the blade recedes. The sheet
is now operated upon by a third blade "capable of sliding to
" and fro on V guides;" the blade in its movement "towards

" the back of the machine" presses against the sheet, releases
it from between the springs, and forces it between a fourth
pair of rollers. The blade "will again recede towards the
" front," leaving the sheet in a position to be acted upon by a
fourth blade "supported by its arms in bearings from the
" main framing." This blade causes the sheet to be folded a
fourth time by its being pressed between a fifth pair of rollers.
The folded sheet is conducted thence by tapes partly round a
drum, and from the drum between a sixth pair of rollers out of
the machine.

The connecting parts of the machine are described in the
Specification, but the patentee does not confine himself "to
" the various details herein shown and described."

[Printed, 1s. 10d. Drawings.]

A.D. 1848, April 27.—No. 12,137.

EDMONDSON, Thomas.—"Improvements in marking and
" numbering railway and other tickets or surfaces, and in
" arranging and distributing tickets."

This invention relates to improvements on and additions to
No. 8538, A.D. 1840.

The Specification contains a detailed description of the machine employed, "parts of which are old and now in use;"
the improvements and additions claimed are :—

1. An ink-trough and a roller connected therewith; the
bottom of the trough is "adjustable to regulate the quantity
" of ink delivered to the roller."

2. A belt for carrying ink from the trough to the inking
rollers.

3. An apparatus for "printing or numbering the units" on
railway tickets, &c.

4. "Stopping the supply of tickets when any given number
" less than ten thousand" has been printed and numbered ;
this is effected by means of "catches and the various pieces
" acting in conjunction therewith."

5. Driving the machine by means of a "pulley" and a
" friction box" actuated by steam or other power.

6. Making the tubes or receptacles for containing railway
tickets, &c. of "plates of metal" instead of "wood and metal
" combined."

7. "The peculiar form and arrangement of the case" for containing railway tickets, &c.

8. "The cutting or stamping of signs or devices" on railway tickets, &c. "to denote the date on which they are issued."

[Printed, 3s. 10d. Drawings.]

A.D. 1848, November 23.—No. 12,340.

ARCHER, HENRY.—"Improvements in facilitating the divi-
"sion of sheets or pieces of paper, parchment, or other similar
"substances."

The improvement is effected by aid of a machine which cuts around the margin of each stamp or ticket (printed on one sheet of paper or parchment) "a consecutive series of holes," leaving a "sufficient adherence of the several stamps," &c. to ensure their retaining the form of a sheet until they are intentionally separated.

"Horizontal bracket arms" are bolted to a cross bar of the framing; they are "provided with V bars, over which a sliding "frame traverses." This frame carries the sheet to be perforated, and for this purpose it is furnished at front and back with a set of clips, one set being stationary, the other "capable "of sliding so as to draw the sheet of paper or other material "to a suitable tension to be pierced." On the side of the frame is a rack, which by means of a pinion moves the frame forward so as to bring a different part of the sheet under the action of punches at each descent of a plunger. "On the top "of the crossbar a slotted plate is bolted," and "over the "slot a perforated plate is fixed." The perforated plate "is "a matrix to receive the ends of the punches." The punches are set in a plate "in such order of lines as will allow of their "circumscribing each stamp of a row of stamps, and punching "corresponding holes in the sheet." This plate is carried by another plate which "is attached to and forms part of the "plunger." The plunger is worked by being connected to an excentric, on the shaft of which a hand wheel is keyed. Before the punches begin to act, provision is made (and described) for moving the frame forward a given distance, and thus "succes- "sive rows of the stamps," &c. will be "pierced at their "circumference as required."

[Printed, 1s. Drawing.]

### A.D. 1848, December 9.—No. 12,361.

TAIT, WILLIAM IRONSIDE.—"Producing outlines on paper,
" pasteboard, parchment, papier mâché, and other like
" fabrics."

The patentee claims 13 improvements; amongst them is one
for taking impressions on paper, &c. "of dotted outlines"
from punctured plates:—The plate is bent and fitted to a
printing cylinder, and an endless web passes between the
printing and the impressing cylinders. To take a plain or uncoloured impression, the paper is laid sheet after sheet on the
web and is passed through between the cylinders. To take a
coloured impression, a sheet coated on its upper surface with
printing ink or other colouring matter is laid on the web, and
thereon is placed "each of the sheets of paper or other sub-
" stance" as it is passed through the press.

Another claim is for engraving outlines of maps and other
subjects on plates of metal and "taking dry impressions
" thereof" by pressure of the plates on paper or of paper on
the plates.

Another claim is for producing "raised outlines on paper,"
&c. for the use of blind persons:—Letters, numerals, &c. are
struck out in metal plates by stamping, perforating, or indenting; impressions are taken on paper from the plates by means
of a letterpress or other press.

[Printed, 7d. Drawing.]

### A.D. 1849, August 30.—No. 12,753.

BAXTER, GEORGE.—"Improvements in producing coloured
" steel plate, copper plate, and other impressions."

Under the above number and date an application was granted
for " an extension for the term of five years of letters patent"
granted to G. Baxter. The specification of the original patent
is numbered 6916 and dated 23rd October, 1835, under which
No. and date an abridgment of the invention will be found.

### A.D. 1850, March 19.—No. 13,007.

EDMONDSON, THOMAS.—"Improvements in the manufac-
" ture of railway and other tickets, and in machinery or appa-
" ratus for marking railway and other tickets."

The tickets are made "either wholly or in part of woven
" fabrics."

The apparatus for printing tickets consists of "certain addi-
"tions to and improvements in" the machine for which the
patentee "obtained former letters patent, the object of the
"present improvements being to obtain a more distinct im-
"pression on the ticket and to render the machine more self-
"acting." The distance between the bottom of the "feeding
"tube" and the point of contact of the printing roller and a
lower roller fixed on the driving shaft is equal to "about
"twice the length" of a ticket, and that between the point of
contact and the "receiving tube" to about "the length of
"four tickets." The "feeding slide" receives motion from a
lever, an excentric "projecting from the driving shaft," and
a connecting link. The type box fits into a dovetailed recess
in the periphery of the printing roller, and if the words are not
printed "across the tickets," it will be necessary "to bevel
"the shanks of the type." The method of supplying ink to
the type and to the numbering wheels is similar to that described in the former letters patent.

The first advance of the slide brings the lowest ticket from
the feeding tube on to a table, and on its next advance the
second ticket pushes the first one forward "until its front edge
"comes over the centre" of the lower roller. "During the
"next back stroke of the slide" the type box arrives in position, and its flanges by compressing the edges of the ticket
against the lower roller "forces the same forward until it rests"
on another table. The printing roller "then performs another
"revolution," and by so doing "the second ticket is brought
"forward and made to push the first one further forward
"along the table." These operations are repeated until the
end of the first ticket comes over a "presser, the upper motion
"of which forces that ticket and that portion of the inking
"ribbon immediately over it against the numbering wheels."
At the next revolution of the driving shaft the first ticket is
deposited in the receiving tube, "the sliding block being then
"elevated to receive it." This block, which has hitherto
been lowered by hand, has a "uniform descending motion"
imparted to it from a "double lever," whereto is jointed a
"long click" taking into the teeth of a ratchet wheel in gear
with a "rack fixed to the back plate of the block." A spring
prevents the block "from descending by its own gravity."

A modification of the foregoing is described, in which "the
" inking ribbon " is dispensed with, and the type is supplied
with ink in a different manner.

The whole of the inking apparatus may be omitted by
making the type and the figures on the numbering wheels of
hard steel or other suitable metal.

The machine for stamping the date on the ticket is composed
principally of (1) a standard, (2) an upper swing frame, (3) a
lower swing frame "jointed to the upper one and guided be-
" low on a projection cast or otherwise fixed to the bottom
" plate " of the standard, (4) steel type, "the upper ends of
" which " bear against a plate held to the upper swing frame
by a thumbscrew, the type being held in place by "a bridle
" screwed at each end to the upper swing frame." The lower
swing frame is furnished with a top plate "having a catch at
" the end which arrests the advance of the ticket when intro-
" duced." A "sharp, clean, and indelible impression" is
obtained "by pushing against the lower swing frame;" this
brings the type down on to the ticket and presses it into the
body thereof.

[Printed, 1s. 8d. Drawings.]

A.D. 1850, April 23.—No. 13,063.

BARANOWSKI, JOSEPH JEAN.—" Improvements in ma-
" chinery for counting, numbering, and labelling."

The improvements "consist especially of a particular ar-
" rangement of wheels or plates " :—A lower wheel formed
with ten notches is moved round one-tenth of its circumference
by the revolution of an upper wheel formed with one tooth.
To the lower wheel is fixed a disc, "the edge of which is en-
" graved with the figures from 0 to 9." To the disc is fixed
a cogged wheel, which "works into a cogged wheel of the
" same size " and is connected to another disc having its edge
engraved in like manner to the former one. Similarly other
cogged wheels and discs may be made to gear with those
already mentioned. The wheels are mounted and revolve
respectively on the axles of the first-named wheels although
" no one of them can move without moving all the others " at
suitable intervals. The notches in the wheels "need not be
" each ten in number."

Among the applications of this invention is one to a " stamping machine, by which the number is stamped and " registered " :—A cylinder moves up and down in a frame, and its top is kept at some distance above the frame by a coiled spring. "The whole of the machinery forms part " of the cylinder and moves up and down with it except a rack and two clicks which are fixed to the frame. There are " two sets " of figured or marked wheels, one above the other " and moved by cogged wheels on a " middle axle "; on the lower set " the numbers project to be used as stamps "; the upper set appear through an aperture " so that each number from " time to time is both stamped and registered." The segment of a wheel, to which is fixed an arm carrying an elastic roller, works into the rack and at each descent of the cylinder is " carried over the under side of the apparatus, and this surface " being charged with printing ink, the roller inks each pro- " jecting figure before it reaches the paper below."

A modification of this machine (which stamps but does not register) is " planned so as to be especially applicable to " stamping numbers on the leaves of ledgers and other books."

Another is to a machine " for printing numbers on cheques " and their counterfoils " :—A drum is mounted on an axle, a series of rollers (of the same diameter as the drum) on another axle, two elastic rollers (charged with printing ink) on another axle, and the figure wheels on another axle " which is fixed " in three of the rollers." The first three axles are connected by wheels, one of which is turned by a winch. The figures project and are used for printing. The drum and the rollers " are covered with flannel, except the space of two inches, " which is always apparent just above the board " whereon the paper is laid, whenever the winch hangs downwards.

Another is to a machine " for printing railway and other " tickets " :—Two circular plates, fixed on the main axle and carrying the figured wheels mounted on another axle, are bound together " on the other side of the axle." As the plates are turned by a winch on the axle, the figured wheels " are " shifted simultaneously by the one-toothed wheel fixed to the " frame of the machine and working into the ten-notched " wheel." One set of figures project and are to be used for printing, the other set are " for registering from time to time " the number of tickets printed." On the periphery of the plates a stereoplate is fixed; it is in contact with a roller which is covered with flannel and pressed against the stereoplate by a screw. A hopper contains the tickets to be printed; a portion of the bottom is removed and replaced by a sliding piece. When this piece is drawn out, "one of the cards drops low " enough to be pushed between the stereoplate and the " roller by the sliding piece as it returns with the bottom of " the hopper." The sliding piece is provided with a rack, and its to-and-fro motion is effected by the revolution of a wheel on the main axle, which drives a wheel of the same size on the axle of the ten-toothed wheel; on the latter axle is an excentric actuating an arm which carries a rack on its top. The inking apparatus consists of "a cylinder moving in a bath " of printing ink, a distributing roller, and an inking roller."

[Printed, 1s. 11d. Drawings.]

A.D. 1850, May 25.—No. 13,081.

RADLEY, WILLIAM, and MEYER, FREDERICK.—"Improve- " ments in treating fatty, oleaginous, resinous, bituminous, " and cerous bodies, in the manufacture and application of " them and of their components and subsidiary products, " together with the apparatus to be employed therein to new " and other useful purposes."

The patentees state in one part of their Specification that they produce a class of compounds "by the union of the acid " components" of fatty, oily, resinous, bituminous, and cerous bodies, and their derivatives, "by double decomposition with " an earthy, alkaline, and metallic salt, or any or either of " them, or by direct combination of these bodies with the " basis of these salts respectively." This class of compounds they apply "per se in admixture with each other and with " other resinoid, oleaginous, spirituous, bituminous, fatty, " and cerous bodies," to the manufacture of pastes and compounds to be used as varnishes, printing inks, and other similar purposes.

In another part they state that they mould rollers for inking printers' types from "oleates, linates, cannabinates, and other " like salts of alumina, and sesqui-oxide of iron, and other " bases, or either or any of them when dissolved by heat and " agitation in a very variable proportion of benzole or highly " volatile oil of coal naptha, and then mixed with common

" coal or wood tar in such proportion as to be fluid at about
" 150° to 200° or at any other temperatures according to the
" discretion of the operator." Instead of coal tar "the least
" volatile oils of coal tar called dead oils" may be used.

[Printed, 1s. 5d. Drawing.]

A.D. 1850, July 17.—No. 13,175.

SMITH, EDWARD N.—"Machinery for folding sheets of paper
" or various other matters or substances capable of being
" folded thereby."

The sheet is laid on a supporting surface consisting of "the
" top surfaces of a series of endless bands" which run round
cylinders or drums. These bands may be connected with a
printing press so as to receive the sheets after they are printed
and delivered from the same. The bands carry the sheet
" directly over a thin horizontal blade" which is arranged
" directly between the two middle endless bands and below
" their top surfaces." The blade "is suddenly elevated
" against the middle part" of the sheet, raises it off the
endless bands, and forces it upwards between two other series
of endless bands, which "grip it and draw it upwards and
" away from the first series." The sheet thus once folded
is conveyed on the top surfaces of one of the two series "in
" the direction at right angles to that in which it was pre-
" viously moved" on the first series over a second blade
" disposed immediately between the two middle bands of the
" series and somewhat below their top surfaces." The second
blade is "suddenly forced upwards so as to strike the sheet
" midway of it and on a line at right angles to that at which
" it was struck by the first blade;" it also raises the sheet
between other endless bands "arranged and operated so as
" to impart to it another double or fold in manner similar to
" those before described."

The machine represented in the sheet of drawings is constructed to fold a sheet four times, the first fold "being across
" the paper," the second "at right angles to the first," the
third "parallel to the second," and the fourth "perpendicular
" to the third;" but the patentee does not confine his invention "to the production of four folds only." The sheet
after the last fold is discharged between rollers on to an
inclined plane.

[Printed, 1s. Drawing.]

A.D. 1850, November 7.—No. 13,315.

BLACK, JAMES.—(*Partly a communication.*)—" A machine
" for folding."

This sheet to be folded is laid by hand on the upper surface
of the lid of a case underneath a folding blade and over a long
slot, which is continued down the case "by means of partitions
" inside, so that there is formed thereby a chamber of the
" same length and depth as the interior of the case," but of
only "about one fourth of an inch in width." Provision is
made for "securing the proper register" of the sheet. The
blade having by preference a serrated edge descends, passes
through the slot carrying the sheet with it, and then rises
again by means of a spring or counter-weight, leaving the
folded sheet in the chamber. A second blade strikes the sheet
crossways and carries it through a slot "into a second and
" similar chamber formed in the side of the first narrow
" chamber," thereby folding the sheet a second time. This
mode of folding may be repeated, the blades being brought
back to their former position by springs. The throw of the
last folder brings the folded sheet "within the grasp of the
" first of two pairs of rollers;" the first pair grasp the folded
sheet "without laying hold of the folder;" the outer pair
covered with cloth "bear against each other with a considerable
" degree of pressure."

[Printed, 10*d*. Drawing.]

---

# PATENT LAW AMENDMENT ACT, 1852.

## 1852.

A.D. 1852, October 6.—No. 263.

WELLS, JOHN GAYLORD.—(*Provisional protection only.*)—
A " self-inking stamping apparatus."

The block or stamp is inked "by the act of lifting the "apparatus from the paper."

The block "is fixed in a swivel frame which turns on stud "axles having their bearings in lugs attached to a tube that "carries the outside case" of the apparatus. On the studs are pinions, "which severally gear into the teeth of a vertical "rack formed on the edge of a slot cut in the sides of an "inner or second tube." This tube is provided on its outer periphery "with two feathers in a line parallel with its axis," and in the outer tube grooves are cut to receive the feathers, the object being to allow the outer tube "to slide over the "inner without receiving any axial motion."

When the apparatus is lifted, the outer tube will first rise, but the weight of the inner tube "will give it a tendency to "remain stationary," and the pinions "will be caused to run "up to the top of their respective racks and invert the position "of the stamp or block." Within the inner tube there is mounted an ink reservoir "with a porous bottom composed of "rolled flannel," which will present a moist surface to the ascending block. The reservoir "must have a tendency to "stand clear of the block when at its highest elevation and "be capable of yielding to a slight pressure put on it," so that it may approach the block and ink the surface thereof. At the foot of the apparatus there is "an elastic shoe," which will yield to the pressure of the hand and allow the block to be brought into contact with the surface of the paper.

[Printed, 3d. No Drawings.]

### A.D. 1852, October 12.—No. 342.

MICHEL, FRANÇOIS ALEXANDRE VICTOR.—(*Provisional pro-tection only.*) — "Stereotyping in copper by the galvano-"plasty."

The inventor claims the application of "the galvanoplasty "for reproducing the engravings in general which are "employed in the typography."

"My process is executed," he states, (1) "in working the "model in copper;" (2) "with gutta percha;" (3) "with "wax;" (4) "with all materials fit to retain a stamp;" (5) "in reproducing with these various models the objects "employed to be stamped."

[Printed, 3d. No Drawings.]

A.D. 1852, November 19.—No. 793.

JOHNSON, John Robert. — "Improvements in the manu-
" facture of type or raised surfaces for printing."

The invention consists in the use of zinc and the alloys of
zinc more fusible than that metal for casting type and other
raised printing surfaces. For type of great hardness, 33 parts
of zinc are added to 59 of tin and used either alone or combined with from two to five per cent. in weight of antimony.
For type of inferior hardness, this alloy is mixed with ordinary
type metal, in proportions varying with the hardness required.
Zinc redistilled, or otherwise purified, zinc and lead, zinc and
tin (in other proportions than above), zinc, lead, and antimony,
zinc, tin, and antimony, zinc, tin, and lead, and zinc, lead,
tin, and antimony, may also be used for the same purpose.
When zinc alone is used, or such a proportion of zinc as to
raise the melting point considerably above that of the ordinary
type metal, the jet or break of the mould is made of earthenware, or if, of metal is covered with white-lead ground in
drying oil or putty to render it imperfectly conducting. The
surface of the fused metal is, to prevent oxidation, covered
with sheet iron, having an aperture for admission of the ladle.
Oxidation of the type from the use of the cleansing ley is
stated not to occur when the alloy of zinc does not exceed
ten per cent. of the whole, and may be altogether avoided by
the use of soft (potash) soap.

Raised printing surfaces may be also formed of the alloys of
zinc by the cliché or "dabbing" process "by adopting the
" well-known apparatus and manipulations at present em-
" ployed," and the alloy of zinc first described.

Printing surfaces may also be formed by stereotyping with
the ordinary alloy of lead and antimony, with the addition of
five to ten per cent. of the alloy of zinc and tin first described.

[Printed, 4d. No Drawings.]

# 1853.

---

### A.D. 1853, April 4.—No. 808.

NEWTON, ALFRED VINCENT.—(*A communication.*)—(*Provisional protection only.*)—A "self-inking stamping appa-
" ratus."

The block or stamp is inked "by the act of lifting the
" apparatus from the paper."

The block is mounted on a horizontal axle which turns in
bearings "formed in a tube that carries or itself forms the
" outside case" of the apparatus. The axle is caused "to
" make a semi-rotation alternately in opposite directions by
" means of a vertical rack carried by an inner or second tube
" gearing into a pinion or pinions on the axle." Thus the
face of the block is alternately (by the mere raising and depressing of the apparatus) brought into contact with the paper
to be stamped and with the inking surface. The inking
apparatus consists of an ink reservoir having "a porous bottom
" composed of rolled flannel;" it is mounted within the inner
tube. The inner tube "is provided on its outer periphery
" with two feathers in a line parallel with its axis," and grooves
are cut in the outer tube to receive the feathers, the object
being to allow the outer tube "to slide over the inner without
" receiving any axial motion."

When the apparatus is lifted, the outer tube will first rise,
" but the weight of the inner tube will give it a tendency to
" remain stationary, and thus through the gearing the axle
" which carries the block will be caused to turn and invert
" the position of the stamp or block."

[Printed, 3*d*. No Drawings.]

---

### A.D. 1853, April 9.—No. 856.

SEARBY, GEORGE.—(*Provisional protection not allowed.*)—
" Improvements in machinery for cutting, carving, and en-
" graving wood, stone, metal, and other suitable materials."

It is proposed to carry out this invention "by the com-
" bination of several parts acting on the principle of the slide
" rest or floating bed and pantagraphs having vertical and
" horizontal movement; with both hollow or open and solid

" beds, in conjunction with a fixed tool or tools consisting of
" cutters, drills, and saws." Facsimiles are thus produced
by the aid of " a tracer pressing over the pattern to be
" imitated."

[Printed, 3*d*. No Drawings.]

### A.D. 1853, May 11.—No. 1164.

BRADBURY, WILLIAM, and EVANS, FREDERICK MULLETT.—
(*A communication.*)—"Improvements in taking impressions
" and producing printing surfaces."

A plant, leaf, feather, insect, or other substance, is laid " in
" a flat and dry state" between a surface of steel and a
surface of polished sheet lead. The two plates are then
subjected to pressure by passing them between rollers or
otherwise. The impression obtained on the lead is used for
the purpose of producing therefrom an electrotype plate of
copper, and it is preferred to use " a solution of sulphate of
" copper." The face of the plate of copper is "to be burnished
" at those parts where the impression does not come," and
from this plate a second electrotype plate is obtained, depositing
thereon (by preference) a solution of sulphate of copper.

The second plate is the one to be used as a printing surface,
and impressions are taken from it " in the ordinary manner of
" printing from engraved plates."

[Printed, 3*d*. No Drawings.]

### A.D. 1853, May 31.—No. 1338.

NEWTON, WILLIAM EDWARD.—(*A communication.*)—"An
" improved construction of hand stamp."

This stamp is so constructed that " by moving it in the
" arc of a circle," it will still come down upon the paper "at
" all points of its surface, although it may strike at an angle
" with the plane upon which the material to be stamped is
" placed."

The shank has at its lower end a ball, which with a corresponding recess in the stamp (or the stock which carries the
stamp) forms a "universal joint, so as to adapt itself to any
" plane surface at whatever angle it may strike such surface."
At a suitable distance above the stamp or stock there is placed
on the shank a collar, against which one end of a coiled spring

rests, the other end resting in a shoulder or recess turned in the top of the stamp or stock. This spring keeps the stamp or stock "in its proper position;" it may however be omitted. The shank is secured to the handle in any convenient manner.

Instead of a ball and socket joint "a gimbal joint" may be used.

[Printed, 6d. Drawing.]

A.D. 1853, June 23.—No. 1532.

ASPINALL, JOSEPH. —(*A communication.*)—(*Provisional protection only.*)—"A self-adjusting stamp."

In this stamp "the die will always lie flat upon the surface " of the paper to be stamped, although the direction of " pressure communicated by the handle may not be directly " vertical."

The handle, instead of being immovably fixed upon the die, " has a ball at its extremity" which works "in a correspond- " ing socket fixed on the top of the die." A spring (by preference a coiled metal spring) is placed round the lower part of the handle, "enclosing the socket and ball, resting " on the upper part of the die and supporting the handle by " acting upon its widened part."

[Printed, 3d. No Drawings.]

A.D. 1853, August 11.—No. 1875.

NEWELL, THOMAS FREDERICK. — (*A communication.*)— " Improvements in machinery for numbering the pages of " books and documents."

Two pages may be simultaneously numbered by this machine. Two printing surfaces, "consisting of the alternate numbers," are placed on either side of a horizontal revolving wheel. The impressions "are taken constantly in the same locality;" the printing surfaces are therefore after printing "moved a distance " equal to that between the succeeding printing surfaces," the ink being applied at the time of their movement. "A set-off " tape" is employed "to prevent the printing-off from the " printed pages."

The machine is set in motion by a weighted treadle, which is connected with a lever carrying the required appendages. The "pressing apparatus" consists of two pressing surfaces, the upper pressing the paper upon the upper printing surface, the lower pressing it against the under surface.

"The inking apparatus" is composed of four rollers, two of them receiving ink from a roller in an ink trough, and distributing it over fixed plates, the other two taking it from the plates and applying it to the printing surfaces.

The set-off tape, as it is rolled from one drum to another, passes over the lower pressing surface. The upper pressing surface "does not require the tape," because "it makes the "first impression upon a leaf of the book" and consequently presses upon a surface "not printed each time it is set in "motion."

A ratchet wheel is fixed on the lower surface of the horizontal wheel.

The workman "places one leaf upon the upper and another leaf against the lower printing surface;" he then presses the treadle, and the two impressions are obtained; "he then "introduces the leaf of the book which was previously upon "the upper printing surface in such manner that it may receive "a fresh impression from the lower printing surface, apply-"ing the fresh leaf of the book to the upper printing surface;" he then again presses the treadle, and so on in succession.

The foregoing arrangement admits of modifications.

[Printed, 11 d. Drawings.]

A.D. 1853, August 24.—No. 1969.

FOSTER, THOMAS.—(*Provisional protection only.*)—"Im-" provements in machinery or apparatus applicable to etching "or engraving upon plain, cylindrical, or other surfaces."

In etching or engraving on plain or flat surfaces, the bar, which carries the tracing point and the etching or marking point or points, is connected "to such a series of levers and "links, or other similar mechanism, as will allow freedom "of action in every direction," and at the same time "ensure "the perfect parallelism of the bar to a given right line at all "times."

In etching or engraving on cylindrical surfaces, the said bar (connected as above described) "is also passed at each end "through a slot in a radial arm, the centre of which is "coincident with the centre of the cylinder."

In etching or engraving on other surfaces, "a suitable

" arrangement of mechanism " must be connected to the said
bar.

[Printed, 3d. No Drawings.]

### A.D. 1853, October 1.—No. 2245.

WOODCOCK, THOMAS. — (*Provisional protection only.*)—
" Improved machinery for carving, cutting, chiselling, and
" engraving."

A tracing point is attached to " a horizontal or vertical lever
" acting upon a moveable joint in order to pass over the
" models or patterns." This lever carries the cutting,
engraving, or other tools over the material to be operated
upon, "whilst the material and model are passing in an
" opposite direction by the action of sliding beds on which
" they rest, moved by a screw."

If preferred, "two centres" may be used, whereon the
material and model "revolve by the action as aforesaid of a
" screw."

By such machinery not only exact copies of the models are
produced, but also copies increased or reduced in size may be
obtained.

[Printed, 3d. No Drawings.]

### A.D. 1853, October 27.—No. 2489.

DOLBY, HENRY.—(*Provisional protection only.*)—" Improve-
" ments in embossing presses."

This press is a hand press, and the impression is produced
" by a sharp blow in place of pressure."

"A barrel or box spring in conjunction with a lever arm
" and link " is used for depressing the plunger. The link
connects the plunger with one end of the lever arm, and the
arm "is secured to the axis of the barrel spring, which is
" previously wound up." The plunger is raised by the
depression of a lever, "which is formed at its extremity with
" two or more teeth," and the teeth take into corresponding
notches "in the top of the plunger." The bearings for the
fulcrum of the elevating lever are " formed with two corre-
" sponding oblique slots, one in each cheek," and the slots
" are inclined and extended back for the pupose of allowing
" the lever to be drawn out to a sufficient extent to enable it

" to be re-engaged" with the notches after the plunger has
been brought down, "thus bringing the press into position for
" the next blow."

[Printed, 3*d*. No Drawings.]

A.D. 1853, November 14.—No. 2631.

HILL, John Singleton Copley, and COTTRILL, Edwin.—
(*Provisional protection only.*) — "Improvements in stamps
" and presses, a part or parts of which improvements may be
" applied to other purposes."

The inventors apply to embossing and other presses (1) an
apparatus to register the number of impressions taken, (2)
mechanism "for preventing the taking of impressions fraudu-
" lently."

They do not limit themselves to any particular registering
machine, but they connect it by an arm to the plunger of the
press, so that it does not register "till the die is brought
" down upon the matrix."

In order to prevent the introduction of paper under the die
before the plunger "has risen sufficiently high to register its
" motion," they place around the matrix "a ring or short
" tube" connected by "a series of levers" with the plunger.

On the rising of the plunger the ring "rises and closes the
" space between the two dies," but when the plunger has
acted on the registering apparatus, it "is disengaged and falls
" down around the lower die."

[Printed, 3*d*. No Drawings.]

---

## 1854.

A.D. 1854, February 28.—No. 478.

DENNY, Theobald.—"Improvements in engraving."

The improvements consist in the "mode of producing en-
" gravings on metallic plates suitable for ordinary surface
" printing."

A plate, by preference of polished steel, is covered with a
coating of dissolved caoutchouc; it is then blackened by

passing it over a wick saturated with spirits of turpentine, after which it is heated underneath until "its oxidation gives " it a bluish white color." This last operation dries the coating ; the surface is made as smooth as possible, and the design is drawn thereon with a lead pencil.

The design is etched with etching needles, "which remove " the coating on the plate and leave uncovered the oxide of " the metal without incising the plate." A solution of virgin wax and petroleum "is passed over the plate and immediately " cleaned off with dry cotton wadding so as to leave the etched " parts damp."

The plate is now plunged "for about two seconds" into a bath of distilled water holding in solution cyanide of potassium, a small quantity of tannin, sulphate of copper, and caustic potash ; "this bath should be employed in the cold state." The plate is again plunged into the bath "to remove any air " bubbles remaining on the etched parts."

The next process is "the complete and perfect coppering " of the drawing" by the electrotype process, which "usually " occupies two hours," after which "the plate is cleaned with " alcohol."

"In order to give greater strength and relief to the coppered " engravings it should be silvered ;" this process is described in the Specification as well as the composition of the silvering bath ; after the plate is cooled, it is cleaned with wadding cotton.

The plate "is finally exposed to the action of an electric " current in a concentrated solution composed of two parts " sulphate of iron and one part sal ammoniac ;" this process also is described. The plate is submitted to the action of the bath "till the required depth is attained, and the other " parts are covered over with colophony dissolved in petro- " leum." Lastly, the plate is exposed for a minute or two "to the action of the battery in the bath of sulphate of " iron and sal ammoniac, in order to remove the polish and " lustre of the engraved surface so as to allow the printing " ink to lay well."

The patentee does not confine himself "to the precise details " herein laid down."

[Printed, 4d. No Drawings.]

A.D. 1854, March 23.—No. 686.

POOLE, MOSES.—(*A communication.*)—(*Letters Patent void for want of Final Specification.*)—"Improvements in pre-
" venting alterations of bank notes, cheques, and other
" documents."

The improvement consists in " combining devices produced
" by puncturing or cutting away of parts of a document
" with printing and writing."

"Portions of the face " of a bank note, cheque, &c. are
punctured or cut through in such manner that " the vacancies
" or perforations" shall be made to represent by numerals,
figures, letters, or other intelligible signs, " the denomi-
" nation or amount of the note, cheque, or other document,
" or the name or part of the name of the bank or promissor,
" or any other essential part " of the note, &c.

Unless the signification of the punctured, cut out, or perforated parts and the written or printed parts agree, it will
at once be ascertained that the document is " a fraudulent
" one."

[Printed, 3*d*. No Drawings.]

A.D. 1854, April 25.—No. 945.

DE BEAUREGARD, FELIX ALEXANDRE TESTUD. — (*Provisional protection only.*)—" Improvements in the manufac-
" ture of inks and in the preparation of papers for receiving
" the same."

These inks and papers " may be employed in stamping and
" printing, as well as in writing."

The paper is prepared by immersing it in a solution of " one
" of the component parts of an ink or pigment." The ink
consists only of " another component part or ingredient " of
such ink or pigment. By this means " the pigment is formed
" upon or in the substance of the paper." The solution may
be otherwise applied to the paper.

An ink, " colourless or nearly so when used, but which
" becomes black upon ordinary unprepared paper," is made
" by dissolving iodide of potassium and iodine in water "
and adding thereto " red chromate of potash and as much
" cyanide of potassium as will decolorize it," and a small
quantity of gum arabic.

[Printed, 3*d*. No Drawings.]

A.D. 1854, May 23.—No. 1143.

ATLEE, THOMAS WILLIAM, and ATLEE, GEORGE JOBSON.—
" Improvements in printed or other forms applicable for
" bankers' cheques, orders for goods, wharfingers' and
" carriers' receipts, taxes and rates collectors' receipts, and
" various other parochial, commercial, or private purposes."

This invention applies to such forms as " are required to
" be separated for the purpose of leaving or preserving a
" check or evidence of the business matter to which such
" torn-off forms may relate ;" it consists in perforating such
forms.

The perforations may be of round, diamond, square, or
other shape, and in one or more straight, undulating, or zigzag
lines, or in any pattern which will admit of being easily torn
asunder. The perforating apparatus preferred by the patentees consists of (1) a number of steel points fixed into a
metallic stock ; (2) a fly press to which the stock is screwed ;
(3) a steel plate fixed in the bed of the press and drilled with
holes corresponding with the points.

The invention is applicable to " excursion, return, or other
" railway tickets ;" these may be perforated " so as to readily
" indicate the peculiar character of their issue."

[Printed, 3d. No Drawings.]


A.D. 1854, October 2.—No. 2107.

WALL, GEORGE. — (*Provisional protection only.*) — "Im-
" provements in the manufacture of railway tickets and other
" similar articles from a substance or material capable of being
" re-used."

These tickets are made of gutta percha, caoutchouc, or any
compound thereof, which may be printed or stamped with the
date, progressive number, &c.

If the ticket is printed upon, the ink may be discharged by
immersion in " any suitable chemical ley ;" if it has been
stamped, the stamp may be effaced by " a gentle heat and
" pressure."

[Printed, 3d. No Drawings.]


A.D. 1854, December 11.—No. 2607.

BEMROSE, WILLIAM, the younger, and BEMROSE, HENRY
HOWE.—" Improvements in the mode of and machinery for
" punching and perforating paper and other substances."

The "main feature" of this invention is the application of "rotating perforators" for the purpose of perforating paper, &c., "when such materials are carried by apparatus also "rotating."

The machine (to the "precise details or arrangements" of which the patentees do not restrict themselves) is worked by a treadle. The paper laid on a table and guided by a moveable gauge is pushed forward until it comes into contact with two rollers. The lower roller "serves as a counterpart" to the upper one, its periphery being perforated with holes corresponding to punches on the periphery of the upper one. The paper, perforated by passing between the rollers, is received on a sloping table.

These rollers do not "actually punch out" a portion of the material, they only perforate it. If the perforations are to be punched or cut out, the perforating part of the upper roller is a disc of thin metal "serrated or toothed at its periphery," and the counterpart "has a continuous slit formed in its "periphery." Provision is made by means of curved pieces of wire or strips of thin brass "to ensure the paper leaving "the perforators after passing through the rollers and to "prevent its being carried round with them."

"Any number of pairs of rollers may be used in one "machine."

[Printed, 7d. Drawing.]

# 1855.

A.D. 1855, May 29.—No. 1233.

JOHNSON, JOHN HENRY.—(*A communication from Carl Heinrich Otto Fänger.*)—(*Provisional protection only.*)— "Improvements in stamping and embossing presses."

The operations of stamping in colours and of embossing in one or more devices are effected "in one press and with one "actuating lever handle." The improvements consist "in "the employment of any required number of different stamps "fitted to work vertically in the overhanging extremity of the

" curved bracket or arm " of the press. The stamps are
" individually brought in contact " with the article to be
stamped " by a lever handle working on a swivel or pivot
" centre in the top of the bracket, so that it may be moved
" laterally in order to be brought on to any one of the stamps
" desired."

The under side of the lever is grooved or slotted to fit over
a projection on the top of the spindle of the stamps, thereby
preventing it " from accidentally slipping off the spindle when
" depressing it." A colour box, perforated at the top and
bottom and covered with absorbent material, is fitted into a
recess in the base of the press so that its upper surface shall
be about flush therewith. Over this box is fitted a cushion,
" working on a centre in the base of the press and capable of
" being pushed on one side by means of a rod and lever and
" button sliding in a guide slot."

When any one of the stamps is to be used, the cushion is
moved on one side; the stamp is brought lightly down on to
the absorbent material; " the button is then released and the
" cushion flies back again to its original position by the aid of
" a spring"; the article is laid on the cushion, and the stamp
is brought down on to it. When one side of the colour box
becomes too dry, it is turned over, and the dry side is placed
downwards.

" On the opposite side of the lever fulcrum " are fitted the
embossing dies, and " as these will require more pressure than
" the stamps, they are placed nearer the working centre of the
" lever." When it is required to use them, " the lever is
" turned round on its swivel fulcrum and brought over any
" one of the dies required." The stamps and dies are raised
by coiled or other springs.

[Printed, 3d. No Drawings.]

A.D. 1855, August 21.—No. 1895.

FIELD, EDWARD.—" Improvements in presses or machinery
" for embossing and colouring."

This invention is an improvement on " the cameo press "
and has for its object " the simplification of that machine and
" a consequent reduction of cost."

In the upper part of a strong framing or standards is a

horizontal shaft carrying (1) a cam ("forged in one piece" with the shaft) which depresses a "compound plunger," (2) a cam ("revolving in a strap") for "working the inking roller " frame," (3) a fast and loose pulley, (4) a fly wheel. To the front of the standards is attached a guide wherein the plunger moves, and in the upper part of the plunger "is fitted an " adjusting fork and nut carrying an antifriction roller." From each side of the plunger a lug projects; similar lugs are cast on the upper part of the guide, and rings of elastic material passed round the lugs raise the plunger when an impression has been struck. In the lower part of the framing is a socket (adjustable as to height), and therein is a piece of metal, "which serves as a support for the force or matrix" consisting of a piece of leather or other soft material. In order to obtain a sharp and well-defined impression on the paper, "a slight rise or incline is made on the cam;" this increases the pressure "at the moment when the die is at its " lowest point."

The sheets of paper are carried beneath the die by endless bands of tape "somewhat similar to those used in feeding " printing machines;" when they arrive beneath the die, " they are arrested by a moveable table" caused to rise and fall by a cam and having its face studded with points; when impressed they travel onward into a box placed at the egress side of the machine.

The inking apparatus is composed of (1) a lever connected to the above-mentioned cam by a ball and socket joint, (2) a traversing frame jointed to the lever, (3) a series of rollers carried by the frame, one having "a serpentine motion, intended " to distribute the ink or colouring matter over the surface of " the die," (4) an ink trough wherein a roller rotates being actuated by a catgut which passes round the fast and loose pulley, (5) "an inverted ink table" adjoining the trough, and (6) "a distributor or scraper, the edge of which may be ad-" justed" against the roller in the trough.

The working of the plunger and of the inking apparatus is described in the specification, but the patentee does not confine himself "to the precise arrangements of the details of the " press herein described."

[Printed, 9d. Drawings.]

A.D. 1855, October 26.—No. 2393.

PINCHES, JOHN.—" Improvements in the construction of
" dies or stamps for marking papers, linen, or other sub-
" stances."

The stem of the handle into which the die is screwed or
otherwise fixed is hollow and cylindrical and fits into a case of
wood or other material. Inside the stem is a coiled spring for
raising the handle and die when pressure is removed therefrom.
Or a "metal bush" may be tightly fitted into the case, and
the stem may slide therein. The coiled spring is held at the
lower part by a pin which passes through slots in the stem and
holes in the case, and at the upper part by a piece of wood
which is pinned to the top of the stem. The bottom of the
case fits into a "pad box" containing the ink.

The operator presses the die on the pad; he then removes
the pad box and "places the bottom edge of the case" upon
the substance to be stamped; by this means "he gets an uni-
" form bearing of such part" and thus presents the die or
" stamp square" with the substance. Then holding the
case with one hand, he strikes the top of the stem with the
other.

[Printed, 6d. Drawing.]

A.D. 1855, November 1.—No. 2440.

PINCHES, JOHN.—"An improved machine or apparatus for
" embossing paper, metal, and other substances by hand."

The object of this invention is to substitute "percussive
" force" for the "power of a lever or screw," and thus to
render embossing machines "more portable and considerably
" less expensive."

The stand is of cast iron; the upper part has formed therein
a cylindrical-shaped hole, into which a hollow stem or die
holder is fitted; and a piece is pinned to the top of the stem,
and the embossing die fits into the lower part thereof, being
secured thereto by a screw. A coiled spring within the stem
is held in position by the piece at the top and at the bottom
by a pin which passes through holes in the stand and slots cut
in the stem. The counterpart is of the ordinary kind and is
screwed to the bottom of the stand. "To ensure coincidence
" of the die with the counterpart thereof," an upright groove

is formed in the stand, and a pin or feather is fixed in the stem.

The operator holds the material to be embossed on the counterpart with one hand, whilst with the other hand he strikes the top of the piece.

[Printed, 6d.  Drawing.]

A.D. 1855, November 3.—No. 2463.

BINNING, JAMES.—(*Provisional protection only.*)—" Im-" provements applicable to embossing presses."

When the press is *not* required " to print the ground of the " embossing in colour," the base is cast in one piece with the frame or standard; otherwise they are made separately and are united in such manner that the standard, carrying the plunger and die ("or force as the case may be"), can be " turned horizontally aside to admit of colour being applied " to the face of the die." The plunger moves through arms projecting from the standard; it is hollow, and inside it is the customary coiled spring for raising it after the impression is struck.

When "coloured work" is being done, it will be found more convenient "to place the force above the die."

[Printed, 5d.  Drawing.]

# 1856.

A.D. 1856, March 31.—No. 779.

NEWTON, ALFRED VINCENT.—(*A communication.*)—" Im-" proved machinery for folding paper."

In this machine the knife by which the folding is in part effected is "stationary"; instead of moving the sheet from the table in the act of folding, it "remains upon the table while " the fold is made;" and instead of pushing or carrying the folded sheet between plates or rollers, it is carried by " nippers which seize the sheet by the middle of the middle " margin."

The framework of the machine is "somewhat similar in"

" appearance to a double printing press," and the machine, is "double in its operation," the two halves being alike. Each table or fly-board has register pins "which are operated in " the usual manner adopted in printing presses." The sheet is seized on its edge by fingers attached to a reciprocating carriage and is carried " under the folding nippers." The fingers are made to open and close by " mechanism com- " monly employed in printing presses," and they are "raised " and dropped at the time of seizing the sheet " by means of "a trip dog " turning upon a pivot. The knife is " at- " tached to and near the end of the carriage," and when by the movement of the carriage it is brought immediately under the nippers, "the carriage stops, and the middle margin of " the sheet is over the edge of the knife." The nippers descend, and their jaws press the sheet over the edge of the knife, thereby making a fold. When the nippers move away from the knife, they carry the folded sheet with them " into " a position to be folded a second time " by a second knife and nippers; these, having completed the second fold, carry the sheet "back to be subjected to a third folding " by a third knife and nippers, and so on as often as the sheet is to be folded; finally the folded sheet " is dropped from the nippers " upon the delivery table."

The drawing represents a machine " for folding octavo " volumes," and the machine " is so arranged that one half " is folded *up* and the other half *down*, the part for folding " from below being similar in construction and operation to " that already described." As the sheet is taken along by the fingers, it is cut into halves by a "rolling cutter," and while one half is carried through and folded as above described, the other "goes through a similar course, except that it passes " under a knife" and is folded by "a nipper which rises up " from below."

An "adjustable check piece" keeps the nippers "from " rising beyond the required position." There are "two sets " of fingers " upon the carriage; two knives on that side of the carriage "where the paper is first carried over the knife ;" and two rolling cutters at the extremities of a rocking bar " to cut the sheets on both sides of the machine." The mo- tions of all the nippers are derived from a cam " operating " upon the lower ends" of two T levers. The carriage is worked by a crank, a slotted connecting rod, a lever, and a link.

[Printed, 11d. Drawings.]

## A.D. 1856, April 18.—No. 925.

BUDDEN, WILLIAM.—(*Provisional protection only.*—"An " improved method of preparing cheques, invoices, and other " papers, so that they may be readily separated from their " counterparts."

By means of this invention the paper "is cut at the same " time that it is printed."

The improvements consist in introducing "a piece of " notched or cut metal " into the cheque, &c. where one part is to be separated from the other, and "overlaying it with " paper or cardboard," so that while being printed "the " metal cuts through the paper at intervals sufficient to render " the paper easily torn, while the part of the metal which is " notched out leaves enough paper uncut to cause sufficient " cohesion" between the parts of the cheque, &c.

[Printed, 3d. No Drawings.]

## A.D. 1856, April 26.—No. 1004.

WALKER, THOMAS.—"Improvements in playing cards."

These improvements consist, first, "in forming playing " cards of a circular form, or of a figure having five, six, " seven, eight, or other number of sides more than four," or of "an elliptical form, or of portions of ellipses, or circles." Secondly, "in marking or placing the entire number of spots " or pips denoting the value of the card near one edge, or " near both edges of the cards." The figures of the king, queen, and knave may be printed in the middle or near the edges of the cards, and have their names printed. The number of spots on each card may also be marked in numeral characters.

[Printed, 6d. Drawing.]

## A.D. 1856, June 2.—No. 1303.

CADET, AUGUSTE.—(*A communication.*)—"Improved stamp " inking apparatus."

The inking bed is fixed in a case of tin, wood, or other material: it consists of a block of wood, on the top of which

sheets of wadding are laid; the sheets are covered over with
" a black oil cloth greased on its under surface" and nailed
round the sides of the block. The bed may be made "self-
" supplying with ink by imbibing it therewith before apply-
" ing the oilcloth," but the inventor prefers to lay the ink on
the outer surface of the oilcloth.

An apparatus is employed in connexion with the inking bed,
" either for pressing out the ink to the surface when the ink
" is applied internally or for equalising it when laid on ex-
" ternally" :—it consists of "a semicylindrical tin box" of
the same length as the width of the inking bed, with rollers
" set horizontally and covered with flannel, the pivots of
" which are set freely in holes made at its two extremities."
This box is provided at its ends with "two circular tin pieces
" which fit to the outsides of the ink bed and serve as guides
" to the flannel rollers."

The case is made with a compartment "to receive the roller
" apparatus and stamp."

[Printed, 3d. No Drawings.]

A.D. 1856, June 12.—No. 1391.

HARDWICK, PHILIP WESLEY. — (*Provisional protection
only.*)—" An improved manufacture of tickets for railway and
" other uses."

The object of this invention is to enable ticket collectors to
ascertain if "the return or season tickets presented to their
" inspection were issued to the person presenting them."

The tickets, as they are issued, are printed or stamped with
" any arbitrary signs, such as letters or figures, which shall
" indicate the age, sex, and chief peculiarities of the person
" demanding a ticket." The printing apparatus may form a
distinct machine or a part of the ordinary dating or numbering
press; the printing surfaces are arranged on blocks or on the
periphery of wheels. If stamping is adopted, a press is provided with dies "for punching out holes in or indenting the
" surface of the ticket."

[Printed, 3d. No Drawings.]

A.D. 1856, June 20.—No. 1456.

CROFTON, MICHAEL THOMAS.—" An apparatus for inking
" stamps used by bankers and others."

The " dabber " is made " in the form of a roller instead of a
" flat surface."

The case of the apparatus is of metal " and fitted into a
" wooden box if necessary." Inside the case are a metal ink
trough, an inking roller, and the dabber roller. The trough
is connected to the case by screws, and other screws pass
through the back of the case " for the purpose of either draw-
" ing back or forcing forward the edge of said trough, which
" is made perfectly straight and serves as a doctor or scraper
" for taking off uniformly some of the ink or other coloring
" matter from the surface of the ink roller." The pivots of
the ink roller work in holes in the case ; one of them projects
and carries a winch handle and also a ratchet wheel, into which
a pawl takes to ensure the roller " being turned only in one
" direction." The dabber roller " works in heart-shaped
" openings" formed in the sides of the case ; its pivots are
inserted into one set of the openings when it is required to
receive ink from the ink roller ; when a supply of ink has been
distributed over its surface, it is removed, and its pivots are
inserted into the other set ; it is now ready for use.

If the case is fitted into a box, the front of the box may be
hinged to the bottom and be covered with elastic substance,
serving when let down as a stamping pad. A portion of the
box " serves as a depository for the stamping instruments."

[Printed, 7d. Drawing.]

A.D. 1856, September 5.—No. 2067.

DUCHATEAU, ALEXIS EUGÈNE. — (Provisional protection
only.)—"Improvements in stamp presses and stamps used
" therewith."

The first improvement consists in making presses in such
manner that the stamp " is inked by the elevation of the lever
" of the press " :—The lever has attached to it and the inking
roller "other small levers ; " so that the roller is caused to
pass under the stamp. The roller is withdrawn by depressing
the lever, and the stamp is forced upon the paper, &c. "by
" the lever coming in contact with the stamp." The stamp
" works in a suitable cylinder attached to the frame of the
" press," and the cylinder contains a spring "which causes
" the stamp to assume a proper position for inking."

The second consists so in making the stamp "that the "figures or letters therein can be altered by a self-acting "motion, or at will, at every inking of the stamp":—Four (more or less) circles of figures or letters, called the units, tens, hundreds, and thousands circles and having inscribed on each figures from 0 to 9, are placed "on a small spindle in the "stamp and are held by a catch or otherwise." The self-acting is effected "by fixing to the inking roller a catch, which "when it moves to and fro under the stamp operates a lever "working a ratchet wheel which is attached to the unit circle, "causing it to revolve." The alterations "at will" are effected "by ungearing the catch on the roller and operating "the lever by hand."

Letters may be engraved on the flat part of the stamp.

"This stamp can be attached to a small handle" and be "operated in all its movements by hand."

[Printed, 3d. No Drawings.]

A.D. 1856, October 1.—No. 2299.

SALTER, ROGER GEORGE.—(*Provisional protection only.*)— "A method of and apparatus for expediting the stamping or "marking of letters, papers, labels, and documents, and im- "provements in and additions to stamping and marking "instruments or apparatus, or in connection therewith."

The inventor employs in connexion with the stamping or marking instrument "contrivances for raising the letter," &c. after the stamping has been performed, "so as to separate it "from the others" :—This he effects "by excluding air from "or by producing a vacuum on the outer surface" of the letter, or "by the employment of an adhesive agent."

The apparatus which he prefers is a cylinder fitted with a piston, connected to a stamp, and having at bottom a flexible ring "nearly flush with the face of the stamp and made to "descend with it on the letter." On the upstroke of the piston "a vacuum will be produced, which will be destroyed "on admitting air through a valve in the cylinder." Or he connects to a stamping instrument a rod "provided at bottom "with a flexible pad or disc or with an adhesive material or "agent," which is made to descend (with the stamp) on the letter and "raises it with it until it be released by coming "against stops."

The stamp and cylinder "are mounted in a convenient
" position with respect to a platform or case which holds the
" letters to be marked." The platform, "carried up a guide
" way by means of ratchet wheels and rack and pinion," is
open on two sides, and under it is a spring. On working a
treadle (or otherwise) the piston is drawn down to the end of
its stroke ; the stamp and cylinder are brought down on to the
uppermost letter (the spring being thereby depressed), and the
proper marks are imprinted. On drawing up the piston a
vacuum will be produced in the cylinder ; the letter will
adhere to the cylinder until " it reaches the top of the guide
" way," when the valve "coming in contact with a stop or
" incline" will be opened, and the letter will be released.
Provision is made for the descent of the platform when all the
letters have been stamped.

The inking of the stamp takes place during its upstroke :—A
reservoir " is fixed on a lever vibrating on a fixed centre ;" it
" overtakes the stamp" and inks it by a sponge or other
agent, "clearing it on its return stroke."

Two or more stamps may be mounted in the same frame and
be worked simultaneously.

[Printed, 3d. No Drawings.]

A.D. 1856, November 13.—No. 2672.

JOHNSON, John Henry.—(*A communication from Cyrus
Chambers.*) — (*Provisional protection only.*) — "Improve-
" ments in machinery or apparatus for cutting and folding
" paper," more particularly applicable " to the folding of
" printed sheets ready for stitching and binding."

The sheet is laid on a table and is so adjusted thereon "that
" the holes made by the register pins of the printing press
" shall coincide with corresponding adjustable registers or pins
" situated between the first of a series of pairs of folding
" rollers." A pressing blade, "having a slightly concave edge
" and fitted with small projecting points," descends, and as
soon as the points come into contact with the sheet, the adjustable pins "are made to descend beneath the rollers so as to
" be entirely out of the way," and the further descent of the
blade " inserts the sheet in a creased form between the folding
" rollers." The doubled sheet is carried along by horizontal

tapes until "its folded edge" comes into contact with a pair of shears which cut the said edge. The cut sheets are now depressed by a second pressing blade and are inserted "be-" "tween two hinged presser plates" placed above a second pair of folding rollers, by which means "a second or cross "fold" is made. A third and last fold "is effected like the "previous one."

Provision is made by means of a roller covered with india-rubber for removing the severed strip from the lower blade of the shears "before another sheet arrives." The second pressing blade has attached to one side of it two "sliding "plates," which carry "diagonal points" just long enough "to penetrate only one thickness of paper." When the blade has descended so as to force the under sheet between the rollers, "the sliding plates are caused by means of a small arm "to recede from each other slightly and force their respective "points in a diagonal or slanting direction into the top sheet, "thereby holding it fixed during the time that the bottom "sheet is continuing its progress along horizontal conduct-" "ing tapes to the third pair of folding rollers."

After the folding the sheet is directed by an inclined flap on to an endless cloth, the inclined flap "ensuring that the "folded sheets shall always be deposited with the same side "uppermost on the endless cloth." The descent of the first pressing blade may be arrested by means of a treadle which raises a stop.

[Printed, 3d. No Drawings.]

A.D. 1856, November 14.—No. 2682.

FONTAINEMOREAU, PETER ARMAND le Comte de. — (A communication.)—(Provisional protection only.)—"An im-" "proved method of forming letters and other devices on "metallic surfaces."

To obtain "an engraving in relief," the required figures, designs, &c., "are formed by the usual means" on a zinc or other metallic plate. "By this means the plate exhibits in "blank the parts cut out," and into these "is poured a metal-" "lic compound" consisting of tin 2 parts, bismuth 2 parts, antimony 1 part; this compound "in contact with zinc and "copper resists the action of acids."

To obtain "an intaglio engraving," the figures, designs, &c.
are cut from the metallic plate, and "are then fixed on a
"thin sheet of zinc and the base filled with the same com-
"position."

[Printed, 3d. No Drawings.]

# 1857.

## A.D. 1857, January 30.—No. 282.

SMITH, HENRY. — "Improvements in window price tickets,
"and which said improvements are also applicable to the
"ornamenting and pricing the wrappers or paper boxes for
"holding fancy and other goods; also in the mode of attaching
"or suspending window tickets."

The patentee claims the application of printing combined
with embossing "to the marking, pricing, and ornamenting"
window tickets, &c., "without any regard to any particular
"ornamental design or to the size or characters to be so
"imprinted or embossed on them."

He does not "pretend to do this by any new process;" he
employs a press, a die, a counterpart, and an inking roller (by
preference self-acting). "All the parts that are white must
"be sunk in the die, while the circular rims, letters, figures,
"&c. would form the face of the die and would therefore be
"readily inked by the roller," so that in the printing "the
"white part would be shewn in relief, and the part colored
"black sunk in."

[Printed, 7d. Drawing.]

## A.D. 1857, February 10.—No. 380.

HERTS, DANIEL BENJAMIN.—(*A communication.*) — (*Provisional protection only.*)—"Improvements in apparatus for
"stamping and embossing."

The stand of this apparatus is fitted with two beds, the one
serving as "a dabber," the other carrying "the requisite
"force." Above the beds is a stamp carrier, "which vibrates
"horizontally on a fixed centre near the back of the stand,"

so as to admit of the stamp being alternately brought over each bed. A coiled spring within the carrier keeps the stamp raised when not acted upon by the striker. The striker is " a lever moving with the carrier and acted upon by a power-" ful blade or other spring, so as to give an effective blow on " the top of the stamp or die spindle." The back end of the striker " works in the groove of a fixed cam," whereby " a figure " of 8 motion " is imparted to the end of the striker " by " simply moving the carrier from one bed to the other." The cam consists of " two angular projections placed side by side, " with their points or apices described inwards or towards each " other, a sufficient space being left between the two apices " for the free passage of the end of the striker." Midway between the apices is " a hinged tongue or guiding piece," which is long enough " to bear against the under side of either " point when deflected laterally by the passage of the end of " the striker."

A buffer of india-rubber or other suitable material is placed on the carrier " below the striking end " of the striker to prevent " fracture of the apparatus by the sudden force of the " blow." A handle in front of the carrier " facilitates its " traverse from one bed to the other."

[Printed, 3d. No Drawings.]

A.D. 1857, February 19.—No. 488.

CLAYTON, THOMAS.—" Improvements in machinery or ap-" paratus for ornamenting and embossing wood, leather, " paper, and other similar materials."

The patentee embosses these materials in either of the following methods, " as the work may require ":—

1. The material is passed between engraved rollers, which are hollow and " raised to the desired temperature by the " introduction of burning gas or other suitable means." As the material passes between the rollers, the pressure required to make the impression of the design thereon is given by means of a weighted lever.

2. Flat dies are used; the lower one is heated on the under side by " ordinary burners ; " the upper one is fixed to a screw, and " a perpendicular motion is procured by guides in the " usual manner."

Colour if required may be applied to the material either before or after the "operation of the machine."

The patentee describes each machine, but does not confine himself to the details set forth.

[Printed, 1s. Drawings.]

## A.D. 1857, March 26.—No. 848.

BENOIST, JEAN JACQUES CONSTANT.—(*Provisional protection only.*)—"A new method of applying marks on paper for " postal purposes."

Each sheet of letter paper or each envelope for letter paper is stamped, so that each sheet or envelope "will indicate the " weight of postage" and thus "save much trouble and the " doubt as to postage dues on the transmission of letters to " any country."

[Printed, 3d. No Drawings.]

## A.D. 1857, May 5.—No. 1264.

HERRERO, JUSTE.—"An improved inking and stamping " machine."

In this machine the inking of the die or type and the impression of the same are obtained by "one single depressing " motion of a handle."

The frame consists of a bracket and a base carrying an inking table and ink reservoir. In the bracket is "a longitudinal " slit," in which works a lever provided at one end with a handle and at the other with a weight "for causing the handle " to ascend spontaneously" after each impression. "Opposite " the fulcrum" the lever has "a projecting part" which carries a coiled spring and a socket "gliding loosely over" the lower end of the said part; the spring pushes the socket constantly towards the inking table. The inking apparatus comprises the table, the reservoir and a roller revolving therein, and three distributing rollers, two of them being mounted on the ends of a cross bar, which "balances on a spindle in the " forked end" of the socket, the third (which inks the die) " revolving on a spindle fixed in the forked end of an elastic " rod, the other end of which is fixed to the socket." Between the handle and the fulcrum of the lever is a slot, wherein

moves a pin " fixed in a slit of the vertical stamp, which latter
" glides loosely in the tubular end of the bracket." The die
or type is attached to the stamp in any suitable manner.

The patentee describes "the mode of acting of this machine,"
which is " exceedingly simple and effectual," adding that "the
" precise details herein-before described" may be modified.

[Printed, 9d. Drawings.]

## A.D. 1857, May 16.—No. 1388.

CRESWELL, George Henry. — " Improvements in appa-
" ratus for supplying ink or other mixture for stamps used
" in stamping letters and other articles."

This apparatus consists of a cylinder covered with woollen
cloth and revolving in a case by means of a winch or handle.

The cylinder fits into the case, "except at the sides, where
" cavities or chambers are formed to receive the ink."
Rubbers, hinged to the sides of the case above the cavities
and faced with woollen cloth at the parts which come into
contact with the cylinder, are pressed with more or less force
against the cylinder by means of screws; they rub off the
superfluous ink as the cylinder is turned round. The top of
the case is removable so as to expose the surface charged with
ink when required for use.

" To ink very large stamps by mere vertical pressure, the
" flat end of the cylinder may be covered with cloth and
" employed instead of the periphery " :—The rubbers are
arranged " to act against the flat end," and the cylinder when
required for use is placed with its axis " in a vertical position."

" If the rotating surface be always turned in the same
" direction," one rubber and one ink chamber will be
sufficient. The rubbers may be brushes or scrapers.

[Printed, 6d. Drawing.]

## A.D. 1857, September 9.—No. 2349.

BERTOU, Leon Louis Honoré.—" Improvements in the
" manufacture or production of ornamental wrappers or
" packings for fabrics or other goods."

The improvements consist in producing on paper or other
fabric trade marks or designs which shall be "indelible and

" of a transparent nature resembling the ordinary water
" mark."

The paper is laid on a metal plate whereon the required
design is engraved in relief. On the paper is placed a copper
or zinc plate; over this one or more sheets of cardboard, and
" finally another zinc plate." The whole is passed through a
copper-plate printing machine or is submitted to pressure in
any other convenient manner.

Any hard substance capable of bearing a design in relief
may be used instead of the metal plate.

[Printed, 3d. No Drawings.]

A.D. 1857, October 6.—No. 2563.

ROBINSON, George Thomas.—" A machine for obliterating
" postage stamps on letters, at the same time stamping the
" post marks and registering the number of letters so
" stamped."

In a casing is a compartment wherein the letters to be
operated on are stacked and held down by a weight. In
the bottom of the compartment is an opening, under which
" elastic fingers" rotate. The fingers pressing against the
lowest letter of the pile carry it forward through a slit between
" a stamping cylinder" and "a plain pressure roller," the
former having on its periphery "the name and number of
" the post office or mark to be printed and also the date
" supplied by moveable type," whilst by the latter "the
" obliterating of the postage stamp and the stamping of the
" post mark is performed, and the letter discharged from
" the machine." The inking apparatus consists of an ink
distributor, an inking roller, and an ink reservoir. "A flexible
" fringe of whalebone or other substance" prevents "more
" than one letter passing at a time."

The registering apparatus is composed of (1) a jointed lever
or pendulum moved "by the passing of a letter," (2) a pawl
attached to the pendulum, (3) a ratchet wheel acted upon by
the pawl, (4) "a train of four other wheels" in connexion
with the ratchet wheel and moved each "one tenth of its
" circumference" by the revolution of the wheel immediately
below, (5) dials on the outside of the machine and connected
to the wheels.

Motion is imparted to the machine "through the shaft on
" which the stamping cylinder is placed."

[Printed, 9d. Drawing.]


A.D. 1857, October 12.—No. 2607.

BEARD, GEORGE.—"Improvements in mechanism for pro-
" ducing impressions on paper or other surfaces."

The patentee claims the construction of an apparatus having
a pad or inking cushion and an inking roller acting in conjunction with a dye or types, and "specially adapted for postal
" purposes."

A pillar on the base of the apparatus is formed with an
upper and a lower projecting arm. To the upper arm is
pinned a "curved lever having a slot" through which a pin
passes so as to connect therewith a plunger. The plunger
(the lower end of which "is provided with a screwed receptacle
" for the impression die") passes through a guide collar at
the outer end of the lower arm. The under side of the lower
arm "is provided with two grooves to receive the flanges
of the inking pad." A "peculiarly formed lever" is hung on
an axis which secures it to the upper arm; its short arm is
slotted, and a guide pin on the plunger works in the slot;
its long arm carries at its lower end the inking roller secured
to it by a rod. This rod is connected to the long arm by
collars; it carries a coiled spring and a screw nut with a
milled head. Another coiled spring is secured by a pin on
the upper projecting arm and by a pin on the plunger. On
the inner side of the plunger is a projection in which is
secured a piece of india-rubber; this "upon the plunger
" being moved up strikes the under side" of the upper arm
to which the lever is hung, "easing the concussion and
" deadening the sound." A catch enables the operator to
keep the mechanism in a proper position "to change or
" handle the impression die, &c." The curved lever is
worked by a handle.

When the apparatus is at rest, "the roller will remain under
" the pad;" when the plunger is raised, the roller "will pass
" under the die," and when it is lowered, it will cause the
roller to be carried back to the pad.

[Printed, 6d. Drawing.]

A.D. 1857, November 5.—No. 2814.

**PALMER,** Henry Robinson.—"An improved stamping and
" endorsing machine."

The patentee claims (1) the employment of "a parallel
" motion" for the purpose of guiding the die holder on to
the inking cushion and then on to the stamping cushion;
(2) the construction of inking pads or cushions with "a dish
" or cavity for containing the ink" and covered with an
absorbent material, whereby the ink "may pass outward to
" the surface of the pad."

A stem, having its upper portion formed so as to be grasped
conveniently by the hand and carrying the die, is formed with
cross arms ; to these are jointed "radius links or bars moving
" on fixed centres attached to the framing of the machine and
" forming a parallel motion." A light blow upon the inking
cushion "covers the surface of the die evenly with ink ;" the
stem is then carried by the hand over the centre, and
another blow is struck upon the material to be stamped on the
stamping cushion.

The inking and stamping cushions are circular and "larger
" than the die intended to be used therewith ;" the former
" is formed with a central pin" which fits into and is free
to revolve in a nut adjustable by means of a screw, "so that
" by making use of both the circular and straight line motions
" the inking pad may be moved to bring all parts thereof
" successively under the action of the die."

One of the figures in the annexed sheet of drawings shows
" a mode of imparting rotary motion to the inking pad by
" means of a ratchet wheel ;" another an "inking pad con-
" sisting of an endless web ;" another the base plate "formed
" so as to admit of stamping papers, &c. at a considerable
" distance from the margin ;" and another "a method of
" driving the machine by a continuous rotary motion."

[Printed, 10d. Drawing.]

# SUPPLEMENT B.

A.D. 1767, December 7.—No. 886.

BERKENHOUT, John.—"A method, entirely new, of dicing,
" flowering, colouring, or marking playing cards, so as to
" render them easily distinguishable from the white cards now
" used." This invention is "to be performed by printing,
" impressing, painting, flowering, dicing, stamping, staining,
" figuring, or otherwise marking or colouring the said cards on
" the back."

The above recited processes are effected in the manner and
method by which such arts "are usually executed."

[Printed, 3*d*. No Drawings.]

A.D. 1832, February 23.—No. 6231.

DE LA RUE, Thomas.—"Improvements in making or manu-
" facturing and ornamenting playing cards." This invention
relates "to that particular part of the operation in the
" making or manufacturing of playing cards which has here-
" tofore been done in water colours by means of what is called
" stencilling ; and which process is by this invention dispensed
" with."

The improvements consist, "first, in printing the colours of
" the têtes or honors and pips of playing cards in colors mixed
" with oil from raised surfaces, either in wood or metal or
" other materials." Secondly, in "printing the colours of the
" têtes or honors and pips of playing cards from lithographic
" stones, when the colours used for that purpose are mixed
" with oil." Thirdly, in ornamenting the pips, &c., "with
" gold, silver, or other metals, or bronze, when such ornament-
" ing is produced by raised surfaces or lithographic printing."

[Printed, 4*s*. 5*d*. Drawings.]

# INDEX TO SUPPLEMENT

[The numbers refer to the pages on which the Abridgments commence. The names printed in *Italic* are those of the persons by whom the Inventions have been communicated to the Applicants for Letters Patent.]

# Patents for Inventions Relating to Printing

ABRIDGEMENTS OF
SPECIFICATIONS

## 1617-1857

First published in 1859
and now reprinted with
a Prefatory Note by

## JAMES HARRISON

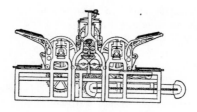

LONDON:
PRINTING HISTORICAL
SOCIETY

A.D. 1822, January 14.—N° 4640.

APPLEGATH, Augustus.—" Improvements in printing ma-
" chines."

The improvements consist, first, in applying the ink to the
form of types, plates, or blocks, " partly on one side of the
" impressing or printing cylinder and partly on the other side."
By this means " the motion of the form is lessened and the quan-
" tity of impressions taken in any given period may be increased
" in the ratio of the diminution of motion," and this not only
in those cases in which the form is caused to pass under the printing
cylinder and inking rollers, but also in those cases in which the
printing cylinder and inking rollers are caused to pass over the
form.

Secondly, in " the combination of two paper feeders with a
" printing cylinder which prints in one direction only."    On
each side at the top of the pressing cylinder are two drums
equal in circumference to half that of the pressing cylinder.    By
the action of a pin in a centre wheel upon arms attached to
two others symmetrically disposed, sheets are fed in above each
drum by an endless web and conducted to the impression and
discharged by endless tapes.

[Printed, 6d. Drawings. London Journal (*Newton's*), vol. 4, p. 57. Rolls
Chapel.]

A.D. 1822, January 29.—N° 4642.

CONGREVE, Sir William.—" Improved methods of multi-
" plying facsimile impressions to any extent."

The first has reference to letter-press work.  Stereotype plates
from a form of matrix types of " brass or other such metal," such
form being " run, together with a thin sheet of prepared pewter or
" other soft metal fit for the purpose, through a rolling press
" similar to a copper-plate press, but stronger.  It is evident a very
" small quantity of this letter in creux would supply the place of a
" very extensive font.  Almost any number of these plates may be
" produced after the matter is set up almost as rapidly as impressions
" may be pulled on paper in a common printing press."

" The second plan for the multiplication of facsimile impressions
" applies to copper-plate work, and is not limited in dimensions
" like the plans at present in use.  The original may be engraved
" on a flat surface of any size and transferred to a second flat

" surface also of any size, and from thence laid down as copies of
" the original upon any number of other flat surfaces by the use
" of plates of different gradations of hardness, as hard and soft
" steel and copper, or soft steel, copper or brass, and pewter.
" The second flat surface should be a thin plate, when a sufficient
" pressure will be obtained to produce the transfers, whatever may
" be the dimensions of the plate, by merely passing the plate
" through a rolling press  .  .  .  such as that above mentioned
"  .  .  .  the rollers of which need not exceed 3 or 4 inches in
" diameter. The size of the plates whereof the facsimiles may be
" thus multiplied is evidently not limited, as it necessarily is where
" the second impression is taken upon the outside of a cylinder."

[Printed, 3d. No Drawing. London Journal (*Newton's*), vol. 5, p. 185. Rolls Chapel.]

## A.D. 1822, March 24.—Nº 4664.

CHURCH, WILLIAM.—"An improved apparatus for printing."

1. Machine for casting the types and arranging them ready
to be transferred to the composing machinery. A matrix bar,
containing a series of matrices, is applied to a mould bar with
a corresponding number of moulds. At the time of casting,
the latter is applied to jets leading from the metal chest, which
is supplied from a metal fountain connected with the metal pot,
and furnished with a valve to prevent the return of the metal.
After the casting, the mould bar, drawn endways, cuts off communication with the metal, and brings the said types beneath a
series of punches, which descend and force them out at the same
time that the matrix bar is unlocked and descends clear of the
types. The types descend into " guides," twisted one-quarter
round in order to bring the bodies of the types side by side, " in the
" same manner as when placed together in a line by a compositor."
The mould bar is kept cool during the process by a stream of water
passing through it. The matrix bar is then locked up, and the
metal bar slidden back for another casting. The metal is injected
by the descent of a plunger in the metal chest. The movements
of each part of this machine are caused by the action of cams upon
the main shaft.

Modification of the above, in which several of the operations are
performed by hand.

2. The types are arranged in " files " in a case at the top of the
machine, each file being directly over a slit in a horizontal frame.

The Printing Historical Society's proposed reprint of the Patent Specification abridgements that relate to printing inventions between 1617 and 1857 will be one of its most important publications. Here in concise yet ample form, are summaries of all printing inventions, successful and established, impracticable and abortive and covering 'the production of copies on all kinds of materials (excepting felted and textile fabrics) by means of types, stereotype, blocks, plates, stone, dies, stencil plates, paper writings, electro-chemicals, and light.' As a source for study it is absolutely unrivalled and it is difficult to imagine anyone interested in the history of printing who can afford to be without the book. The original edition has for some time been virtually unobtainable. Mr James Harrison of the Patent Office has contributed a prefatory note on Bennet Woodcroft the indefatigable patent agent and prototype industrial archaeologist who alone was responsible for the original publication.

This republication must be entirely self-supporting and cannot be assisted by the Society's general funds. Everything depends on an *immediate* response to this prospectus. The facts are these: the book will be a Crown octavo of 640 pages; it will be printed by lithography and case bound in cloth. Its manufacturing cost (delivered to subscribers) will be 17s per copy for the proposed edition of 1,000. We must therefore secure a subscription of 500 copies at 35s before we can proceed – even this is less than half the minimum commercial price. The cost to non-members will be 3 guineas.

We have arranged a production schedule that will enable us to despatch your copy to you by 17 January 1969, *provided 500 subscriptions are received by 31 October.* Please fill in and despatch your subscription form NOW, to:

The Publications Secretary, Printing Historical Society
St Bride Institute, Bride Lane
London EC4

*A typical opening is reproduced overleaf*

STELLAR PRESS BARNET HERTS